Transboundary Air Pollution:
Acidification, Eutrophication and Ground-Level Ozone in the UK

ISBN 1 870393 61 9

For further copies, please contact:

Mhairi Coyle
CEH Edinburgh
Bush Estate
Penicuik
Midlothian
EH26 0QB
UK

mcoy@ceh.ac.uk
tel. ++44(0) 131 445 8528
fax. ++44(0) 131 445 3943

Dr. Alison Vipond
Air and Environment Quality Division
Department for Environment, Food and Rural Affairs
Ashdown House, Zone 4/D11
123 Victoria Street
London, SW1E 6DE
UK

alison.vipond@defra.gsi.gov.uk

The report is also available in electronic format at http://www.nbu.ac.uk/negtap/.

For technical enquires, please contact:

Prof. David Fowler
CEH Edinburgh
Bush Estate
Penicuik
Midlothian, EH26 0QB
UK

dfo@ceh.ac.uk
tel. ++44(0) 131 445 4343
fax. ++44(0) 131 445 3943

NEGTAP 2001

Prepared by the National Expert Group on Transboundary Air Pollution (NEGTAP) at CEH Edinburgh on behalf of the UK Department for Environment, Food and Rural Affairs, Scottish Executive, The National Assembly for Wales/Cynulliad Cenedlaethol Cymru, Department of the Environment for Northern Ireland.

DEFRA Contract EPG 1/3/153

National Expert Group on Transboundary Air Pollution

http://www.nbu.ac.uk/negtap/

D Fowler (Chairman)	
M Coyle (Secretary)	Centre for Ecology and Hydrology Edinburgh
H M ApSimon	Department of Environmental Science and Technology, Imperial College of Science, Technology and Medicine
M R Ashmore	University of Bradford
S A Bareham	Cyngor Cefn Gwlad Cymru/Countryside Council for Wales, Joint Nature Conservancy Committee
R W Battarbee	University College London
R G Derwent	Meteorological Office
J-W Erisman	Energy Research Center of the Netherlands
J Goodwin	AEA Technology Environment
P Grennfelt	Swedish Environmental Research Institute
M Hornung	Centre for Ecology and Hydrology Merlewood
J Irwin	Environment Agency
A Jenkins	Centre for Ecology and Hydrology Wallingford
S E Metcalfe	University of Edinburgh
S J Ormerod	Cardiff University
B Reynolds	Centre for Ecology and Hydrology Bangor
S Woodin	University of Aberdeen

Terms of Reference

The National Expert Group on Transboundary Air Pollution (NEGTAP) is an advisory, Non-Departmental Public Body. Its work spanned 24 months and the Terms of Reference are:

To review current knowledge and advise Ministers on:

- ❖ biological and chemical trends in the UK environment, and the prospects for recovery, as a result of current and projected deposition of transboundary air pollutants

- ❖ UK critical load, and critical load exceedance maps for acidity and eutrophication and advise Ministers on their further development

- ❖ requests from the Government on other transboundary air pollution issues.

Information on the Expert Group is available on the internet at http://www.nbu.ac.uk /negtap/, and includes membership, agendas, minutes of meetings, and a register of interests. This report will also be available on the internet at this address. The group will build on the reports from previous groups such as the Review Group on Acid Rain, Photochemical Oxidants Review Group and the Critical Loads Advisory Group.

The views expressed in this report are those of the authors and not necessarily those of the organisations they represent or the commissioning bodies.

Executive Summary

This report provides a detailed description of the current status of the problems of acid deposition, eutrophication and ground-level ozone pollution in the UK, including emissions, atmospheric concentrations and deposition of the major pollutants, and the impacts on soils, vegetation and freshwaters. A summary of impacts throughout Europe is included to provide a perspective for the assessment.

- Emissions of the major pollutants SO_2 and NO_x in 1999 have declined by 80% and 40% of their respective peak emissions and are projected to decline further by 2010, in line with UK commitments within international protocols. Emissions of NH_3 have changed little since the peak emissions in the mid 1980's, but a decline of 12% relative to 1990 is expected by 2010.

- The deposition of sulphur and oxidized nitrogen in the UK has declined since the peak in emissions by 50% for sulphur and 16 % for oxidized nitrogen. However, substantial non-linearities in relationships between emission and deposition have been detected and will continue, so that in some areas of the country the reduction in deposition may continue to be much smaller than the national reduction in emissions.

- The acidity of UK rainfall more than halved over large areas of the UK between 1985 and 1999.

- Ground-level ozone concentrations regularly exceed the thresholds for effects on vegetation and human health throughout the UK, but the peak concentrations declined by 30% between 1986 and 1999.

- The assessment of future pollutant concentrations and deposition rely heavily on numerical models that have improved steadily over the last decade and represent current understanding of the underlying processes, with all their uncertainties.

- Reduced inputs of acidity and nitrogen from the atmosphere may provide the conditions in which chemical and biological recovery can begin, but the time scales of these processes are often very long (decades) relative to the time scales of reductions in emission.

- Widespread acidification of acid sensitive UK soils occurred through the 20th century and as yet, there is little direct evidence of recovery despite the reduced deposition.

- Acidification of freshwaters has been widespread in the uplands of the UK from 1850 onwards. There is clear evidence of chemical change consistent with the beginning of recovery and the first stages of biological recovery have been detected. However, the original species may never become re-established and active site management may be necessary to promote biological recovery.

- Critical loads for acidification are currently (1997) exceeded in 71% of UK ecosystems, and this is expected to decline to 47% by 2010 by which time deposited nitrogen will be the major contributor to acidification.

- Critical loads for eutrophication are currently (1995-1997) exceeded in *ca* 25% of UK 1 km x 1 km grid squares with sensitive grasslands and *ca* 55% with heathland. These percentages are expected to decline to *ca* 20% and *ca* 40% respectively in 2010, with reduced nitrogen (NH_3 and NH_4) being the main contributor.

- The reduction in SO_2 concentration over the last three decades has virtually eliminated direct effects on vegetation, leading to an expansion of some lichen species. However, current deposition of nitrogen is probably changing species composition in many nutrient-poor habitats and these changes may not be readily reversed. Current O_3 concentrations threaten crops and forest production. The effects of ozone and nitrogen deposition are likely to remain significant beyond 2010.

- The major ecological problems due to air pollution are common to large areas of Europe where, like the UK, sulphur emissions and deposition have declined substantially and where N deposition has changed relatively little. In continental Europe the deposition of N and the presence of elevated ozone concentrations represent the major ecological problems and while deposition and effects by 2010 will be reduced, widespread exceedances of critical loads and levels will still occur.

- The long-term operation of UK networks monitoring the major gaseous, particulate pollutants and those in rain have provided the necessary data, which underpin this assessment. The networks will be vital to demonstrate compliance with international protocols as well as scientific assessment of the state of the UK environment in the future.

Technical Summary

This report provides a detailed description of the current status of the problems of acid deposition, eutrophication and ground-level ozone in the UK, covering the emissions, atmospheric concentrations and deposition of the major pollutants and the effects on soils, freshwaters and vegetation. The scope of the report is therefore broad and this short summary identifies the main findings. The subject is presented in order, following the pollutant pathway from source to receptor, which also matches the chapter headings.

Emissions (Chapter 2)

The UK emissions of most of the pollutants contributing to acid rain, eutrophication and ozone production in (and downwind of) the UK, including sulphur dioxide (SO_2), the nitrogen oxides (NO_x), carbon monoxide (CO), and non-methane volatile organic compounds (NMVOCs) have declined substantially over the last decade, as detailed below. The exception, ammonia (NH_3), shows emissions which have changed little over the last 15 years and are least certain. In the Gothenburg Protocol (to abate acidification, eutrophication and ground-level ozone), the UK agreed annual emission ceilings for SO_2 (625 kt-SO_2), NO_x (1181 kt-NO_x), NH_3 (297 kt-NH_3) and NMVOCs (1200 kt) to be reached from 2010. The proposed EU National Emissions Ceilings Directive will set the emission ceilings for the same four pollutants. During negotiations, the UK has agreed to more stringent ceilings for SO_2 and NO_x. The emissions are expressed as kt (thousands of tonnes), in the case of sulphur and nitrogen as the elements S and N.

- Annual UK emissions of sulphur dioxide peaked in 1970 at 3259 kt-S, declined to 594 kt-S by 1999 and will decline further to around 312 kt-S by 2010.

- Annual UK emissions of nitrogen oxides peaked in 1980s at *ca* 850 kt-N and declined to less than 500 kt-N by 1999. They will continue to decline to around 359 kt-N by 2010.

- Annual UK emissions of ammonia are the least certain of all the pollutants that contribute to acidification and eutrophication; they reached approximately 300 kt-N annually in the late 1980s and are expected to decline by 11%, relative to 1990, by 2010.

- Annual UK NMVOC emissions peaked in 1989 at 2500 kt, declined to 1700 kt and are set to decline further to 1200 kt by 2010.

- Annual CO emissions peaked in 1970s at *ca* 8500 kt, declined to less than 5000 kt by 1999 and will decline to 2800 kt by 2010.

- Emissions of base cations (and other long-range transport metals) are very uncertain, and have been estimated to be 74 kt annually. Emissions have probably declined as industrial particle filtration systems have improved.

Concentrations and Deposition of Sulphur, Nitrogen, Ozone and Acidity in the UK (Chapter 3)

The concentrations and deposition of sulphur compounds have declined over the UK as a whole. Between 1986 and 1997 the change of about 50% is roughly the same as the reduction in emissions. However, the spatial pattern of the deposited sulphur has changed, with a much greater reduction in deposition in the East Midlands, and very small reductions in the west coast uplands. This is important because the most acid sensitive ecosystems in the UK are found in the areas which have experienced the smallest reductions in sulphur deposition. The reduction in sulphur deposition is accompanied by a similar decrease in rainfall acidity, throughout the UK. For the nitrogen compounds, data show a reduction in deposition of 16%.

The detection of these changes emphasises the requirement for the monitoring networks and a process of evaluation for the data.

For ground-level ozone, the peak concentrations have declined by about 30% since the 1980s, and the average concentrations are showing a slight increase, which is expected to continue over the coming decades.

- Deposition of non-seasalt sulphur in the UK declined by 52% between 1986 and 1997 during which emissions declined by 57%

- Between 1986 and 1997 the wet deposition of sulphur declined by 42% while dry deposition declined by 62%.

- In the East Midlands, the decline in deposition and concentrations of sulphur in the atmosphere were very large (>70%), while at west coast sites, few reductions in SO_4^{2-} in precipitation have been detected.

- A substantial decrease (30 to 50%) in rainfall acidity has been recorded throughout the UK between 1986 and 1997.

- Deposition of nitrogen oxides in the UK has declined by about 16%, following a reduction in NO_x emissions of *ca* 45% since the emissions peak in 1990.

- Total N deposition in the UK is dominated by reduced N (as NH_3 and NH_4^+) and has changed little since 1986.

- The potential acidification from nitrogen deposition now substantially exceeds that of sulphur.

- Non-linearities in the relationship between the emission and deposition patterns for sulphur have been detected, these will lead to slower reductions in acidity related critical loads exceedance in the uplands of western Britain than expected.

- The import of sulphur from shipping sources to the south and west of the UK is slowing the recovery from acid deposition.

- Rates of dry deposition of SO_2 have increased with time in response to changes in the relative amounts of SO_2 and NH_3 in the air.

- Ground-level ozone continues to exceed thresholds for effects on vegetation and human health over large areas of the UK, although the peak concentrations have declined by about 30% during the last decade.

- There is evidence that the mean ground-level ozone concentration over the UK is increasing.

Modelling Concentrations and Deposition (Chapter 4)

Modelling the transport, chemical transformation and deposition of pollutants provides the **only** available instrument to integrate current knowledge of the processes quantitatively and predict the concentrations and deposition of pollutants at future dates. By their nature, models can only be as good as our current understanding, and in general are some way behind the latest developments in the underlying science. It follows that there are always uncertainties in modelled output values, and where possible, measurements are used. Even with current uncertainties in the science, and hence in the models, it is clear that substantial further reductions in sulphur and acid deposition in the UK will take place over the coming decade. The largest uncertainties remain in the nitrogen compounds, and especially ammonia, where the short lifetime in the atmosphere produces large gradients in concentration, deposition and effects over small horizontal distances. This fine scale structure is not well captured using the current models.

- The EMEP Eulerian model has replaced the Lagrangian models for work under the CLRTAP. It integrates acidifying and photochemical pollutants.
- The EMEP model reproduces observed concentrations of ozone across the UK and the overall deposition of sulphur for the UK.
- The EMEP models still operate at a scale which is coarse in the context of the UK, and UK scale models have a role in assessing UK policy options.
- UK scale models are able to reproduce the general patterns of deposition of S, oxidised and reduced N but remain deficient in the overall totals.
- It is still difficult to reproduce the reduced N budget for the UK using current emissions inventories. It seems likely that these underestimate actual NH_3 emissions.
- Current reduction plans (the Gothenburg Protocol) are predicted to result in a significant reduction in S deposition and a smaller reduction in oxidised N deposition across the UK; reductions in reduced nitrogen under this protocol are too small to have a significant impact in the UK.
- Peak concentrations of ozone will probably be reduced with the implementation of the Gothenburg protocol, but should be considered in the context of an increasing global background.
- From about the middle of this century it is likely that annual mean ozone concentrations in the UK will be substantially larger than current values and may pose a threat to vegetation and human health.

Effects on Soils (Chapter 5)

Soils vary in their sensitivity to acidifying inputs, and the UK, in common with the Scandinavian countries, has large areas of acid sensitive soils, many of which have been receiving large inputs of acidifying pollutants for more than a century. The main processes of acidification of soils by sulphur are reasonably well known, but there remain important gaps in our understanding of the fate and chemical and biological effects of deposited nitrogen compounds in UK soils. While there is widespread evidence of soil acidification, it is not surprising that there is no direct evidence of recovery since timescales for recovery of soils, especially the acid sensitive soils with inherently low weathering rates, are long.

- There is evidence from the UK that acid deposition has resulted in acidification of acid sensitive soils and these findings are consistent with studies in other parts of Europe.
- There is experimental evidence that a reduction of strong acid anion inputs (sulphate and nitrate) results in a rapid increase (*ca* 1 year) in soil water acid neutralising capacity (ANC).
- Recovery of soils by an increase in base saturation will take much longer (decades) than recovery of soil water ANC. Change is dependent on base cation supply from weathering (slow) and atmospheric inputs.
- Results of modelling studies are consistent with these experimental data and indicate that recovery of soil and soil waters from acidification will take decades. For some upland soils, models predict that soil base saturation may never return to predicted values prior to the onset of acid deposition.

- There is currently little unequivocal evidence of recovery from soil acidification in the UK as there are few data collected from appropriate soil types. Most available data suggest continuing acidification of soils under semi-natural vegetation into the 1990s but a re-sampling study in 1998/99 suggests an increase in pH in some upland soils since 1978. Re-sampling exercises on arable and intensive grassland soils show a decrease in acidity over the last 10 to 20 years.

- Desorption of sulphate from the soil may slow the increase in soil water ANC following a reduction in sulphate deposition. Manipulation experiments suggest that it may take up to 20 years for sulphate outputs to reach a new steady-state with inputs.

- There is experimental evidence from forest systems that a reduction in the amount of deposited oxidised-N results in an immediate decrease in soil water nitrate concentrations and an increase in soil water ANC. However our ability to predict the future consequences of nitrogen deposition for soil acidification and recovery is limited due to inadequate understanding of N dynamics and limited representation of N processes in soil acidification models.

Effects on Freshwaters (Chapter 6)

The sensitivity of many upland soils to acidification is carried into the freshwaters within the same catchments. Thus the large areas of the UK with acid sensitive soils are co-located with many sensitive freshwaters, and the best long-term record of environmental acidification in the UK is to be found in the lake sediments. These records show lake acidification in the latter part of the 19th century, largely from UK industry and domestic emissions. The freshwaters also provide clear signs of chemical recovery, detailed below and in Chapter 6. The timescale for recovery is slow, especially for biological recovery, and there is evidence of an important interaction between climate and freshwater chemistry in the UK.

- Acidification of freshwaters has been widespread across the uplands of the UK from the 1850s onwards.

- The main cause of surface water acidification is deposition of anthropogenic S, although N compounds contribute significantly in some areas.

- There is clear evidence of chemical changes that indicate the start of recovery from acidification in most areas since the 1970s, consistent with large reductions in S emission/deposition. This trend is important in indicating that target ecosystems are potentially recovering as a result of emission control.

- Since the mid-1980s S deposition has declined appreciably around source areas but very little in more remote areas. This is reflected in trends over the last 15 years, whereby SO_4^{2-} concentrations have decreased at sites across the UK. The spatial extent of this decline is not constant, however, and S concentration has decreased, with pH recovery, in 'near source' surface waters but with less change in remote areas, consistent with the observed changes in S deposition.

- There are indications of biological recovery from acidification but by contrast with the results from chemical assessments these are modest and restricted to a small number of locations. This might be because regional chemical trends have not yet been sustained or substantial enough to allow re-colonization, but for streams, limits imposed by continuing acid episodes cannot be ruled out.

- Predictions into the future show a continued chemical recovery if agreed emission reductions are achieved but significant time lags (decades) are likely.

- During the last 10 years, surface waters across the UK have shown a significant increase in the total organic carbon concentration (TOC). This is not thought to be related to decreased acidic deposition, but probably results from a change in the climatic regime with increased temperatures in recent years.

Effects on Vegetation (Chapter 7)

Vegetation clearly suffered from the effects of large SO_2 concentrations in the 1960s and 1970s, but the large reductions in concentration have provided an opportunity for recovery, especially of some of the lower plants and lichens. The current SO_2 concentrations and especially those of 2010 and beyond will pose little or no threat to vegetation. The main pollutant threats to the health and productivity of UK vegetation are from nitrogen deposition and ozone. In the case of nitrogen deposition, the semi-natural plant communities in areas of large deposition show evidence of change, (e.g. reductions in diversity) both in survey data and in site specific studies, and current emission controls will not greatly reduce the current threat. In the case of ozone, there have been reductions in the peak concentrations, but summer concentrations still reach values which pose a threat to the health and productivity of semi-natural and crop plants in the UK.

- Decreases in SO_2 concentrations over the past two to three decades have had detectable effects on vegetation, including substantial increases in the distribution of many lichen species, improved tree growth in certain areas and increased likelihood of sulphur deficiency in crops.

- Instances of change in vegetation composition observed throughout the UK are consistent with effects of nitrogen deposition. Community composition in several nutrient poor habitats is changing towards species associated with higher nitrogen availability. Effects of habitat management are also implicated in these changes.

- There is no field evidence of recovery of vegetation composition in the UK in response to reduced N deposition, and such responses are expected to lag by several decades. Simple reversal of change may not be possible, and active site management may be needed to promote recovery.

- Current O_3 concentrations in the UK have been shown experimentally to reduce tree growth, cause visible leaf injury, reduce crop yield and affect semi-natural vegetation. Peak concentrations are falling but the implications of this for vegetation are uncertain.

- The AOT40 exposure index currently used for O_3 risk assessment in Europe has several limitations, most notably the fact that data from the experimental conditions in which it was derived are not directly applicable in field conditions.

- Surveys of tree condition since 1987 have not identified a chronic deterioration in the UK, related to air pollution. However, there is clear evidence of the effects of drought, and insect and fungal attack on some species in specific areas, and air pollution may play a role in predisposing trees to such effects.

- By 2010, most of the country will be protected from the direct adverse effects of SO_2. However, ozone and nitrogen deposition are likely to still pose a major threat to vegetation in the UK.

- The empirical critical loads for nutrient nitrogen which are currently used for UK mapping may be to too high to reflect adverse ecological change in some ecosystems, and need to be reviewed.

- Critical levels of SO_2 and NO_x may be exceeded close to some major roads, industrial works and urban areas, and the implications of such exceedances on sites of high nature conservation value in such locations need to be examined in more detail.

- More sophisticated methods of ecological risk assessment need to be developed to provide a closer link between critical loads and levels and actual impacts on vegetation, taking into account factors such as land management, climate, soil water and nutrient status and initial species composition.

The European Perspective (Chapter 8)

The changes observed in the pollution climate of the UK during the last two decades are similar to those observed elsewhere in Europe, where, overall, a similar reduction in emissions of sulphur has taken place. The change from a pollution climate dominated by sulphur to one currently dominated by nitrogen compounds, and ozone, is also common across much of Europe. However, there are areas of continental Europe which experience particular air pollution problems, and are a valuable guide to the magnitude of the problems within some areas of the UK. For example, within the Netherlands, ammonia and the environmental, political and scientific problems with which it is associated are especially important. In southern Europe, the problems of elevated ozone concentrations for vegetation and human health are particularly important. Thus a comparison of the field data and the analyses of the issues by research groups elsewhere in Europe provide a very helpful perspective for this report.

- Emissions of sulphur in Europe declined by 41% between 1990 and 1998. During the same period, emissions of NO_x declined by 21%, NH_3 by 14% and NMVOCs by 24%. European policy to decrease emissions was much more successful than that of the US.

- A substantial decrease in sulphur deposition and rainfall acidity has been recorded throughout Europe.

- Nitrogen deposition in Europe has changed little over the last two decades, and, in most countries of Europe, is dominated by reduced nitrogen as NH_3 and NH_4^+.

- Base cation deposition measured in the open field and in throughfall has declined during the last decade.

- Scenario studies show that by 2010 the Gothenburg protocol will lead to a substantial reduction of the exceedances of critical loads of acidity in Europe. For nutrient nitrogen, however, critical load exceedances are unlikely to change very much.

- Non-linearities in the relationship between the emission and deposition patterns for sulphur and oxidised nitrogen have been detected, leading to slower reductions in critical loads exceedance in remote areas than expected.

- Ground-level ozone continues to exceed thresholds for effects on vegetation and human health. The peak concentrations have declined during the last decade but mean ozone concentrations show signs of an upward trend.

- It is expected that global background ozone concentrations will continue to rise, due to increased precursor emissions, particularly in Eastern Europe and Asia. Emission control strategies in N America and Europe will lead to a reduction in peak episodic concentrations in those regions.

♦ Signs of recovery both of freshwater chemistry and biology have been shown in many ecosystems severely damaged by deposition during the 1970's and 1980's. The recovery is still limited and model calculations indicate that the recovery process may take many decades.

♦ Particulate matter has become an issue of increasing concern over Europe and North America and is considered to be the most important driving force for future control of the substances under the Gothenburg Protocol and the NECD.

Recovery (Chapter 9)

The core chapters of this report provide a detailed assessment of the emissions, deposition and effects of acidifying pollutants, eutrophication by nitrogen and ground-level ozone on UK ecosystems. The commitments by the UK to reduce emissions of sulphur, nitrogen and volatile organic compounds during the last two decades and over the coming decade, will greatly reduce pollutant concentrations and deposition within the UK and the contribution to pollutant deposition throughout Europe. This chapter summarises the evidence for recovery of air quality and effects on soils, freshwaters and vegetation of the above pollutants.

♦ Current (1995 to 1997) exceedance of critical loads for acidification extends over 71% of the area of sensitive ecosystems in the UK, and is expected to decline to 46% by 2010.

♦ Deposition of reduced nitrogen is a major part of the exceedance and will become the dominant component by 2010.

♦ There is evidence of chemical recovery in some upland soils from the effects of acidification, with the largest increases in soil pH occurring in the uplands of England and Wales.

♦ There is evidence of chemical recovery of some freshwaters from the effects of acidification in Galloway. Cumbria, the Pennines, North Wales and the SE England.

♦ Chemical recovery of UK freshwaters is not uniform and large areas show no recovery.

♦ Biological recovery of freshwaters is a slow process and signs of recovery are few in the UK. However, there are signs of recovery of epilithic diatoms in some areas of Scotland and Wales.

♦ Critical loads for eutrophication are currently (1995-1997) exceeded in ca 25% of UK 1 km x 1 km grid squares with sensitive grasslands and ca 55% with heathland. These percentages are expected to decline to ca 20% and ca 40% respectively in 2010, with reduced nitrogen (NH_3 and NH_4^+) being the main contributor.

♦ The reductions in nitrogen emissions have produced only small decreases in nitrogen deposition in the UK so far (16%). For eutrophying effects there is no evidence of chemical or biological recovery. When deposition is reduced sufficiently to allow recovery to begin, the recovery process is expected to be very slow.

♦ For ozone, there has been a substantial decline in the peak ozone concentrations (30% since the mid-1980s), although the mean concentrations show evidence of an increase and are expected to increase further over the coming decades. The net effect of these changes in the ozone climatology of the UK on terrestrial ecosystems remains unknown.

Contents

Contents

Chapter 1: Introduction

Long-range transport of air pollutants between the countries of Europe was identified as an important ecological and political issue during the late 1960s, and formalised by Sweden at the United Nations Conference on the Human Environment (Sweden 1971). The early work focussed strongly on the role of sulphur as the major contributor to acid deposition, and monitoring and research programmes throughout Europe were stimulated by the political implications of inter-country exchange of pollutants.

The primary pollutants are generally emitted as gases SO_2, NO, NO_2 and NH_3. The acidifying gases SO_2, NO and NO_2 are oxidised in the atmosphere to their respective acids, H_2SO_4 and HNO_3. In the process of oxidation the gaseous SO_2 is transformed to particle SO_4^{2-}, while HNO_3 may be present as a gas or within particles or cloud droplets. The pollutants are removed from the atmosphere either directly by absorption at the ground or washed out by rain and snow, giving rise to the expression "acid rain". The processes of emission, chemical transformation and deposition are illustrated in Figure 1.1, for the major acidifying pollutant emissions SO_2, NO_2 and NH_3. With residence times for these pollutants of 1 to 3 days and average transport distances by wind in the lower atmosphere of 500 to 1000 km per day it is easy to see how substantial quantities of these pollutants are exchanged between the countries of Europe. The long-range transport of pollutants in Europe is the subject of a UNECE protocol (http://www.unece.org/env/lrtap/), within which an international monitoring network and modelling of inter-country exchange of pollutants are the primary activities. The UNECE long-range transport convention also provides the framework within which protocols have been developed (Table 1.1). Thus, the analysis provided within this report for the UK forms part of activities throughout Europe, which are described on a continental scale by the reports of EMEP (http://www.emep.int/). A chapter of this report on the wider European picture forms an important perspective for this report.

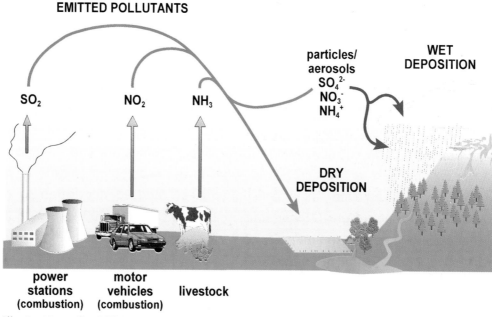

Figure 1.1 Illustration of acidifying and eutrophying pollutant emission and deposition processes.

The first international protocol to reduce pollutant emissions, the Thirty per cent Reduction in Sulphur Emission (the '30% Club') in 1984, was followed in 1988 and 1991 by protocols on oxides of nitrogen (NO_x) and non-methane volatile organic compounds (NMVOCs) to reduce the effects of acidification and photochemical smog. Sulphur emissions were subject to a further protocol to reduce acidification effects in 1994. In 1999 a major protocol to further reduce emissions of SO_2, NO_x, NMVOCs and NH_3 (included in the process for the first time) was opened for signature. Table 1.1 summarises these protocols and the emission reduction targets for the EU are shown. Substantial political action to reduce effects of the major pollutants responsible for acidification, smog and eutrophication has therefore been made.

The effects of these protocols on the pollutant concentrations, deposition and effects to date (and where possible into the future) form an important focus for this report. The individual pollutant gases have quite short residence times in the atmosphere, varying from a few hours for NH_3 to a few days for NO_2. However, the effects on terrestrial ecosystems have much longer time constants for recovery from the effects of acid deposition. This is a consequence of the buffering capacities of the chemical and biological systems and the magnitude of pollutant burden within the ecosystems. In the case of some slowly weathering soils recovering from acidification or an ecosystem recovering from N deposition these time scales extend to several decades.

With the substantial magnitude of reductions in sulphur emissions in the UK (and elsewhere in Europe) over the last two decades we should, given a satisfactory monitoring and assessment programme, be able to detect resulting improvements in air and environment quality. The observed changes in concentration, deposition and effects on soils, freshwaters, vegetation and other targets in the natural as well as the built environment form a common thread to the analysis. There are also important interactions between the pollutants which may have influenced the atmospheric processing and/or terrestrial fate and effects. Such interactions may have introduced non-linearities in the relationships between emissions, concentrations, deposition and effects.

The format of the report follows the pathway of the pollutants from emission and ambient concentrations to deposition followed by a consideration of the effects on freshwaters, soils and vegetation.

The UK has extensive networks to monitor concentrations of the gases SO_2, NO_2, NH_3, O_3 and wet deposition of the major ions associated with acid deposition and eutrophication, see Appendix B. A comparison between trends in emissions of the primary pollutants and both concentration and deposition, develops the background for an assessment of the current effects of acid deposition and eutrophication on the soils, freshwaters and flora of the UK. An important focus for this part of the analysis is 'what is the current magnitude of the effects, and is there evidence of recovery as a consequence of reduced deposition to date? It is important to note here that current (1999) emissions of sulphur (*ca* 600 kt-S) are 20% of the peak in 1970 of *ca* 3000 kt-S, so the majority of S emission reduction has already taken place. For nitrogen oxides the reduction from peak emissions (840 kt-N in 1990) is about 60% to 488 kt-N in 1999.

The following questions summarize the approach and the focus of the report

❑   How has UK air quality changed in response to the international protocols (Table 1.1)?

❑   Are the observed changes in concentrations and deposition of the major pollutants consistent with the current understanding of the emissions, atmospheric processes, transport and deposition of pollutants?

❏ When will the full effect of the changes required by the protocols be observed by the monitoring networks?

❏ What is the current extent of environmental effects of acidification in the UK and can we detect signs of recovery?

❏ Will the ecosystems of the UK be protected by the current protocols from the effects of acid deposition, eutrophication and ozone?

❏ What is the expected time course of recovery from the effects of acid deposition, eutrophication and ground-level ozone?

Critical loads and levels

The potential for the air pollutants to damage the natural or built environment provides the motivation for much of the control measures to date, as well as this report. However measuring and quantifying the damage by pollutants is not a simple matter. Similarly measuring the gain in environmental quality resulting from legislative action requires quantitative measures of environmental sensitivity to pollutant inputs followed by an assessment of deposition and a comparison between them. **The common measure of environmental sensitivity is the critical load. This is defined as a quantitative estimate of exposure to one of more pollutants below which significant harmful effects on sensitive elements of the environment do not occur according to present knowledge.** Appendix D describes the methods used to calculate critical loads for the UK and they have been quantified for acidification of soils and freshwaters (Chapters 5 and 6 respectively). Effects of SO_2, NH_x, NO_x and ozone on vegetation are considered in Chapter 7. Critical loads (and in the case of gaseous pollutants, also critical levels) have been used with measured and modelled exposure and deposition data to gain the maximum reduction in effects for the investment in control measures. There is in many cases a gap between the estimated deposition or exposure following implementation of a protocol and the critical load or level. The gap is revealed as an exceedance of the critical load or level and provides an indication of the areas in which ecosystem effects of the pollutants may be present. The strategies for introduction of pollutant control measures have been developed to provide the greatest reduction in areas in exceedance of critical loads and levels. These gap-closure strategies have been at the heart of policy development within the UNECE.

Critical loads currently offer the only quantitative methodology to assess environmental impacts of acidifying deposition at national or regional scales. The exceedance of critical loads or levels is **not** a quantitative estimate of damage to the environment; it represents the potential for damage. The time scales for damage vary greatly among the environmental targets and pollutant combinations, and some time scales for damage are very long (10-100 years). Recovery of ecosystems may also be rapid or very slow, again depending on the environmental target and pollutant.

In quantifying areas of the country in exceedance of critical loads or levels, great quantitative precision is of course possible through the mapping and calculation procedures. These must not be confused with accuracy, as the combination of data sets, all with their respective uncertainties conceal large uncertainties for which there are currently no rigorous procedures to quantify.

The application of critical loads and critical level methodologies has proved very useful for policy development and has provided cost effective control measures. This has all been achieved despite large uncertainties in the actual magnitude and location of damage in the field. However, the large uncertainties in exceedance values and their uncertain relationship with actual damage cautions against the over interpretation of mapped or accumulated exceedances. In this report we have presented critical loads and levels data and estimates of the exceedances to illustrate the current and projected potential for effects of pollutants on UK ecosystems.

This report describes the current deposition and exposure of the UK terrestrial environment to air pollutants, the changes in the last 20 years and it also estimates the effects of the protocols agreed in Gothenburg in 1999 on soils, freshwaters and vegetation in the UK up to the year 2010.

Table 1.1 International pollutant emission control protocols within the UNECE - CLTRAP (United Nations Economic Commission for Europe – Convention on Long-Range Transboundary Air Pollution) and the EU (European Union).

UNECE – CLRTAP Protocol (common name)			Objectives		
	Open for Signature & [Entry into Force[1]]	Number of signatures & ratifications (as of 1st Sep. 01)[2]	Pollutant	Base Year/ Target Year	Reduction %
Acidification, Eutrophication and Ground-level Ozone[3] (Gothenburg Protocol)	1999	31, 1	Sulphur dioxide Nitrogen oxides Non-methane VOCs Ammonia[3]	1990/2010	75 50 58 12
Persistent Organic Pollutants (POPs)[4]	1998	36, 7	eliminate any discharges, emissions and losses of POPs.		
Heavy Metals[4]	1998	36, 10	cadmium lead mercury	Reduce, control or eliminate the use of heavy metals.	
Further Reduction of Sulphur Emissions[5] (2nd S protocol or Oslo protocol)	1994 [1998]	28, 23	Sulphur dioxide	1980/2000	62
Volatile Organic Compounds[6]	1991 [1997]	23, 21	Non-methane VOCs	1987/1999	30
Nitrogen Oxides[6]	1988 [1991]	25, 28	Nitrogen oxides	1987/1994	stabilisation
Thirty per cent Reduction in Sulphur Emissions (1st S protocol or the "30% club")	1985 [1987]	19, 22	Sulphur dioxide	1980/1993	30
European monitoring and evaluation programme (EMEP)	1984 [1988]	22, 38	Long-term financing of EMEP.		
EU	Year initiated		Objectives		
EU – 5th Environmental Action Programme (5EAP)	1993		Sulphur dioxide Nitrogen oxides Non-methane VOCs	1985/2000 1990/2000 1990/1999	35 30 30
National Emissions Ceilings Directive[7] (NECD)	1999		Sulphur dioxide Nitrogen oxides Non-methane VOCs Ammonia	1990/2010	77 55 54 14

1 Sixteen ratifications are needed for a protocol to enter into force
2 Updated status can be found at http://www.unece.org/env/lrtap/
3 The percentage emission reduction target for the EU is shown, which corresponds with the overall effect of the different emission ceilings for each Member State.
4 POPs and heavy metals will not be considered further in this report.
5 The different emission ceilings for each Member State correspond to a 62% emission reduction for the EU.
6 These are the same for individual Member States and for the EU.
7 Proposed targets from the common position (June 2000) for a national emission ceilings directive (NECD).

Chapter 2: Emissions

> ➤ Annual UK emissions of sulphur dioxide peaked in 1970 at 3259 kt-S, declined to 594 kt-S by 1999 and will decline further to around 312 kt-S by 2010.
>
> ➤ Annual UK emissions of nitrogen oxides peaked in the 1980s at *ca* 850 kt-N and declined to less than 500 kt-N by 1999. They will continue to decline to around 359 kt-N by 2010.
>
> ➤ Annual UK emissions of ammonia are the least certain of all the pollutants that contribute to acidification and eutrophication; they reached approximately 300 kt-N annually in the late 1980s and are expected to decline by 11%, relative to 1990, by 2010.
>
> ➤ Annual UK NMVOC emissions peaked in 1989 at 2500 kt, declined to 1700 kt and are set to decline further to 1200 kt by 2010.
>
> ➤ Annual CO emissions peaked in the 1970s at *ca* 8500 kt, declined to less than 5000 kt by 1999 and will decline to 2800 kt by 2010.
>
> ➤ Emissions of base cations (and other long-range transport metals) are very uncertain, and have been estimated to be 74 kt annually. Emissions have probably declined as industrial particle filtration systems have improved.

2.1 Introduction

This chapter describes the UK emissions of the primary pollutants that lead to acid deposition, eutrophication of the environment and photochemical oxidant formation and deposition. The current emissions and trends in the UK over the last three decades form the focus of this chapter while emissions from the rest of Europe and other countries are discussed in Chapter 8. However, the emphasis elsewhere in the report on the changes in concentrations, deposition and an assessment of the effects of these changes requires this chapter to detail important changes in the spatial pattern and nature of sources. In particular, any change in source characteristics that might influence the pattern of deposition is important. Emissions are estimated from statistical information such as fuel use, km of travel or production and use. Emission factors describe, for example, the amount of a pollutant emitted per unit of fuel used or km driven. The UK inventory (National Atmospheric Emission Inventory (NAEI) at NETCEN AEA Technology, http://www.aeat.co.uk/netcen/airqual/naei/) is compiled on an annual basis and provided all data used in this chapter unless stated otherwise. Each year the full time-series is updated to take account of improved methodologies and updated fuel use or activity data. The robustness, quality and uncertainties of the inventories vary between pollutants and depend on the complexity of the emitting processes and the availability of representative data (emission factors). Sulphur (S), for example, is primarily emitted from the sulphur contained in fuels. This is relatively stable for different fuels across a wide range of combustion conditions and consequently the sulphur inventory is very reliable. However, estimates of NO_x emissions are more uncertain as they depend on the conditions of combustion, which can vary considerably depending on engine maintenance, operation and type. Other pollutants have increased uncertainties due to a shortage of information to form a reliable UK picture or complexity in the release process as in the case of ammonia from agriculture where emissions depend on animal feed, housing and waste management techniques.

2.2 Sulphur Emissions

Sulphur emissions arise principally from the S in solid and liquid fuels which have traditionally been burned in large quantities for electricity generation, domestic and industrial heating and for transport. Natural and process emissions also contribute to atmospheric concentrations of S.

2.2.1 SO$_2$ Trends

The UK emission profile, Figure 2.1 (Goodwin *et al.* 2000), exhibits a steady decline of 82% between 1970 and 1999 with the exception of small peaks in 1973 and 1979, which correspond to the harsh winters in those years. There is also a short period at the end of the 1980s when emissions were relatively constant from year to year. The comparatively small decrease in emissions between 1997 and 1998 is due to the failure of the flue gas desulphurisation (FGD) plant at a major UK power station.

Table 2.1 shows UK emissions broken down by source sector and fuel categories (Goodwin *et al.* 2000). The two main fuels contributing to S emissions are solid fuel and petroleum products (92% in 1999). Emissions from solid fuel use declined by 76% between 1970 and 1999 and those from petroleum by 91%.

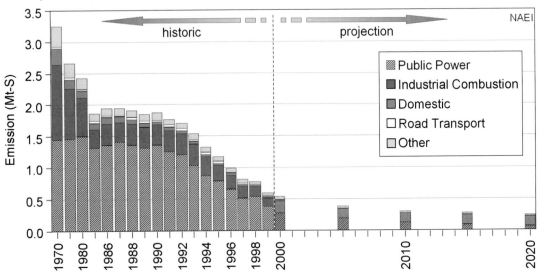

Figure 2.1 UK emissions of sulphur (Mt-S) 1970 – 2020. Note: Estimates from 2000 - 2020 are based on projections using: DTI fuel demand and economic growth data, regulation of "S" content in fuel and expected "S" reductions in the power, refinery and cement industries.

Reductions in emissions from coal are from wide scale replacement of coal with natural gas as a fuel for domestic, commercial, industrial and in later years power station uses. In addition, fitting of FGD at the Drax and Ratcliffe power stations has further reduced coal related emissions since 1995. The most important factors in the fall in emissions from petroleum use are the decline in fuel oil use and the reduction in the sulphur content of gas oil, fuel oil and diesel. The reduction in the sulphur content of gas oil is particularly significant in sectors such as domestic heating, commercial heating and off-road sources, where gas oil is used extensively. The sulphur content of diesel has steadily declined in recent years, to reduce the particulate emissions to the atmosphere from vehicles (QUARG 1996). SO$_2$ emissions from diesel in the early 1990's were relatively constant, however between 1994 and 1998 this source of sulphur declined by 72%.

Figure 2.2 shows emission trends from urban sources of SO_2 including road transport, commercial and public service and domestic emissions. Emissions have reduced steadily and significantly since 1970.

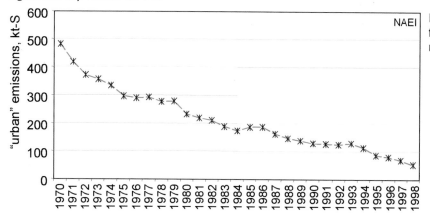

Figure 2.2 S emissions (kt-S) from urban sources (commercial, road transport & residential).

Table 2.1 UK emissions of sulphur by UN/ECE[1] source category and fuel type (kt-S).

	1970	1980	1990	1991	1992	1993	1994	1995	1996	1997	1998	1999	%99
Comb. in energy prod.													
Public power	1457	1504	1362	1268	1217	1042	881	796	660	513	536	388	65%
Petroleum refining plants	121	131	77	81	73	74	68	71	72	67	49	47	8%
Other comb. & trans.	151	36	21	19	8	7	5	5	5	7	6	8	1%
Comb. in comm/inst/res													
Residential plant	261	113	54	58	52	57	46	34	36	32	27	27	4%
Comm/pub/agri Comb.	226	109	45	43	45	48	40	30	29	24	17	11	2%
Combustion in industry													
Iron & steel comb.	217	64	44	43	33	38	35	33	29	29	23	21	4%
Other ind. comb.	707	388	185	193	217	214	183	140	114	95	81	57	10%
Production processes	47	39	24	21	18	17	15	14	14	13	10	9	1%
Extr./distrib. of fossil fuels	3	3	8	3	4	3	3	3	4	3	3	1	0%
Solvent use	1	1	1	1	1	1	1	3	2	3	3	2	0%
Road transport	22	21	32	29	31	30	32	26	19	14	12	6	1%
Other trans/mach[2]	47	31	24	26	25	24	24	22	23	21	19	18	3%
Waste	2	3	3	3	3	2	2	2	1	1	1	2	0%
By fuel type													
Solid	1837	1571	1385	1337	1288	1085	922	821	679	577	591	437	74%
Petroleum	1273	774	406	374	373	423	361	303	280	194	148	112	19%
Gas	96	47	42	39	30	15	15	15	16	19	15	17	3%
Non-fuel	54	49	45	36	34	31	36	37	32	30	31	29	5%
Total	3259	2440	1877	1784	1724	1553	1333	1174	1005	819	784	594	100%

1 UK emissions reported in IPCC format (Salway, 2001) differ slightly due to the different source categories used.
2 Including railways, shipping, naval vessels, military aircraft and off-road sources

2.2.2 Assessment of Reductions from "High Stack" and "Low Level" SO_2 Sources Between 1970 and 1998

In assessing the impact of changes in the SO_2 emission inventory, it is important to examine the change in total emissions, their spatial distribution and the height of the source. In considering the transport and fate of SO_2 the height at which the SO_2 is emitted to the atmosphere has a very important effect on the local concentration field and the potential for both local removal by dry deposition and terrestrial effects close to the source.

This section provides details of the relative trends in "high stack" and "low level" emissions for comparisons with observed (concentration) trends by separating the NAEI SO_2 estimates into low and high level sources see Table 2.2 below.

Table 2.2 Allocation of emissions to high stack and low level sources.

High Level	Large industrial processes (sulphuric acid, aluminium, coke production, collieries, refineries, cement & lime)
	Industrial combustion (Large Combustion Plant (LCP) component from refinery, industry and iron & steel)
	Power stations
	Municipal waste incineration
	Flaring
Low Level	Non-industrial (domestic, commercial, transport and agriculture)
	Industrial combustion (non-LCP component from refineries, industry and iron & steel)

Refineries, iron and steel production and other industrial plant emit SO_2 from a variety of high stack and low-level combustion sources. LCP (Large Combustion Plant) returns have been used to separate the combustion emissions into high and low level components. LCP emissions are reported from 1991 to the latest year (currently 1998). The NAEI total for the sector can thus be separated into LCP (high stack) and non-LCP (low level) emissions by subtracting the LCP component from the total NAEI estimate. However, LCP data are not available for 1970 – 1990. In order to estimate the LCP and non-LCP component for 1970 – 1990 the %LCP from 1991 has been assumed for all earlier years. Table 2.3 shows the %LCP assumed for 1970 – 1990 refinery, industry, iron and steel and power station emissions.

Table 2.3 %LCP SO_2 assumed for 1970 – 1990.

NAEI Sector	LCP as % of SO_2 total for sector	
	1970 –1991	1998
Refinery combustion	77	51
Industrial Combustion	39	67
Iron and Steel Combustion	12	13
Power Stations	100	100

Figure 2.3 shows a significant contribution from reductions in "low level" sources to the overall SO_2 reductions from 1970 to 1990. During this period "high stack" emissions contributed only 37%. In contrast for more recent years, 1990 – 1998, over 84% of emission reductions have been as a result of reductions from "high stack" sources.

The majority of emission reductions between 1970 and 1990 (63%) were from low level sources. This reduction resulted from a switch from solid and liquid fuels high in S to low S natural gas across the industrial, domestic and commercial sectors. In addition a downward trend in liquid fuel sulphur contents has helped to reduce emissions further. The impact of these changes had less of an influence over the large "high stack" emitting sources during the 1970 – 1990 period. Since the early 1990s with de-regulation of gas use in electricity generation and implementation of integrated pollution control (IPC) on large plants, emissions from large "high stack" sources have declined dramatically, contributing 84% of the 1990 – 1998 SO_2 emission reduction.

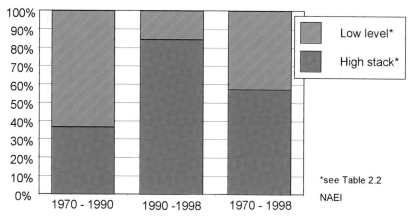

Figure 2.3 Contribution to SO₂ emission reductions.

2.2.3 SO₂ Emission Maps

The geographical distribution of SO₂ emissions compiled for the NAEI (Goodwin *et al.* 1997 & 2000) is shown in Figure 2.4 aggregated to 10 km x 10 km. A large fraction of the SO₂ emissions are concentrated into relatively few 1 km x 1 km grid squares containing the major point sources such as refineries and power stations and large industrial plant. The resulting map highlights the main urban areas and some major roads. High emissions around Belfast are from a combination of industry and domestic sources burning coal and oil for heating. The large urban areas of London and Birmingham, which are covered by Smoke Control Areas, show relatively low SO₂ emission levels. Emissions from UK shipping are evident in large port areas.

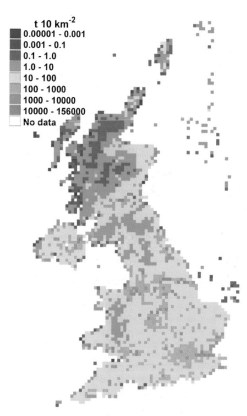

Figure 2.4 1998 UK spatial emissions of SO₂ at 10 km x 10 km.

2.2.4 Policies & Progress: Sulphur Dioxide

The 1st Sulphur Protocol laid down a target of 30% reduction from 1980 by 1993 for all countries (Table 1.1). The United Kingdom did not sign this protocol but did in fact meet the requirement and is likely to achieve its CLRTAP target for 2010 of 313 kt-S through continued action to reduce "S" in liquid fuels, switching to natural gas, FGD abatement and use of low "S" coal in power plants. Figure 2.5 shows the driving forces for, and achievements of, emission reductions in the UK power industry.

In Figure 2.5 the reference line (thick black) shows how emissions would have increased with increasing energy demand with "no structural change" made to the industry in terms of efficiency, fuel use or nuclear substitution.

1. Nuclear power (pink), introduced prior to 1980, offered nominally SO₂-free energy and shows a saving of 0.75 Mt-S in 1998 from the "no structural change" reference scenario.

2. After taking account of nuclear power, efficiency improvements (blue line) are responsible for an additional reduction of 13% or 0.3 Mt-S by 1998.

3. Fuel switching (green dotted), which began in 1992/3, achieved an additional reduction of 23% or 0.5 Mt-S by 1998.

4. By 1993/4 FGD (dark green dashed) was being fitted at two plants in the UK. This action achieved an additional 5% or 0.1 Mt-S reduction by 1998.

5. Throughout the period 1980 to 1998 the average "S" content of coal fluctuated. By 1998 the average "S" content was on a consistent downward trend. This effect has contributed to an additional 3% or 0.075 Mt-S reduction by 1998.

The combination of these measures and actions brings us to the actual emissions (thin black line) and represents an annual saving of 1.8 Mt-S and a reduction of 77% for 1998 from the reference estimate based on electricity demand in 1998 and the 1980 industry structure.

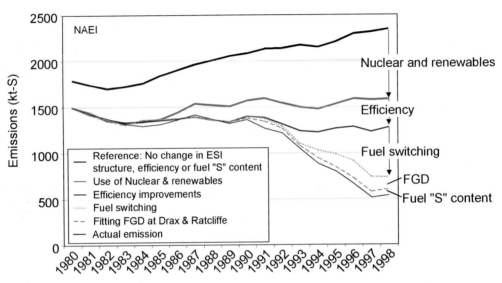

Figure 2.5 Driving forces for emission reductions in the UK power industry (kt-S y^{-1}). The reference line (thick black) is detached from the other lines as the use of nuclear power began prior to 1980.

2.3 Ammonia Emissions

Emissions of ammonia are mainly from a broad range of agricultural sources (Misselbrook *et al.*, 2000; Dragosits, 1998), amounting to about 242 kt-N annually with an additional 46 kt–N from non-agricultural sources (Sutton *et al.*, 2000a). However, the number and complexity of NH_3 sources in the landscape has made it difficult to quantify the emissions. Furthermore, there is evidence from the monitoring data for atmospheric NH_3, wet deposition and aerosol concentrations that there is more reduced nitrogen in the atmosphere, deposited to the UK landscape and advected out from the UK shoreline by the wind than can be accounted for using the current inventory (Sutton *et al.*, 2000a). There are similar problems in accounting for the measured air concentrations of NH_3 and aerosol NH_4^+ using official NH_3 emissions in the Netherlands (Erisman *et al.*, 1998a & 2001), which are described in more detail in Chapter 8.

The estimates of UK NH_3 emissions range from 70 to 595 kt-N (Sutton *et al.*, 1995a) and while important progress has been made in quantifying both agricultural and non-agricultural emissions, there remain very large uncertainties in the emissions in the UK and elsewhere in Europe. The following section on the trends in UK NH_3 emissions should therefore be treated with caution because, while the animal numbers are known well, changes in agricultural practice and their effects on NH$_3$ emission are much less certain.

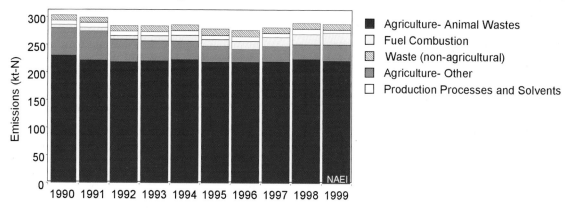

Figure 2.6 Emissions of ammonia (kt-N).

2.3.1 Ammonia Trends

Recent estimates of the UK emissions of ammonia are shown in Table 2.4 and Figure 2.6. The inventory is based on data compiled by a working group on ammonia emissions comprising DEFRA, Silsoe Research Institute, Institute of Grassland and Environmental Research, ADAS, Imperial College and CEH Edinburgh (Misselbrook *et al.*, 2000; Dragosits 1998), modified by AEA Technology for consistency with the NAEI (Goodwin *et al,.* 2000). Much work has been done over recent years to improve the estimates from both agricultural and non-agricultural sources. Emissions for years prior to 1990 have not been estimated.

Table 2.4 UK emissions of ammonia (kt-N).

	1990	1991	1992	1993	1994	1995	1996	1997	1998	1999	%1999
Agriculture (cultivation with fertiliser)	41	44	34	30	29	25	20	23	22	25	9%
Agriculture (livestock)	223	214	212	214	215	211	211	213	217	215	75%
Combustion (stationary)	5	6	5	5	5	4	4	4	3	4	1%
Combustion (road transport)	1	1	1	3	5	7	10	12	14	16	6%
Fertiliser production	4	4	4	4	4	4	5	3	5	2	1%
Other industrial processes (coke, paper, sugar beet, chemicals)	2	2	2	2	2	2	2	2	2	2	1%
Landfill	4	4	4	4	4	4	4	4	4	4	1%
Other (waste burning, pets, market gardens)	16	16	15	14	14	14	14	14	14	14	5%
Sewage sludge disposal	5	5	5	6	6	6	7	6	6	6	2%
Total	301	296	283	283	284	278	276	281	288	287	

Ammonia emissions are dominated by agricultural sources with emissions from livestock and their wastes comprising 82% of the total emission. These emissions derive mainly from the decomposition of urea in animal wastes and uric acid in poultry wastes. Emissions depend on animal species, age, weight, diet, housing systems, waste management and storage techniques. Hence emissions are affected by a large number of factors that make the interpretation of experimental data difficult and emission estimates uncertain (Pain *et al.*, 1998; Sutton *et al.*, 1995a). The other agricultural sources included are emissions from fertiliser use, crops and decomposition of agricultural crops. These are particularly uncertain owing to the complexity of the processes involved. The category non-agricultural sources comprises a number of diverse sources. The total emission from these sources is estimated at around 20% of the total, however these are very uncertain due to a lack of data (Sutton *et al.* 2000a). Emissions of ammonia from road transport, although relatively small, are increasing as a result of the use of three way catalysts.

2.3.2 Ammonia Emission Maps

Figure 2.7 shows 5 km x 5 km UK emissions for 1999 from the CEH Edinburgh/University of Edinburgh model (the methodology used was described by Dragosits *et al.*, 1998). The areas of highest emission occur in relation to cattle farming (west and north west England, Northern Ireland), as well as in pig and poultry farming areas (East Anglia, North East England, central Scotland). By contrast, emissions are low in upland areas such as the North Pennines and Lake District of Northern England and in the Scottish Highlands.

Figure 2.7 UK Spatial Emissions of NH$_3$ at 5 km x 5 km (Source: CEH Edinburgh).

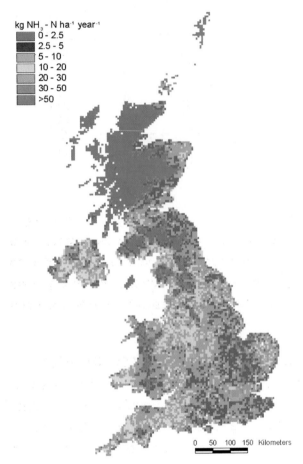

2.3.3 Policies & Progress: Ammonia

The Gothenburg protocol and proposed National Emission Ceiling Directive are the first agreements to have set targets for reductions in ammonia emission. For the UK, it is anticipated that the target will be the same for both agreements: a modest reduction of around 11% by 2010 from emissions in 1990. From forecasts of changes in agricultural activity, it is anticipated that this target will be met. More stringent targets would require technical abatement programmes. Section 8.2.3 describes the agreements in more detail and their implications for emissions across the rest of Europe.

2.4 Nitrogen Oxide Emissions

Emissions of nitrogen oxides come mainly from road vehicle combustion engines and the high temperature combustion processes used in power production.

2.4.1 NO$_x$ Trends

Figure 2.8 shows a 30% reduction in total UK NO$_x$ between 1970 and 1998 (Goodwin *et al.*, 2000). However this decrease has not been constant. Between 1970 and 1984 UK NO$_x$ emissions changed little except for small peaks in 1973 and 1979, which were due largely to the cold winters in those years.

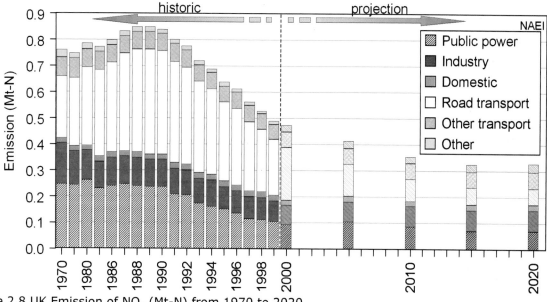

Figure 2.8 UK Emission of NO$_x$ (Mt-N) from 1970 to 2020.

From 1984, emissions increased markedly as a result of the growth in road traffic reaching a peak in 1989 (Table 2.5). Since 1989, total emissions have declined by 38% as a result of a 53% reduction from power stations and 42% decrease from road transport, the latter due to the growing fraction of vehicles fitted with a catalytic converter. The penetration of catalysts into the road vehicle fleet will further reduce emissions from road transport by 74% between 1998 and 2010.

2.4.2 The Contribution of Soil NO Emissions to the Total NO$_x$ Budget

Biological nitrification and denitrification processes in soil produce and emit NO. Rates of emission depend on substrate availability (mineral N) and soil physical properties. In industrial countries, well-aerated N fertilised arable soils are the largest sources of soil NO emission. Emission rates may exceed those of N$_2$O emission and can be as large as 1 mg-N m^{-2} h^{-1} (Thornton *et al.*, 1995).

In order to assess the contribution of soil NO emissions to the total NO$_x$ emission budget, a number of methodologies have been developed. Williams *et al.* (1992) and Stohl *et al.* (1996) calculated NO emission from a land use factor and soil temperature, to produce soil NO emission inventories for the US and Europe. Other methodologies attempted to derive soil NO emissions as a function of N fertiliser input (i.e. Skiba *et al.*, 1997) and more recently as a function of N input (by fertiliser and atmospheric deposition) and the water filled pore space of the soil (Sozanska, 1999; Skiba *et al.*, 2001). Several of these methodologies have been used to calculate soil NO emissions for the different countries throughout Europe (Simpson *et al.*, 1999). Estimates of the soil contribution to the total NO$_x$ budget ranged from 2 to 23% (Simpson *et al.*, 1999). Large regional variations were found by all methodologies. For the UK, for example, the contribution of soil to the total annual NO$_x$ budget may vary from 1 to 6%, but for Spain the most generous methodology estimated that soils are responsible for almost 30% of the total NO_x budget (Simpson *et al.*, 1999).

Work by Stohl *et al.* (1996) suggests large seasonal variations. On hot summer days the soil contribution to the total NO_x budget was larger than the annual average, and for some countries the magnitude of soil emissions was comparable to that of emissions from combustion and other non-biological processes.

❑ Estimates of soil NO emissions are very uncertain. In Europe, soils contribute between 2 to 23% to the total NO_x budget of individual countries.

❑ To reduce uncertainties, we need better estimates of the NO emission induced by N fertiliser.

❑ The importance of soil NO varies with season and country. In the warmer, less industrialised countries of Europe soils are a more important NO source than in the cooler highly industrialised countries.

❑ In all countries, soils contribute more to the total NO_x budget in summer than winter because the source is strongly influenced by soil temperature and soil water content, and so this source of NO_x can make an important contribution to photochemical smog formation.

Table 2.5 UK emissions of nitrogen oxides by UN/ECE[1] source category and fuel type (kt-N y^{-1}).

	1970	1980	1990	1991	1992	1993	1994	1995	1996	1997	1998	1999	%1999
Comb. in Energy Prod.													
Public power	247	262	238	208	204	173	160	151	137	113	111	103	21%
Petroleum refining plants	13	13	12	12	12	11	10	10	10	10	11	9	2%
Other comb. & trans.	19	14	19	20	20	20	23	15	15	15	16	17	3%
Comb. in Commercial Institutional & Residential													
Residential plant	19	19	19	22	21	22	21	20	23	21	22	22	4%
Comm/pub/agri Comb.	23	14	11	12	12	12	12	11	12	11	10	10	2%
Combustion in industry													
Iron & steel comb.	23	8	7	7	7	7	8	8	8	8	7	7	2%
Other ind. comb.	99	75	60	57	56	55	57	52	50	51	48	44	9%
Production processes	5	5	4	3	3	3	3	2	2	2	2	2	0%
Extr./distrib. of fossil fuels	0	0	0	0	0	0	0	0	0	0	0	0	0%
Road transport	234	301	397	388	373	349	330	303	291	268	239	217	44%
Other trans/mach	0	0	0	0	0	0	0	0	0	0	0	0	
Off-road sources	37	32	27	28	28	27	27	26	27	26	27	25	5%
Other	38	37	40	40	39	38	36	36	37	36	33	31	6%
Waste	2	4	3	3	2	2	3	3	2	1	1	1	0%
Land use change	3	5	3	2	2	0	0	0	0	0	0	0	0%
By fuel type													
Solid	267	263	234	209	204	166	152	143	126	103	99	91	19%
Petroleum	423	434	506	495	477	453	428	394	383	351	319	289	59%
Gas	32	53	66	69	71	75	81	75	81	82	86	88	18%
Non-fuel	39	37	34	29	26	25	28	26	23	25	24	20	4%
Total	760	787	840	802	778	719	689	637	614	562	528	488	

1 UK emissions reported in IPCC format (Salway, 2001) differ slightly due to the different source categories used.
2 Including railways, shipping, naval vessels, military aircraft

2.4.3 UK NO$_x$ Emission Maps

Figure 2.9 shows the total 1998 UK emissions of NO$_x$ at a scale of 10 km x 10 km, compiled from the NAEI 1 km x 1 km emission map (Goodwin *et al.*, 1997 & 2000). Approximately 30% of the total emission is concentrated in a few grid squares that contain point sources. Another 33% of the UK NO$_x$ emission is derived from major road links. These two elements are the most reliable data and together contribute 63% of the mapped emissions. For NO$_x$, road transport dominates and vehicles travelling at high speeds contribute the most. As a result, the major route-ways (e.g. Motorways and primary routes) are visible on the map. Urban areas and city centres show high emissions resulting from large volumes of road transport, residential and commercial combustion. A combination of high national shipping emission and relatively few large ports result in significant localised emissions from shipping in port areas.

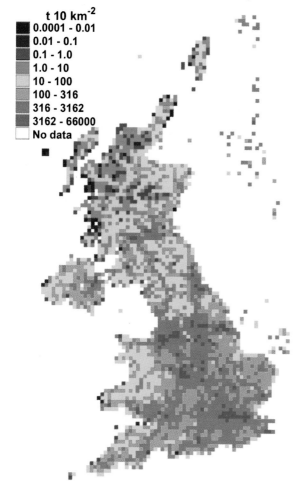

t 10 km^{-2}
0.0001 - 0.01
0.01 - 0.1
0.1 - 1.0
1.0 - 10
10 - 100
100 - 316
316 - 3162
3162 - 66000
No data

Figure 2.9 1998 UK emissions of NO$_x$ at 10 km x 10 km.

2.4.4 Policies & Progress: Nitrogen Oxides

The first CLRTAP Nitrogen Oxide Protocol target (Table 1.1) was achieved by the UK and some other European countries (see Section 8.2.2). The Fifth Environment Action Programme target of a 30% reduction by 2000 with respect to 1990 was achieved by the UK in 1997 and emissions have continued to decline ever since.

Emission reductions for NO$_x$ are generally more difficult than for SO$_2$ where a relatively small number of well-known large sources (power plants and some industries) are responsible for the majority of emissions. Switching from oil to natural gas only provides small NO$_x$ emission reductions. The low-NO_x burners fitted to many large power plants are not as effective in reducing emissions as FGD is for SO_2. Furthermore the large and increasing number of motor vehicles are more difficult to control. In the UK, as in many Western European countries, measures to reduce emissions from road transport have begun to take effect. Figure 2.10 shows the UK emission trends from road transport against a baseline of no change in vehicle technology or fuel switching since 1980.

The filled areas show the actual emission trends for different road transport types, from 1980 to 1999, taking into account the major driving forces for emission reductions in the UK fleet. Based on assessing the emissions without improvement measures (the reference, black line), the effect of certain measures can be evaluated. This assessment provides hypothetical estimates of emission savings in 1999 by comparing the reference and successive emissions to the measure below.

1. By the early nineties, three way catalysts were being introduced to UK petrol engined vehicles. This measure (orange line) ensured a further downward trend in emissions and contributed to a 29% reduction, a saving of 102 kt-N in 1999.

2. Fuel switching only provided a modest 1 kt-N contribution to emission reduction (blue line).

3. Improvements in diesel vehicle technology began to contribute to significant reductions in NO_x in the early nineties. HGV and bus improvements contributed significantly to an additional 14% reduction, a 44 kt-N saving on 1999 emissions.

Overall these measures have reduced road transport emissions by an additional 44% in 1999 a emission saving of 146 kt-N for 1999. Emissions are expected to continue to decrease as old vehicles are replaced with those with improved vehicle technology.

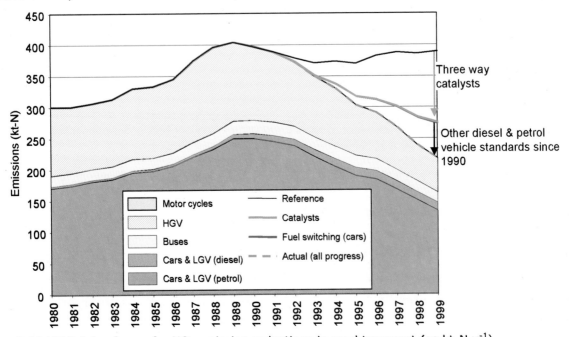

Figure 2.10 UK Driving forces for NO_x emission reductions in road transport (as kt-N y^{-1})

2.5 Non-Methane Volatile Organic Compounds and Carbon Monoxide Inventory

Non-Methane Volatile Organic Compounds (NMVOCs) and carbon monoxide (CO) emissions contribute to the formation of tropospheric ozone. This ozone forms from the reaction of NO_x, CO and NMVOCs in the presence of sunlight (see Chapter 3). Ozone is both harmful to human health and to vegetation. CO and certain NMVOC species have also been found to be toxic to human health. NMVOCs and CO are emitted from a large number of sources including combustion, predominantly where combustion is inefficient such as in road vehicles and small residential boilers. NMVOCs are also emitted from industrial processes using solvents, the manufacture of chemicals and petroleum refining and distribution. Natural emissions of NMVOCs also occur from vegetation. Emissions from forests (178 kt/y) are included in the NAEI, however emissions from other biogenic sources are currently excluded.

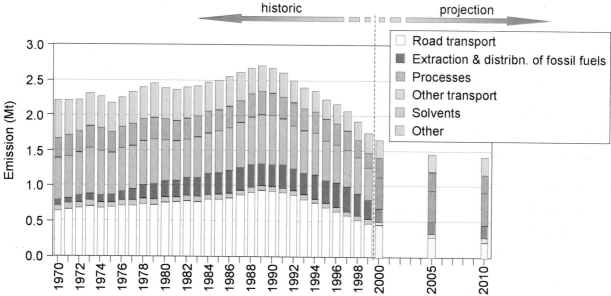

Figure 2.11 NMVOC emissions in the UK 1970 - 2010.

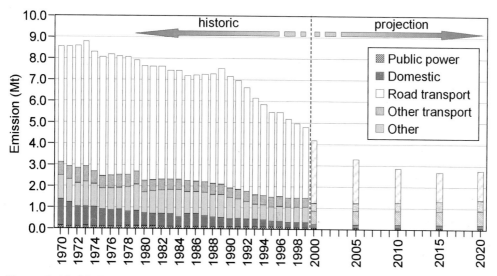

Figure 2.12 CO Emissions in the UK 1970 - 2020.

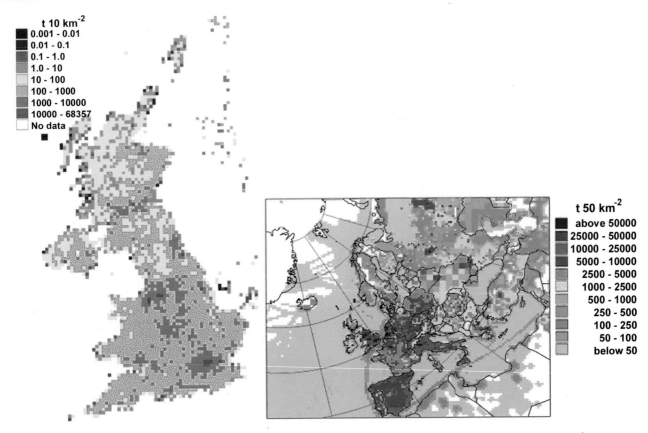

Figure 2.13 a. UK NMVOCs for 1998 at 10 km x 10 km.

b. 1998 European emissions of NMVOCs at 50 km x 50 km (from EMEP/MSC-W).

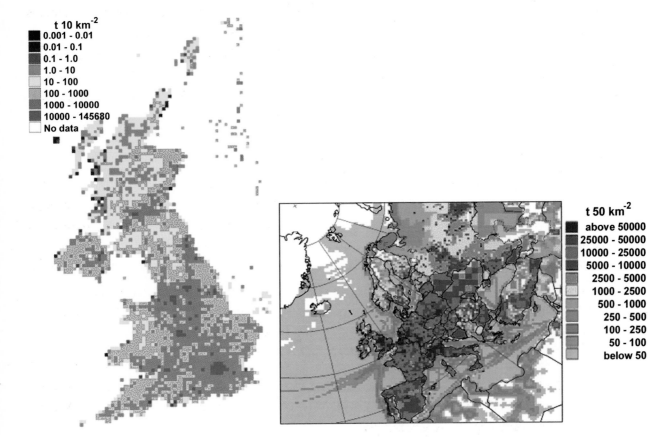

Figure 2.14 a. UK CO for 1998 at 10 km x 10 km.

b. 1998 European emissions of CO at 50 km x 50 km (from EMEP/MSC-W).

2.5.1 NMVOCs and CO trends

Emissions of NMVOCs (Figure 2.11) and CO (Figure 2.12) declined by 25% and 31% respectively between 1990 and 1998, primarily as a result of the addition of catalytic converters to road vehicles. This reduction is expected to continue into the future as new cars with increasingly effective emission controls replace older vehicles. By 2010 NMVOC emissions are expected to have declined by a further 27%. By 2020 CO emissions are expected to have declined by a further 41% from 1998 levels. In the UK in 1998 73% of CO and 27% of NMVOC emissions were from road transport. Recent efforts to reduce fugitive emissions from industrial processes and from solvent use have and will continue to have an impact in reducing NMVOC emissions.

2.5.2 NMVOCs and CO Maps

Figures 2.13 and 2.14 show the spatial distribution of emissions of NMVOCs and CO in the UK and across Europe. Emissions are large in areas with high road traffic density and where industrial processes and refineries are located. CO emissions are particularly high in city centres where road traffic speeds are low.

2.5.3 Policies & Progress: NMVOCs

Emissions of NMVOCs are covered by the Gothenburg protocol, the NECD and the VOC protocol. The VOC protocol commits the UK to a 30% reduction in emissions of volatile organic compounds by 1999 from a 1987 baseline. This has been achieved with a 34% reduction reported in the 1999 UK inventory. UK emission reductions have been achieved through the addition of three-way catalysts to road vehicles and also through tighter controls on industries using solvents through the Solvents Directive. Tightening authorisations and action from industry has also contributed to reductions in NMVOC emissions in recent years. Both the Gothenburg and NECD agreements set more stringent targets to be achieved by 2010. Reaching these targets will require substantial further emission reductions in the UK and many other member states.

2.6 Base cation inventory

The deposition of base cations (notably Ca^{2+} and Mg^{2+}) helps to neutralise the effects of the acidity generated by S and N deposition, which in their mobile anionic form as SO_4^{2-} and NO_3^- leach Ca^{2+} and Mg^{2+} from the soil profile, as described in Chapter 5. The first NAEI estimates have recently been completed for calcium, magnesium, potassium and non-seasalt sodium. These estimates are very uncertain and are presented here for the first time, in Tables 2.6 to 2.9 and Figures 2.15 to 2.18 below. These NAEI estimates show reducing base cation emissions that follow reductions in PM10 emissions as a result of particulate abatement and the switch from coal to natural gas as a primary energy source.

Total Ca^{2+} estimates from the NAEI for 1995 amount to 2.2 kt compared with 74.3 kt estimated by Lee and Pacyna (1999). The main difference is in the emissions from the non-point source energy use sector (domestic and commercial fuel combustion) and demonstrates the potential uncertainty in these estimates.

Table 2.6 Calcium (tonnes).

Source	1990	1991	1992	1993	1994	1995	1996	1997	1998	1999
Public power	838	830	776	645	608	581	536	452	464	389
Petroleum refining plants	6	7	7	7	8	7	7	7	7	6
Other comb. & trans.	6	6	4	2	1	0	0	0	1	1
Residential plant	634	655	593	564	397	258	278	272	292	357
Comm., public & agri. Comb	65	60	50	45	40	29	31	34	21	17
Iron & steel combustion	55	54	52	52	54	55	56	57	56	53
Cement plant & other industry combustion	1295	1150	1118	1106	1197	1160	1130	1146	1117	1067
Iron & steel	72	68	67	67	69	71	73	75	72	68
Processes in industry	95	80	72	72	80	77	78	81	81	81
Other mobile sources	0	0	0	0	1	1	1	0	0	0
Total	3066	2910	2740	2561	2455	2238	2191	2127	2111	2039

Table 2.7 Potassium (tonnes).

Source	1990	1991	1992	1993	1994	1995	1996	1997	1998	1999
Public power	64	64	60	50	44	34	25	21	22	17
Other comb. & trans.	0.3	0.3	0.2	0.1	0.1	0.0	0.0	0.0	0.0	0.0
Residential plant	30	31	28	26	19	12	13	13	14	17
Comm., public & agri. comb	3	3	2	2	2	1	2	3	1	1
Iron & steel combustion	0.03	0.02	0.01	0.03	0.03	0.02	0.01	0.00	0.02	0.02
Other comb. In industry	13	15	17	16	15	14	11	10	8	8
Processes in industry	0.3	0.3	0.3	0.3	0.2	0.2	0.2	0.2	0.1	0.1
Road transport combustion										0.01
Total	111	113	107	94	80	61	51	47	45	43

Table 2.8 Magnesium (tonnes).

Source	1990	1991	1992	1993	1994	1995	1996	1997	1998	1999
Public power	107	107	100	83	74	56	52	35	36	28
Other comb. & trans.	0.5	0.4	0.3	0.2	0.1	0.0	0.0	0.0	0.0	0.0
Residential plant	50	51	46	44	31	20	22	21	23	28
Comm., public & agri. comb	5	4	4	3	3	2	2	4	1	1
Iron & steel combustion	8	8	7	6	7	7	7	7	7	7
Other comb. in industry	22	24	28	26	24	23	19	17	14	13
Iron & steel	11	10	9	9	9	9	9	10	10	9
Processes in industry	1	0.5	0.4	0.4	0.4	0.3	0.3	0.3	0.2	0.2
Total	203	206	195	172	148	117	110	95	91	87

Table 2.9 Sodium (tonnes).

Source	1990	1991	1992	1993	1994	1995	1996	1997	1998	1999
Public power	99	96	88	73	64	49	46	30	30	24
Petroleum refining plants	4	5	5	5	5	5	5	5	5	4
Other comb. & trans.	0.37	0.35	0.25	0.15	0.07	0.03	0.03	0.03	0.03	0.03
Residential plant	40	41	37	35	25	16	17	17	18	22
Comm., public & agri. comb	6	6	5	5	5	4	4	5	2	2
Iron & steel combustion	1	1	1	2	2	2	1	1	1	1
Other comb. in industry	25	28	30	29	27	23	19	17	13	11
Processes in industry	0.4	0.4	0.3	0.3	0.3	0.3	0.2	0.2	0.2	0.2
Other mobile sources & machinery	0.2	0.2	0.2	0.3	0.4	0.4	0.3	0.3	0.2	0.1
Total	175	178	168	149	127	99	92	74	70	65

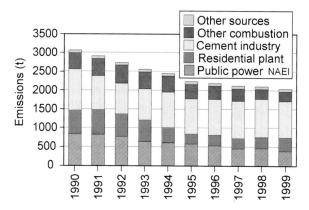

Figure 2.15 UK calcium emission estimates.

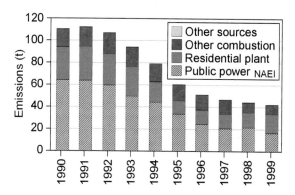

Figure 2.16 UK potassium emission estimates.

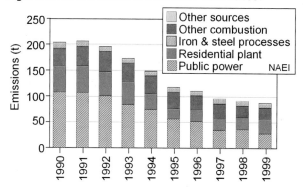

Figure 2.17 UK magnesium emission estimates.

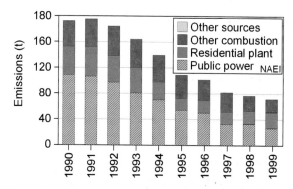

Figure 2.18 UK sodium emission estimates.

2.7 Uncertainties

Due to the variety of methods used to estimate inventories, a simple quantitative treatment cannot be provided for the accuracy of emission estimates. However, an indication can be made of the systematic errors in a qualitative way for each pollutant. For individual years, there are considerable uncertainties associated with the emission estimates. However, trends over time are considered to be more reliable.

SO_2 emissions are likely to be the most accurate as they depend largely on the sulphur content of fuels. Hence a comprehensive analysis of coal and fuel oil consumption by power stations, agriculture, industry and domestic sectors will give accurate emission estimates. The main uncertainty is in estimates of sulphur retention in ash and results in emission totals with an accuracy of ±10-15%.

NO_x emissions are less accurate than SO_2 because they are based on relatively few measurements of emission factors and depend on combustion conditions that vary widely. For example, the amount of NO_x emitted from vehicles varies as a function of speed as well as being dependent on the type of vehicle (this particular example is taken into account when estimating emissions from the road transport sector). In addition, many of the data used have been derived from small samples which contain margins of error e.g. vehicle speed distributions. It is estimated that NO_x emissions are accurate to ±30%.

Ammonia emissions are much more uncertain due largely to the nature of the major agricultural sources. Emissions depend on animal species, age, weight, diet, housing systems, waste management and storage techniques. Hence emissions are affected by a large number of factors which are difficult to measure and which make the interpretation of experimental data difficult and emission estimates uncertain.

The development of an accurate emission inventory for NMVOCs is hindered by a number of factors. First, the number of species covered by the term NMVOCs is very large and they arise from a diverse range of processes. Within a single industry, such as printing, the variation in the quantity and composition of organic solvents used in the inks, the different printing processes used and the varying extent and types of abatement used on the different printing presses make it difficult to apply a single, generally valid, emission factor across the industry. The cost of measuring emission factors for all of the different processes would be large and not entirely satisfactory since the measurement of emission factors is also problematic. Many commonly employed measurement techniques such as flame ionisation detection do not respond with uniform sensitivity to all compounds. Large errors can therefore be introduced if emitted compounds are poorly detected by the measurement technique used. Methane is also associated with NMVOC emissions from many sources, for instance combustion processes, transport, and the oil and gas industries. Emission factors derived from measurements of these sources often include a methane component. In addition data relating to individual industrial processes and solvent use are incomplete. Significant improvements have been made to the NMVOC inventory over the last few years, in particular regarding speciation and obtaining more detailed information from a host of industrial processes. As a result the uncertainty associated with the NMVOC emission estimates is considered to have significantly reduced. It is estimated that UK NMVOC emissions are probably accurate to $\pm 30\%$.

CO emissions depend on the technology employed and the specific combustion conditions. The emission factors used in the inventory have been derived from relatively few measurements of emissions from different types of boiler, hence they are less accurate than CO_2 and SO_2.

Base cation inventories are currently highly uncertain as these inventories have not been widely reviewed. Inventories for base cations are not widely compiled and there is a lack of measurement data and research.

> ➤ Deposition of non-seasalt sulphur in the UK declined by 52% between 1986 and 1997 during which emissions declined by 57%.

> ➤ Between 1986 and 1997 the wet deposition of sulphur declined by 42% while dry deposition declined by 62%.

> ➤ In the East Midlands, the decline in deposition and concentrations of sulphur in the atmosphere were very large (>70%), while at west coast sites, few significant reductions in SO_4^{2-} in precipitation have been detected.

> ➤ A substantial decrease (30 to 50%) in rainfall acidity has been recorded throughout the UK between 1986 and 1997.

> ➤ Deposition of nitrogen oxides in the UK has declined by about 16%, following a reduction in NO_x emissions of ca 45% since the emissions peak in 1990.

> ➤ Total N deposition in the UK is dominated by reduced N (as NH_3 and NH_4^+) and has changed little since 1986.

> ➤ The potential acidification from nitrogen deposition now substantially exceeds that of sulphur.

> ➤ Non-linearities in the relationship between the emission and deposition patterns for sulphur have been detected, these will lead to slower reductions in acidity related critical loads exceedance in the uplands of western Britain than expected.

> ➤ The import of sulphur from shipping sources to the south and west of the UK is slowing the recovery from acid deposition.

> ➤ Rates of dry deposition of SO_2 have increased with time in response to changes in the relative amounts of SO_2 and NH_3 in the air.

> ➤ Ground-level ozone continues to exceed thresholds for effects on vegetation and human health over large areas of the UK, although the peak concentrations have declined by about 30% during the last decade.

> ➤ There is evidence that the mean ground-level ozone concentration over the UK is increasing.

3.1 Introduction

This chapter describes concentrations and the deposition of major gaseous pollutants, SO_2, NO_2, NH_3, and the products of their chemical transformation in the atmosphere to SO_4^{2-}, NO_3^-, NH_4^+ and H^+ in the UK. The chapter also provides an update of ground-level ozone concentrations and trends with time provided by the 4th PORG report (1998).

The 'current' concentrations and deposition form part of a time series, as the pollution climate of the country changed substantially in response to controls on major sources of SO_2, NO_x and NMVOC pollutants. It is useful therefore in this chapter to identify:

(1) the current concentrations and deposition of pollutants contributing to the acidification and eutrophication of UK ecosystems and the presence of ground-level ozone,

(2) the changes in concentrations and deposition during the period for which high quality measurements are available,

(3) the extent to which the observed changes in concentrations and deposition are consistent with the current understanding of the transport, transformation and deposition processes,

(4) the changing importance of individual pollutants over the last 20 years and their probable role in future environmental problems.

The controls on emissions introduced to date are largely a consequence of international protocols described in Chapter 1, the focus of which was initially sulphur and acid deposition. The controls over emissions of NO_x (and NMVOCs) were introduced later and have had a smaller impact so far on the overall magnitude of emissions (Chapter 2). For NH_3, the most recent agreements (the Gothenburg protocol and NECD) represent the first international effort to regulate this pollutant, although for most countries the expected reductions in annual emission over the coming decade are very small.

3.2 Acid Deposition in the UK

3.3 Sources of Acidifying Pollution

The acidity deposited from the atmosphere in the UK arises from oxidation of SO_2 to H_2SO_4, giving rise to two H^+, and of NO_2 to NO_3^- producing one H^+ ion. These sources of acidity provide the majority of the deposited acidity in precipitation, the so-called 'acid rain'. The oxidation processes may occur in the gas phase (homogeneous reactions), or in atmospheric aerosols, or in cloud or rain droplets by heterogeneous processes (Figure 3.1) As some coal contains a significant Cl^- content, and following combustion is emitted as HCl to the atmosphere, there is a contribution from HCl to the production of acidity from coal combustion, but overall it is small relative to that from SO_2 and NO_x (Chapter 2).

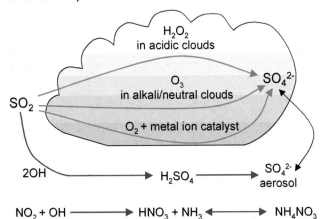

Figure 3.1 Sulphur dioxide and nitrogen dioxide oxidation processes.

Acid deposition is not limited to the acidity contained in precipitation. The acid gases SO_2 and NO_2 may also be deposited directly onto terrestrial surfaces by dry deposition. Acidity is generated as these gases are oxidised within or on the surfaces of vegetation or soil. Similarly, the deposition of other important atmospheric pollutants may also acidify soils. In the case of gaseous ammonia in particular, this highly soluble pollutant may be taken up and absorbed as NH_3, readily forming NH_4^+ in solution on or within vegetation or soil. If the NH_4^+ ion is metabolised by plants it is transformed to $R-NH_2$, which in the process effectively liberates a hydrogen ion H^+ and may be considered to be acidifying (Sutton *et al.*, 1993). Alternatively, if the NH_4^+ is oxidized to NO_3^- and leached from the soil profile, this is also acidifying. Thus, in order to quantify the contribution of individual nitrogen pollutants to the acidification of ecosystems, it is necessary to know the chemical fate of the N atoms deposited. This complication makes it difficult to define precisely the actual acidifying input to the landscape. Simplifying assumptions allow progress for mapping acid deposition (Figure 3.2). The simplest approach is to calculate the **potential** acidifying input assuming the deposition of a sulphur atom generates two H^+, and oxidized and reduced nitrogen each contribute one H^+. Thus to quantify acid deposition it is necessary to measure wet deposition of SO_4^{2-}, NO_3^- and NH_4^+ and dry deposition of the gases SO_2, NO_2, HNO_3 and NH_3 and the aerosols containing SO_4^{2-}, NO_3^- and NH_4^+. The processing of pollutants and the degree to which these acidify soils and freshwaters are considered in Chapters 5 and 6. In assessing the net acidification from atmospheric inputs, it is also necessary to consider the deposition of base cations of anthropogenic origin (Ca^{2+} and Mg^{2+}), which neutralize acidity deposited or generated in soil and vegetation.

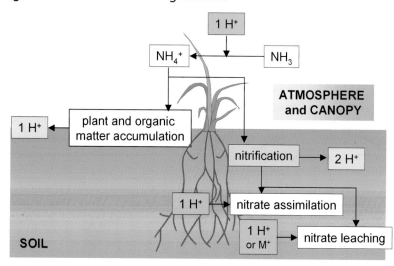

Figure 3.2 Illustration of the processes that produce acidity from NH_x deposition (after Sutton *et al.*, 1993).

3.3.1 Natural Sources of S and N

The pollutant sources of SO_2 and NO_x are not the only sources of atmospheric S and N or acidity as these elements are emitted from a range of entirely natural processes and, prior to the presence of human activity on the planet, the biogeochemical cycling of S and N formed an essential component in the mineral nutrition of terrestrial and aquatic ecosystems (Graedel and Crutzen, 1993). The 'natural' sulphur deposited originates from marine sources, derived either from sea-spray or emission of gaseous S compounds and volcanic sources while the fixed nitrogen originates largely from soil emissions of NO from terrestrial ecosystems, from biomass combustion and from lightning. Atmospheric NH_3 is emitted from vegetation and animal waste in natural as well as agricultural land use.

A detailed consideration of the role of natural sources of S and N in deposition to the UK is beyond the remit of this chapter, but the subject is considered briefly as a knowledge and understanding of the 'background' natural biogeochemical cycling of S and N is necessary to quantify the baseline on which the pollutant deposition is superimposed. It is unfortunate that the technology necessary to quantify atmospheric inputs developed long after substantial anthropogenic emissions began. There are therefore few reliable measurements on which to base estimates of the S and N deposition before 1950. The subject of natural biogeochemical cycling of S and N has generally been treated at a global scale, and recent analyses of the available literature show that in the case of nitrogen, the anthropogenic gaseous emissions to the atmosphere of both oxidized and reduced N contribute roughly 70% of the total emissions (Figure 3.3). The conclusion that on global scales anthropogenic emissions now dominate the atmospheric cycling of reactive nitrogen also extends to sulphur (Figure 3.4).

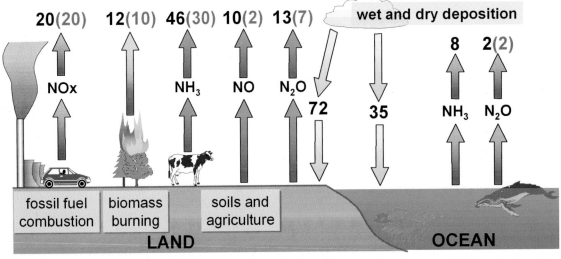

Figure 3.3 Global atmospheric nitrogen budget (Tg-N y^{-1}). Man-made contributions are shown in brackets (Fowler, 1999).

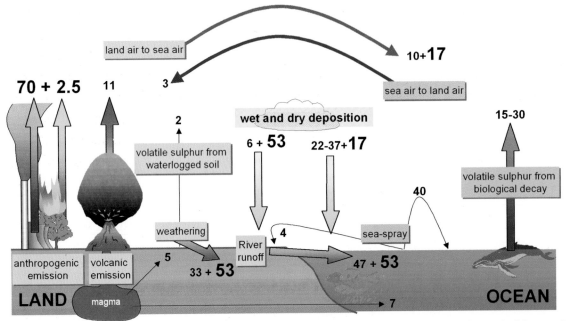

Figure 3.4 Global sulphur budget (Tg-S y^{-1}). Man-made contributions are shown in large bold type (after Graedel and Crutzen, 1993).

A substantial reduction in UK and European emissions of both S and N must therefore be considered in a global context, as the global emissions of both S and N are increasing due to greater increases in emissions within rapidly developing regions relative to the decreases in Europe. In North America for example, pollutant emission controls have also been introduced, especially for the photochemical oxidant precursors NO$_x$ and NMVOCs. However, despite widespread evidence of acidified freshwater ecosystems in the North-East of the continent, emissions of SO$_2$ in the USA declined by only 12% between 1985 and 1997, the period during which European sulphur emissions declined by approximately 50% (EMEP, 1999). Similarly, emissions of NO_x in the USA changed by less than 1% over the same period as the growing number of sources compensated for the introduction of control measures.

There is therefore a global perspective to the issues of long-range transport which has generally been ignored in developing emission control protocols. A focus at country or regional scale has been entirely appropriate for the problems to date, but with the growing global emissions and greater attention to tropospheric ozone and issues linked to perturbation of the global nitrogen cycle, it will become increasingly important to consider emissions and control measures at a hemispheric and global scale.

Natural emissions and anthropogenic emissions outside Europe are considered in more detail later in the chapter as they contribute a substantial fraction of deposited non-seasalt sulphur along the west coast of the UK, and limit the extent to which acid deposition in the UK can be reduced using legislation which applies only within Europe.

3.4 The Deposition Processes and Measurement Networks

3.4.1 Wet Deposition

This is simply the process whereby pollutants are removed from the atmosphere by precipitation. The process contributing the majority of the concentration of pollutants in rain and snow is nucleation scavenging, in which aerosols containing the pollutant act as the condensation nucleus on which cloud droplets form. Other minor contributors also include diffusion and impaction of aerosols onto cloud droplets and rain and direct uptake of the gases by cloud and rain drops (Fowler, 1984) (Figure 3.5). Wet deposition removes most of the aerosols containing SO_4^{2-} and NO_3^-, which are predominantly present in the size range 0.2 to 1.0 µm (diameter) from the atmosphere as these aerosols are too small to deposit to the surface at significant rates by gravitational settling and are only captured directly at terrestrial surfaces at significant rates by forests or other aerodynamically rough surfaces.

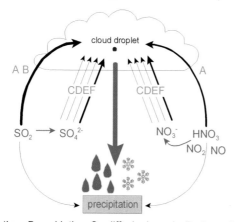

A - dissolution   B - oxidation   C - diffusiophoresis   D - brownian diffusion
E - impaction   F - cloud condensation nuclei pathway

Figure 3.5 The pathways and mechanisms for the transfer of sulphur and nitrogen containing compounds to the ground in precipitation (see Appendix A for a definition of the terms A to F).

Orographic enhancement of wet deposition

Rainfall very efficiently removes aerosol phase SO_4^{2-}, NO_3^- and NH_4^+, and thus the areas of the country with large rainfall tend to be the areas of largest wet deposition even though the concentrations of pollutants are smaller in the high rainfall areas. The aerosols represent the form of the pollutant S and N by which long-range transport mainly occurs. The uplands of the UK are consistently areas of enhanced rainfall, and therefore wet deposition. A substantial fraction of the additional rainfall in the uplands of Britain occurs by seeder-feeder scavenging, in which the hill (orographic) cloud is formed above the uplands as the air is forced to rise by the orography. (Figure 3.6a). The hill clouds contain larger concentrations of most of the anthropogenic ions than higher level cloud simply because the orographic cloud forms largely within boundary layer air which contains larger concentrations of the pollutant derived aerosols. The precipitation from the higher level cloud washes out the hill cloud, increasing rainfall amount and concentrations of the major ions reaching the ground. This process of seeder-feeder enhancement of rainfall and wet deposition has been extensively studied in the UK (Fowler *et al.*, 1988; Choularton *et al.*, 1988; Inglis *et al.*, 1995; Dore *et al.*, 1992) and has been shown to increase substantially the wet deposition throughout upland Britain in mechanistic studies of individual events (Inglis *et al.*, 1995) in long-term studies using the naturally occurring radiotracer ^{210}Pb (Fowler *et al.*, 1998a) and in catchment mass balance studies (Reynolds *et al.*, 1997). A detailed consideration of the literature is beyond the scope of this chapter, however, the additional wet deposition resulting from this process throughout the UK makes an important contribution to precipitation, wet deposition of pollutants and exceedances of critical loads.

The processes of seeder-feeder enhancement are illustrated in Figure 3.6a, along with measured cloud water concentrations from studies at Great Dun Fell during field experiments in Figure 3.6b.

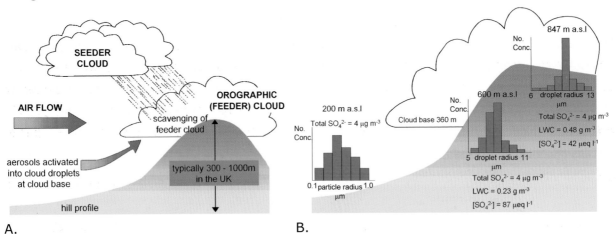

A.   B.

Figure 3.6 a) Illustration of the seeder-feeder wet deposition process and (b) measurements of sulphate concentration in aerosol and cloud droplets over Great Dun Fell.

Measurements of wet deposition in the UK

Measurements of acidity (H^+) and the major anions with which it is associated (SO_4^{2-} and NO_3^-) in precipitation have been routinely made in the UK at a network of sampling stations using a consistent methodology since 1985 (RGAR, 1997; Appendix B). Thus wet deposition has been measured directly for approximately 15 years. Some of the earlier measurements date back to the last century (Laws *et al.*, 1861), but the methodology, sampling and analysis protocols and characteristics of these early measurements have not yet been analysed sufficiently to use them to construct a long-term chronology of acid deposition in the UK.

Interest in acid rain prompted measurements at a range of sites throughout northern Britain in the 1970s (Fowler *et al.*, 1982). These measurements showed that rainfall acidity, concentrations of SO_4^{2-} and NO_3^- and deposited acidity values in northern Britain were similar to those in southern Scandinavia. At this stage, despite measurements at sites in Scotland, Central England and East Anglia (Martin and Barber, 1984), there were too few measurements to construct a wet deposition map for the UK from the measurement data alone. The data analysed and presented in this chapter are therefore restricted to the period 1986 – 1998, for which wet deposition monitoring is available for the entire UK with similar monitoring equipment, collection protocols and analytical methods.

The current network

The composition of rain and snow in the UK is monitored at a rural network of 39 sites using bulk collectors mounted 1.5 to 2 m above-ground sampled weekly, and at 1 site using a wet-only collector that is sampled daily (RGAR, 1997) (Appendix B).

In general, the monitoring sites are used to define the broad spatial patterns in rainfall composition, but they do not sample the full range of the distribution of precipitation amount or composition. This is largely a practical constraint because the hill tops where precipitation values are largest are generally avoided because such sites are difficult to access in winter conditions, are very windy and where a significant fraction of the annual deposition occurs as snow which is not collected efficiently. However, as Figure B3 shows, the monitoring sites cover the majority of the country and have proved suitable for defining the regional distribution of precipitation chemistry (RGAR, 1997).

The weekly and daily samples are used to define the precipitation weighted annual mean concentrations of the major ions present in precipitation: SO_4^{2-}, NO_3^-, Cl^-, H^+, Na^+, NH_4^+, K^+, Ca^{2+} and Mg^{2+}. These are then used to map the patterns of concentration. The mapping of precipitation weighted mean concentrations relies on Kriging methods (Webster et al., 1991), assuming that the variation in space is locally random even though there is a spatial correlation.

Having mapped the precipitation weighted concentrations of each of the ions, the wet deposition is calculated as the product of the annual precipitation amount obtained from the UK Meteorological Office and provided at a scale of 5 km x 5 km. The Met Office data are used because the precipitation maps are constructed using a much larger network of gauges (in excess of 2000), which sample at ground-level. The precipitation chemistry network relies on just 40 sites and uses collectors mounted nearly 2 m above ground. The precipitation chemistry collectors have the advantage that they avoid some of the locally re-suspended contamination from soils but they under-catch precipitation amount because of the exposure of the collector to wind.

A further step in the calculation of wet deposition is required because the network does not adequately sample the high precipitation regions of the uplands where the wash-out of hill cloud by falling rain considerably increases wet deposition (Fowler et al., 1988 & 1995a) as shown in Figure 3.6. The procedure used to modify the maps relies on empirical observations of the relationship between concentrations of major ions in orographic cloud and that of the upwind seeder rain (Dore et al., 1992). The orographic enhancement of precipitation amount is assumed to occur entirely through seeder-feeder scavenging of orographic cloud (Figure 3.6a).

The resulting maps of wet deposition were produced at a grid resolution of 20 km x 20 km from 1986 to 1994 and have recently been improved to 5 km x 5 km using a revised methodology which allows for the effects of wind-drift of falling raindrops.

Concentrations of the major ions in rain

Concentrations of all the major ions show large regional variation over the UK. In the case of the ions derived from pollutants, including SO_4^{2-}, NO_3^-, NH_4^+, and H^+, the concentrations are largest in the east, and smaller, often by as much as 50% in the west. The gradients arise through a combination of two processes, the predominantly westerly airflow over the country brings generally less polluted air from the Atlantic and the rainfall amount is substantially larger on the west coast, as a consequence of seeder-feeder processes (Figure 3.6). However, while broadly correct, this is a considerable simplification of the spatial patterns in concentrations of the individual ions.

The wet deposition patterns, which are a product of precipitation amount and concentration, show the largest deposition in the high rainfall regions. It is important therefore to distinguish between the concentration and deposition patterns.

Acidity

The focus of the acid rain issue was initially the free acidity in precipitation, but since the concentration of H^+, depends on the concentrations of all the other ions present, its value in understanding processes is limited and in this section the report will concentrate on the major ions. However, the acidity is of interest and the network measurements in 1986 showed that weighted mean acidity in precipitation in the east of the UK was typically pH 4.2 to pH 4.1 (60 to 80 μeq H^+ l^{-1}). The acidity has declined steadily with time and current H^+ concentrations are smaller by between 30% and 50%, so that typical precipitation weighted concentrations are now between pH 4.3 and pH 4.4 in the same eastern areas of the UK (40 to 50 μeq H^+ l^{-1}) as shown in Figure 3.7a and 3.7b.

SO_4^{2-}

For the pollutant derived SO_4^{2-}, in the mid 1980s the largest concentrations were in the east and south of England with mean concentrations of 80 to 100 μeq l^{-1} and the smallest concentrations in NW Scotland (15-20 μeq l^{-1}) (Figure 3.8a). The value of background SO_4^{2-}, i.e. pollutant SO_4^{2-} from non-UK sources is important and is not known precisely. However, values at remote sites in NW Europe from the EMEP network indicate values of the order of 7 to 10 μeq l^{-1}, so even the remote sites in the UK receive at least half of their non-seasalt SO_4^{2-} from pollutant sources. The current (1997) concentrations of non-seasalt SO_4^{2-} are shown in Figure 3.8b and these also show a large NW-SE gradient in the UK with values in NW Scotland remaining close to 20 μeq l^{-1} while the peak concentrations in the East Midlands of England are about 60 μeq l^{-1}. There is also a clear west to east gradient with larger concentrations along the east coast of the UK. The change in SO_4^{2-} concentration between 1986 and 1999 is large and represents a reduction by almost 50% in the English Midlands and East Anglia and is accompanied by a reduction in acidity of the same magnitude in the source regions.

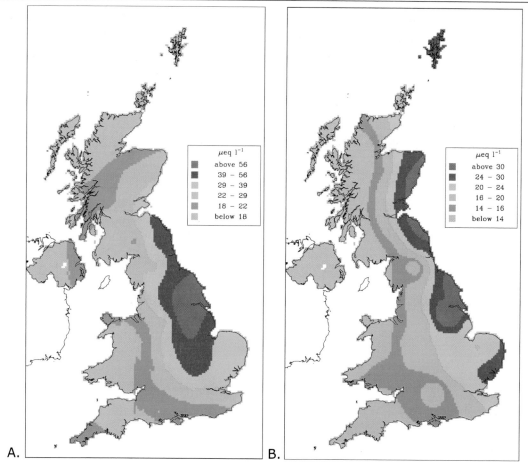

Figure 3.7 Concentration of H$^+$ (acidity) in UK rainfall a) 1986 and b) current (1997).

The changes in SO_4^{2-} (and acidity) with time at sites on the west coast of the UK are much smaller both in relative and absolute terms. At some of the west coast sites the trends in non-seasalt SO_4^{2-} are largely non-significant and this is a surprise, as this monitoring period covers a time in which emissions of SO_2 in the UK and Europe declined by almost 50%. The NH_4^+, NO_3^- and H$^+$ concentrations show similar spatial patterns to those of non-seasalt SO_4^{2-} with a marked E-W gradient and peak values in East Anglia. The absolute magnitude of the E-W gradient in NO_3^- concentration is similar to that in SO_4^{2-} i.e. 40 to 50 μeq-NO_3^- l^{-1} across the country in the most polluted areas. However, the relative gradient is larger for NO_3^- because in the remote regions of NW Scotland concentrations of NO_3^- were very small, typically 2 to 5 μeq-NO_3^- l^{-1} in the mid 1980s. The values in the polluted areas of 40 to 50 μeq l^{-1} are therefore an order of magnitude larger than those at the remote sites. Differences between SO_4^{2-} and NO_3^- concentration gradients also arise because of the presence of a background in the SO_4^{2-} concentration. Seasalt contains appreciable quantities of SO_4^{2-}, and in calculating non-seasalt SO_4^{2-} a correction is made for marine SO_4^{2-} by assuming the Cl$^-$:SO_4^{2-} and Na^+:SO_4^{2-} ratios in bulk sea water apply in the case of precipitation. At remote locations in the west and north of Britain this is a reasonable assumption, but in the East Midlands of England Cl$^-$ is present as HCl and non-seasalt Cl$^-$ in aerosols from the high Cl$^-$ coals produced from some East Midlands coalfields. The marine correction for these areas relies on the Na^+:SO_4^{2-} ratio to quantify the non-seasalt Cl$^-$ deposition.

There is also SO_4^{2-} in the atmosphere from marine emissions of dimethyl sulphide (DMS) which is oxidized in the atmosphere, ultimately to SO_4^{2-} and contributes to non-anthropogenic background SO_4^{2-} deposition. The emission of SO_2 from shipping in the North Atlantic and transport from North America also contribute to sulphur deposition in the UK, and are considered in more detail later in the chapter.

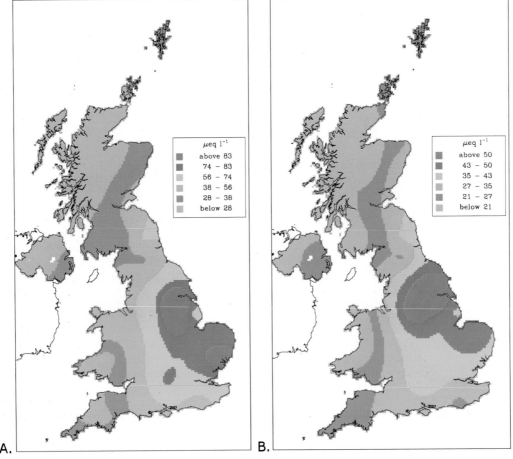

Figure 3.8 a) 1986 non-seasalt SO_4^{2-} concentration in rainfall and b) the current (1997) concentration of non-seasalt SO_4^{2-} in rainfall in the UK.

NO_3^-

The concentrations of NO_3^- are largest in the East Midlands and East Anglia, with precipitation weighted annual mean values of about 40 μeq l^{-1} and smallest in the north west of Scotland, with values in the range 5 to 12 μeq l^{-1} (Figure 3.9). The east-west gradient across the UK is larger for NO_3^- than SO_4^{2-}, because, there is no contribution from marine sources to the NO_3^- in rain.

NH_4^+

Concentrations of NH_4^+ in rain, like those of NO_3^-, are larger in central and eastern areas of the UK than at west coast locations. The gradient across the country is similar to that of NO_3^-, with values in the range 40 to 60 μeq l^{-1} in East Anglia and values of typically 10 μeq l^{-1} at the west coast locations (Figure 3.10). The emissions and atmospheric processing of the precursor gases leading to NH_4^+ and NO_3^- in rain are very different, and there are clear differences in the spatial patterns of these two ions, with NH_4^+ concentrations being generally larger than those of NO_3^- in central and eastern England, while the concentrations of NO_3^- are generally larger than those of NH_4^+ in the remote regions of the north and west.

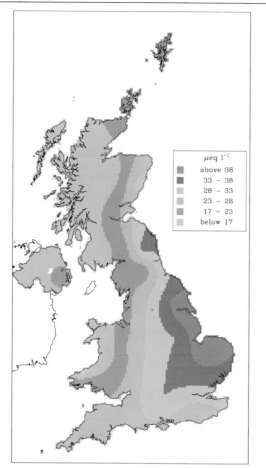

Figure 3.9 Current (1997) concentration of NO_3^- in UK rainfall.

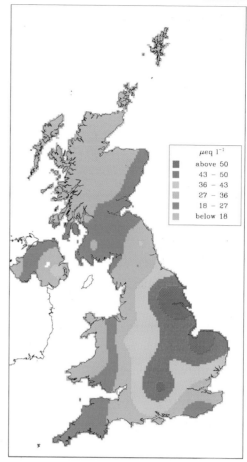

Figure 3.10 Current (1997) concentration of NH_4^+ in UK rainfall.

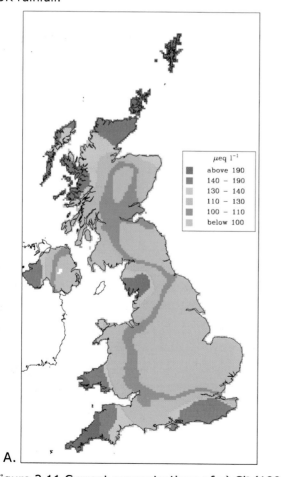

A.

B.

Figure 3.11 Current concentrations of a) Cl^- (1997) and b) Na^+ (1997) in UK rainfall.

Na^+ and Cl^-

The marked E-W gradients in concentrations of the major pollutant derived ions contrast strongly with the marine derived ions especially Na^+ and Cl^-. These ions' concentrations at the west coast sites are in the range 200 to 400 $\mu eq\ l^{-1}$ (Figure 3.11a and b). Seasalts dominate the ionic composition of precipitation and provide the majority of the total SO_4^{2-} deposition along the west coast. The inland and east coast sites in contrast show marine Na^+ and Cl^- concentrations in the range 50 $\mu eq\ l^{-1}$ to 70 $\mu eq\ l^{-1}$ and at these sites marine SO_4^{2-} contributes only 10% to 20% of total SO_4^{2-} in precipitation. The relative contributions of marine and pollutant derived ions to the total ionic strength of precipitation therefore changes across the UK.

Wet deposition

Combining the concentration fields with precipitation amount, and correcting for the orographic effects in the UK uplands provides the wet deposition maps. As the gradients across the country in precipitation amounts are generally larger than the gradients in concentration of the major ions, the wet deposition maps show a stronger influence of precipitation field than of major ion concentration.

The main features of the wet deposition maps are illustrated in maps for 1986 and 1997 for non-seasalt SO_4^{2-} (Figures. 3.12a and 3.12b). The peak in sulphur wet deposition in 1997 of 25 kg-S ha^{-1} in the Pennine hills of northern England and in Cumbria is appreciably smaller than in 1986 (50 kg-S ha^{-1}). The rainfall amounts vary between years but there are no monotonic regional trends in precipitation amount over the 12 year period. There are therefore areas of the country in which substantial reductions (i.e. up to 50%) in wet deposition have occurred since the mid 1980s.

The wet deposition of non-seasalt SO_4^{2-} at west coast sites, and in the north and west of Scotland show no clear differences between 1986 and 1997.

The spatial distribution in wet deposition of NH_4^+ and NO_3^- are shown in Figures. 3.13 and 3.14, for 1997, again illustrating the dominance of the precipitation field in controlling the pattern of wet deposition.

The deposition of nitrogen both wet and dry, are considered in more detail later in the chapter.

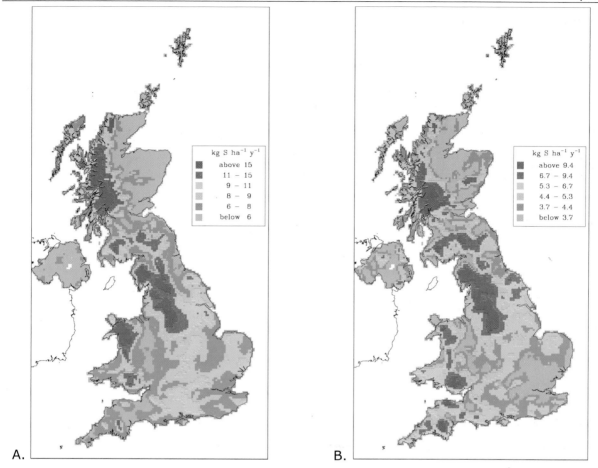

A.　　　　B.

Figure 3.12 Wet deposition of non-seasalt SO$_4^{2-}$ for (a) 1986 (b) 1997.

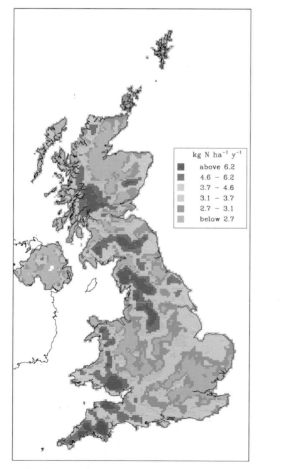

Figure 3.13 Wet deposition of NO$_3^-$ for 1997.

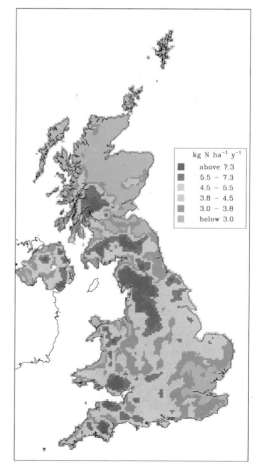

Figure 3.14 Wet deposition of NH$_4^+$ for 1997.

3.4.2 Dry Deposition

Deposition of gases and aerosols directly to the Earth's surface is referred to as dry deposition and, unlike wet deposition, until recently has not been monitored routinely anywhere in the world. New reliable instrumentation has made it possible to monitor rates of dry deposition of gases such as SO_2, NH_3 and O_3 (Erisman *et al.*, 1998b; Fowler *et al.*, 1998b). In the UK, SO_2 dry deposition is monitored at two stations, an arable farming site in rural Nottinghamshire, and a moorland site in the Scottish Borders, to provide the input parameters for a dry deposition model (Smith *et al.*, 2000) which is used to estimate dry deposition throughout the UK.

To estimate dry deposition to the UK landscape, concentrations of the gases are monitored directly with networks of monitoring stations for SO_2, NO_2 and HNO_3 (Table 3.1). The measured concentration field is combined with a deposition model using measured or climatological average meteorological inputs (wind speed, air temperature, solar radiation, surface wetness) to calculate the deposition velocity (v_d), as illustrated in Figure 3.15, using a resistance analogy of the deposition process. Monthly and annual deposition inputs are calculated to provide the annual maps for the UK at a resolution of 5 km x 5 km and the values for each grid square are weighted for each of the five classes of land cover for which the deposition model calculates the deposition (forests, moorland, grassland, urban and arable). The calculation procedure differs between the different gases depending on the availability of measured data and the underlying process (Smith *et al.*, 2000). In particular, the net exchange of NH_3 is complicated by the bi-directional nature of the exchange process over vegetation due to the presence of a compensation point (Sutton *et al.*, 1995b).

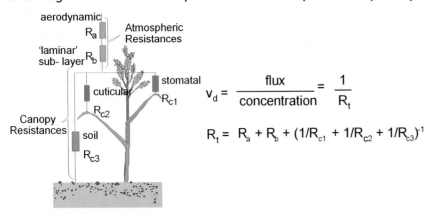

$$v_d = \frac{\text{flux}}{\text{concentration}} = \frac{1}{R_t}$$

$$R_t = R_a + R_b + (1/R_{c1} + 1/R_{c2} + 1/R_{c3})^{-1}$$

Figure 3.15 Illustration of the resistance analogy for dry deposition.

Table 3.1 Measurements and models used to estimate dry deposition to the UK (for full details of the monitoring networks see Appendix B).

Gas	Rural monitoring stations	Deposition model
SO_2	40 daily and weekly monitors + *ca* 10 continuous. 2 continuous flux monitors	Resistance model
NO_2	21 monthly diffusion tube sites. 7 continuous monitors No flux monitors	Resistance model
NH_3	84 two weekly/monthly monitors. 1 continuous flux monitor	Canopy compensation point model
HNO_3	12 monthly denuders, 1 daily denuder	Resistance model

In addition to the gases, aerosols are dry deposited, and this provides an important input of metals (base cations Ca^{2+}, Mg^{2+}, K^+, Na^+ and heavy metals Pb, Cu, Zn) which are not present in the gas phase. Deposition of base cations from the atmosphere provides an important source for soils in areas with slowly weathering parent mineralogy (especially granites). However, the measurements on which current estimates of dry deposition input of base cations are based, is limited to the few sites at which measurements have been made, where scavenging ratios (the ratio of the mass in precipitation to that in air) may be estimated directly from measurement. These data are then used with the wet deposition measurements to estimate country-wide aerosol base cation concentrations (CLAG, 1997).

SO_2

The measured concentration fields (Figure 3.16a) are interpolated to provide 5 km x 5 km maps for the country. Because urban areas, representing ca 10% of the country, experience enhanced SO_2 concentrations from local sources, urban concentrations are larger than those in the surrounding rural areas. The urban area SO_2 concentrations are increased using an empirical relationship between the emission inventory S emissions and monitored SO_2 concentrations (Stedman et al., 1997a). The mapped SO_2 concentrations are used to calculate dry deposition using a resistance analogy model (Smith et al., 2000), as shown schematically in Figure 3.15.

The SO_2 concentration field for the UK in Figure 3.16a shows the largest concentrations in the East Midlands, with values of approximately 5 ppb and a corridor of relatively large concentrations between the Midlands and London. To the south, east and west of this area, concentrations decline steadily, and in the remote areas of the UK and especially in the uplands of Scotland and Wales, the concentrations are very small, and substantially less than 1 ppb. Dry deposition, calculated using a process-based model (Smith et al., 2000) is shown in Figure 3.16b, with the largest values corresponding with the areas of high concentrations. Trends are considered elsewhere in this chapter in more detail, but it is important to note that the concentrations and deposition of SO_2 have declined by approximately an order of magnitude in the areas of largest concentrations, since the early 1970s.

NO_2

The concentrations of NO_2 in the UK, are largest in the major conurbations throughout the country, with annual average values of typically 20 ppb (Fig 3.17a). In extensive rural areas of the Midlands and south-east England concentrations of NO_2 are in the range 10 to 15 ppb and exceed those of SO_2 by a factor of 5 or more. Outside these areas, the NO_2 concentrations decline to values below 1 ppb in the highlands of Scotland and the west coast. The rapid decline in NO_x emissions in recent years, as a consequence of catalytic converters on motor vehicles and fuel substitution for some of the large combustion plant has resulted in a marked reduction in NO_2 concentrations throughout the UK. Figure 3.18 shows the mean NO_2 concentration for all rural monitoring stations, which declines between 1990 and 1998 from about 9 ppb to 5 ppb, a reduction approaching 50%, and consistent with the reduction in emissions during the same period (Chapter 2).

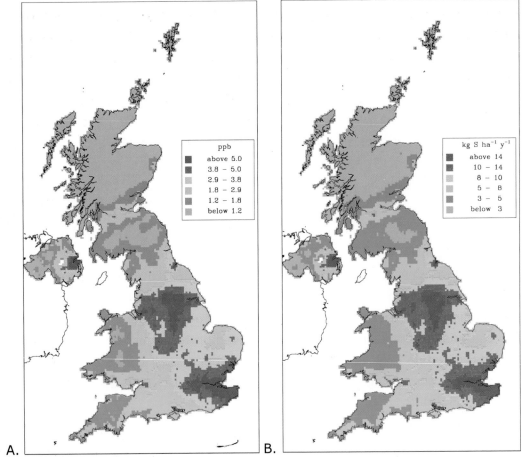

Figure 3.16 1997 (a) atmospheric concentration and (b) dry deposition of SO_2 to the UK.

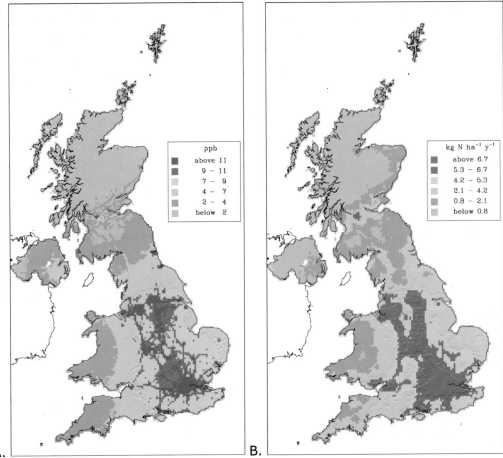

Figure 3.17 a) Atmospheric concentrations of NO_2 during 1997 and (b) dry deposition of NO_2 for 1997.

The procedure for calculating NO_2 deposition follows that for SO_2, with measured ambient NO_2 concentrations at rural sites providing the underlying UK map. The concentrations of NO_2 in urban areas are increased following the method described by Stedman *et al.* (1997b). The deposition model for NO_2 is simplified considerably relative to that for SO_2, since NO_2 does not deposit to external surfaces of vegetation (Figure 3.17b). The process is reduced largely to stomatal uptake, and therefore shows large seasonal variations in deposition with removal rates during the winter being very small and maximum deposition rates during the spring and summer.

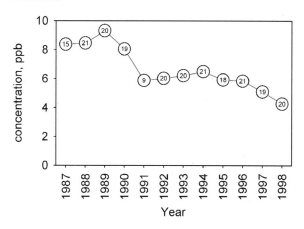

Figure 3.18 Rural NO_2 diffusion tube sites (see Appendix B, Table B3) trend in the network average (numbers indicate the number of sites in the average, only years with data capture in excess of 75% are included).

Nitric acid (HNO₃) and aerosol NO_3^-, NH_4^+ and SO_4^{2-}.

Within the last three years, a network has been established to monitor ambient concentrations of nitric acid and the aerosol concentrations of NO_3^-, NH_4^+ and SO_4^{2-}. (Appendix B) These measurements show concentrations of HNO_3 to be largest in the south east of England, with average concentrations of approximately 1.5 μg-HNO_3 m^{-3} and a steady decline to the north and west of the UK, with concentrations in Scotland averaging typically 0.2 μg-HNO_3 m^{-3} and are mapped in Figure 3.19 (Sutton *et al.*, 2001a).

Figure 3.19 HNO_3 concentration map, interpolated from Sept. 1999 to Nov. 2000 network measurements.

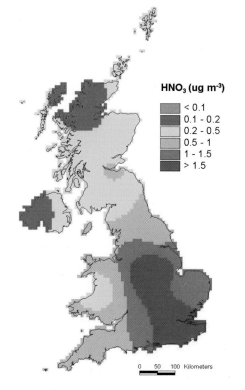

HNO_3 (ug m⁻³)

	< 0.1
	0.1 - 0.2
	0.2 - 0.5
	0.5 - 1
	1 - 1.5
	> 1.5

0   50   100 Kilometers

NH₃

Ambient concentrations of NH₃ in the UK are monitored directly with a network of approximately 80 stations (Sutton *et al.*, 2001b; Appendix B). The emissions of NH₃, largely from livestock farms, show great local variability, and with this scale of spatial variability, a concentration field interpolated directly from measurements fails to capture much of the fine structure in the concentration field. The UK NH₃ concentration field is therefore provided using a long-range transport model (FRAME), described in Chapter 4. The resulting map of NH₃ concentration in Figure 3.20a, shows the largest values in the livestock farming areas of the border counties of England and Wales, in Cumbria, Lancashire and in south west England.

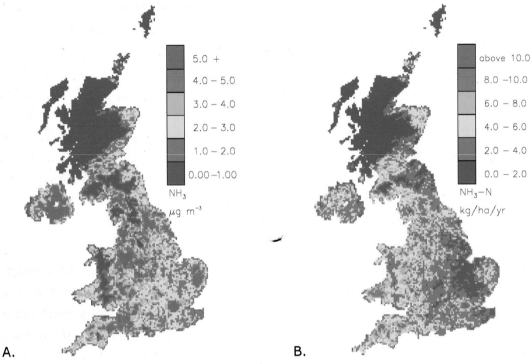

A.   B.

Figure 3.20 FRAME 1996 (a) NH₃ concentrations and (b) dry deposition of NH₃.

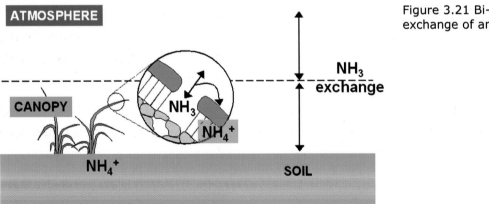

Figure 3.21 Bi-directional exchange of ammonia.

The surface exchange of NH₃.

The surface exchange of NH₃ is treated as a bi-directional process reflecting the fact that NH₃ exhibits a compensation point (χ_s), so that at ambient concentration excess of χ_s NH₃ is deposited and when concentrations are smaller than χ_s NH₃ is emitted (Figure 3.21). The deposition of NH₃ is therefore calculated using a process based model, which simulates the compensation point exchange process for all fertilized vegetation (Sutton *et al.*, 2000b & 2001c). For semi-natural vegetation, a simpler approach is adopted, using a fixed canopy resistance because the compensation point is too small and insufficiently well known to justify the application of a compensation point approach. The dry deposition of NH_3 using a canopy compensation point model for all of the fertilized vegetation, and a canopy resistance model for all other surfaces, is shown in Figure 3.20b.

3.4.3 Cloud Droplet Deposition

Wet and dry deposition represent the dominant pathways for pollutant deposition within the UK, but for those areas of the landscape which are in cloud for a significant fraction of the time (the uplands, especially in the west) the direct deposition of cloud droplets to vegetation represent an important contribution to the deposition total (Crossley *et al.*, 1992). For sites at altitudes above 600 m in western Britain the cloud frequency lies between 3% and 10% and with this fraction of the time 'in cloud', the deposition of cloud water becomes an important component of the total. For example, at forest sites above 500 m asl in the Scottish borders, the majority of the sulphur and nitrogen input may be deposited as cloud (or occult) deposition (Crossley *et al.,* 1992). This deposition pathway is also included because the exposure of vegetation to the largest concentrations of pollutant ions in the liquid phase occurs through the deposition of polluted cloudwater (Fowler *et al.,* 1990). The total deposition maps for acidity S and N for the UK therefore include cloud deposition to provide estimates of the total deposition and to identify sites and components of the ecosystem at risk from effects of the pollutants through different deposition pathways.

3.5 Changes in Deposition with Time

The main features of the regional patterns in wet deposition and the concentrations of major ions in precipitation have remained fairly constant throughout the monitoring period reported here, 1986-1999, with a clear gradient of increasing concentration from the west coast towards the east, for all ions derived from the major pollutants, and a decreasing concentration from west to east of the seasalt ions (Na^+ and Cl^-). The changes with time that have been observed, include a large reduction in non-seasalt SO_4^{2-} concentration, especially in central and eastern regions of the UK, a marked reduction in the acidity of rain, almost everywhere by up to 50%, and small, but significant reductions in NO_3^- concentrations in the East Midlands, but no significant overall trend in NO_3^- concentration throughout the country and no change in NH_4^+ concentration.

The concentrations and deposition of sulphur in precipitation have declined and the change has been much greater in the source regions than elsewhere. These trends in concentrations and deposition provide an important background for the interpretation of the measurements of trends in composition of surface waters within the Acid Waters Monitoring Network, (AWMN). For the trend analysis there are two key questions.

(1) Have the reductions in UK (and other European) emissions of sulphur led to reduced S deposition in the UK and to any change in the spatial pattern of deposition?

(2) Are observed changes in concentration and deposition consistent with current understanding of the processes?

3.5.1 Changes in the sulphur budget of the atmosphere over the UK, and the relative importance of wet and dry deposition

In Chapter 2, the UK emissions of SO_2 are shown to have declined between 1986 and 1997 by 57%. Similarly, non-UK European S emissions declined by 45% between 1986 and 1997. These large changes provide a large 'signal' to examine the measurement data. The mapped wet and dry deposition using a consistent methodology for the 12 year period allow the mass balance of the atmosphere over the UK to be quantified. This is shown in Table 3.2. The total deposition of non-seasalt sulphur declines from 492 kt-S in 1986 to 234 kt-S in 1997, a reduction of 52%. So overall the emission and deposition changes are approximately equal. However, the partitioning of the total deposition in the UK between wet and dry deposition shows an important change over the monitoring period. The wet deposition declines by 42% while dry deposition declines by 61% over the 12 years. There are also regional differences with the bulk of the improvement in the central and eastern Midlands of England and the smallest changes in the high rainfall areas of western Britain.

Table 3.2 UK sulphur emission and deposition 1986 to 1997 and the atmospheric budget over the country (all values kt-S).

Year	1986	1987	1988	1989	1990	1991	1992	1993	1994	1995	1996	1997
UK emissions	1966	1961	1923	1860	1882	1790	1753	1584	1354	1176	1014	830
I/Ps non-UK European	120	102	75	94	80	100	86	92	78	73	90	75
Dry deposition	262	246	234	227	201	231	185	187	159	123	125	102
Wet+cloud deposition	230	226	251	229	226	223	215	186	198	155	171	132
Total deposition	492	472	485	456	427	454	400	373	357	278	296	234
Exported emissions	1594	1591	1513	1498	1535	1436	1439	1303	1075	971	808	671

Clearly therefore, the answer to the first question is that there has been a marked reduction in S deposition in response to emission reductions but the area in which deposition has declined is largely restricted to the source regions. Thus the answer to question 2 is that the observed change in deposition is unexpected. In particular, the very large reduction in dry deposition, primarily as a consequence of a reduction in ambient SO_2 concentrations in the source region (within 100 km of the major sources) is the main cause of the much greater reduction in dry deposition. There is empirical evidence that the rate of dry deposition has increased in the source regions in response to changes in the relative concentrations of SO_2 and NH_3 (Fowler *et al.,* 2001), which have not been incorporated in the UK deposition budgets in Table 3.2. The extent of the relative changes in wet and dry deposition is therefore underestimated in the data in Table 3.2.

3.6 Trends in the Sulphur Content of Precipitation

The observed decline in SO_4^{2-} concentration in precipitation (Table 3.3 and Figure 3.22) is clear at the sites in the East Midlands and Yorkshire, the major source areas. In these areas (within 100 km of the major power stations) the non-seasalt SO_4^{2-} concentration declines at approximately 3 μeq-SO_4^{2-} y^{-1} throughout the 12 years and the (linear) trends are highly significant. At the sites close to the west coast of England, Wales and Scotland and in the west of N. Ireland there is also a decline in non-seasalt SO_4^{2-} but for each of these sites considered individually the decline is small and is not statistically significant. When all 'west coast' sites are considered together a small statistically significant linear trend of decreasing SO_4^{2-} is established.

The sites at distances of 100 km to 200 km from the major sources (Eskdalemuir, Redesdale, Mharcaidh and Achanarras, Barcombe Mills and Compton) show significant decreases in SO_4^{2-} averaging between 1 and 2 $\mu eq\text{-}SO_4^{2-}\ l^{-1}\ y^{-1}$.

Thus the reduction in wet deposition is clearest in the same areas as the dry deposition reduction. The reduction in dry deposition on precipitation collectors contributes about 25% of the observed decline in wet SO_4^{2-} deposition in the source regions.

The trends are therefore smallest at the remote, high rainfall sites and it is only possible to detect statistically significant trends at these remote sites by grouping the data for all remote sites. At the individual monitoring sites at these west coast locations, the observed decline in non-seasalt SO_4^{2-} is not significant.

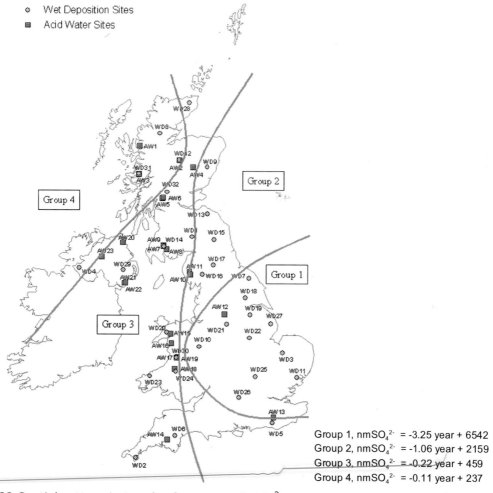

Group 1, nmSO$_4^{2-}$ = -3.25 year + 6542
Group 2, nmSO$_4^{2-}$ = -1.06 year + 2159
Group 3, nmSO$_4^{2-}$ = -0.22 year + 459
Group 4, nmSO$_4^{2-}$ = -0.11 year + 237

Figure 3.22 Spatial pattern in trends of non-seasalt SO_4^{2-} at monitoring sites across the UK.

The cause of this may partly be the inter-annual noise in the meteorology masking a small signal. However, this raises the question of stationarity, i.e. are all other conditions remaining constant during the 12 years of monitoring? The first and most obvious indicator is precipitation amount, which shows considerable inter-year variability. However, analysis of the data shows that for precipitation amount there is no monotonic trend. The relative frequency of winds which transport pollutants from the source areas in the UK and other countries of Europe to remote regions of the UK has been examined in earlier analyses of UK acid deposition (RGAR, 1990 & 1997). This in turn is influenced by larger scale phenomena including interactions between ocean and atmosphere over the North Atlantic and the relative frequency of winds from oceanic and continental sources over the UK.

Table 3.3 Linear trend analysis of non-seasalt SO_4^{2-} in precipitation at UK monitoring sites 1986-1997. The statistically significant trends are listed in the final column.

	Site*	slope	standard error	probability	sig. slope
Group 1	**Stoke Ferry**	**-3.0610**	**0.6128**	**0.001**	**-3.0610**
	High Muffles	**-2.0060**	**0.6574**	**0.012**	**-2.0060**
	Preston Montford	-0.7790	0.9001	0.407	
	Flatford Mills	**-3.6040**	**0.7125**	**0.000**	**-3.6040**
	Thorganby	-2.4080	1.1719	0.067	
	Jenny Hurn	**-4.7900**	**0.8817**	**0.000**	**-4.7900**
	Wardlow Hay Cop	**-1.4800**	**0.6322**	**0.041**	**-1.4800**
	Bottesford	**-4.8090**	**0.7266**	**0.000**	**-4.8090**
	Woburn	**-3.5150**	**0.6058**	**0.000**	**-3.5150**
	Compton	**-3.2970**	**0.9557**	**0.006**	**-3.2970**
	Driby	**-2.6530**	**0.7876**	**0.007**	**-2.6530**
Group 2	**Barcombe Mills**	**-1.5870**	**0.4544**	**0.006**	**-1.5870**
	Glen Dye	-0.2300	0.7861	0.776	
	Whiteadder	**-1.3930**	**0.5654**	**0.033**	**-1.3930**
	Redesdale	-1.3510	0.6268	0.057	
	Bannisdale	-0.3780	0.3305	0.280	
	Cow Green Reservoir	-0.7010	0.3539	0.076	
	Hillsborough Forest	-1.5070	0.8724	0.128	
Group 3	**Eskdalemuir**	**-0.4840**	**0.1258**	**0.003**	**-0.4840**
	Goonhilly	-0.2730	0.4059	0.516	
	Yarner Wood	0.0160	0.4124	0.970	
	Loch Dee	-0.7710	0.4224	0.098	
	Beddgelert	-1.5200	0.8512	0.108	
	Tycanol Wood	-0.3910	0.2678	0.175	
	Llyn Brianne	-0.3900	0.2183	0.104	
	Achanarras	**-0.8490**	**0.3012**	**0.018**	**-0.8490**
	Pumlumon	-0.1390	0.3707	0.718	
	Balquhidder	-0.2070	0.4458	0.653	
Group 4	Lough Navar	-0.0600	0.1405	0.680	
	Strathvaich Dam	-0.1900	0.2802	0.514	
	River Mharcaidh	-0.6060	0.2779	0.054	
	Polloch	-0.5740	0.4342	0.243	

*See Appendix B for site details.

The North Atlantic Oscillation (NAO) has been recognised as an important influence on European climate (Hurrell, 1995) and is discussed at length in the Acid Waters Monitoring Network 10 year report (UK AWMN, 2000). The NAO provides an index of 'westerlyness' in the airflow over the UK. Large NAO values (or large pressure gradients) are associated with strong 'zonal airflow' over the country and a succession of fronts and precipitation over the UK. If marked changes of the NAO occur during the 12 years of the available wet deposition data for the UK, then it may be argued that this would introduce additional variability into the precipitation chemistry measurement and mask trends. The annual NAO values plotted in Figure 3.23 show a clear maximum in NAO in the years 1990, 1992 with smaller positive values in 1986, 1989, 1991 and 1994, while 1987, 1988, 1995, 1996 and 1997 all show negative values (reduced westerlyness). A simple correlation of Cl^- concentration against NAO, using annual data reveals relatively little structure with the exception that the largest positive value is associated with the largest mean Cl^- concentration. Thus, the precipitation chemistry data at annual scales, as used for the deposition maps, shows a weak association between these two variables.

The annual Cl^- deposition however, is highly episodic, with a substantial fraction of the deposition contributed by a few rainfall events each year. The data from the UK primary precipitation chemistry sites which provide daily collection, show that all sites in the primary network are highly episodic in Cl^- deposition (defined as sites receiving >30% of the wet deposition in < 5% of the precipitation events). Furthermore, the Cl⁻ deposition is largely a winter phenomenon, with 80% of the deposition in the winter months. In conclusion, while variability in the weather has masked some of the trends in deposition, the changes in the 'westerlyness' of UK weather are not the cause of the change in partitioning of sulphur between wet and dry deposition in the UK.

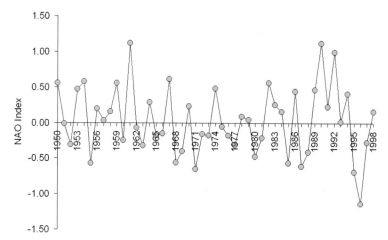

Figure 3.23 Annual variation in the NAO index.

3.7 Trends in Concentrations of Long-Range Transported Pollutants from the UK

Over the last decade, the downward trends observed in the concentrations of a number of air pollutants in the United Kingdom have also been observed across Europe. Many of the factors that have influenced UK emissions have been active throughout Europe. In the paragraphs below, the trends in SO_2 and particulate sulphate have been examined in air masses which have passed over the UK en route to the remote background monitoring station, Birkenes, in southern Norway.

Figure 3.24 presents the annual mean SO_2 and particulate sulphate concentrations in all air masses that arrive at the Birkenes site from the wind direction sector from 210-270° using the EMEP daily wind sector allocations. The Birkenes site is in the southern part of Norway and the air masses which arrive in this particular sector will have passed over the United Kingdom during the previous 1-3 days. Over the period from 1985-1996 inclusive, significant downward trends have been reported (Torseth et al., 2000) both in SO_2 and particulate sulphate.

The sum of the airborne concentrations of SO_2 and particulate SO_4^{2-} appear to been declining by about 2% per year (on a µg-S m⁻³ basis) over the period of 1985-1996. Over the corresponding period, UK SO_2 emissions have declined by about 6% per year, which is significantly faster than the observations in Figure 3.24. The observed decline should be seen in the context of the large year-on-year variability and the low overall level of the daily concentrations detected which precludes a great level of accuracy. The small reduction in concentrations of sulphur in the gas and aerosol phase observed relative to the reductions in emissions is consistent with the observations at remote locations in the UK, and provides further evidence that the main consequence of emission reduction has been in reduced dry deposition rather than reduced long range transport.

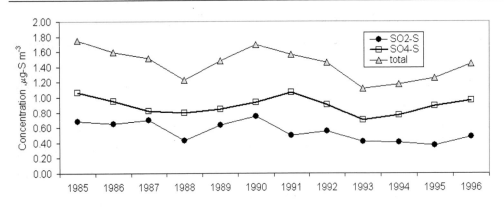

Figure 3.24 Trends in SO$_2$ and particulate sulphate and their total observed at Birkenes, Norway from 1985-1996 in air masses arriving from the United Kingdom.

3.8 Non-Linearity

The observed changes in the spatial deposition patterns in the UK show that the relationship between pollutant emission and deposition varies both across the country and with time. It is not surprising that the different meteorology and distances to sources across the country should produce complexity in the observed spatial pattern in deposition. However, it is a little surprising that the spatial pattern should vary with time in the way it has. The term 'non-linearity' has been used to illustrate the fact that as emissions decline, the rates of reduction in concentrations and deposition vary across the deposition footprint. The term is not new and was discussed in reports of the Review Group on Acid Deposition (1987 and 1994) and by Clark *et al.* (1987). In the UK as a whole, the reduction in emission of sulphur is roughly linear with the deposition. However, during the time the UK emissions declined by 50% the decline in deposition in the East Midlands of England was approximately 70%, while in the west of Wales the reduction in deposition was closer to 30%. Changes in the pattern of deposition and the partitioning into wet and dry deposition is therefore introducing non-linearity into the spatial relationship between emission and deposition of S in the UK and the degree to which the effect is observed depends on the scale at which the analysis is performed. It is important to note here that the demand for analysis of effects of pollutants on the environment is towards finer spatial detail, and with this trend comes an increasing requirement to be able to quantify and validate the fine structure in deposition. The observed non-linearities show that a monitoring network is essential to underpin an assessment of the effects of control strategies. If the current assessment had relied solely on models developed to simulate the emission, transport and deposition processes, rather than on monitoring networks, these changes would not have been detected.

Several processes may have contributed to generate the change in the partitioning of wet and dry sulphur deposition in the UK .

    (1) A much larger reduction in low level than high level sources of SO$_2$.

    (2) An observed change in the rate of SO$_2$ dry deposition which has gradually increased in the source regions as SO$_2$ concentrations have fallen.

    (3) An oxidant limited conversion of SO$_2$ to SO$_4^{2-}$ in the atmosphere.

    (4) A change in the background concentration of non-seasalt SO$_4^{2-}$ from sources to the west of the UK (notably shipping S sources).

All four processes may have combined to cause the observed non-linearity in sulphur deposition and these are considered in turn.

3.8.1 Non-Linearity: Source Height

The UK emissions contain a range of sources that can be separated according to the height at which the pollutant is injected into the atmosphere. The power stations which contribute the majority (80%) of the UK total have tall stacks (100 m to 200 m). With high temperatures and large exit velocities, stack gases are generally injected into the atmosphere at effective heights of 300 m to 500 m. Smaller industrial sources with smaller stacks have much smaller emission heights and domestic emission and vehicle diesel combustion are effectively ground level. These low level sources dominate the urban SO_2 concentrations as illustrated by Figure 3.25. However, urban areas represent less than 10% of the country and only a small fraction of S emission, declining from 7% in 1986 to 3% in 1997. The decline in low level emissions has contributed to the observed decline in dry deposition in the source regions, but the changes in this contribution to UK deposition are too small to explain the change in wet deposition over the UK and especially at west coast sites.

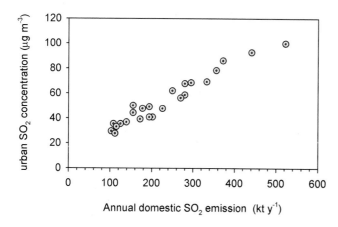

Figure 3.25 Relationship between low-level (domestic) SO_2 emissions and the annual mean concentration in urban areas.

3.8.2 Non-Linearity: Changes in Rates of Dry Deposition

Early applications of deposition velocities within models to calculate dry deposition assumed a constant rate of dry deposition to the landscape (Fisher, 1978). More recent applications have recognised the spatial variability in SO_2 deposition with differences in land cover and meteorological conditions (EMEP, 1999; RGAR, 1997). It is recognised therefore that deposition velocity is very sensitive to changes in both surface and atmospheric conditions. Measurements of SO_2 dry deposition over seasonal time scales show that the affinity of absorbing surfaces is strongly influenced by the presence of surface water (Fowler et al., 1995b) and the chemical composition of the surface water (Flechard et al., 1999; Erisman et al., 1996b). The most important chemical species in solution influencing the magnitude of the surface resistance for SO_2 (r_c) appears to be NH_4^+, and in particular the ratio of the concentrations of NH_4^+ to SO_4^{2-} in solution on leaf surfaces. Changes in ambient SO_2 concentration may therefore be expected to increase the ratio of NH_4^+/SO_4^{2-}. Field data for the UK shows a substantial influence of the NH_4^+/SO_4^{2-} ratio on the deposition velocity for SO_2. With the substantial reduction in SO_2 concentration in source areas of the UK, from typically 10 to 20 ppb in the 1970s and 1980s to little more than 1 to 4 ppb in the late 1990s, the potential for change in deposition velocity is clear.

As NH_3 emissions have changed relatively little during this period, the change in the NH_4^+/SO_4^{2-} ratio over large areas is typically an order of magnitude and may be expected to have changed r_c (and v_g) substantially. A set of measurements of the canopy resistance to dry deposition in the 1970s and 1990s shows a reduction from 130 sm^{-1} to 85 sm^{-1} over the 20 year period. Quantifying these changes spatially would be a speculative exercise given the lack of historical ambient NH$_3$ concentrations. However, the change would have increased the rate of dry deposition removal of SO$_2$, especially in the source regions, which would have experienced the greatest change in NH$_4^+$/SO$_4^{2-}$. In conclusion, it is probable therefore that changes in dry deposition rates have made a substantial contribution to the observed non-linearity. The necessary analysis to quantify the magnitude of the change throughout the country remains to be completed.

3.8.3 Non-Linearity: Effects of Changes in SO$_2$ to SO$_4^{2-}$ Oxidation on Deposition

The oxidation of SO$_2$ to SO$_4^{2-}$ outlined in Figure 3.1 occurs by both homogenous (gas phase) and heterogeneous processes occurring in cloud droplets or on aerosols. The bulk of the SO$_4^{2-}$ produced over the UK appears to result from heterogeneous oxidation processes, especially in stratiform cloud through reaction with O$_3$ or H$_2$O$_2$ (Figure 3.1). The changes in SO$_2$ emissions would lead to changes in the NH$_4^+$/SO$_4^{2-}$ and the pH in cloud water, and this would change rates of SO$_4^{2-}$ production by the O$_3$ pathway. The reduced SO$_2$ emissions would tend to increase the fraction of the emitted SO$_2$ oxidized in source regions.

An attempt was made to reproduce the "observed" deposition trends using a Lagrangian acid rain model (TRACK, see Chapter 4 for more information on this model). The chemical scheme used in the model is a simplified treatment of the oxidation of sulphur and nitrogen species (Hayman et al., 2000). The chemistry is treated explicitly as daytime and night-time reactions, rather than being diurnally averaged. Sulphur dioxide is oxidised to sulphate via a number of homogenous and heterogeneous pathways. The individual chemical reactions are not represented explicitly in the model. Instead, the overall oxidation rate of SO$_2$ to sulphate aerosol is expressed as:

$$\frac{d[SO_4]}{dt} = (k_1[OH] + k_2) * [SO_2]$$

Where:

        $k_1[OH]$ is the gas phase rate constant

        k_2 is the aqueous chemistry rate coefficient

The aqueous phase rate coefficient may be expected to increase in areas where the concentrations of sulphur dioxide have decreased significantly. This will lead to an increase in the pH of the rainwater. The aqueous phase chemistry of SO$_2$ and ozone is very sensitive to the pH of rainwater. To simulate this change, the aqueous oxidation rate coefficients used in TRACK were increased from 2.0×10^{-6} to 3.4×10^{-6}. Wet and dry deposition budgets were then determined for these coefficients and emission fields appropriate for 1990 (Figure 3.26). Not surprisingly, the wet deposition budget did increase. A rate co-efficient of 3.4×10^{-6} produced the relative proportion of wet to dry deposition observed in 1997.

This work shows that the chemical processes alone probably play only a small role in the observed trends.

3.8.4 Non-Linearity: Effects of Changes to S Emissions Outside Europe

European, and especially UK, emissions declined by *ca* 50% over the period 1986 – 1997. However, emissions for the US changed little (-12%) and more importantly emissions for shipping in the North Atlantic have increased substantially as traffic and the S content of fuel have both increased. The contribution of shipping sources to sulphur deposition in the UK has been studied by Vincent *et al.* (2000), who show that shipping may contribute 12% of the sulphur deposition at west coast sites. The precise effect of the changes in shipping emissions is difficult to quantify, as the S emissions from shipping cannot be spatially disaggregated with great precision. Modelling studies at a global scale show that the regional background S deposition for shipping and N American emission lead to a deposition of approximately 200 mg m^{-2} to the west of the British Isles (Figure 3.27). The deposition of 200 mg-S m^{-2} as SO_4^{2-} would lead to a concentration of SO_4^{2-} in precipitation of approximately 12 µeq-SO_4^{2-} l^{-1} in a precipitation of 1000 mm (typical of the west coast). The precipitation chemistry at the west coast sites show typical SO_4^{2-} concentrations of 15 to 20 µeq^{-1}. For a linear response to changes in UK emissions, concentrations at these west coast sites would therefore have been expected to decline by 7 to 10 µeq l^{-1}. Thus an increase in background of 5 to 10 µeq l^{-1}, would have offset changes in the SO_4^{2-} concentration in rain from UK and other European sources due to emission reductions.

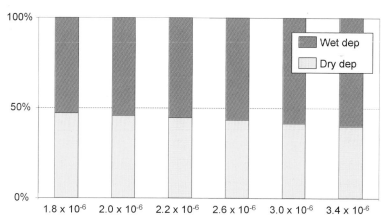

Figure 3.26 Relative contributions of wet and dry deposition to total deposition budget as a function of the aqueous phase rate constant.

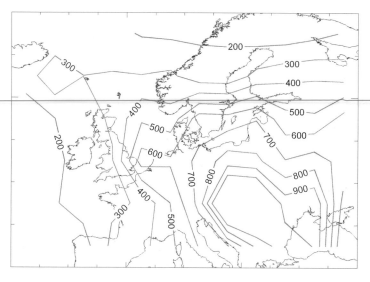

Figure 3.27 Wet deposition of sulphur to the European region (mg-S m^{-2} y^{-1}) from both natural and man-made sources of both SO_2 and DMS, calculated with the STOCHEM global model (Stevenson *et al.*, 1998). Man-made emissions of SO_2 are from the EDGAR database for 1992, which includes stationary combustion, smelting, biomass burning and shipping.

3.8.5 Non-Linearity: Conclusion

Overall, therefore, the processes of chemical transformations involved in wet and dry deposition have not remained constant over the monitoring period and have responded to changes in the chemical climatology of the air over the UK. In particular, there is evidence that the different pollutants interact in both the chemical processing and removal rates.

The two main contributors to the observed non-linearity are changes in the canopy resistance to dry deposition, which has increased the deposition velocity with time, and an increase in the 'background' SO_4^{2-}, in air from the Atlantic, largely from shipping, although an increasing contribution from North American sources is also possible.

An important consequence of the change in background SO_4^{2-} concentrations is that to reduce S deposition sufficiently in western Britain, especially Wales, Cumbria, Galloway and the western Highlands, to values small enough to allow recovery of damaged ecosystems, it may be necessary to control shipping emission sources (and other major sources to the west of Europe).

3.9 Nitrogen Deposition

The acidifying inputs from the atmosphere include oxidized N compounds (NO_3^- in rain and aerosols, and dry deposition of NO_3^- aerosols, NO_2, HNO_3, HONO and PAN) and reduced nitrogen as NH_4^+ in rain and aerosols and dry deposition of NH_3. However, these compounds are also of interest for their part in terrestrial ecosystem eutrophication resulting from the role of N as a major nutrient. Furthermore, as acidification of soils and freshwaters declines with the reduction in sulphur emissions, the role of nitrogen and eutrophication are becoming more important.

3.9.1 Changes in Nitrogen Deposition 1986 -1999

The wet deposition of NO_3^- and NH_4^+, outlined earlier, shows smaller changes over the period 1986 to 1999 than those of SO_4^{2-}. However, there are important changes, and these should be examined in the light of the changes in emissions during the same period. The concentrations of NO_3^- in precipitation declined by about 10% over the country as a whole. However, in a statistical sense the trend in concentration throughout the country is not significant. It is useful to consider the different areas of the country, in the same way as for SO_4^{2-}, earlier in this chapter and shown in Figure 3.22. Considering the sites in group 1 (the sites in the East Midlands and SE of England), the trend in NO_3^- is statistically significant, averaging almost 1 µeq l^{-1} per year over the 10 year period 1989 to 1999 and representing a decrease of about 20% from 42 to 34 µeq l^{-1} (Figure 3.28 and Table 3.4).

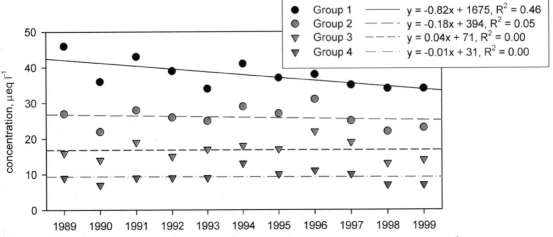

Figure 3.28 Trends in NO_3^- in precipitation, averaged with sites grouped as for SO_4^{2-} (Figure 3.22).

Table 3.4 Trends in NH_4^+ and NO_3^- concentrations in precipitation from 1986 to 1999. Statistically significant trends (95%) are highlighted.

	Site*	Ammonium (NH_4^+)			Nitrate (NO_3^-)		
		Slope	R^2	Probability	Slope	R^2	Probability
Group 1	**Stoke Ferry**	**-1.2924**	**0.3297**	**0.032**	**-0.7271**	**0.3398**	**0.029**
	High Muffles	-0.2778	0.0225	0.608	**-0.6187**	**0.2953**	**0.045**
	Preston Montford	-0.8551	0.1734	0.139	-0.2080	0.0176	0.651
	Flatford Mill	-0.9857	0.1808	0.148	-0.5641	0.1637	0.151
	Thorganby	-1.1907	0.0691	0.386	**-0.8123**	**0.4392**	**0.010**
	Jenny Hurn	-0.5211	0.0423	0.481	-0.4214	0.1574	0.160
	Wardlow Hay Cop	0.1785	0.0096	0.738	-0.0866	0.0054	0.803
	Bottesford	-0.5497	0.0753	0.342	**-0.9802**	**0.5339**	**0.003**
	Woburn	-0.6109	0.0989	0.273	-0.3122	0.0850	0.312
	Compton	-0.9705	0.1301	0.205	**-0.8489**	**0.4215**	**0.012**
	Driby	-1.0560	0.2125	0.097	-0.2430	0.0516	0.435
	whole group	*-0.7476*	*0.1738*	*0.138*	*-0.5293*	*0.3508*	*0.026*
	whole group: 89-99	*-1.2984*	*0.2562*	*0.112*	*-0.8209*	*0.4559*	*0.023*
Group 2	**Barcombe Mills**	**-1.5214**	**0.4681**	**0.007**	-0.3642	0.1210	0.223
	Glen Dye	-0.0997	0.0044	0.830	-0.0791	0.0034	0.850
	Whiteadder	-0.3992	0.0894	0.299	-0.5929	0.2092	0.100
	Redesdale	0.5391	0.0836	0.316	-0.1040	0.0135	0.693
	Bannisdale	0.0236	0.0006	0.932	0.2136	0.1699	0.143
	Cow Green Reservoir	0.2503	0.1055	0.257	-0.0776	0.0197	0.632
	Hillsborough Forest	-0.8366	0.1241	0.288	-0.0677	0.0029	0.876
	whole group	*-0.0696*	*0.0045*	*0.820*	*-0.1893*	*0.0864*	*0.308*
	whole group: 89-99	*-0.4113*	*0.0925*	*0.363*	*-0.1843*	*0.0461*	*0.526*
Group 3	Eskdalemuir	0.0743	0.0813	0.575	0.0743	0.0270	0.575
	Goonhilly	-0.1953	0.0197	0.632	0.1307	0.0141	0.686
	Yarner Wood	0.3479	0.0474	0.455	0.3685	0.0819	0.321
	Loch Dee	-0.4984	0.1941	0.115	-0.0905	0.0188	0.640
	Beddgelert	0.7669	0.2654	0.105	0.1829	0.0338	0.588
	Tycanol Wood	0.1704	0.0612	0.394	0.0902	0.0254	0.586
	Llyn Brianne	0.1282	0.0502	0.441	0.0831	0.0259	0.582
	Achanarras	**-0.7960**	**0.9740**	**0.002**	-0.3080	0.1155	0.235
	Pumlumon	-0.1565	0.0213	0.669	-0.0003	0.0000	0.999
	Balquhidder	0.1703	0.0459	0.462	0.0085	0.0001	0.974
	whole group	*0.0197*	*0.0009*	*0.917*	*0.0210*	*0.0012*	*0.908*
	whole group: 89-99	*-0.0944*	*0.0122*	*0.747*	*0.0438*	*0.0028*	*0.876*
Group 4	Lough Navar	0.2115	0.1365	0.194	0.1265	0.0473	0.455
	Strathvaich Dam	0.0874	0.1588	0.177	0.0175	0.0025	0.872
	River Mharcaidh	-0.0736	0.0281	0.567	-0.0152	0.0008	0.925
	Polloch	**-0.3217**	**0.4645**	**0.043**	-0.4217	0.3958	0.069
	whole group	*-0.0166*	*0.0034*	*0.843*	*-0.0076*	*0.0004*	*0.946*
	whole group: 89-99	*0.0114*	*0.0014*	*0.914*	*-0.0108*	*0.0004*	*0.953*

*See Appendix B for site details.

The emissions and the rural concentrations of NO_2 in the UK declined by about 40% during the period 1990 to 1999. There are no statistically significant trends in any other region of the country and for most regions, there is no downward trend at all. These relatively small trends, when combined with precipitation amount, show evidence of a modest decrease in NO_3^- in wet deposition. Furthermore, the large decrease in NO_2 concentrations throughout the country also lead to reduced nitrogen deposition. The measurements of HNO_3 concentrations only began in 1998 and do not provide a sufficiently long time series for trend analysis.

However, the decreases in NO_3^- in rain are a good indication of the trend in HNO_3, which would probably be downwards by about 10% over the country during the last decade.

The trends in NH_4^+ are less clear than those in NO_3^-, because NH_4^+ data are inherently more variable. The concentrations of NH_4^+ in precipitation show no consistent changes over the country. In the groups of sites, used to analyse the data for SO_4^{2-} and NO_3^-, there are no groups that show a statistically significant trend, but the trends are negative in 3 out of the 4 groups (Table 3.4). Only 4 individual sites, which are scattered throughout the UK, show statistically significant trends, all show a reduction in NH_4^+, but the underlying cause is uncertain and could be the result of local site factors rather than a general, UK wide phenomenon. The emissions of NH_3, which are the least certain of all major pollutants, are not known to have changed significantly during the period of the wet deposition measurements. It is also uncertain therefore, whether any change in the dry deposition of NH_3 has occurred since 1986.

3.9.2 Changes in the Relative Contributions of Nitrogen and Sulphur to Acid Deposition

While the total deposition of potential acidity in the UK has been declining due to reduced S deposition, the relative contribution by NO_3^- and NH_4^+ has been increasing. Current wet deposition of NH_4^+ and NO_3^- exceeds that of non-seasalt SO_4^{2-} (expressed in chemical equivalents). Typical rainfall weighted concentrations of NO_3^- and NH_4^+ (each 40 to 50 µeq l^{-1} in the polluted regions) exceed non-seasalt S concentration by almost a factor two. When the total deposition to the UK of oxidized and reduced nitrogen (27 Gmol-N y^{-1}) is compared with non-seasalt sulphur deposition (14.5 Gmol-S y^{-1}), the total potential acidification is now dominated by the oxidized and reduced nitrogen input (Figure 3.29).

The actual acidification of soils and freshwaters however, cannot be allocated to the components of nitrogen and sulphur so simply, because it is necessary to know the chemical and biological fate of the deposited nitrogen to quantify the acidification (Figure 3.2) and the fate of the deposited nitrogen remains poorly known. This is a very important point, as the effects of deposited sulphur, through its acidification of soils and freshwaters, are much better understood than the role of deposited nitrogen in acidification.

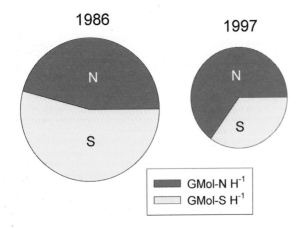

UK Gmol y^{-1}	1986	1997
N	27	27.0
S	32	14.5
Total	59	41.5

Figure 3.29 Potential acidification by N and S.

3.9.3 Total Nitrogen Deposition

The total annual deposition of nitrogen of 380 kt-N (27 Gmol-N) is split 43% oxidized N and 57% reduced N, even though emissions of reduced nitrogen are considerably smaller (287 kt-N) than those of oxidized nitrogen (560 kt-N). The annual total deposition of nitrogen at 380 kt-N averages approximately 17 kg-N ha^{-1} throughout the country, approximately an order of magnitude larger than N deposition in the 19th century (Laws *et al.,* 1861). The spatial distribution of the annual total N deposition in the UK is shown in Figure 3.30; the areas of large deposition include much of the uplands of northern England, Wales and parts of western Scotland. However, unlike acid deposition, there are also substantial areas of south west England and East Anglia which receive large nitrogen deposition, the latter mainly a consequence of NH$_3$ deposition.

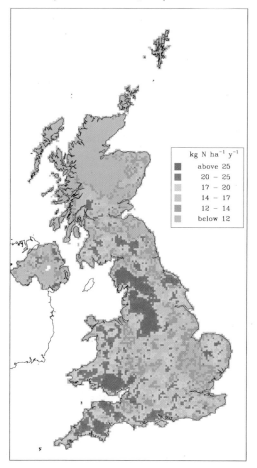

Figure 3.30 Total N deposition to the UK for 1997, calculated as the average deposition to each grid square accounting for different land cover types.

The frequency distribution of N deposition in the UK (Figure 3.31) shows that the majority of the grid squares in the UK receive substantially larger nitrogen deposition than the remote areas of northern Europe (< 10 kg-N ha^{-1} y^{-1}).

Separating the nitrogen deposition by major land uses and into oxidized and reduced nitrogen (Figure 3.32) shows that forests receive the largest annual inputs, averaging 33 kg-N ha^{-1}, but that for all surfaces reduced nitrogen dominates the input, averaging two thirds of the total. These different forms of fixed nitrogen in the atmosphere have very different average lifetimes and travel distances. For example, the mean residence time of reduced nitrogen is 5 hours, while that of oxidized nitrogen is approximately 30 hours, and mean travel distances for reduced and oxidized nitrogen are 150 km and 1000 km respectively.

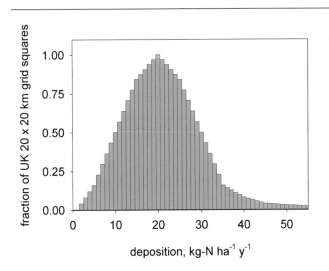

Figure 3.31 Relative frequency distribution of N deposition to the UK 20 x 20 km grid squares.

total deposition: 335 kt-N

	reduced	oxidized
	218	117

	Forest	Moorland	Grassland	Arable
Total N Deposition, kt	60	109	86	109
Area, x 10^6 ha	2	7.9	6.5	7.9
Mean Deposition, kg-N ha^{-1}	33	16	15	16
% Reduced N	69%	58%	50%	58%

Figure 3.32 Partitioning of total N deposition to the UK by land class (1995-97).

The result of the very different atmospheric behaviour of reduced and oxidized nitrogen is that their environmental effects occur at different distances from the source. In the case of reduced nitrogen, with a relatively short atmospheric lifetime, the effects of UK emission occur largely within the UK, whereas for oxidized nitrogen, 85% of which is exported from the UK, the effects primarily occur outside the UK. The individual components of the atmospheric nitrogen budget for reduced and oxidized nitrogen over the UK illustrate these differences (Figure 3.33).

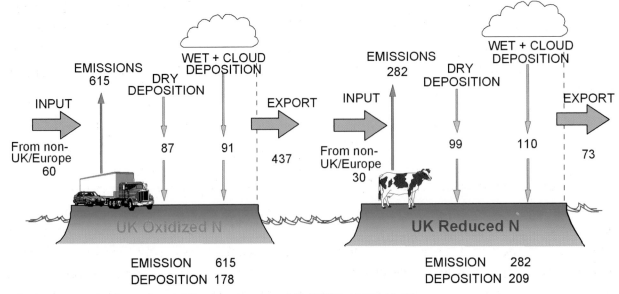

Figure 3.33 UK budgets for oxidised and reduced N (1996-1997, kt-N).

Reduced nitrogen therefore dominates the nitrogen deposition budget within the UK and the terrestrial effects due to nitrogen deposition. The characteristics of NH_3 sources within the country, being very widely distributed and close to the surface, lead to a substantial fraction of heterogeneity in the deposition being sub-grid scale relative to the map shown in Figure 3.20. In the map, the N deposition is shown at a resolution of 5 km x 5 km. However, recent field studies show that individual NH_3 sources lead to deposition gradients from 40 to 5 kg ha^{-1} y^{-1} all within 270 m of the source. An example of this very local scale variability in NH_3 deposition is provided in Figure 3.34, taken from Fowler et al. (1998c), which shows the gradients in ambient concentrations of NH_3 and the deposition gradient within 270 m of a poultry farm. The data also show that, despite the local deposition, the majority of the emitted NH_3 evades capture by the woodland and contributes to the regional pollution field. It is probable in the case of NH_3 deposition in the UK that most of the major terrestrial effects occur as sub-grid scale features at the very large number of small area deposition 'hot-spots', close to intensive livestock units (Sutton et al., 1998).

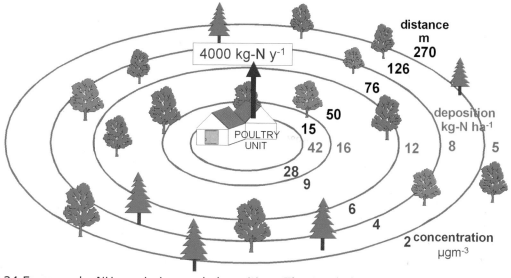

Figure 3.34 Farm scale NH_3 emission and deposition. The total deposition within 270 m of farm in woodland is 4% of the emissions (155 kg-N y^{-1}, Fowler et al., 1998c).

A similar effect is also present for NO_2 in the proximity of major sources, roads and urban source areas. However, the relatively small rates of dry deposition of NO_2 and the large background values reduce the importance of this effect. The other 'hot spot' for N deposition in addition to the variety of large sources of NH_3 includes uplands exposed to frequent hill cloud in the polluted regions of the country. Such sites, especially if wooded, may receive more than 50 kg-N ha^{-1} annually.

The marked differences between oxidized and reduced nitrogen transport and removal times from the atmosphere lead to very different regional scale deposition footprints for the emissions of oxidized and reduced nitrogen, and are illustrated in Figure 3.35. This figure, derived from a combination of the UK monitoring and assessment provided in this report, and results from the EMEP analyses, shows the areas in which 66% of the deposition occurs. The data show that the deposition of reduced nitrogen is largely limited to the UK, with only a small fraction of the emission travelling distances greater than 1000 km. For oxidized nitrogen the footprint of influence of UK emission extends over much larger distances, with the majority of the UK emissions being exported from the UK coastline and travelling on for distances in excess of 1000 km.

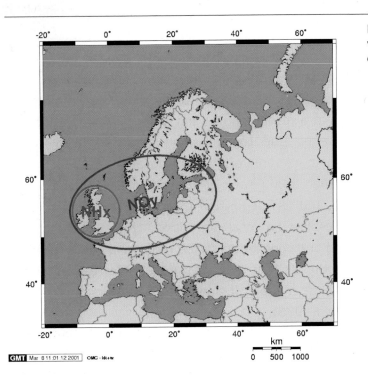

Figure 3.35 Illustration of the footprints in which 66% of UK nitrogen emissions are deposited.

3.10 Ground-Level Ozone

Ozone is present throughout the lower atmosphere with a large peak in concentration in the stratosphere, known as the ozone layer (15 - 50 km). The largest fraction and concentrations are in the stratospheric ozone layer (90%, SORG, 1999) but as tropospheric (ground-level) ozone is being investigated here, stratospheric ozone is not discussed specifically (for further information see SORG, 1999). However some stratospheric ozone is transferred to the troposphere during events such as tropopause folding and cut-off lows (Kentarchos *et al.,* 1999; Beekmann *et al.,* 1997) where it contributes to the global average background concentration of 20-30 ppb. The rest of the ozone in the troposphere is produced by photochemical reactions involving nitrogen oxides (NO_x), carbon monoxide (CO), oxygen and volatile organic compounds (NMVOCs). Ozone is termed a photochemical oxidant, as photons (hν) are required for the chemical reactions that produce it. Although other photo-oxidants such as peroxyacetyl-nitrate (PAN) and hydrogen peroxide (H_2O_2) are generated in the boundary layer, ozone has the greatest potential to cause harm. The trends and maps of ozone are discussed in the following section, while effects on vegetation are considered in Chapter 7.

Reactions of NO, O_3 and NO_2 (equations 1 to 3 below), govern the concentration of O_3 in an unpolluted atmosphere and can generate a few ppb of ozone depending on the initial concentrations of each gas. Under typical daytime conditions with a well-mixed atmosphere the 3 reactions reach equilibrium and no net chemistry occurs.

$$NO + O_3 \rightarrow NO_2 + O_2 \quad (1)$$
$$NO_2 + h\nu \rightarrow NO + O \quad (2)$$
$$O + O_2 \rightarrow O_3 (+ M) \quad (3)$$

where hν = sunlight with wavelength 280-430 nm
M = any molecule e.g. N_2 or O_2

Where other daytime chemical reactions supplement the available NO_2 for reaction (2) without consuming ozone, net ozone production can occur. The processes that produce additional O_3 are very complex involving several hundred NMVOCs, radicals and NO_x, however the reactions can be summarised as follows (PORG, 1998):

$$OH + RH \rightarrow R + H_2O \quad (4)$$
$$R + O_2 (+M) \rightarrow RO_2 (+M) \quad (5)$$
$$RO_2 + NO \rightarrow RO + NO_2 \quad (6)$$
$$RO \rightarrow \text{carbonyl products(s)} + HO_2 \quad (7)$$
$$HO_2 + NO \rightarrow OH + NO_2 \quad (8)$$

where: OH = hydroxy radical; RO_2 = alkyl peroxy radical; RO = alkoxy radical; R = alkyl radical; HO_2 = hydroperoxy radical; RH = saturated hydrocarbon (e.g. alkane)

As OH is regenerated in reaction (8) the process forms a catalytic cycle and several molecules of ozone can be produced from the oxidation of a single hydrocarbon compound. The oxidation of carbon monoxide (CO) also involves hydroperoxy and alkyl peroxy radicals and this process may also perturb the photostationary state and generate ozone (PORG, 1998).

Prior to the industrial revolution natural sources of NO_x and NMVOCs would have generated ozone in the troposphere, adding to that transported from the stratosphere. However the large amounts of NO_x and NMVOCs released by human activities have led to a large increase in the northern hemisphere background concentration. Evaluations of historical ozone measurements indicate that since the early 1900s European annual mean concentrations have increased from 10-15 ppb to ca 30 ppb (Volz & Kley, 1988; Anfossi and Sandroni, 1997). Modelling studies have attributed this rise to the increase in emissions of ozone precursors (Hough & Derwent, 1987; Wang & Jacob, 1998) and indicate that global ozone concentrations are likely to rise further in the next 100 years or so.

Anthropogenic emissions of the ozone precursors can also cause large transient increases in ozone concentration, termed episodes or smogs. These occur when high concentrations of precursors coincide with weather conditions favourable for ozone production such as when the air is warm and slow moving. It was the occurrence of eye irritation, breathing problems and visible plant damage during smogs in southern California in the 1950s that led to increased research into ozone photochemistry and effects. Tropospheric ozone is also a greenhouse gas, as it absorbs long-wave radiation and a fraction of solar radiation, making an important contribution to anthropogenic climate change (IPCC, 1995). Berntsen *et al.* (2000) estimated that the mean global radiative forcing due to changes in tropospheric ozone concentration since 1850, increased from 0.05 W m^{-2} in 1900 to 0.34 W m^{-2} in 1990 (25% of the current value for CO_2).

3.10.1 The Ozone Climate of the UK

The majority of biological and industrial activity takes place on the earth's surface, in the lowest part of the troposphere called the planetary boundary layer (PBL). There are 4 processes that influence the instantaneous concentration of ozone in this boundary layer:

(1) photochemical production (as outlined above)

(2) chemical destruction (mainly by reaction 1 with NO)

(3) atmospheric transport (horizontal advection and vertical transport by diffusion or turbulence)

(4) surface dry deposition (direct removal at the Earth's surface by reaction with materials or absorption by vegetation)

These processes lead to ozone concentrations being highly variable, spatially and temporally. The annual average ozone concentration measured at sites in the UK varies considerably across the landscape from low values of around 10 ppb in urban/industrial regions to 25 ppb in the countryside and 35 ppb in upland areas. During the summer months there is a broad regional gradient from low concentrations in the NW to higher concentrations in the SE, towards mainland Europe. This summer-time spatial pattern extends across Western Europe and is caused by regions where ozone production occurs more frequently in a combination of precursor emissions (NO_x and NMVOCs), high solar radiation and temperatures. During the winter this spatial pattern is reversed with the highest concentrations occurring in the NW and the lowest in the SE as a consequence of ozone destruction in the NO polluted atmosphere of the dense urban/industrial regions of the southern UK and continental Western Europe.

There is also a seasonal cycle in ozone concentration, with a peak during the spring and summer. There are two processes involved in producing this cycle: the summer peak is due to warm, sunny weather and the accumulation of precursor species in anti-cyclonic conditions increasing the photochemical production of ozone; the spring peak is less well understood but may be partly due to tropospheric production from precursors accumulated over the polar region during the winter (PORG, 1998). At less polluted northern sites the seasonal cycle tends to show a pronounced peak in the spring whereas at more polluted southerly sites the peak is spread from April to September, as illustrated by the plots in Figure 3.36.

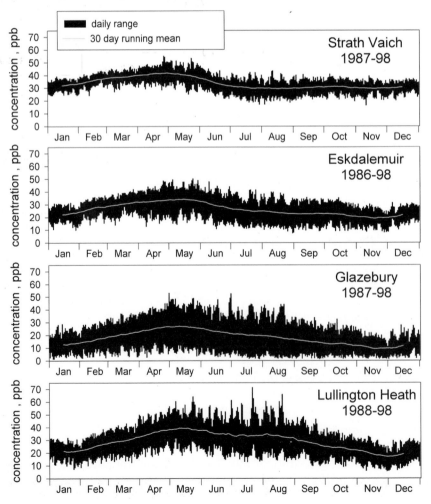

Figure 3.36 Examples of seasonal cycles in ozone concentration from a northerly remote rural site (Strath Vaich) to a rural site in the more polluted south of the UK (Lullington Heath).

At rural sites a diurnal cycle in ozone concentration is observed, typically with a mid-afternoon peak and night-time minimum (Figure 3.37a). This cycle is governed by the dynamics of the PBL, although photochemical production also plays a part. During the daytime, turbulent mixing in the PBL leads to entrainment of ozone from the free troposphere (Stull, 1989). In sunny weather the presence of NO_x and NMVOC emissions can also lead to photochemical production and so enhanced ozone concentrations. These processes produce an afternoon peak in ozone concentration when the atmosphere is most turbulent and UV levels are at a maximum. During the night and early morning the lower regions of the PBL become thermally stratified and stable as the surface cools, greatly reducing entrainment of ozone from the free troposphere. The ozone concentration decreases rapidly as losses to dry deposition are not replenished by mixing from above and photochemical production cannot occur. The minimum concentration is usually reached between midnight and dawn, although increases may be observed over short periods when sporadic turbulence breaks through the stable layer and mixes down ozone from the free troposphere (Garland & Derwent, 1979; Corsmeier *et al.,* 1997). The diurnal cycle is most pronounced in warm anti-cyclonic conditions as the daytime peak is enhanced when very slow moving air masses and increased convective mixing allow the build up of large concentrations of ozone during the day. Strong temperature inversions occur during the night as the surface rapidly loses heat to clear skies, nocturnal ozone depletion increases and a large drop in concentration occurs. During anti-cyclonic periods large amounts of precursor emissions can lead to episodes of high ozone concentration across large areas of the country, often reaching or exceeding air quality standards.

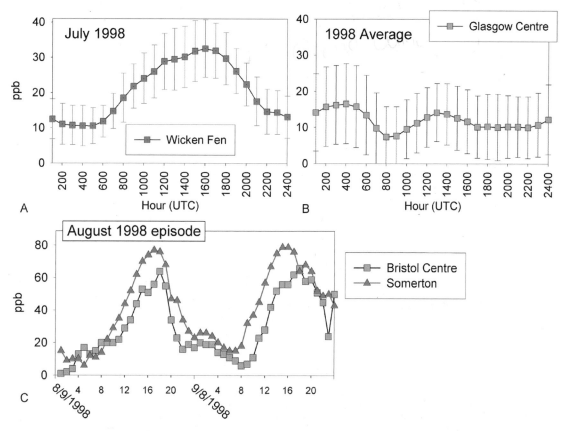

Figure 3.37 Example of diurnal cycles in ozone concentration for (a) a rural site, (b) an urban site and (c) a rural site and nearby urban site during a photochemical episode (error bars show the standard deviation of hourly means).

In urban areas there is also a diurnal cycle but in this case it is mainly influenced by NO emissions from traffic, as O_3 rapidly reacts with NO to produce NO_2 (reaction 1). Generally, the urban cycle has minima during the morning and evening rush-hours when traffic levels peak, and a maximum overnight with intermediate values during the afternoon (Figure 3.37b). However, during episodes of higher than average ozone concentration urban sites may measure concentrations similar to those in the surrounding area, as illustrated in Figure 3.37c which shows a plot of the hourly means measured in central Bristol and Somerton (rural site ~45 km south of Bristol) during a small episode on the 8th and 9th of August 1998.

3.10.2 Maps of Ozone Effects Indices for the UK: Annual Mean, AOT40 and 8 Hour Running Mean

The methods used to map ozone concentration were described in PORG (1998) and the underlying theory is examined in Coyle *et al.* (2001). A brief description of the theory and methods is given here. It can be shown that during the afternoon, when the PBL is well developed, rural monitoring sites observe concentrations that are representative of a wide geographical area (within approx. 100 km radius). Hence a map can be produced by interpolating the afternoon value of a variable from rural sites then modifying the resulting grid cell values to account for the diurnal cycle in ozone concentration. For the 24 hour mean ozone concentration this is done using the variable $\Delta O3$, which is the difference between the mean concentration observed during 24 hours and that during the afternoon period. This variable is then related to the location's altitude (h) using the empirical relationship:

$$\Delta O3 = a + b.e^{c.h}$$

The magnitude of the diurnal cycle in ozone concentration at a given location generally depends on the wind speed and atmospheric stability. However wind speed measurements are not available at all monitoring sites and so altitude is used as a surrogate.

The resulting maps are only valid in rural areas and overestimate concentrations in and around conurbations where emissions of NO deplete ozone by the reaction to NO_2. Measurements from the urban network of monitoring sites in the UK can be used to account for this urban influence by investigating the relationship between the measured mean and that calculated for the 1 km x 1 km grid square containing a site. The urban influence (UI) can be defined as (Stedman, 1997a):

$$UI = (mapped\ value - measured\ value)/mapped\ value$$

and this variable can be related to the NO_x concentration (NOxc) in the grid square. To summarise the method of calculating UK ozone concentration maps:

❑ afternoon values from the national network of rural monitoring sites are interpolated to a 1 km x 1 km grid, using a minimum-curvature algorithm

❑ the afternoon value in each grid square is adjusted for the diurnal cycle in ozone concentration

❑ the rural value is modified to account for ozone depletion by reaction with NO using a relationship derived from the national network of urban monitoring sites.

Annual mean ozone concentration map for effects on materials.

The mechanisms of damage to materials by ozone and the concentrations at which they occur are not well defined as yet (PORG, 1998), although research programmes have been undertaken (Lee *et al.*, 1995 & 2001; Leith & Cape, 1998) and a provisional level of an annual mean O_3 concentration of 20 ppb was set for an acceptable rate of materials deterioration at a UNECE workshop in 1993 (UNECE, 1993).

The rural annual mean is calculated by interpolating the 1200 h UTC to 1800 h UTC afternoon ozone concentrations at the rural network sites and adjusting them for the diurnal cycle using $\Delta O3 = 1.5 + 6.06.e^{-4.43 \times 10^{-3} h}$, as outlined above. The depletion of O_3 by titration with NO is accounted for using UI = 0.0062 NOxc, where NOxc is the annual average NO_x concentration (mapped at 1 km x 1 km, Stedman *et al.*, 1997b). The resulting map for 1996 is shown in Figure 3.38 below. The 20 ppb critical level for damage to materials, is exceeded in 93% of the country, however this includes only 19% of urban areas where 'at-risk' materials are concentrated.

AOT40 for crops, semi-natural vegetation and forests

A full description of the AOT40 effects indices can be found in Chapter 7, along with maps calculated using the method described below.

The same procedure used to map the annual mean is applied for the AOT40 values but in this case the altitude relationship has a linear form:

$$\frac{\text{AOT40 daylight hours}}{\text{AOT40 well-mixed hours}} = b.\text{altitude} + c \text{, where altitude} = \text{height above sea level in m.}$$

All three AOT40 critical levels for wheat, semi-natural vegetation and forests, are calculated over the summer months when a "well-mixed" period of 1300 h UTC to 1800 h UTC is most appropriate. Statistical analysis indicated that the gradient of the altitude relationship is the same for all AOT40 indices but they have different intercepts (Coyle *et al.*, 2001) with the parameters given in Table 3.5 below.

Table 3.5 Linear regression parameters for the AOT40 ratio to altitude relationship.

AOT40 index	$b \times 10^{-4}$	c
crops and semi-natural vegetation	7.401	1.42
forests	7.401	1.35

Number of days per year the 8 hour running mean exceeds 50 ppb

The effects of ozone on human health have been extensively studied since the 1960's. Ozone is a highly reactive gas and is considered to be one of the most irritant of common air pollutants. The mechanism for ozone effects in humans is quite well understood and involves inflammation of the respiratory tract and lungs induced by the oxidation by ozone. A threshold for effects has been found in some studies, although it varies between individuals and the ozone exposure regime used (PORG, 1993). The UK Expert Panel on Air Quality Standards (EPAQS, 1994) recommended an 8-hour running mean of 50 ppb as the critical level for ozone effects. The UK government adopted this as its air quality standard, with an objective that by the end of 2005, the 97th percentile of daily maximum 8-hour running mean should not exceed 50 ppb (DoE, 1997). This level is quite low in respect to the likely threshold for effects on an average person, however it should protect the most susceptible individuals in the population, such as asthmatics and those with respiratory disease (DoE, 1997).

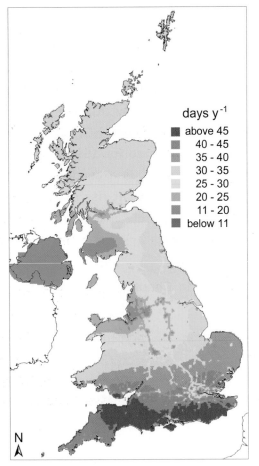

days y^{-1}

■ above 45
■ 40 - 45
■ 35 - 40
■ 30 - 35
■ 25 - 30
■ 20 - 25
■ 11 - 20
■ below 11

N

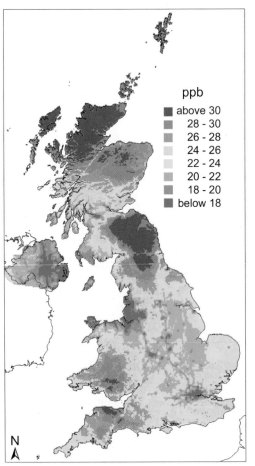

ppb

■ above 30
■ 28 - 30
■ 26 - 28
■ 24 - 26
■ 22 - 24
■ 20 - 22
■ 18 - 20
■ below 18

N

Figure 3.39 The number of days during 1996 when the 8-hour running mean ozone concentration exceeded 50 ppb, used to assess to potential for effects on human health.

Figure 3.38 1996 annual mean ozone concentrations, used to assess the potential for damage to materials.

Mapping the number of days per year on which the 8-hour running mean exceeds 50 ppb (8hrm) is quite straightforward. This variable is not affected by the diurnal cycle in ozone concentration and so the definition of an altitude relationship is not required. The 8hrm observed at rural sites will be representative of a wide area and can be mapped using a simple bilinear interpolation from the rural network sites. However, to assess the risk of adverse human health effects the map must be adjusted for the effect of urban NO emissions, as the majority of the population live in urban areas. In this case the urban influence is given by UI = 0.01 NOxc and the resulting map for 1996 is shown in Figure 3.39. The air quality standard adopted by the UK government equates to the 8-hour running mean exceeding 50 ppb on fewer than 11 days per year. The map, Figure 3.39, shows that the standard was not met across most of the country (99.95%) during 1996, with the exception of a few small areas in central London, the Midlands and northern England. The standard is designed to protect the most ozone sensitive individuals, and so the majority of the population is not likely to be affected by this degree of exceedance. The map shows that susceptible people should be aware of the risk, particularly if they live in the south of England where the level of exceedance is greatest.

The spatial pattern is quite different in the map of 8hrm (Figure 3.39) compared to the annual mean (Figure 3.38), as the 8hrm is largest in the summer months when the positive NW to SE ozone gradient dominates. The annual mean includes the winter measurements when the gradient is reversed and higher concentrations occur in the NW.

3.10.3 Future Global Ozone Baseline Levels

A global three-dimensional Lagrangian chemistry model, STOCHEM, has been used to calculate the influence of the projected increases in emissions of methane, carbon monoxide and nitrogen oxides from human activities through to the year 2100 on the global distribution of ozone. The emissions from the Intergovernmental Panel on Climate Change Special Report on Emissions Scenarios have been used and specifically the A2 variant (SRES A2). Surface ozone concentrations are predicted to rise steadily throughout the next century. With this background, ozone baselines are expected to increase within the British Isles. Figure 3.40 presents the modelled seasonal cycles in ozone, for a model grid square covering central England, in each of the years 1990, 2030, 2060 and 2100. The spatial resolution of the global model results in a seasonal cycle representative of the northern hemisphere baseline with only a slight influence from European regional scale photochemical episodes.

Annual mean ozone concentrations increase from 34 ppb in 1990, to 39 ppb in 2030, 44 ppb in 2060 through to 52 ppb in 2100. The percentage increases in baseline ozone, relative to the 1990 case, are 14% in 2030, 27% in 2060 and 51% in 2100. European regional scale summertime photochemical episodes will be superimposed on this baseline. This projected rise in the background ozone concentration could also have significant impacts on vegetation, as the 40 ppb threshold will be exceeded throughout most of the year (see Chapter 7 for more information on ozone effects on vegetation).

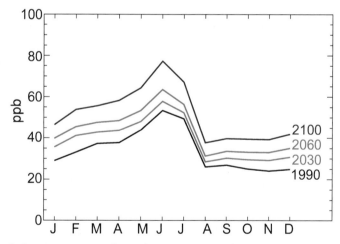

Figure 3.40 Current and future seasonal cycles in ozone for central England, predicted using the STOCHEM global model with the IPCC SRES A2 emission scenario.

3.10.4 Trends in Ground-Level Ozone Concentration in the UK

Routine monitoring of ozone concentrations in the UK began in the early 1970s with measurement campaigns for short periods and a national network of 16 rural monitoring stations was established in 1986 (PORG, 1998), measuring continual hourly averages. The National Air Quality Information Archive: http://www.aeat.co.uk/netcen/airqual/welcome.html holds recent data as well as most of the earlier measurements. With more than 10 years of data available we would anticipate that trends due to the reduction in European precursor emissions and the predicted rise in the global background ozone concentration to be detectable. However many factors influence annual ozone statistics and make simple trend analysis by linear regression difficult to interpret. For example: local site characteristics such as ozone dry deposition rates and NO_x emissions vary; annual large scale meteorological patterns, such as the prevalence of anti-cyclonic conditions, affect the long-range transport of ozone and precursor emissions.

Previous analysis of annual mean and maximum ozone concentration trends in PORG 1998, Coyle *et al.* 1999 and Coyle *et al.* 2000 (using data up to 1995, 1996 and 1999 respectively) showed an overall picture of an increasing background ozone concentration and decreasing concentrations during photochemical episodes, although few of the sites had statistically significant trends (at a 5% probability level) . A large decline was found in monthly maximum ozone concentrations, with a decrease in peak values of the order of 30 ppb from the 1970s to 1990s, which has continued into 2000 (Figure 3.41). The trend statistics for: annual maxima; the number of days per year the 8 hour running mean exceeds 50 ppb (8hrm); AOT40 crops and forests (W40 and F40) and annual averages, for the period starting *ca* 1980 to 2000 are given in Appendix E.

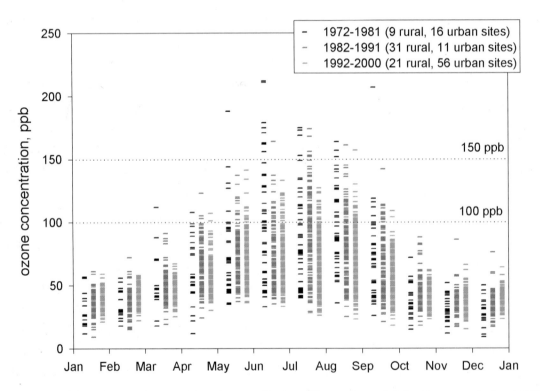

Figure 3.41 Monthly maxima from UK ozone monitoring sites grouped into three periods, 1972-1981, 1982-1991 and 1992-2000 (NB The number and type of sites has changed over the period).

Most of the sites show a downward trend in the annual maxima that is statistically significant at 8 of the sites (average –3 ppb y^{-1}). In comparison to the earlier analysis the magnitude of the trend at many sites has increased and in some cases it has become statistically significant. These results indicate that the downward trend in peak ozone concentrations is continuing. They are comparable to the results of Gardner & Dorling (2000) who found a downwards trend of -0.7 to -2.3 ppb y^{-1} in 1984 to 1998 meteorologically adjusted summer daily maxima at Eskdalemuir, Harwell, Lullington Heath, Sibton and Yarner Wood.

The change in peak values is also reflected in the 8hrm and AOT40 trends. Twelve of the 15 sites have statistically significant downward trends in their 8hrm, averaging *ca* 2 days y^{-1}, indicating that although the air quality standard will not be met across the whole country by 2005, the magnitude of exceedance will be reduced. Most sites have downward trends in their AOT40s, although few are statistically significant due to the large inter-annual variability in this statistic (on average ±50% variation between years). Although AOT40 data indicate a downward trend this is likely to be offset by increases in the background ozone concentration. Analysis of the number of exceedances of 40 ppb and 60 ppb per year (from 1986 to 1999) indicate that although fewer large exceedances of 40 ppb occur, there are more hours when 40 ppb is exceeded. See Sections 7.6.2 and 7.8 for more discussion of the implications of these changes for vegetation.

For the annual average, most sites have small upward trends, *ca* 0.1 ppb y^{-1}, and 3 sites have statistically significant trends of over 0.2 ppb y^{-1}. These results are indicative of an upwards trend in the annual average ozone concentration but most sites show very little change and the increases predicted by modelling are not yet clearly discernible in the data using this method of analysis.

Within the EUROTRAC sub-project TOR-2 (EUROTRAC-2, 1998) work is underway to improve the analysis of trends by accounting for the various factors that cause inter-annual variability (e.g. precursor emissions and weather patterns). One method being examined is to segregate ozone measurements by their source region using air-mass back trajectory data. This approach was used by Simmonds *et al.* (1997) with data from Mace Head during 1987 to 1995. They found a slight increase in unpolluted concentrations (+0.19 ppb y^{-1}), representative of the northern hemisphere background, and a decrease in concentrations from polluted European areas (-0.39 ppb y^{-1}). Some results using this method at Strath Vaich and Mace Head are presented here.

The trajectories used were 5-day back trajectories from the ECMWF, provided by the BADC (http://www.badc.rl.ac.uk/) that are launched at 1200h UTC 900 mb from a regular grid of points covering the UK. As the grid points and site locations do not coincide, the 4 grid points closest to the sites were chosen. The sectors at Mace Head were set following those in Simmonds *et al.* (1997) (North, Atlantic, South and Europe). At Strath Vaich sectors for the North, Atlantic and Europe were chosen as dictated by the site's location. In this preliminary analysis a day's 24 hourly values were assigned to a sector when at least 3 trajectories were within it. Although none of the trends is statistically significant at the 5% level, analysis shows that they are different in each sector and some patterns can be seen.

At Mace Head:
- results are similar to those of Simmonds *et al.* (1997) for 1987 to 1995 data;
- the annual average is lower from the European sector and there is a small non-significant upward trend;
- the annual average from the "clean" North and Atlantic sectors are *ca* 3 ppb larger than the European and have larger upwards trends that approach 10% statistical probability of significance;
- annual maxima have upwards trends from the "clean" sectors and a large downwards trend in the European sector.

At Strath Vaich:

- although trends in the annual average are virtually identical for each sector the concentrations in the "clean" sectors are *ca* 2 ppb higher than those from Europe;
- there is a large downwards trend in the annual maximum from Europe but not from the other 2 sectors.

Overall the results from this analysis are consistent with the assessment of decreasing peak ozone concentrations and an increasing background concentration. Similar trends of decreasing peak values and either increasing annual mean concentrations or no change have been observed at rural monitoring sites in Germany (Beilke and Wallasch 2000). Ozone concentrations and trends across the rest of Europe are considered further in Chapter 8.

The main conclusions from Chapter 3 are summarized in the bullet points at the beginning of the chapter (page 43).

Chapter 4: Modelling Concentrations and Deposition

> ➤ The EMEP Eulerian model has replaced the Lagrangian models for work under the CLRTAP. It integrates acidifying and photochemical pollutants.

> ➤ The EMEP model reproduces observed concentrations of ozone across the UK and the overall deposition of sulphur for the UK.

> ➤ The EMEP models still operate at a scale which is coarse in the context of the UK, and UK scale models have a role in assessing UK policy options.

> ➤ UK scale models are able to reproduce the general patterns of deposition of S, oxidised and reduced N but remain deficient in the overall totals for most pollutants.

> ➤ It is still difficult to reproduce the reduced N budget for the UK using current emissions inventories and it seems likely that these underestimate actual NH_3 emissions.

> ➤ Current reduction plans (the Gothenburg Protocol) are predicted to result in a significant reduction in S deposition and a smaller reduction in oxidised N deposition across the UK; reductions in reduced nitrogen under this protocol are too small to have a significant impact in the UK.

> ➤ Peak concentrations of ozone will probably be reduced with the implementation of the Gothenburg protocol, but should be considered in the context of an increasing global background.

> ➤ From about the middle of this century it is likely that annual mean ozone concentrations in the UK will be substantially larger than current values and may pose a threat to vegetation and human health.

4.1 Introduction

The need to model long range transport of acidic sulphur pollutants across Europe was first established through the Long Range Transport of Air Pollution (LRTAP) programme of the Organisation for Economic Cooperation and Development (OECD, 1977). This modelling programme then passed to the United Nations Economic Commission for Europe (UNECE) and has become a cornerstone of the EMEP (Co-operative programme for Monitoring and Evaluation of the Long-range Transmission of Air Pollutants in Europe) programme which was set up in 1977. The UNECE Convention on Long Range Transboundary air pollution (CLRTAP), signed in 1979, was the first international agreement to tackle air pollution across broad regions. Protocols to the convention have addressed not only setting targets for future emission reductions, but also the scientific and administrative framework to monitor and assess progress (Murley, 1995). The Geneva Protocol to that Convention (1984) established a mechanism to ensure the long term funding of EMEP. EMEP now oversees a programme of monitoring air and precipitation quality, the collection of emissions data (a task now shared with CORINAIR) and modelling atmospheric dispersion.

The EMEP modelling effort addresses four issues: acidification and eutrophication; ground-level ozone; persistent organic pollutants (POPs) and heavy metals. The models yield estimates of both present day and future concentrations and deposition. Source-receptor matrices allow the fate of emissions from any individual country to be quantified. Output from the EMEP models feeds into Integrated Assessment Models (e.g. RAINS, ASAM) to allow the costs and benefits of proposed emissions reductions to be assessed (Alcamo *et al.*, 1990; Schoepp *et al.*, 1999;

Warren and ApSimon, 2000). As a result, the EMEP models lie at the heart of policy formulation within both the UNECE and the EU. The UK recognised that in terms of both the scale of outputs and the representation of processes, the EMEP models may not meet the needs of domestic policy. To this end, a range of other models are in use in the UK, some of which are described below. Output from the EMEP acidification and ozone models is compared with data from the UK's monitoring networks and results from UK-scale models. The effects of both past and possible future emissions scenarios are also modelled for the UK.

Given current concern about changes in the earth-atmosphere system, it is important to consider the interactions between changing emissions, concentrations of pollutants in the air and climatic conditions. Two different issues are explored using a UK scale model and a global model.

4.2 Recent Developments in the EMEP Models

The original EMEP model was a receptor orientated, single layer, Lagrangian trajectory model for S only (Eliassen and Saltbones, 1983), running on a 150 km x 150 km grid. A coupled chemical scheme including oxidised and reduced N was introduced from 1986. The EMEP Lagrangian Acid Deposition Model (LADM) served as the operational model within EMEP until 1999. A detailed description of LADM is given in Barrett and Berge (1996). Estimates of transboundary fluxes across Europe for the period 1985 to 1996 are presented in EMEP/MSC-W Report 1/98 (EMEP, 1998). In the Lagrangian model, a proportion of deposition could not be attributed to particular source countries (described as un-attributable deposition). The problem of un-attributable deposition was greatest for S and oxidised N and could partly be explained by the transport of pollutants through the boundary layer and into the free troposphere and then back again. This process could not be modelled using the single layer Lagrangian model.

It was recognised that the horizontal resolution of the Lagrangian model was coarse and that a range of tropospheric processes (such as cloud chemistry, vertical wind shear, venting to the free troposphere) required a multi-layer model (Berge and Tarrason, 1992). To address these issues, an Eulerian model has been developed. The Eulerian model required a range of inputs at higher resolution than LADM including emissions, meteorological data and appropriate advection schemes. Meteorological inputs are provided by the Operational Numerical Weather Prediction model of the Norwegian Meteorological Institute (HIRLAM). The original meteorological sub-model (LAM50E) calculated meteorological conditions every 6 hours for a total grid area coincident with that of LADM (Berge, 1993). The most recent version of the Eulerian model uses a new meteorological model (PARLAM-PS) that calculates meteorological data every 3 hours and covers a larger model domain, which includes all signatories to CLRTAP (Tarrason and Schaug, 1999). The extra computational demands of the Eulerian model meant that parallelisation was an appropriate strategy, although the model run time is still substantially longer than LADM, even running on multiple processors. As with the Lagrangian model, the Eulerian model initially included S only (Berge, 1993), with other pollutants being included as the model developed (Jonson and Berge, 1995). The main features of the Lagrangian and Eulerian models are summarised in Table 4.1.

Outputs from the Lagrangian and Eulerian models have been compared by Barticki and Tarrason (1998) and the Eulerian model compared with data from the EMEP monitoring network for 1996 (Olendrzynski *et al.*, 1998). The Eulerian model was used to calculate source-receptor flux budgets under the terms of the CLRTAP for the first time for 1997. The model has undergone extensive development and modification and the version used to assess transboundary acidification and eutrophication for 1998 is not the same as that used earlier. The 1998 model is described in detail in Olendrzynski (2000). Output from the Lagrangian model, which has provided the basis for the negotiation of the protocols to the LRTAP convention, is not available for 1998.

Table 4.1 Comparison of Lagrangian and Eulerian EMEP models after Bartnicki and Tarrason, 1998; Tarrason and Schaug, 1999.

	Lagrangian	Eulerian
Resolution		
horizontal	150 km x 150 km	50 km x 50 km
vertical layers	1	20
upper boundary	mixing height	100 hPa
meteorological input	LAM50E	PARLAM-PS
chemistry	10 components	9 components
wet deposition	Scavenging ratios	Scavenging ratios in cloud and sub cloud
Dry deposition	Resistance analogy	Resistance analogy
Boundary conditions	Climatological, monthly variations	Climatological, monthly variations
CPU requirements for source allocation, 1 y	*ca* 8 hrs CRAY T3E, 16 processors	*ca* 486 hrs CRAY T3E, 16 processors

One of the major advantages of the Lagrangian formulation was its suitability for calculating the source-receptor relationships that are so important in policy development. In an Eulerian model, non-linear effects make such relationships more difficult to establish. Once source-receptor relationships have been computed, however, the Eulerian model reduces the amount of un-attributable deposition. Output from the Eulerian model for 1998 is presented later in this chapter and is based on the latest EMEP matrices (Tarrason and Schaug, 2000). Results from the latest version of the EMEP model were not available for 1997 at the time of this study.

EMEP began work on an ozone model in 1989 in the context of UNECE interest in developing policy to reduce concentrations of photochemical pollutants, especially ozone. The original Lagrangian model adopted the same meteorological inputs and transport algorithms as LADM (Simpson, 1993). The ozone model employs the UNECE estimates of anthropogenic emissions of SO_2, NO_x, CO and NMVOCs and calculated natural emissions of isoprene from forests. NMVOCs are speciated by source sector following the scheme suggested in PORG (1993). The model estimates ozone concentrations every 6 hours (at 0, 6, 12 and 18 hr UTC) and these values are used to calculate the mean of daily maximum ozone (April to September), AOT40 and AOT60 (Simpson *et al.*, 1997). The Lagrangian Model for Ozone (LMO) was modified to include a simplified representation of the effects of stomatal closure at temperatures above 25°C. Photolysis rates were updated based on the UK Photochemical Trajectory Model (Jenkin *et al.*, 1997) and some background concentrations changed to reflect new estimates. The LMO was highly demanding of processing time and, as a result, was parallelised in the same way as the Eulerian model described above. The parallel version allows source-receptor matrices to be calculated for use in integrated assessment models (e.g. IIASA RAINS-ozone). IIASA have been using a reduced-form version of the EMEP ozone model which uses regression analysis to capture the response of ozone levels to changes in national NO_x and NMVOC emissions (Heyes et al., 1997). The relationships between precursor emissions and ozone concentrations have been based on the output of a large number of runs of the EMEP model. In this chapter we use output from the LMO for 1995.

4.3 Modelling at the UK scale

4.3.1 Modelling S and N Deposition

The latest EMEP models provide estimates of concentrations and deposition of pollutants at a spatial scale of 50 km x 50 km. Given the size of the UK and more particularly, the size of areas of particular habitats of recognised conservation value (e.g. SSSIs), this scale is rather coarse. As referred to above, there are also processes not represented in the EMEP models that are known to be important for the pollution climate of the UK. Here we describe models designed to operate at the UK scale, but within the context of the wider EMEP area: the Hull Acid Rain Model (HARM); the Edinburgh-Lancaster Model for Ozone (ELMO); Trajectory Model with Atmospheric Chemical Kinetics (TRACK) and the Fine Resolution Ammonia Exchange Model (FRAME). Although desirable, it should be noted that there has been no rigorous assessment of the uncertainties associated with the outputs of the different models. As the uncertainties will reflect those in the emissions inventories, our understanding of the processes and the model's ability to represent those processes in some form, it would be anticipated that the uncertainties would be least for S and most for reduced N.

A number of acid deposition models in use in the UK were reviewed in the most recent report of the Review Group on Acid Rain (RGAR, 1997). HARM is used extensively by DEFRA in the context of formulating policy with regard to reducing deposition of potentially acidifying and eutrophying sulphur and nitrogen. In common with the EMEP LADM, HARM is a receptor orientated, Lagrangian model producing estimates of annual concentrations and deposition of compounds of oxidised S and N, reduced N and HCl. Unlike the EMEP model, the meteorological elements of HARM (e.g. wind speed, boundary layer height) are fixed and highly simplified. Wet removal is assumed to occur through constant drizzle. The standard model employs 72 straight-line trajectories for air parcels to travel along towards each receptor site. Unlike the EMEP models (both Lagrangian and Eulerian) HARM includes a simplified representation of the seeder-feeder effect. Seeder-feeder enhancement has been identified as causing a significant increase in wet deposition of S and N to the uplands of the UK (see Chapter 3). As this process is included in national deposition estimates, models which do not attempt to represent seeder-feeder are unlikely to be able to reproduce the national figures (RGAR, 1997). The development and validation of HARM against data from the UK's monitoring networks has been described in the literature (Metcalfe et al., 1995; Metcalfe et al., 1998a) and the emphasis here will be on developments of the model not covered in these publications. The version of HARM used for the RGAR report operated for the UK at a spatial scale of 20 km x 20 km. The current version (HARM11.5) works at 10 km x 10 km exploiting input data for emissions, rainfall and land-use dependent deposition velocities available at this resolution. Across the rest of the EMEP area, emissions are held at 50 km x 50 km. One of the major limitations of HARM, in common with other single layer models, was its inability to reproduce estimated patterns or quantities of dry NH_x deposition across the UK (RGAR, 1997). HARM11.5 employs an alpha factor approach (a fraction of NH_3 emission in each grid square which is directly dry deposited in that square) to try to capture some of the highly variable behaviour of ammonia in a relatively low resolution model. The alpha factors were derived from the multi-layer FRAME model (Singles *et al.*, 1998) by Mark Sutton (CEH, Edinburgh). The implementation of the alpha factors has improved HARM's ability to reproduce estimates of dry NH_x deposition based on a combination of measured and modelled air concentrations, whilst not seriously compromising its ability to model wet NH_x deposition.

The HARM model has been run for 1997 and compared with the best estimates of deposition for that year, based on data from the UK's monitoring networks (see Chapter 3). HARM uses 1997 emissions for the UK (where available) and for land based emissions across the EMEP grid area. Natural emissions of sulphur from marine algae and volcanoes are for 1995. A 1997 rainfall field has been employed. Deposition estimates have been generated for a 10 km x 10 km grid across the UK. Data from CEH have been produced at a scale of 5 km x 5 km and are derived from a 1996 gas concentration data (for dry S and dry NO_x deposition), 1997 rainfall concentrations (for wet deposition) and 1996 measured and modelled data (for dry NH_x). Deposition patterns and amounts have been compared by regression analysis, national scale mapping and the calculation of deposition budgets.

Regression analysis has been carried out by comparing HARM modelled deposition with the CEH data for the 32 grid cells across the UK which contain sites of the Acid Deposition Monitoring Network (see Chapter 3 and Appendix B). It should be borne in mind that these cell values are calculated at different scales (HARM 10 km x 10 km; CEH 5 km x 5 km). As in previous data/model comparison exercises, the model output has been used as the independent variable. The results of the regression analysis are summarised in Table 4.2 below.

Table 4.2 Results of regression analysis comparing HARM11.5 with CEH data for 1997.

	R^2	Slope	Intercept
Wet S	0.56	1.35	0.14
Dry S	0.67	1.20	0.02
Wet NO_y-N	0.55	0.98	0.41
Dry NO_y-N	0.83	0.77	-0.58
Wet NH_x-N	0.62	1.75	0.01
Dry NH_x-N	0.41	2.28	0.81

For wet S, the model shows a general tendency to underestimate compared with the data based on measurements. This is most apparent over northern England, south east Scotland and mid-Wales. The model performs worst at the site of Wardlow Hay Cop (central England), where HARM deposition is less than half that based on the measurements. Dry S deposition shows quite a close correspondence between modelled values and those from the measurements. HARM tends to underestimate dry S deposition at sites close to the east coast of England (especially at Flatford Mill in Essex). As in previous data – model comparison exercises, HARM is able to reproduce the overall pattern of wet deposition of oxidised N. There is model overestimation at most sites across southern and central England and underestimation in northern England and southern Scotland. Modelled deposition exceeds observed most clearly in south east England (e.g. Barcombe Mills). For dry oxidised N deposition HARM values consistently exceed the values based on the monitoring networks. As explained in Chapter 3, the CEH maps of dry oxidised N deposition are based on NO_2 only, although the UK budget includes HNO_3. HARM output includes HNO_3 in its estimate of dry N deposition. HARM underestimates both wet and, more particularly, dry deposition of reduced N although it is able to reproduce the spatial pattern of NH_x deposition. For wet NH_x, underestimation is most pronounced in the uplands of northern England (e.g. Bannisdale, Cumbria). The challenge of modelling dry deposition of reduced N for single layer models such as HARM has been noted previously (RGAR, 1997). Changes to the representation of dry NH_x deposition in HARM have improved model performance (Metcalfe *et al.*, 2001), but it still underestimates compared with the CEH data. Two sites near the east coast of England (Stoke Ferry and High Muffles) and one near the Welsh coast (Tycanol Wood) show very severe underestimation of deposition. It seems likely that UK emissions of NH_3 have been underestimated and model runs increasing these emissions (e.g. by 30%) certainly help to improve the match between modelled and CEH data. The likely underestimation of UK NH_3 emissions has also been suggested by Lee *et al.* (2000a). The output from a specialised ammonia model FRAME (Fine Resolution AMmonia Exchange) is described below.

Maps of HARM and CEH Edinburgh deposition (see Chapter 3) are shown in Figures 4.1 and 4.2. The Figures generally confirm the patterns suggested by the regression analysis. For S and oxidised N, HARM is able to reproduce the overall pattern of deposition across the UK. The maps emphasise the model's underestimation of S deposition in the British uplands (wet) and south east England (dry), although the latter may be a result of the urban enhancement applied to the CEH data. For wet oxidised N, HARM generally overestimates deposition in the south and east and underestimates in the north and west. National budget estimates are presented in Table 4.3. The HARM values are not area weighted, while the CEH values are for GB only.

Table 4.3 National budgets of S and N deposition (kt-S and kt–N).

	CEH	HARM	FRAME	EMEP
Wet S	139.5	121.5	-	79.7
Dry S	106.5	89.5	-	250.7
Total S	246.0	211.0	-	330.4
Wet NO_y-N	97.0	107.3	-	67.8
Dry NO_y-N	20.1*	47.8	-	101.9
Total NO_y-N	117.1	155.1	-	169.6
Wet NH_x-N	108.8	72.6	106	64.0
Dry NH_x-N	109.6	56.1	98	109.5
Total NH_x-N	218.4	128.7	204	173.5

*based on NO_2 only

Output from HARM has also been compared with deposition for 1998 modelled using the EMEP Eulerian model (data provided by K. Olendrzynski, EMEP/MSC-W). EMEP modelled wet and dry S, NOy and NH_x deposition are shown in Figure 4.3 and should be compared with the equivalent Figures in Chapter 3 (3.12b, 3.13, 3.14, 3.16b, 3.17b and 3.20b) and Figures 4.1, 4.2 and 4.4 in this chapter. The budgets for the UK are included in Table 4.3. It is clear that the EMEP model is not yet able to reproduce either the spatial distribution or quantity of S deposition across the UK indicated by the measurements or HARM. The EMEP model overestimates the area of high (> 6 kg) dry S deposition, particularly in Wales, Scotland and south west England. For wet S, the EMEP model cannot reproduce the high levels of deposition in the uplands of Britain, particularly in western areas. For oxidised N, the EMEP model reproduces the spatial distribution, but not the amount of dry deposition and has too little wet deposition which is not over the western uplands as indicated by the CEH data. Modelled output for reduced N shows a reasonable spatial distribution, but again too little wet deposition. The modelled dry NH_x is very close to the CEH total. These differences were also apparent when the Lagrangian model was in use and the change to an Eulerian formulation has not resulted in any significant improvement. It appears that retaining a UK scale modelling capability to develop policy options for the UK is well justified.

4.3.2 Other Long Range Transport Models

The last report by the Review Group on Acid Rain (RGAR, 1997) included an inter-comparison of a number of long range transport models in use in the UK (including HARM and the EMEP model). This exercise has not been repeated, but output from the FRAME and TRACK models are used in this report and their basic structures and assumptions will be outlined.

The TRACK (Trajectory Model with Atmospheric Chemical Kinetics) model (Lee et al., 2000a, b & c) has been used in Chapter 3 to explore possible changes in S oxidation pathways. TRACK is a receptor orientated Lagrangian model which employs straight-line trajectories. Unlike HARM, it can operate in single or multi-layer modes. Land based emissions are used at the same resolution as HARM (10 km x 10 km for the UK, 50 km x 50 km for EMEP). Additional emission sources of NO_x included in TRACK are aircraft, soil and lightning. The model's chemical scheme has been outlined in Chapter 3. In common with HARM, TRACK indicates patterns of deposition and source attribution that are significantly different from the EMEP models.

Emissions of base cations in Europe are very uncertain. The first emissions inventory, for calcium in particles smaller than 5 μm was constructed by Lee and Pacyna (1999) for Europe at a grid resolution of 50 km x 50 km and was used, with the TRACK, model to estimate the base cation deposition over Europe (Lee et al., 1999) (see Chapter 8 for more detail). The total source strength was estimated at 750 to 800 ktonnes annually and is dominated by cement factories, power generation, and iron and steel production. The overall quality of the statistical data on which the inventory is based was described as 'poor'. This inventory also omits the particles re-suspended by the wind, which make an important contribution to the deposition of base cations in many areas.

The FRAME model is a Lagrangian trajectory model which was developed specifically to address the spatial patterns of ammonia deposition for Great Britain (Singles, 1996; Singles et al., 1998). The model is structured with 33 vertical layers, providing a level of detail sufficient to permit simulation of ground-level NH_3 concentrations. FRAME may be run using instantaneous diffusion, as with single-layer models, and this demonstrates the importance of the multi-layer approach in modelling NH_3 concentrations. Although the focus is on NH_x, the model includes coupled chemistry with SO_x and NO_y in order to deal with the interactions between these pollutants. The model was developed from the TERN model (ApSimon et al., 1994), and established for Great Britain using statistically weighted straight-line trajectories, constant drizzle and incorporating orographic enhancement of wet deposition allowing for the seeder-feeder effect. The version of FRAME used here includes a diurnally variable boundary layer height. The new scheme has enhanced the washout rate of NH_x which was underestimated in previous version of the model. This change results in closer agreement with measured values (see Table 4.3).

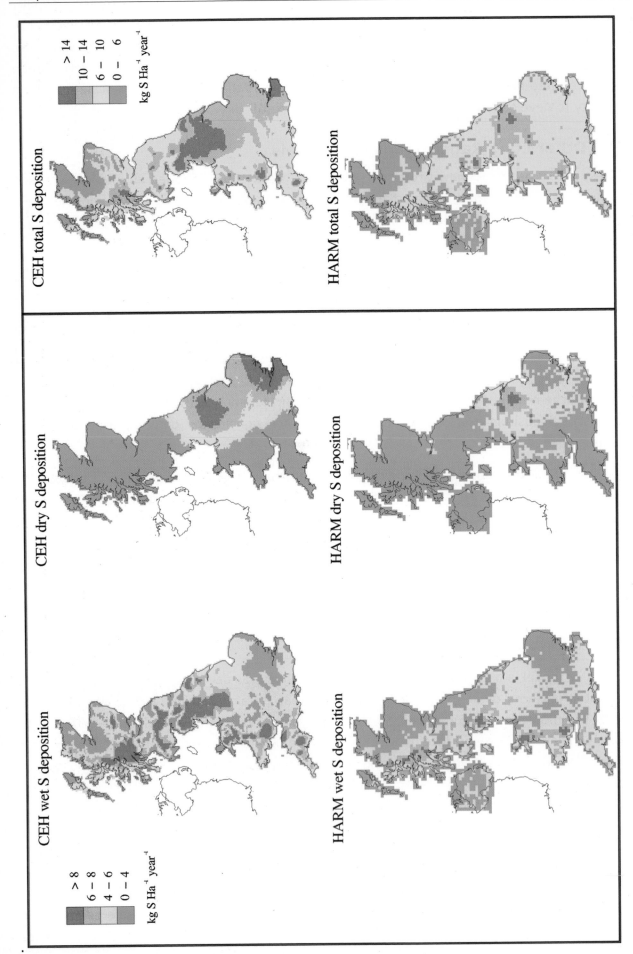

Figure 4.1 HARM 1997 vs. CEH S deposition.

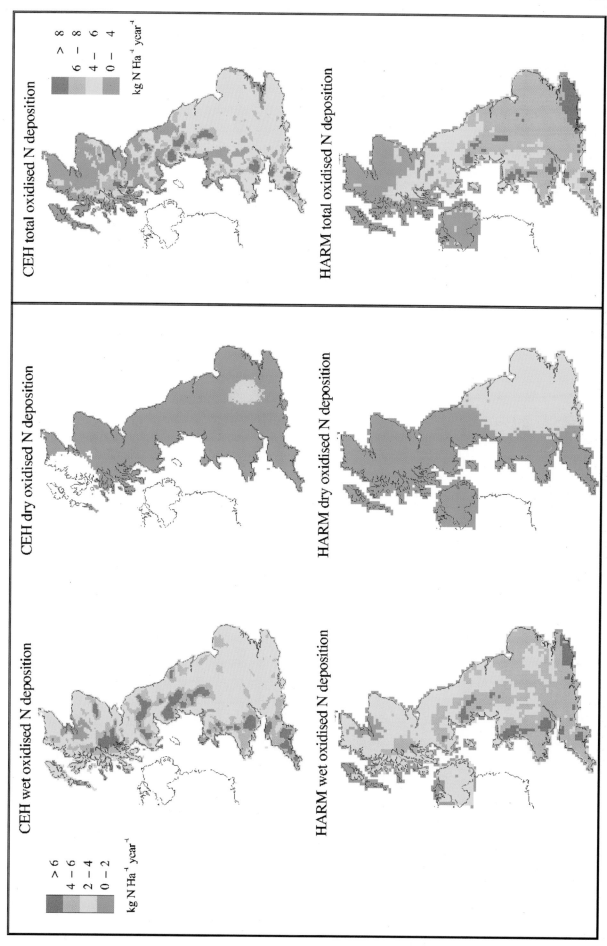

Figure 4.2 HARM 1997 vs. CEH oxidised N deposition.

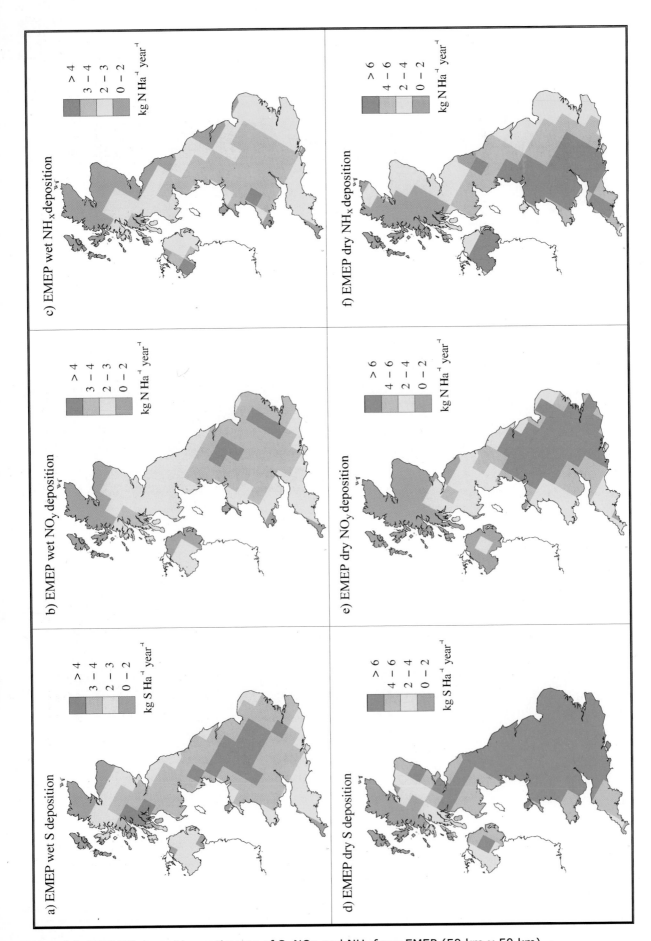

Figure 4.3 1998 UK deposition estimates of S, NOy and NH$_x$ from EMEP (50 km x 50 km).

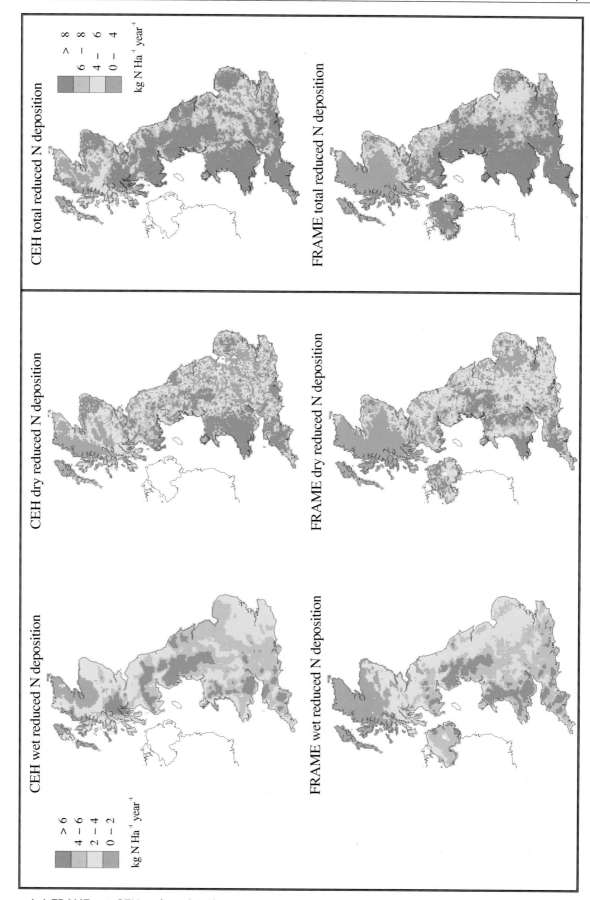

Figure 4.4 FRAME vs. CEH reduced N deposition.

As its name implies, a key interest in FRAME is the analysis of spatial patterns at a fine resolution, and the model was established at the outset to provide 5 km resolution estimates of NH_x deposition (Singles, 1996) to aid the assessment of environmental impacts of nitrogen deposition and for comparison with monitored concentration fields. A central feature of FRAME is its explicit treatment of dry deposition to different ecosystem receptors. Using land-cover data and a land-cover dependent resistance analysis, FRAME is able to estimate nitrogen inputs to ecosystem receptors for comparison with critical loads. The sum of these different dry deposition fields is then used to provide the average map of ammonia dry deposition across the country. More recently FRAME has been extended to cover all of Britain and Ireland, with a more detailed treatment that incorporates the bi-directional exchange of NH_3 as governed by vegetation NH_3 compensation points (e.g. Sutton *et al.*, 1995b). Although FRAME uses the same emissions totals as HARM, one difference is the use of a high resolution (5 km x 5 km) NH_3 emissions inventory for the Republic of Ireland. For 1996, FRAME estimates dry NH_x deposition at 98 kt-N and wet deposition at 106 kt-N, with a total deposition of 204 kt-N to the UK (see Figure 4.4). Overall, this is similar to the EMEP and CEH estimates. However, as with the other models, total NH_x deposition is underestimated, which reflects underlying uncertainties in the UK NH_3 budget.

4.3.2 Modelling Ground-Level Ozone Concentrations

ELMO is another single layer Lagrangian model running at a scale of 10 km x 10 km over the UK. Emissions inventories for anthropogenic NMVOCs, isoprene and CO are employed in addition to those used in HARM. The emissions used in ELMO are for 1995. Rather than using some representation of an annual average climatology, ELMO uses a wind rose, boundary layer depth (1400 m), temperature and humidity derived from measurements taken at Heathrow in 1995 for all days when the maximum hourly mean ozone concentration exceeded 50 ppb at any of the UK's monitoring sites. The model runs along the same number of trajectories as HARM (72), but uses a lower wind speed (3.6 m s^{-1}). The arrival time for each trajectory is set at 1800 h. The chemical mechanism in ELMO is a condensation of that in the Master Chemical Mechanism (Jenkin *et al.*, 1997) and involves 160 chemical reactions. These describe the fast photochemistry which drives ozone production in the polluted boundary layer over the UK (and the rest of north-west Europe). ELMO estimates the concentrations of the free radicals OH and HO_2, which drive ozone production through the oxidation of hydrocarbons. The model represents the degradation of 9 hydrocarbons (methane, ethane, propane, butane, ethylene, propylene, isoprene, toluene and o-xylene) and the reactions of the resulting organic peroxy radicals (RO_2) and alkoxy radicals (RO) with NO and NO_2 which in turn give rise to photochemical ozone. The model assumes cloud free conditions and photolysis rates are set for July at 50°N with realistic values for surface albedo, stratospheric ozone concentration and background aerosol loading. ELMO is described in detail in Metcalfe *et al.* (in prep.). ELMO is effectively a model for peak ozone concentrations, estimating values for late afternoon on a sunny, summer's day. The standard output is for ambient ozone concentration, but a series of empirical functions have been developed to calculate statistics such as AOT40, AOT60 and exceedances of EPAQS standards, which are based on hourly values. These functions have been derived from an analysis of the hourly data from the rural ozone monitoring network for 1995 and a comparison of these data against ELMO output.

ELMO output has been compared with measured ozone concentrations at the UK's rural monitoring sites for 1995. ELMO is able to reproduce the overall south-north gradient across the UK, but underestimates the absolute peak hourly values at the sites. This is unsurprising given the highly simplified meteorology assumed in ELMO and the complex nature of the actual back trajectories associated with the measured peaks. When ELMO values are compared with the 95th percentiles for the monitoring sites, the overall level of agreement is good (see Figure 4.5). The model overestimates for sites in south east England and underestimates at Strathvaich Dam in the north of Scotland.

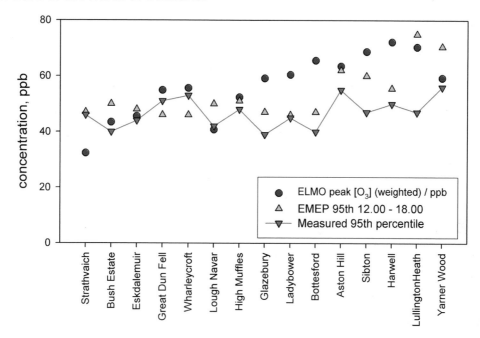

Figure 4.5 Modelled and measured ozone concentrations for 1995, ELMO and the EMEP Lagrangian model.

Figure 4.5 also shows the ozone concentrations for the sites modelled by the EMEP Lagrangian Photochemical model (data supplied by David Simpson, EMEP/MSC-W). Here the 95th percentiles of model output for 1200 and 1800 h have been plotted. As with ELMO there is generally good agreement with the observations except for the two coastal sites in southern England (Sibton and Lullington Heath). Based on this comparison it seems reasonable to use ELMO to explore the effects of future changes in emission of the major ozone precursors. The spatial scale at which ELMO operates and the availability of emissions data for a range of source categories makes it more suitable than the EMEP model for policy development within the UK.

4.4 Modelling Trends Through Time

When emissions inventories and other input data, such as rainfall fields, are available, it is possible to run models for different years in the past. These 'hindcasts' can be compared with monitoring data (see Chapter 3) to give a further guide to how well models are able to reproduce what is happening in the atmosphere. Such an assessment will help to assess the reliability of forecasts produced by the same models when run with proposed future emissions scenarios.

4.4.1 Modelling Historical Data

Modelled 'hindcasts' can help to complete series of measurement-based data which have gaps resulting from a lack of original data and/or changes in methodology. They also offer the potential to explore the changing importance of different source categories over time (see Chapter 2). Spatially disaggregated emissions inventories only became available for the UK (on a regular basis) from the mid-1980s (see Chapter 2). Emissions data have been obtained for most years since 1986 (i.e. the period covered by the monitoring networks) with information also being available for 1970, 1980 and 1983. As there is little information on the historical emissions of reduced N (NH_x) and uncertainties in the inventories remain very large (see Chapter 2), these have been held constant in this sequence of model runs. The limitations imposed by making this assumption must be recognised as there is a complex relationship between NH_3 and acidic species to generate ammonium aerosol, especially through the oxidation of SO_2 (ApSimon et al., 1994). HARM has been run with year-specific rainfall. All other model variables (e.g. wind speed, deposition velocities) have been held constant. The inputs for the 'hindcasts' are summarised in Appendix F.

Given the wider availability of data relating to S than to N, model results for S will be discussed in more detail than those for N. Modelled S budgets for the UK and the percentage changes in total deposition and UK emissions are shown in Table 4.4. Figures for S deposition in parentheses are from Chapter 3 and represent those estimates based on data from the monitoring networks, not those based on interpolation. Data-based estimates for both wet and dry S deposition are available for 1987, 1992, 1995 to 1997.

Table 4.4 S budgets for the UK from HARM11.5 showing changes in deposition and emissions used in the model. Totals in parentheses are 20 km estimates from the monitoring data (see Chapter 3).

Year	Dry S (kt-S)	Wet S (kt-S)	Total S (kt-S)	% change from previous modelled year	UK S emission (kt-S)	% change in emissions between years UK + (EMEP)
1970	277.5	344.2	621.7		2893	
1980	243.0	327.2	570.2	-8.3	2447	-15
1983	196.5	259.3	455.8	-20.1	1922	-21.5
1986	190.0	258.7	448.7	-1.6	1922	slightly up
1990	180.3	217.0	397.3	-11.5	1894	-1.5 (-14)
1991	175.8	207.3	383.1	-3.6	1868	-1.4
1992	159.4	228.1	387.5 (400)	+1.1	1741	-6.8
1993	147.9	206.0	353.9	-8.7	1597	-8.3
1994	128.7	191.2	319.9	-9.6	1358	-15
1995	117.0	149.9	266.9 (278)	-15.0	1179	-38 (-32)
1996	109.0	127.1	236.1 (296)	-11.5	1017	-13.7
1997	89.5	121.5	211.0 (234)	-10.6	826	-30 (ca -20)

The overall modelled pattern of change in S deposition across the UK between 1986 and 1997 is illustrated in Figure 4.6 (cf Figure 3.12). Over the period since 1986, modelled total deposition has fallen by 53% (see Table 4.4). Budgets based on measurements show an overall decline of 52%. What is not apparent from these figures, however, is the spatial and temporal variability in changes in wet and dry S deposition across the UK. These are clearer when data for individual grid cells and different time periods are considered. Modelled depositions have been taken for the 10 km grid cells which contain one of the UK's precipitation composition monitoring sites (see Appendix B).

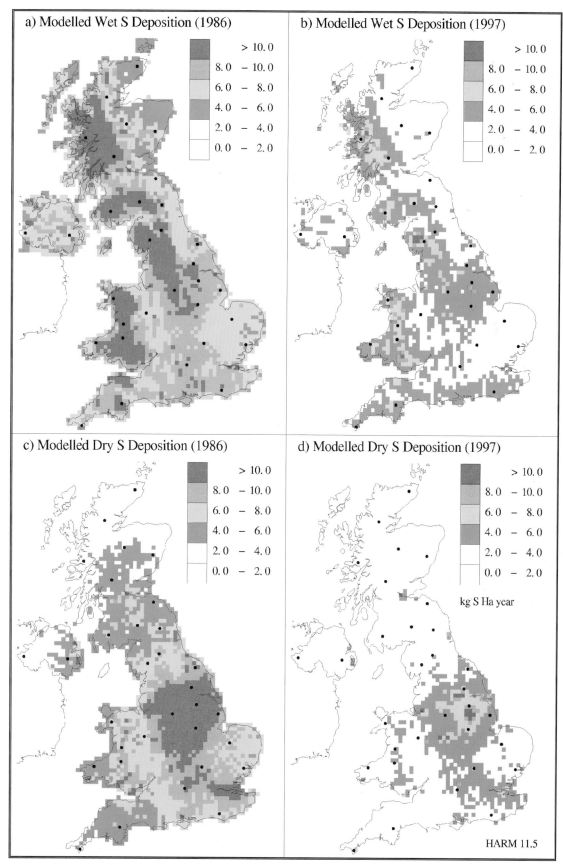

Figure 4.6 HARM modelled wet and dry S deposition 1986 and 1997.

Comparisons have been made between changes in wet and dry deposition at the different sites over the periods 1986-90, 1990-95 and 1995-97. The results for the 5 primary sites (Strathvaich Dam, Eskdalemuir, Lough Navar, High Muffles and Yarner Wood) are illustrated in Figure 4.7. Results from Bottesford and Pumlumon have also been included to improve the geographical spread of the sites. These seven represent two 'clean' sites – Lough Navar and Strathvaich Dam, three intermediate sites and two high deposition sites (High Muffles and Bottesford). Overall reductions in deposition have been greater at the more polluted sites than the 'clean' sites with the greatest reduction in deposition at the site with the highest proportion of dry deposition (Bottesford) (Figure 4.7a). The trends for dry and wet deposition separately are illustrated in Figure 4.7b and c and show different behaviours between sites and between time periods. There is a particularly clear downward trend in dry S deposition and a more mixed pattern for wet deposition, but going generally down.

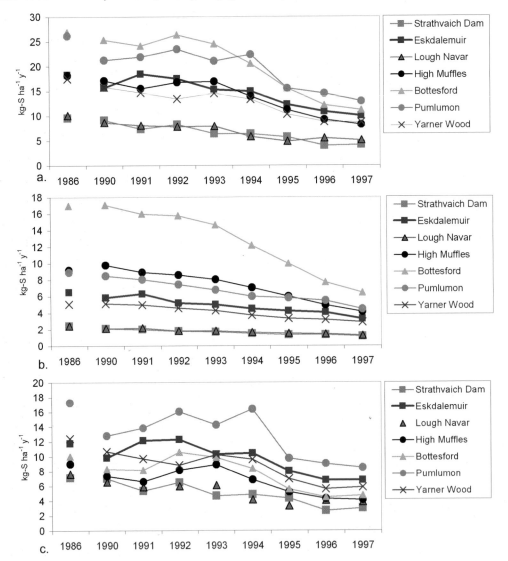

Figure 4.7 Sulphur deposition at selected UK sites 1986-1997 as modelled with HARM: a) total, b) dry and c) wet.

Using the model results for all 32 network sites regional trends become more apparent. Figure 4.8 shows the percentage change in dry or wet deposition over particular time periods. Between 1986 and 1990 there is a modelled increase in dry S deposition over Lincolnshire and East Yorkshire, which is most pronounced at Jenny Hurn (5118), Driby (5136) and High Muffles (5009). There are also small increases indicated for the south coast of England. The greatest modelled reductions in S deposition over this time period occur in north east England and over much of Scotland. The results for wet deposition also show a slight increase over parts of Lincolnshire and East Yorkshire. The greatest reductions in wet deposition occur over the remainder of England and Wales and into eastern Scotland. There is little reduction in wet deposition in northern and western Scotland or Northern Ireland. Over this time period modelled deposition shows the poorest agreement with deposition based on measurements than in any other time period. For 1986-90 the model yields a 5% reduction in dry deposition and a 16% reduction in wet deposition, while the data based on measurements show a 23% reduction in dry and a 2% reduction in wet. Over this period, however, UK emissions of S only fell by 1.5%, while emissions over the EMEP area fell by 14%. Within the UK, emissions from power stations actually increased in line with increasing coal consumption by this sector (up 1.6%) (DTI, 1999). Over the same period, domestic coal consumption fell by 42%. As described in Chapter 2, the majority of reductions in emissions over the period 1970 to 1990 were from low-level sources. HARM is a single layer model which does not treat emissions from different source heights in different ways. It is possible, therefore, that HARM has underestimated dry S deposition from low level sources and hence the impact of emissions reductions from this source category.

The patterns for 1990-95 (Figure 4.8) show much larger percentage reductions in deposition (see also Figure 4.7a). Modelled reductions in dry deposition are greatest in central and southern England, while the largest reductions in wet deposition occur on the east side of the UK, parts of western Scotland and Northern Ireland. Both the model and the data from measurements show greater reductions in dry deposition (> 35%) than wet (about 30%). UK S emissions fell 38% over this period, but the reduction in EMEP emissions was less, at about 32%. Within the UK there was a massive decline in emissions from public power generation (down 42% over this period, largely due to a switch to gas) and this is reflected in the modelled deposition pattern.

For 1995-97 (Figure 4.8), the model output shows the greatest reductions in dry S deposition in north east England, with a declining gradient of change towards the extreme south west and north east of the UK. The pattern for wet deposition is rather confused, with the greatest reductions in east/central England and the highlands of Scotland. The modelled percentage changes in wet and dry deposition are higher than, but consistent with, those from the data. One of the trends over the period is that although the rate of decline in dry deposition remains faster than that for wet deposition, they are getting closer. For the first time over this time period, UK S emissions showed a greater percentage reduction (30%) than emissions over the EMEP area. The steep downward trend in emissions from power stations continued (36% drop over the period). There was a particularly marked fall in emissions from a number of the large coal fired power stations in the lower Trent and Yorkshire Ouse valleys. Emissions from Cottam, Ferrybridge, Eggborough and Drax all fell by more than 40%.

Over the whole period, HARM can be used to estimate the percentage of total S deposition derived from UK sources compared with those elsewhere across the EMEP grid. The modelled attribution to UK sources for 1970 is about 65%, staying at 60% by 1986. From the mid 1990s, UK emissions of SO_2 began to fall more rapidly than those from the rest of EMEP and this is reflected by their decreasing contribution to total S deposition (53% for 1997).

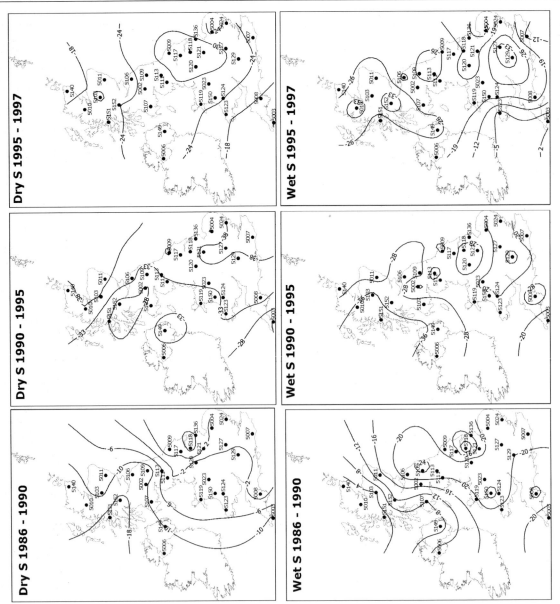

Figure 4.8 Percentage changes in wet and dry S deposition 1986 – 1990, 1990 – 1995, 1995 – 1997 modelled with HARM for 32 monitoring sites (for site names please refer to Table B3 in Appendix B).

Overall reductions in modelled S deposition between 1986 and 1997 (53%) are very similar to those from the measurements (52%). An analysis of data from the EMEP sites within the UK also indicates that over the period 1980 to 1995 S deposition has been cut by 30-40% in eastern England and by >50% elsewhere (Barrett *et al.*, 2000). The reduction in total deposition is similar to the percentage reduction in UK emission over the same period (57%). There is a difference, however, in the attribution of the reductions between modelled and measured. The measurements indicate a greater reduction in dry deposition than in wet (Chapter 3). Both model output and measurements show that the greatest changes have occurred at the highest deposition sites. This report presents clear evidence of non-linearity in the relationship between sulphur emissions and deposition in the UK (Chapter 3) with the reductions in emission leading to proportionally smaller reductions in deposition in some areas and larger reductions in deposition in others. These effects are important to understand and simulate with models to quantify the changes in exceedance of critical loads resulting from protocols for future emission reductions. As discussed earlier the areas of the UK with large non-linearities are the uplands of Wales and the East Midlands. At much larger scales, these effects are not observed, and the total budget for deposited sulphur declines approximately linearly with sulphur emissions. An EMEP analysis of non-linearity reports little evidence of non-linearity for sulphur in a numerical experiment based largely on Germany (Bartniki 2000). This analysis is not in serious conflict with that presented here because the author notes that the non-linearities increase with distance between source and receptor and are largest at the sites towards the boundaries of Europe. It is also important to note that the analysis is focused on the county to country exchange, and at the UK scale the EMEP model and the UK deposition estimates presented here are in good agreement.

The decline in emissions of oxidised N has not been as large as that for SO_2 (see Chapter 2), with an increase in the UK through to about 1989, followed by a steady decline. It is to be expected, therefore, that changes in NOy deposition will not be as pronounced as those for S. There are fewer year specific estimates of deposition based on measurements for NOy than for S. Since 1986, both wet and dry deposition figures are only available for 1993, 1996 and 1997. Modelling changes in oxidised N deposition has used the same approach as for S. The resulting modelled budgets for the UK are shown in Table 4.5.

Table 4.5 NO_y budgets for the UK from HARM11.5 showing changes in deposition and emissions used in the model.

Year	Dry NOy (kt-N)	Wet NOy (kt-N)	Total NOy (kt-N)	% change from previous modelled year	UK NOx emission (kt-N)	% change in emissions between years UK + (EMEP)
1986	63.7	122.5	186.2		2416	
1990	68.4	119.5	187.9	+1	2776	+15
1991	66.4	116.7	183.1	-2.6	2683	-3.4
1992	61.5	126.9	188.4	+2.9	2451	-8.6
1993	57.0	121.4	178.4	-5.3	2240	-8.6
1994	53.9	120.3	174.2	-2.2	2102	-6.2
1995	54.2	110.6	164.8	-5.4	2141	+1.8
1996	53.3	102.9	156.2	-5.2	2009	-6.2
1997	47.8	107.3	155.1	-0.7	1892	-5.8

Over the period since 1986, modelled total NO_y deposition has reduced by 16.7%, with a 12.4% cut in wet deposition and a 25% cut in dry deposition. Trends for the same monitoring sites used for S are shown in Figure 4.9. As with S, there has been least change at the two cleanest sites (Strathvaich Dam and Lough Navar). The patterns of change in dry deposition are more consistent than those for wet deposition. A number of sites show an increase in dry deposition between 1986 and 1990 in response to the increase in UK and EMEP emissions over that period. Modelled wet deposition shows no clear trend until after 1994 (when it declines) and may reflect the importance of long range transport of oxidised N from the rest of the EMEP area. Plotting percentage changes for all 32 precipitation concentration sites (Figure 4.10) highlights the differences between dry and wet deposition and between a period of general increase in emissions (1986 – 1990) and one of decrease (1990 – 1997). For 1986 – 1990, most of the UK shows an increase in dry deposition, while the pattern for wet is much more varied, with some reduction over England and southern Wales and an increase over north Wales and Scotland. For 1990 – 1997 the whole of the UK shows a sharp decline in dry deposition, with wet deposition also reduced over much of the country, particularly over Scotland.

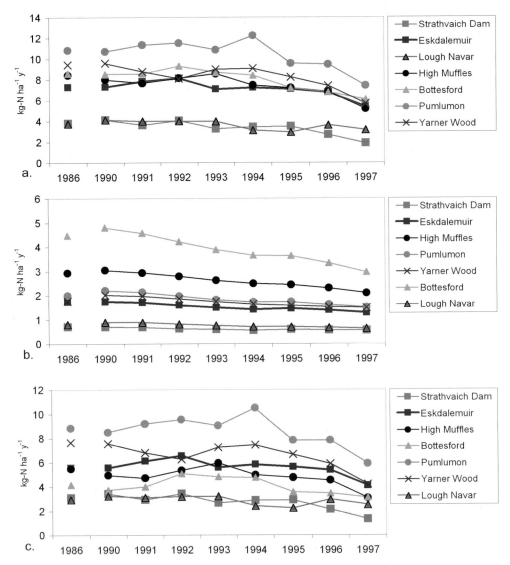

Figure 4.9 Oxidised N deposition at selected UK sites 1986 – 1997 as modelled with HARM a) total, b) dry and c) wet.

Measurement based data for the monitoring sites also show a mix of patterns in terms of wet NO_y deposition (see also Barrett *et al.*, 2000). The majority of sites, however, show some decline between 1986-88 and 1997. Dry deposition estimates are only available for 1991, 1992-94 and 1996, all of which post-date the emissions peak. The majority of sites show a slight reduction over this period, with the greatest declines at the highest deposition sites.

As described above, UK emissions of NH_3 were held at 1996 levels for all model runs, while those across the EMEP area were varied according to published figures. Given the coupling of the S and reduced N chemistry in HARM, through the formation of ammonium aerosol, some changes in reduced N deposition might be anticipated (Metcalfe *et al.*, 1998b). Over the period from 1986, all sites except Goonhilly show a reduction in HARM modelled wet NH_x deposition; at 10 of the sites this reduction is in excess of 1 kg-N ha y^{-1}. This decrease in modelled wet NH_x deposition will reflect the modest overall reduction in NH_3 emissions across Europe and the impact of reductions in SO_2 emissions on the formation of ammonium sulphate aerosol. HARM shows no clear trends in dry NH_x deposition. It has been suggested that reductions in SO_2 concentrations may reduce the transport distance of reduced N, but up to 1997 HARM shows no clear evidence for this. HARM has been run using a reduced N emission of about 370 kt-N

(450 kt-NH₃), which may reflect the emission peak in the mid 1980s. When this higher figure is used in the context of a low S emission (from the Gothenburg protocol – see below), then the change in transport distance is apparent, with increased modelled dry NH$_x$ deposition.

One of the significant changes of the last decade has been the shift from inputs of acidity dominated by S to a situation where N has become increasingly important. Output from HARM can be used to illustrate this trend and to highlight some of the variability between sites. Figure 4.11 shows the HARM modelled deposition of S and total N (oxidised and reduced) expressed in keq H$^+$ for six sites across the UK. All sites were S dominated at the start of the period (1986). This figure highlights the areas with the greatest reduction in acid inputs are in the south and east, with smaller changes to the north and west. These findings are consistent with the analysis of data from the monitoring networks (see Chapter 3).

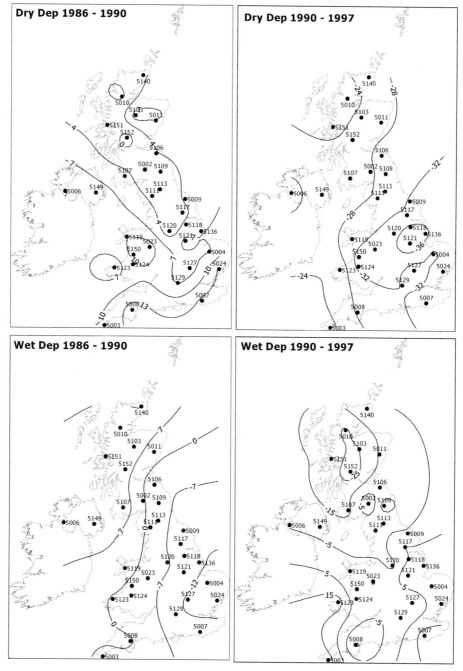

Figure 4.10 Percentage changes in wet and dry NO$_y$ deposition 1986- 1990, 1990 – 1997 modelled using HARM for 32 monitoring sites (for site names please refer to Table B3 in Appendix B).

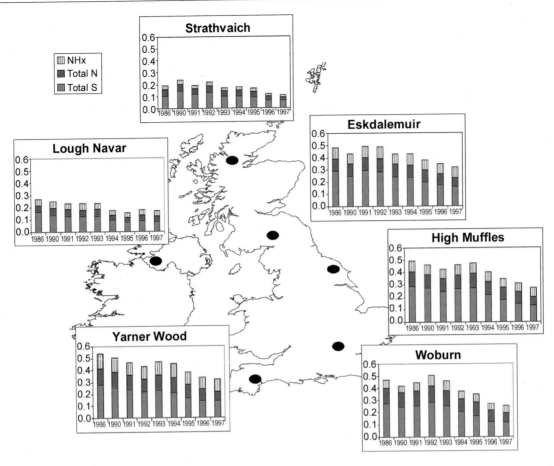

Figure 4.11 Trends in HARM modelled S and total N (NO$_y$ and NH$_x$) deposition in keq H$^+$ at selected UK sites 1986 – 1997.

4.4.2 Model Forecasts

HARM, FRAME and ELMO have been run to assess the effects of meeting emissions targets agreed in the Gothenburg Protocol. In these scenarios both UK and UNECE country emissions were set to the agreed emission limits. Emissions of carbon monoxide were not covered by the protocol, but were set to current published reduction plans. UK emissions under the protocol are compared with the base year of 1990 in Table 4.6 (see also Table 1.1).

Table 4.6 UK emissions for 1990 and 2010 as reported for the Gothenburg Protocol (kt).

Pollutant	1990 emission	Gothenburg (2010)
SO$_2$	3736	625
NO$_x$ (as NO$_2$)	2788	1181
NH$_3$	329	297
NMVOCs	2667	1200
CO*	6938	2872

*not covered by Protocol

The impact of Gothenburg on deposition of S and N modelled using HARM and FRAME is illustrated in Figure 4.12. In this case, both models have used a long-term rainfall field (1961-1990). The budget numbers are: S 102 kt-S, NO$_y$ 102 kt-N, NH$_x$ 159 kt-N and should be compared with the figures in Table 4.3. Modelled source attribution indicates that only 39% of S deposition to the UK may be from UK sources by 2010. As might be expected the steepest decline is in S deposition, with the lowest for reduced N. Following a modelled decrease in UK NH$_3$ emissions of 14% from 1990, FRAME wet deposition of NH$_x$ is reduced by 31% to 76 kt-N.

By contrast FRAME NH$_x$ dry deposition, which provides ecosystem specific deposition estimates, decreases by only 11%. This is due to a substantial reduction in import of NH$_x$ to the UK; the reduction in the sum of import plus UK NH$_3$ emissions between 1990 to 2010 is 23%, which is broadly consistent with the reduction in deposition.

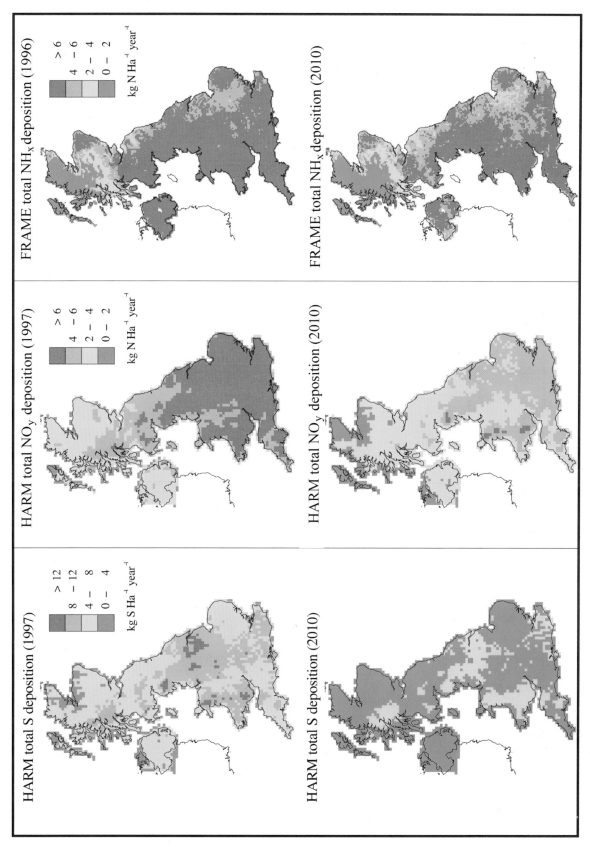

Figure 4.12 HARM modelled S and NOy and FRAME NH$_x$ deposition assuming implementation of the Gothenburg protocol.

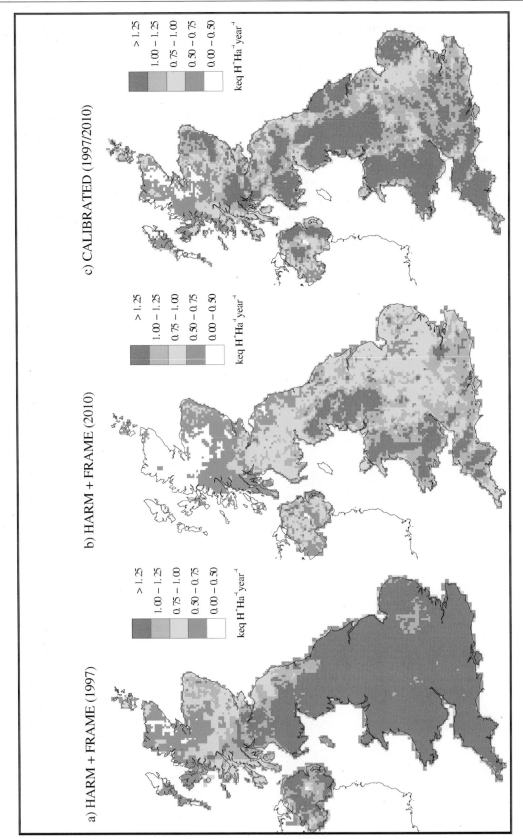

Figure 4.13 The potential deposition of acidity (H$^+$) to the UK modelled using: (a) HARM for SO$_x$ and NO$_y$ and FRAME for NH$_x$ with 1997 emissions; (b) the Gothenburg emission scenario for 2010 with HARM (SO$_x$ and NO$_y$) and FRAME (NH$_x$) and (c) the calibrated model output for 2010.

Figure 4.13 shows total deposition of H$^+$ under Gothenburg using S and oxidised N from HARM and reduced N from FRAME. It is this combined model approach that is used elsewhere in this report to assess future total acidifying deposition and critical load exceedances. Deposition maps based on the measurements (see Chapter 3), are also used to estimate critical load exceedance. Differences between models and measurements are always present and to reduce the effects of differences between models and measurements being interpreted as real trends with time, the model deposition estimates have been calibrated against the measurement data. In this report, the grid square average annual deposition derived from the measurement data for the period 1995 to 1997 has been used to deduce calibration factors for the models. These calibration factors are assumed to apply for the model runs for future emission scenarios. Calibrated H^+ deposition in 2010 is illustrated in Figure 4.13c showing that in some parts of the UK this process has a significant effect on modelled future acid inputs.

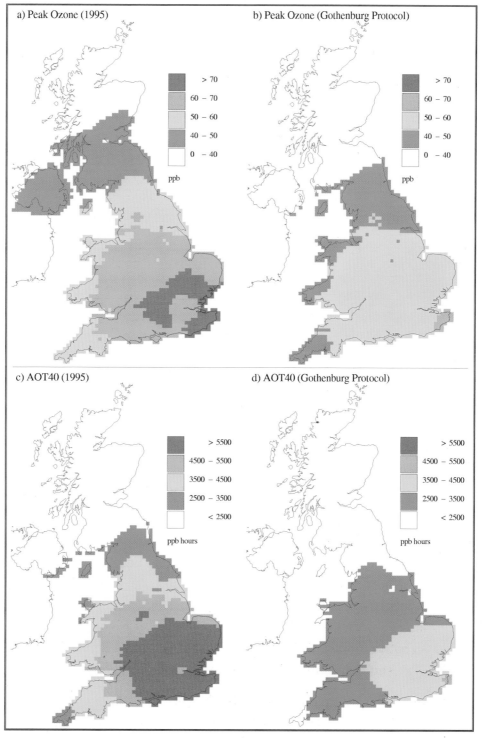

Figure 4.14 ELMO modelled ozone concentrations and AOT40 1995 and assuming implementation of the Gothenburg protocol. The AOT40 is derived from the peak value and is effectively the AOT40 for crops.

The effects of the proposed emissions reductions on ground-level ozone concentrations and AOT40, based on ELMO output, are illustrated in Figure 4.14. In this case, the reference year is 1995. Under this scenario, mean peak ozone is reduced from 52 ppb (1995) to 44 ppb (Gothenburg). It should be noted that this future scenario does not include any change in background ozone concentrations (see Section 4.5). Implementation of the protocol appears to reduce concentrations across the whole of the UK except northern Scotland where levels are generally low. The very distinctive 'doughnut' of high concentrations around the Thames Valley disappears by 2010. ELMO estimates of AOT40 can be compared with those derived from RAINS (using a cut-down version of the EMEP model, see Section 4.2) using 1995 and Gothenburg protocol emissions (Figure 4.15). Note that output from RAINS is expressed in ppm hours, not ppb hours (1 ppm h ≡ 1000 ppb h). The ELMO and RAINS output for 1995 look similar, with values in the south and east above 5000 ppb hours. For 2010, RAINS indicates more persistent values of high AOT40 in south east of England than does ELMO.

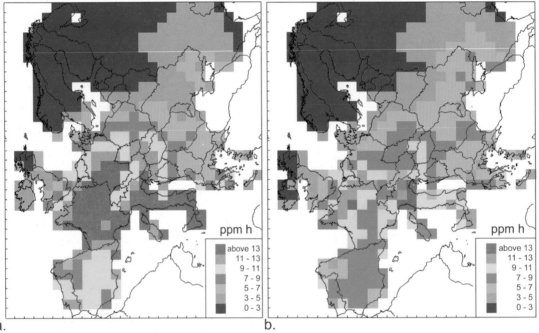

a.   b.

Figure 4.15 AOT40 crops for (a) 1995 emissions and (b) 2010, predicted using the Gothenburg emission scenario, from the EMEP model.

4.5 Modelling Air Pollution in the Context of Global Change

Consideration of issues such as acidification and eutrophication has generally taken place independently from studies of global climate change and its effects. This has partly been because of the structuring of the research process and partly because the issues were initially perceived to operate at fundamentally different spatial and temporal scales. The recognition of the importance of sulphate aerosols in radiative forcing (IPCC, 1994) started to change that perception. It has also been recognised that future changes in tropospheric concentrations of ozone and methane (both radiatively active trace gases) will have an effect on the production of potentially acidifying and eutrophying S and N compounds through changes in the oxidising capacity of the atmosphere. Inevitably, attempts to formulate policy to control episodes of photochemical pollution must also take into account these broader scale changes in the atmosphere. The meshing of issues across spatial scales, particularly regional and global, is now being reflected in modelling efforts.

It is well established that summertime ozone episodes across Europe are superimposed on a global ozone baseline. Ozone monitoring at the Montsouris Observatory near Paris and Montcalieri near Turin in the late 19th century indicates that ozone levels were then about 30% to 50% of modern values (Anfossi *et al.*, 1991). Computer modelling studies have shown that this increase in O_3 concentrations is consistent with the known changes in anthropogenic emissions of nitrogen oxides, methane and carbon monoxide. The global, 3-dimensional Lagrangian chemistry model STOCHEM (Collins *et al.*, 1997) has been used to calculate the influence of the projected increases in emissions of nitrogen oxides, methane and carbon monoxide on the global distribution of ozone through to 2100. The A2 emissions scenario from the IPCC Special Report on Emissions Scenarios (IPCC, 2000) has been used. A2 assumes an increasing world population (with slow convergence of fertility patterns) and fragmented, slow economic growth and technological development. A notable feature of A2 is the high level of methane emission beyond 2050. The results of model runs for 2030, 2060 and 2100 show a steady rise in surface ozone concentrations over the next century. Areas where ozone concentrations exceed 60 ppb are predicted to expand considerably, initially over Europe and North America (by 2030, Figure 4.16b) and then expanding to cover most of the populated continental areas by 2100 (Figure 4.16d). The modelled outcomes for central England have been described in Chapter 3 Section 3.10.3. It is clear from this global scale modelling that the success of policy to control regional scale ozone production across Europe will also depend on changes at the global scale. In particular, it appears that future anthropogenic emissions of ozone precursors in North America and Asia will play a key role in determining outcomes across Europe (Collins *et al.*, 2000b).

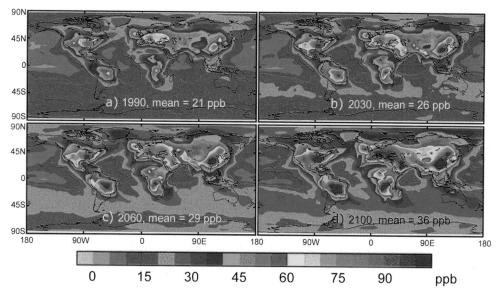

Figure 4.16 Global surface ozone distributions for (a) 1990, (b) 2030, (c) 2060 and (d) 2100, during July of each model year. Modelled using STOCHEM with the IPCC SRES A2 emissions scenario (IPCC, 2000).

Given the important role of ozone in the troposphere as a source of OH and related radical species (see Section 3.8), the impact of increasing background levels on S and N deposition across the UK have been explored by re-running HARM for the Gothenburg emissions scenario with 40 ppb of ozone rather than the usual 30 ppb. Modelled wet NOy deposition increases by 11.5% and is concentrated in the uplands of Wales, north-west and south-west England where

>0.5 kg-N ha y^{-1} would be deposited. The implications of this for damage estimation should be considered.

The possible impact of climatic change on the global pattern of S deposition has been explored using STOCHEM with emissions scenarios developed for the IPCC. Figure 4.17a and b show modelled wet S deposition for the year 2030 with and without climate change. Both model runs use the same emissions (IPCC B2 scenario), but in one case 1990 meteorology was used and in the other 2030 meteorology. The maps show very similar features. The impact of Asian SO$_2$ emissions on the wet S deposition fields is clearly apparent across much of the northern hemisphere. Transport of acid sulphur compounds across the North Atlantic is also evident following the implementation of strict SO$_2$ controls in Europe. There is some indication that the trans-Atlantic contribution to S deposition in the UK may increase, but it is difficult to say whether this is a robust feature of future deposition patterns. The lack of difference between the maps may be a result of the rather limited climate change expected by 2030.

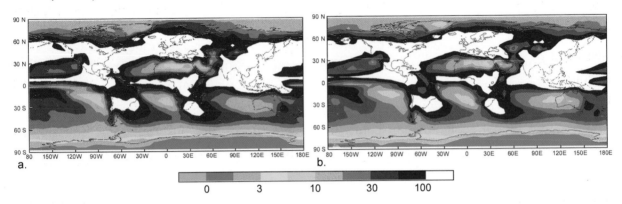

Figure 4.17 STOCHEM modelled global S deposition (mg m^{-2} y^{-1}) in 2030 (a) with and (b) without climate change. Both use the IPCC B2 emission scenario with (a) using meteorology from 1/3/1990 to 30/2/1991 and (b) from 1/1/2030 to 30/2/2031.

There are clearly many issues associated with future global change that are of importance in developing successful policy to control the concentrations and deposition of pollutants at the regional scale. Changes in the oxidation capacity of the atmosphere, dominant weather patterns (temperature, rainfall etc) and, over the longer term, land use will all affect the ways in which pollutants are transformed, transported and deposited. Global climate change will also affect the nature and pattern of energy consumption and hence future emissions. Setting emissions targets will have to consider these broader issues. The development of the UK's position with respect to the Gothenburg protocol (see above) also had to take into account the country's commitments under the Kyoto protocol to the UNFCCC. As the timeframe for future scenarios relating to deposition of S and N compounds and photochemical pollutants moves forwards in to the mid-21st century, so more issues relating to global change will have to be taken into consideration even in simple, regional scale models.

4.6 Conclusions

Long-range atmospheric transport models have been developed to explore the pollution climate within the UK and across Europe. At both scales, they play a key role in developing policy to cut emissions of those pollutants associated with acidification, eutrophication and the creation of excess ground-level ozone. The EMEP models, which underpin policy formulation within the UNECE and EU, have undergone considerable development in recent years. Both within EMEP and within the UK, there has been a general trend towards models operating at a finer spatial resolution exploiting the availability of higher resolution input data.

- Comparison of UK S and N deposition based on measurement data with output from the EMEP Eulerian model and a UK scale model (HARM), indicates that the UK scale model provides a better representation of this deposition.

- The modelling of reduced N is problematic, even using a specialist model such as FRAME and reflects the many uncertainties associated with this pollutant.

- Both the EMEP Lagrangian photochemical model and the UK scale ELMO are able to reproduce observed peak ozone concentrations and distributions.

- The availability of UK scale models is important for impacts assessment, but also offers the opportunity to explore policy options within the UK in more detail using the available emission source category data.

- Historical deposition estimates can be compared with measurement data (when available). Results suggest that although the models capture the overall effect of emissions reductions, they are not able to reproduce all of the elements of the observed changes.

- Implementation of the Gothenburg protocol seems likely to result in further substantial reductions in S deposition across the UK and to shift most of the country to a situation where inputs of H^+ are dominated by nitrogen deposition.

- Peak ozone levels will also be reduced but, in any given year, these are highly dependent on meteorological conditions.

- Background ozone levels are likely to continue to increase and will also have an effect on the path (wet vs. dry) and the amount of acid deposition inputs. Although the impact of climate change may not be significant within the time frame of current UNECE protocols and EU directives, it seems likely that it will have a greater effect on the pollution climate from the middle of this century and should be taken into account.

Chapter 5: Effects on Soils

> - There is evidence from the UK that acid deposition has resulted in acidification of acid sensitive soils and these findings are consistent with studies in other parts of Europe.
> - There is experimental evidence that a reduction of strong acid anion inputs (sulphate and nitrate) results in a rapid increase (*ca* 1 year) in soil water acid neutralising capacity (ANC).
> - Recovery of soils by an increase in base saturation will take much longer (decades) than recovery of soil water ANC. Change is dependent on base cation supply from weathering (slow) and atmospheric inputs.
> - Results of modelling studies are consistent with these experimental data and indicate that recovery of soil and soil waters from acidification will take decades. For some upland soils, models predict that soil base saturation may never return to predicted values prior to the onset of acid deposition.
> - There is currently little unequivocal evidence of recovery from soil acidification in the UK as there are few data collected from appropriate soil types. Most available data suggest continuing acidification of soils under semi-natural vegetation into the 1990s but a re-sampling study in 1998/99 suggests an increase in pH in some upland soils since 1978. Re-sampling exercises on arable and intensive grassland soils show a decrease in acidity over the last 10 to 20 years.
> - Desorption of sulphate from the soil may slow the increase in soil water ANC following a reduction in sulphate deposition. Manipulation experiments suggest that it may take up to 20 years for sulphate outputs to reach a new steady-state with inputs.
> - There is experimental evidence from forest systems that a reduction in the amount of deposited oxidised-N results in an immediate decrease in soil water nitrate concentrations and an increase in soil water ANC. However our ability to predict the future consequences of nitrogen deposition for soil acidification and recovery is limited due to inadequate understanding of N dynamics and limited representation of N processes in soil acidification models.

5.1 Soil Acidification

5.1.1 The Nature of the Soil

One of the most important chemical characteristics of the soil is the cation exchange complex, which arises from the presence of negative charges on the surfaces of clay minerals and soil organic matter. The acidity of the soil is determined by the relative proportions of base cations (Na^+, K^+, Ca^{2+}, Mg^{2+}), protons and acid aluminium species occupying the exchange complex. In neutral soils, base cations will dominate, whereas in acid mineral soils, the exchange complex will be dominated by acid aluminium species such as Al^{3+}, $Al(OH)^{2+}$, $Al(OH)_2^+$. In acid organic soils, protons may be the dominant exchangeable cation.

Any processes that either remove exchangeable base cations or increase the number of negative charges without adding further base cations will acidify the soil. In contrast, addition of base cations to the soil by mineral weathering or from an external source such as liming will counteract acidification. Loss of organic matter from soil by burning will reduce the negative charge and thus ameliorate acidification.

The process of soil acidification can be considered in terms of a careful application of the mobile anion concept (Reuss and Johnson, 1986). This states simply that as the soil solution must remain electrically neutral, cation leaching must be accompanied by an equivalent amount of anions. Thus for soil acidification to occur, there has to be a source of protons to exchange for base cations and a supply of mobile anions to accompany the leached cations. There are several processes whereby this occurs naturally.

5.1.2 Processes of 'Natural' Soil Acidification

Respiration: Carbon dioxide, evolved in respiration by roots and soil micro-organisms, dissolves in the soil solution to form carbonic acid which dissociates to yield protons and bicarbonate anions. The protons exchange for base cations on the exchange complex, and bicarbonate provides the accompanying 'mobile anion' for leaching. Carbonic acid is a weak acid and dissociation is negligible below pH 4.5. Thus acidification resulting from respiration is self-limiting and unimportant in acid soils.

Organic acid production: Decomposition of organic matter leads to the formation of soluble organic acids. These acids are stronger than carbonic acid and can therefore dissociate to give protons and organic anions at a pH below 4.5. The role of organic acids in soil acidification remains an area of debate, as the quantitative importance of organic acids will vary with soil type and degree of acidification. Furthermore, organic acid production depends on the decomposition of organic matter, a process that is also susceptible to the effects of acidification (Wookey *et al.*, 1991; Wookey and Ineson, 1991).

Base cation uptake: Plants require base cations for growth, exuding protons from the roots to maintain electrical neutrality. Thus plant growth is an acidifying process that is temporary under conditions where plant death and decay returns the base cations to the soil. If the plants are harvested, as in forestry, permanent depletion of the base cation store will occur (Reynolds and Stevens, 1998), although the amount removed will depend on tree species, site conditions, timing and type of harvesting (Hornung, 1985).

Organic matter accumulation: Organic matter accumulation can acidify because it consists largely of weak acids with few base cations. Thus the cation exchange capacity of the soil can increase while the base cation status remains unchanged. This effect can be large where organic matter is accumulating rapidly as in some peat bogs and young forests.

Seasalt deposition: The so-called 'seasalt effect' is a particular example of the mobile anion effect, whereby protons are released from organic soils by ion exchange in response to the input of neutral salts (Skartveit, 1981; Langan, 1989). The effect is a short-term (days to months) acidification of the soil solution rather than a soil acidification process *per se* (Hendershot *et al.*, 1991).

5.1.3 Processes of Acid Neutralisation

Weathering: The most important acid consuming process in soil is mineral weathering. This process is the source of base cations from the soil and the rate of weathering is fundamental to the soil response to acid rain and the definition of critical loads. Unfortunately the rate of weathering is one of the most difficult processes to quantify (Hodson *et al.*, 1998; Hodson and Langan, 1999) because it depends on a wide range of internal and external factors such as abundance of weatherable minerals, soil texture, climate, slope etc. At any one site these factors will interact to define the weathering rate.

Sulphate adsorption: Sulphate adsorption takes place on the surfaces of iron and aluminium oxides that are abundant, for example, in the B horizons of podzolic soils in the UK uplands. Sulphate adsorption consumes protons and sulphate but the process is concentration dependent, with the capacity of the soil to adsorb/desorb sulphate changing with the solution sulphate concentration (Chao *et al.*, 1962). This has important implications, as it means that a decline in input concentrations will cause sulphate to be desorbed until equilibrium is achieved. Thus recovery from acidification following a reduction in sulphur deposition will be slowed if there is a significant pool of sulphate adsorbed in the soil. Relatively little work has been done nationally in the UK to study the influence of sulphate adsorption on acidification and recovery. Given the widespread occurrence of podzolic soils, sulphate dynamics may be important in determining the rate of recovery of some acidified soils and waters.

Sulphate reduction: Microbial reduction of sulphate to sulphide is an important process in anaerobic soils, particularly in wetlands and bogs, resulting in the formation of pyrite (FeS_2) and/or loss by volatilisation of hydrogen sulphide or other gaseous compounds. The process of sulphur storage in wetlands and peatlands is reversible if the system is allowed to dry out allowing re-oxidation of the sulphides.

Liming: Agricultural liming has been practised for centuries in order to counteract soil acidification resulting from cultivation and nitrogenous fertiliser additions. In the uplands, where most acidic soils occur, liming has been used to improve the productivity of grazing land often in association with other agricultural treatments. In effect, liming introduces a source of rapidly weatherable minerals to the soil, which can increase soil base saturation and pH. Addition of lime to organic soils can also increase the cation exchange capacity as the surface charge on soil organic matter is pH dependent.

Liming has also been used to counter excessive acidification of forest soils and much information is available from Scandinavian studies. Generally the effects are to increase base saturation, mainly in the surface layers of the soil, although very long-term studies have observed some changes at depth (Derome *et al.*, 1986; Andersson and Persson, 1988). However, lime dissolution rates in forest soils can be very slow, with between 65-75% of the lime remaining in the top 20 cm, 25 years after liming. Liming can also increase mineralisation of organic carbon and nitrogen in the forest floor (Persson *et al.*, 1989; Kreutzer *et al.*, 1989) resulting in a nitrification pulse and large nitrate concentrations in seepage waters (Kreutzer *et al.*, 1989). This can lead to temporary acidification of subsoil waters as the nitrate is initially leached from the surface more rapidly than the added calcium, which has a longer transport time to the lower horizons.

Liming has resulted in an undesirable reduction in growth volume in some pine and spruce species (Foster *et al.*, 1988), but few other biological effects have been observed in forest soils (Andersson and Persson, 1988; Robinson *et al.*, 1991 & 1992). Liming of peats and wetland soils can cause damage to plants, particularly *Sphagnum spp* (Howells and Dalziel, 1992; Clymo *et al.*, 1992), although there are no reports of damage to other plants such as cotton sedge (*Eriophorum vaginatum*), bell heather (*Erica tetralix*) and bog asphodel (*Narthecium ossifragum*) that are typically found on acid, peaty upland soils.

5.1.4 Effects of Acid Deposition

If soil acidification is regarded in the light of the 'mobile anion' concept, then acid deposition provides both a source of protons to exchange for exchangeable base cations and mobile anions (SO_4^{2-} and NO_3^-) to accompany the displaced cations. For sulphur deposition, the process of sulphate adsorption reduces the acidifying effect by effectively removing both the sulphate and hydrogen ions, but this is a temporary effect until new equilibrium conditions are established. The processes determining the role of nitrogen in the acidification of soils is, however, more complex.

The nitrogen cycle is intimately linked with acid-base relationships within the soil as shown by Figure 5.1, which is a schematic representation of how nitrogen transformations affect the proton balance of the soil.

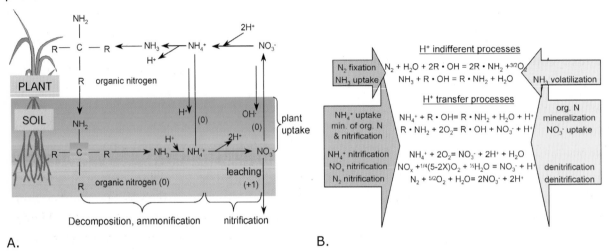

A.   B.

Figure 5.1 a) Schematic representation of acid-base relationships of the nitrogen cycle. Numbers in parentheses refer to the net production (+) or consumption (-) of protons in the soil system starting with soil organic nitrogen. b) Important acid-base reactions of the nitrogen cycle. R-OH and R-NH$_2$ refer to generic organic nitrogen compounds associated with soil organic matter. (after Reuss and Johnson, 1986 and Driscoll and Schaefer, 1989).

In the absence of nitrate leaching and external inputs of nitrogen, there is no net proton production associated with the nitrogen cycle. The cycle within the plant and the soil is balanced. However, in broad terms, the balance between nitrogen supply and utilisation by plants and the soil microbial biomass will be the main control on nitrate leaching.

The most important forms of atmospheric nitrogen deposition are NH_3, NH_4^+ and NO_3^- and their relative acidifying effects on ecosystems, summarised in Figure 5.2, depend on the nitrogen transformations that occur in the soil. If all reduced nitrogen inputs in excess of biological requirements are transformed to nitrate, then on a per mole basis, NH_3 and HNO_3 are equally acidifying. Over a period of years to a few decades, increased biotic uptake of nitrogen can temporarily prevent soil acidification but ultimately, NO_3^- leaching in response to excess nitrogen deposition will be acidifying irrespective of the form of the incoming N. If increased nitrogen inputs also stimulate growth of biomass, uptake of base cations will increase soil acidification if the biomass is removed through harvesting. The key issues are therefore whether or not deposited NH_4^+ will be nitrified and the capacity of the system to immobilise deposited mineral N in the soil and biomass.

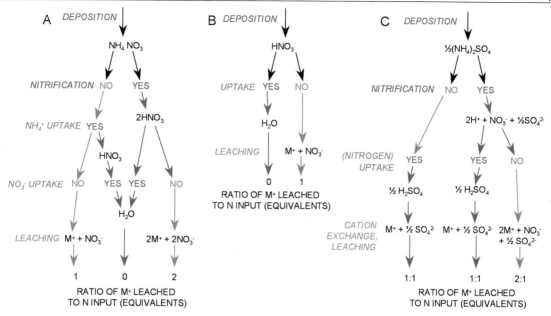

Figure 5.2 Acidification effects associated with inputs of a) ammonium nitrate, b) nitric acid and c) ammonium sulphate. (after Reuss and Johnson, 1986).

5.1.5 Soil Biological Responses

Nitrogen deposition may affect soil biological processes and in particular N cycling both through direct and indirect effects. One of the most widely reported indirect effects is through a change in plant litter quantity and quality. For example, increases in N concentration of tree foliage litter have been observed across N deposition gradients (Tietema and Beier, 1995) although changes in the total N flux in litter appears only to be observed in broadleaved stands (Gundersen, 1995). This change in litter quality, in combination with the direct effect of increased N availability in soil solution on abiotic and biotic processes, is thought to accelerate initial stages of decomposition but retard later stages. These effects have been reviewed by Fog (1988), Berg *et al.* (1996), and most recently by Berg and Matzner (1997). Generally, a decrease in microbial activity in response to increased N supply is greatest in litter from low fertility sites or substrates with high C/N ratios (e.g. Bååth *et al.*, 1981). It is suggested, by Berg and Matzner (1997), that this is due to a suppression of lignolytic enzymes in white rot fungi thus reducing decomposition rates in the latter stages. Combined with reactions of both ammonium and nitrate with lignin and phenolic components forming chemically stable compounds, Berg and Matzner (1997) suggest this may result in an increase in N accumulation rates with N deposition.

Aber *et al.* (1998) have argued that the major mechanism for increased nitrogen storage in forest soils, as nitrogen deposition increases, is mycorrhizal assimilation. Reduced decomposition rates could delay the release of internally cycled nitrogen but would not account for the large accumulation of externally deposited N in the soil (Nadelhoffer *et al.*, 1999). Rates of abiotic fixation are insufficient to account for the magnitude of retention reported and carbon limitation of assimilation by soil microbes would prevent microbial immobilisation. Aber *et al.* (1998) therefore argue that only mycorrhizal fungi have a sufficient carbon supply to account for the large N accumulation in the soil. This nitrogen would be cycled within the soil pool through assimilation and exudation. Continued deposition of nitrogen could result in a decline in mycorrhiza, thus reducing competition for N from other soil microbes such as nitrifiers. Much of this type of work has been conducted in forest systems and there is a need to increase the work in semi-natural systems. Changes in soil N availability and uptake can also lead to changes in plant species composition due to influences on plant competition and changes in sensitivity to environmental stress. These effects are considered further in Chapter 7.

5.2 Indicators of Change

The acid status of soils has been considered in terms of intensity versus capacity related indicators and effects (e.g. Reuss and Walthall, 1989). Capacity factors deal with amounts, e.g. the amount of exchangeable cations in a soil or of exchangeable acidity. These parameters generally change slowly over a timescale of decades, and often the pool size in the soil is large and spatially heterogeneous. Thus over a short time scale, for example 5 years, their value for detecting change may be limited by the 'noise' in the measurements, particularly if the magnitude of change is small relative to the size of the pool. Capacity factors can be compared with input loads or input-output budgets to assess impacts.

Intensity factors relate to concentrations and apply mainly to soil solutions. Although they can be highly variable in space and time, these factors can change rapidly by a large amount in response to changes in concentration in the inputs at a seasonal or single event timescale. They should be compared with concentrations of ions in deposition inputs to assess impacts.

5.2.1 Capacity Factors

Soil pH: This is the most commonly, and often the only, quoted measure of soil acidity. As generally determined it is essentially a measure of the water, or weak salt solution exchangeable protons in a soil. The methodology generally used to measure soil pH is based on the assumption that the soil comes rapidly to equilibrium with an added solution and it is the H^+ ions in this solution that are measured. Soil pH is not necessarily the best measure of soil acidity because it can vary over a range of timescales depending on the volume and salt content of the soil solution. The method of measurement can also influence the result as can variability between pH electrodes, making it difficult to compare results between studies. However, a very useful conceptual model of the acid buffering reactions occurring within different soil pH ranges has been developed by Ulrich (1987), which gives a broad indication of the likely response of soils to increasing acidic inputs (Table 5.1).

Exchangeable acidity: This quantifies the hydrogen plus aluminium ions held on exchange sites in soils. It is actually measured as the ions displaced from exchange sites by the cation in an added solution; the most commonly used extractants are ammonium acetate, potassium chloride (KCl), and barium chloride ($BaCl_2$). In mineral soils aluminium is the dominant form of exchangeable acidity. Once again care must be taken when comparing studies as the results are influenced by the extractant and precise methodology used. To be used in the 'capacity sense' the parameter should be converted into a quantity per unit volume of soil, e.g. mol m^{-3}. This indicator also has limited application in acid soils because acid deposition fluxes are usually very small relative to the pool of exchangeable acidity, so that it is unlikely that measurable changes would occur except in heavily impacted systems over many decades.

Base saturation: A more useful index of soil acidification in acid soils is the decrease in soil base saturation (the proportion of the exchange complex occupied by base cations). This occurs as aluminium species replace base cations on the exchange complex with subsequent leaching of the base cations from the soil in association with 'mobile' acid anions. The quantity of base cations held on exchange sites in soils is determined by extraction of the cations with a solution containing an exchanger ion.

Table 5.1 Buffer systems and their pH ranges in soils (Ulrich, 1987).

Soil buffering component	Soil pH range	Main reaction product (Chemical change in soil)
Carbonate buffer range: $CaCO_3$ & $MgCO_3$	8.6 > pH > 6.2	$Ca(HCO_3)_2$ in solution (leaching of calcium)
Silicate buffer range: Primary silicate minerals	Whole pH range (dominant buffer reaction in carbonate free soils pH > 5)	Weathering of primary silicates to clay secondary minerals; (increase in CEC)
Cation exchange buffer range: Clay minerals	5 > pH > 4.2	Formation of non-exchangeable hydroxy Al species; (blockage of permanent charge sites causing reduction in CEC)
Cation exchange buffer range: Manganese oxides	5 > pH > 4.2	Exchangeable Mn^{2+}; (reduction in base saturation)
Cation exchange buffer range: Interlayer hydroxy aluminium species	5 > pH > 4.2	Aluminium hydroxysulphate (accumulation of acid in case of sulphate inputs)
Aluminium buffer range: Interlayer hydroxy aluminium species	4.2 > pH	Al^{3+} in solution (Al displacement, reduction in permanent charge)
Al / Fe buffer range: As Al buffer range, but including soil hydroxy-iron compounds	3.8 > pH	Organic Fe complexes (Fe displacement, bleaching)
Fe buffer range: Ferrihydrite	3.2 > pH	Fe^{3+} in solution (Fe displacement, bleaching, destruction of clay minerals)

Nitrogen status: The most commonly used measure of soil nitrogen status is percent total N of a particular soil depth band or pedological horizon. More rarely the N content per unit weight or volume is calculated. Water, or weak salt extractable NO_3^- is sometimes used as a measure of readily available N. The amount of ammonium held on the soil cation exchange complex gives an indication of the amount of readily available ammonium. It is determined as the ammonium removed using an extractant, most commonly KCl. However, changes in percent N content or total amount of N per unit weight or volume will generally represent small changes in a large pool.

5.2.2 Intensity Factors

In many ways, measurements of soil solution chemistry and assessment of its acidity is simpler than for bulk soil. The chemical determinations are generally made on the filtered solution. The measures are generally of the total or ionic form of an element and may be reported as the element or as the ion actually measured. pH can be measured directly. The way in which the soil water/solution is extracted from the soil can have a major impact on the chemistry, mainly on the concentration of the various solutes. Sample handling, pre-treatment and analytical methodology can also affect the results. The concentrations of other ions in soil solution, e.g. calcium or aluminium, would be intensity factors.

Increasing dominance of the exchange complex by aluminium and protons is reflected in the chemistry of the soil solution, which becomes increasingly acidic and enriched in dissolved aluminium species. A useful index of this change is the effect on the acid neutralising capacity of the soil solution (ANC; see Appendix C), which declines as the soil water is progressively acidified.

For nitrogen, concentrations of nitrate and ammonium can be measured directly in soil solution. Total N in solution is also sometimes determined, usually following a digestion. Dissolved organic nitrogen (DON) is another measure of soil solution N that is usually derived by subtracting measured inorganic-N from total determined N.

5.2.3 Indirect Measures of Change

The availability to plants, the extractability and mobility of a number of elements or ions vary with soil acidity. Thus, several trace metals become more readily extractable and more mobile with increasing acidity. Phosphate ions, in contrast, are less available to plants at low pH when they are adsorbed more firmly onto anion exchange sites on iron and aluminium hydroxides. Hence, acidification can lead to P deficiency in vegetation as the phosphate becomes less available. Phosphorus availability is also reduced at high pH in the presence of calcium carbonates when precipitation as various forms of calcium phosphate may occur (Frossard *et al.*, 1995).

The molar ratio of dissolved calcium or base cations to aluminium has been used as a critical chemical indicator for potential growth reduction effects on trees and plants (Sverdrup and Warfvinge, 1993; Cronan and Grigal, 1995). The concept, originally proposed by Ulrich (1983), arose from the need to generate a quantitative link between forest vitality and soil acidification. Following an exhaustive review of mainly laboratory experimental studies of aluminium toxicity to a wide range of trees and plants, Sverdrup and Warfvinge (1993) observed that the most consistent correlations with growth effects were obtained with the (Ca+Mg+K)/Al molar ratio of the solution surrounding the roots. From the data, simple ion exchange models were developed to predict growth reductions in response to changes in the (Ca+Mg+K)/Al molar ratio of the soil solution. Several authors have subsequently criticised the approach (Högberg and Jensén, 1994; Cronan and Grigal, 1995; Lökke *et al.*, 1996; Skeffington, 1999), although few alternatives have been proposed.

In some instances, parameters other than those that directly measure N or N compounds can be valuable indicators of changes in N status or availability. An increase in plant available N, due for example to increased atmospheric inputs, can lead to increased plant growth. This will result in an increased demand for other essential nutrients and, if this increased demand cannot be met, induced deficiencies in elements such as P, K^+ or Mg^{2+} can result. In the case of P, this can lead to changes in P mineralisation from soil organic matter, with the supply from this source becoming more important. Changes in enzymes related to mineralisation of P from soil organic matter can therefore be valuable indicators of P stress; such changes have been reported from N addition experiments.

Similarly, the ratio of exchangeable ammonium to K^+ or Mg^{2+} is a useful indicator in sites receiving large inputs of NH_x. Accumulation of nitrogen in the soil can lead to a decrease in the soil C/N ratio. The C/N ratio of the forest floor has proved to be a useful index of the onset of nitrate leaching in forest ecosystems (see Section 5.4.2).

5.3 Evidence of Change: Monitoring and Resampling

5.3.1 Acidity

There are very few long-term UK monitoring studies of soil chemistry and none of soil biota. However, chemical data are available for a few specific sites, from a small number of regional studies and from three national studies. In view of the paucity of UK studies, this section will also briefly review European literature to identify factors relevant to the UK. Potential confounding factors in the interpretation of trends and changes in soil chemistry will also be examined.

Evidence from site specific studies in the UK

The longest run of data and the most famous is that from the Rothamsted long-term plots. The Geescroft Wilderness is an area of former arable land which has been left untended since 1886 and which has, over the years, reverted to woodland. The soils have shown a decline in pH of the surface horizon from *ca* 7 to just above 4 in the 110 years since management ceased, and similar declines in two lower soil layers. Johnston *et al.* (1986) estimated that "atmospheric inputs may comprise up to 30% of acidifying inputs at or near neutral soil pH and more as soil pH decreases". The results of an application of the SAFE model also suggested that acidic deposition was a major cause of the acidification (Sverdrup *et al.,* 1995). A more recent, detailed study (Blake *et al.,* 1999) involving the construction of proton budgets concluded that acidic deposition had been the major factor in the acidification in the Geescroft Wilderness and also in the unfertilised and un-limed Park Grass.

Evidence from UK regional studies

There have been five relevant studies in the UK: one in Wales, two in England and two in Scotland.

In a study in North West Wales, Kuylenstierna and Chadwick (1991) re-sampled 13 sites: 4 brown soils, 7 podzolic soils, one peat ranker and one peat. All the soils were under grassland dominated by *Festuca spp*, *Agrostis spp* and *Nardus stricta*. The first sampling was carried out in 1957 and the re-sampling in 1990; it involved between one and three sampling depths at the various sites, giving a total of 31 samples. The original pH values ranged between 4.4 and 6.4 and all the separate samples showed reductions in pH with the decline ranging from 0.1 to 1.6 pH units and with the decline in pH 'broadly positively correlated to the original pH' (Figure 5.3). The sites sampled represented a range in altitude from *ca* 130 to 915 m with consequent variations in precipitation and deposition of pollutant and non-pollutant ions. The variation in the magnitude of pH change with deposition was not explored.

Adamson *et al.* (1996) re-sampled 32 soil profiles on the Moor House-Upper Teesdale NNR. The original sampling took place between 1963 and 1973 and the re-sampling in 1991. A range of soil types was involved, including rankers, rendzinas, brown soils, podzolic soils and stagnogleys. Between one and four horizons were sampled at each location, depending on soil morphology; the total number of samples involved was 100. The changes in soil chemistry, analysed by soil horizon and soil type are presented in Table 5.2, where rendzinas and rankers have been grouped as lithomorphic soils. Organic and A horizons showed a consistent increase in acidity of between 0.4 and 1.0 units between samplings; the initial pH values for these horizons varied between 3.5 and 5.8 for the O horizons and between 3.9 and 7.5 for the A horizons. Brown soils and lithomorphic soils showed an increase in acidity throughout their depth but gleys and podzols showed a decrease in acidity at depth, contrasting with the increase in the surface horizons. Correlations with other determinands showed a positive relationship between the changes in pH and extractable base cations, suggesting increased leaching of base cations over the time period.

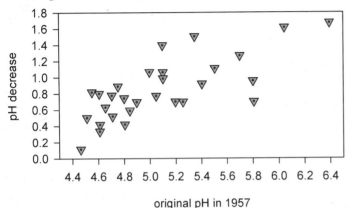

Figure 5.3 The measured pH decrease for soils in north-west Wales originally sampled in 1957 and re-sampled in 1990. (after Kuylenstierna and Chadwick, 1991).

pH decrease

original pH in 1957

Table 5.2 Mean changes in pH between samplings by soil horizon and major soil group. Horizons are defined by Hodgson (1974) and major soil groups by Avery (1980). O, H and Ah horizons have been combined into the organic horizons category and podzolic soils and surface-water gley soils have been combined into a single category. All horizons for which there are initial data have been included and the number of horizons in each category is shown in brackets. (From Adamson et al, 1996).

Horizon	Lithomorphic soils*		Brown soils		Podzolic/Gleys		Average	
Organic	-0.500	(2)	-0.840	(4)	-0.350	(6)	-0.538	(12)
A	-0.665	(6)	-0.960	(9)	0.063	(4)	-0.652	(19)
E					0.117	(7)	0.117	(7)
B	-0.125	(2)	-0.420	(13)	0.110	(21)	-0.094	(36)
C			-0.504	(8)	0.506	(5)	-0.115	(13)
Average	-0.524	(10)	-0.632	(34)	0.089	(43)	-0.263	(87)

*Includes rendzinas and rankers

A study at Wytham Wood in Oxfordshire (Farmer, 1995), involved sampling of soils from a series of permanently marked quadrats, each 10 m². In 1974, 150 quadrats were sampled with 4 soil samples collected from fixed positions along the sides of each quadrat. Each soil sample was divided into three depth bands. In 1990, soils were re-sampled from 50 of the original quadrats. Eighteen of the 50 sites were in ancient woodland and 16 in recent woodland; the published paper concentrates on these 34 sites. The soils were mainly gleys or pelosols. Farmer (op. cit.) reported "a tendency for a decline in pH" with "the mean pH change always negative when analysed by woodland type or soil depth". The mean change for ancient woodland was -0.155 and for recent woodland -0.17, from initial mean pH values for the ancient woodland of 4.79 and for the recent woodland of 5.63. Only the declines in the lowest soil layer were statistically significant. The data also showed an increase in soil nitrogen, which was significant for the soils from both woodland types and for each soil depth.

A series of 15 soil profiles in forests in North East Scotland were re-sampled by Billet *et al* (1988; 1990a & b) 37 years after the original sampling in 1949 and 1950. The soils included brown forest soils, gleys, podzolic soils and peats and were sampled by pedological horizon. The first paper based on the study only considered soil pH while the later paper (based on a detailed study of 9 of the soils) considered pH, extractable cations, cation exchange capacity and base saturation. The results showed that the surface organic horizons had been acidified by 0.07 to 1.28 pH units in 80% of the sites and that at 70% of the sites, the mineral horizons had been acidified below 40 cm. For more detailed analyses of the data, the sites were split into two groups: those below tress planted in the nineteenth century and those planted in the 50 years prior to sampling. Acidification and organic matter accumulation were greatest under the older trees. Under the younger trees, freely drained soils showed acidification while poorly drained soils showed increases in pH. Acidification was found in all soil types under the older trees except where the site had formerly been dominated by Calluna that had now died back. All the soils in the 'older' group showed a decrease in exchangeable calcium at all depths but only two of the younger group showed this trend. Ninety-six percent of the individual soil samples showed an increase in extractable aluminium over time, with very large increases, 26- and 19-fold in two of the soils. The older sites and only one of the younger soils showed an overall trend towards a reduction in base saturation.

The authors conclude that base cation accumulation in the trees, litter and organic horizons was the main driver of acidification in the near surface layers but that acid deposition "may be contributing to mineral soil acidification below the rooting zone".

Also in North East Scotland, soil profiles originally sampled between 1973 and 1975 were re-sampled in 1997/98 at Roseile, Altyre plus a number of locations on the Glensaugh Experimental Farm (Miller *et al*, 1999). The soils were all acid podzols. The results showed an increase in exchangeable hydrogen, a decrease in exchangeable base cations and in percentage base saturation throughout the profile. The declines in base saturation at Glensaugh were from 14.4 to 3.8% for the H horizon, 5.0 to 1.0 for the Eh and 2.1 to 0.8 for the Bs.

Evidence from UK national surveys

There have been three national soil re-sampling exercises in the UK: the re-sampling of a subset of the National Soil Inventory (NSI) sites by SSLRC; the Representative Soil Series (RSS) by ADAS and the Countryside Survey by CEH. The National Soil Inventory of England and Wales was first carried out between 1978 and 1981 and involved sampling of 5692 points on a 5 km grid. In 1994/95, 902 of the 2547 arable and ley sites were re-sampled and in 1995/96, 768 of the 1803 permanent (managed) grassland sites. A wide range of soil analyses was carried out on the samples. The re-sampling of the arable and ley sites showed an increase in pH which was most marked in the soils with pH >6.5. The permanent grassland soils also showed an increase in pH, mainly in the soils with an initial pH less than 5.5.

The RSS was started in 1969 and is carried out by DEFRA/ADAS (Skinner and Todd, 1998). It involves annual surveys of soil pH, nutrient and organic matter levels on farms in England and Wales. The sampling uses a subset of farms from the Survey of Fertilizer Practice (Chalmers *et al.*, 1990). The methods are described in Skinner *et al* (1992). In the early years of the study

120 farms were sampled each year but the number was increased to 240 in 1980. The scheme was stopped for a year in 1984 and when restarted in 1985 used 180 farms per year, comprising 60 farms sampled 10 and 5 years previously, 60 sampled only 5 years previously and 60 new farms. When farms have been sampled three times they are discarded from the study. On each farm four fields are selected at random for sampling. The results from the sampling show that in the first 25 years there was no significant change in the pH of arable soils but there was a linear decline of the pH of grassland soils, over the period, from a mean of just over 5.7 to 5.4. A more detailed analysis of the data shows a decrease in the proportion of arable soils with a pH below 6.0, from 10% in 1969-73 to 4% in 1990-93. In the grassland soils, the proportion of soils with pH below 6.0 increased from 39% in 1969-73 to 56% in 1990-93.

The Countryside Survey sampled the surface soil at 5 locations in each of 268 1 km sample grid squares distributed throughout Great Britain in 1978. The sample of squares was designed to sample all the main landscape types and the soils sampled therefore represented all the main soil groups in Great Britain and a wide range of land uses. The sampling was repeated in 1998/99. Samples were collected, using a 15 cm corer, from a fixed position within a 200 m^2 vegetation quadrat. The initial samples were analysed for pH and loss on ignition. The 1998/99 samples are being analysed for pH, loss on ignition, trace metals, organic pollutants and biota. A total of *ca* 950 soils were re-sampled in 1998/99. The data analysis is still in progress but the data show both increases and decreases in pH between 1978 and 1998 with an overall trend towards an increase in pH (Figure 5.4). The data are being analysed by soil group and by environmental zone; future analyses will also separate the soils under agricultural and semi-natural habitats. Results to date suggest an increase in mean pH in all major soil groups except pelosols and in all environmental zones (Haines-Young *et al* 2000). The largest increase is seen in the uplands of England and Wales, and the smallest increase in the uplands of Scotland.

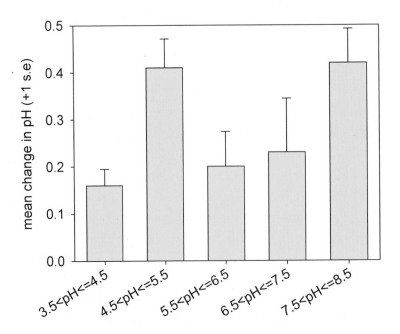

Figure 5.4 Mean change in pH for CS2000 soils from 1978 to 1998/9 by pH interval [soil pH(1978+1998/9)/2], 767 soil samples (0-15 cm depth) from fixed locations across Great Britain.

Evidence from regional correlations with deposition chemistry.

Skiba *et al* (1989) examined the relationship between patterns of peat pH and base saturation at 123 sites with modelled atmospheric deposition. Peats with the highest acidity, pH(CaCl$_2$)<3.0 and the lowest base saturation, <10%, occurred mainly in areas where deposited acidity was greater than 0.8 kg-H$^+$ ha^{-1} y^{-1}. The authors concluded that the correlation provided "..strong evidence for acid deposition having caused further acidification of peats in Scotland over and above natural levels.". They also suggested, on the basis of results from laboratory equilibration studies, that recovery of peat acidity should be evident within a few decades following the reductions in pollutant emissions that were taking place.

White and Cresser (1995 and 1998) examined the chemistry of podzols developed in granitic material, sandstones or quartzites across a pollution gradient in eastern Scotland. They showed strong positive relations between soil pH and rainfall mean pH, and between soil pH and deposition fluxes of strong acid anions. Extractable aluminium increased with acid inputs in the granitic soils but the strongest relationships for the sandstone and quartzite soils were with the flux of strong acid anions.

Evidence from soil solution chemistry

A number of authors have reported that soil solution chemistry is a good indicator of changes in soil status and acidification. On theoretical considerations one would expect changes in soil solution chemistry to be seen before changes in bulk soil chemistry. Soil solution data also provide a clearer link to drainage water chemistry than bulk soil chemistry. The longest dataset of soil solution data for UK upland soils derives from a site in a tributary catchment of the Afon Cyff, itself a headwater tributary of the River Wye, in the Cambrian Mountains of Mid-Wales. A number of shorter datasets are available for individual sites, usually linked to specific manipulative experiments. Monitoring of soil solution chemistry is now a part of the ECN protocols and is carried out at each of the 12 ECN terrestrial sites. However, this sampling programme has only been running for between 3 and 5 years, varying between sites. The following discussion is therefore based on the 10-year dataset from Mid-Wales.

Data are available from soil water samplers in an agriculturally unimproved stagnopodzol soil at Plynlimon covering a period from September 1984 to September 1994. Samples were collected every two weeks up to September 1988 and every 4 weeks thereafter. Samples were analysed for monovalent and divalent base cations, ammonium, sulphate, nitrate, chloride, total dissolved aluminium (Altot), dissolved organic carbon (DOC) and pH. Organic anion concentrations were estimated from DOC and pH using the simple model proposed by Thurman (1985).

Time-series plots for pH and ANC in both the surface organic and mineral horizons reveal a gradual upward trend but with considerable variability in the data between sampling occasions (Figure 5.5). Episodic seasalt deposition, which results in temporary soil water acidification, is responsible for much of the noise in the data. During these events, soil water Na$^+$:Cl$^-$ ratios become very low, departing significantly from the theoretical seawater value, and large depressions in soil water pH and ANC occur, implying ion exchange of Na$^+$ for H$^+$ in the surface horizons, with release of Al in the subsoil.

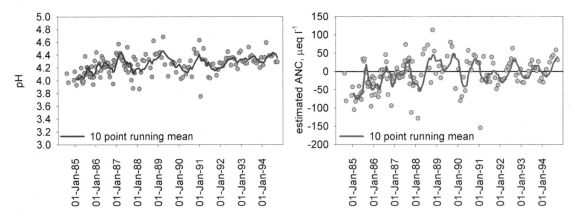

Figure 5.5 Time series of pH and ANC in soil waters collected from the surface organic horizon of a peaty podzol in a subcatchment of the Afon Cyff at Plynlimon in mid-Wales. Points are observed values; solid line represents a 10-point moving average trend line.

In the surface organic horizon, pH variations are buffered by reactions with dissolved organic matter that effectively behave like weak acids. The concentration of organic anions varies seasonally, with largest concentrations in the summer coinciding with the period of greatest DOC production. During the summer, organic anions can contribute up to 50 % of the total anion charge. The cyclical variation in organic and strong acid anion concentrations results in a similar variation in ANC, which becomes positive (exceeding +50 µeq l^{-1} in individual samples) during the summer, but becoming negative (between -100 and -150 µeq l^{-1}) in the winter. Within the Bs horizon, Al concentrations are more than double those in the Oh horizon, with approximately 75% present as inorganic aluminium (Hughes *et al.*, 1990). The resulting effect is that ANC values are predominantly negative and much lower than seen in the Oh horizon. The highest ANC values in the Bs horizon are observed in the summer/early autumn, which coincides with lowest strong acid anion concentrations and largest concentrations of organic anions. Soil water pH variability is low and has a limited role for reactions with dissolved organic matter, so other buffering processes must be operating in this horizon. Most probably these are reactions involving Al hydroxy species either on surfaces or in solution or the weathering of silicate minerals. Increased weathering is indirectly indicated by larger silica concentrations in the Bs horizon, which are more than double those in the Oh horizon. The pool of weatherable minerals also increases with depth in the soil.

5.3.2 Re-Sampling and Monitoring Studies in Other European Countries

Increases in soil acidity over the last 50 years have been reported from studies in a number of other European countries. Thus, Berden *et al* (1987) collated and reviewed 21 published studies from Europe and North America; the bulk of the studies were from Germany but also some from Sweden, Czechoslovakia, Austria and the UK. The studies covered periods of between 15 and 60 years and included a wide variety of soil types but mostly under forest. The great bulk of the reported analyses showed a decline in pH over the period between sampling. For example, 289 out of 325 reported analyses of A horizon samples showed a decline in pH, most of less than 1 pH unit. Those studies which considered base cations and base saturation also reported reductions in these parameters.

One of the largest national monitoring programmes in Europe is the Swedish National Survey of Forest Soils and Vegetation (Wilander & Lundlin, 1999). This involves 23,500 plots in which analyses of the pH of the humus layer are carried out on *ca* 20,000 samples and of the B horizon from 2,000 sites. More detailed soil analyses, including exchangeable cations, are carried out on between 500 and 1,000 samples from each horizon. The survey was started in 1963 with the two latest samplings taking place in 1983-87 and 1993-2002. The median humus horizon pH was 3.95 in the 1980's and 3.76 in the 1990's, and for the upper part of the B horizon 4.74 in the 1980's and 4.54 in the 1990's. A study of the subset of sites with trees of the same age, thus removing the effect of tree growth, showed reductions in the median pH of 0.13 units for the humus horizon and 0.21 for the B horizon. Re-evaluation of the results and comparison of the analytical methods used in the 1980's and '90's suggests that the pH values determined in the 1980's were 'roughly 0.1 pH unit too high'. After allowing for this, it is suggested that the decline in mean pH for both the humus and B horizons was *ca* 0.1 units between the 1980's and 1990's (Wilander & Lundlin, 1999). The study also showed reductions in extractable Mg^{2+} and K^+, and an increase in extractable Al in the B horizon over the ten year period; calcium showed regional variations with increases in some areas and decreases in others.

Studies which have included soils with a range of pHs at the time of the initial sampling have commonly reported that the magnitude of the reduction in pH declined with initial pH. Thus, Grenzius *et al* (1984), Riebling and Schaefer (1984) and Glatzel *et al* (1985), working in Austria and Germany, reported the largest declines in pH in soils with higher initial pH. Falkengren-Grerup (1986), working in Southern Sweden and Dahl (1988) in southern Norway found increasing or unchanged pHs in the most acid soils. Bjornstad (1991) re-sampled, in 1987, surface horizons of soils from 21 marked plots in Sogne, Southern Norway. He reported declines in pH, of up to 1.3 units, from the less acid soils (initial pH >4.0) but an increase in more acid soils of up to 0.2 units. The base saturation had decreased in 80% of the plots.

In a study in Southern Sweden Lundstrom *et al* (1998) carried out a forest status survey that included both extractable soil chemistry and soil solution chemistry. The authors concluded that the main pattern of variation in soil variables could be related to differences in acidic deposition. The authors also concluded that soil solution composition, particularly total Al, inorganic Al and pH in the B horizon, were the best indicators for measuring anthropogenic soil acidification. A study of soil acidification in Southern Switzerland between 1987 and 1997 (Blaser *et al.*, 1999) was also based on soil solution chemistry. Significant long-term trends were detected in addition to short-term seasonal variations. Thus, base cation concentrations declined in all horizons while Al decreased in the upper horizons but increased in the lower horizons. The BC:Al ratio declined in all mineral horizons. The latter two studies show the value of soil solution based studies rather than those based on bulk soil analyses. The Swiss study was also interesting in that the acidification it reported was during a period when acidic deposition was decreasing. The authors ascribe the detected acidification to "..a memory effect of the high acid loads between 1965 and 1985."

5.3.3 Interpreting Soil Acidification Trends: The Role of Confounding Factors

In terms of the role of acid deposition, the interpretation of much long-term soil acidification data is confounded by factors such as vegetation succession, management and other environmental changes. These can alter the rates of key processes such as base cation accumulation in biomass and the generation of organic acids as a product of forest floor decomposition. Several authors have commented on the relationship between acid deposition and these other possible causes of acidification, based either on the evidence of the measured soil chemistry or a consideration of the underlying concepts and theories of soil acidification.

There have been many studies of soil acidification by forests or individual trees (e.g. Hornung, 1985) which show that the direction and the magnitude of the changes in soil chemistry vary with the initial soil status and the tree species. In general, fast growing conifers increase the acidity of near surface layers compared with hardwoods (*cf.* Ovington, 1953; Alban, 1982) and there have been many reports of acidification following replacement of hardwoods with conifer plantations (Miles, 1978).

Hallbacken and Tamm (1986) used regression approaches to explore the causes of acidification over a 50 to 60 year period under spruce stands. In the near surface horizons there was an inverse relationship between stand age and pH in the data from the initial and repeat samplings, suggesting the importance of base cation accumulation in biomass. There was no relationship for deeper horizons. More recent sampling showed a further decrease in pH at all soil depths but with no relationship to stand age. The authors concluded that in the recent trends especially, acidification below the rooting zone was probably driven by acidic inputs. Similarly, Falkengren-Grerup (1987) in an extensive study of forest soils in southern Sweden, concluded that there was no relationship between the measured soil acidification, in both the surface and mineral soils, and biomass changes. Ulrich (1989) also argued, from theoretical grounds as well as field evidence, that ecosystem internal processes can be excluded as a cause of the recent acidification of subsoils. An evaluation of the data from the Swedish National Survey of Forest Soils and Vegetation for the 1980's and 1990's has tried to separate out the effect of forest growth. It was concluded that 'forest growth combined with air pollution has caused acidification corresponding to a decrease in pH of around 0.1 units over a 10 year period and that the acidifying effect of growth is responsible for one-tenth of the pH decrease observed' (Wilander and Lundlin, 1999).

Chronosequence studies on glacial moraines show rapid acidification in natural successions once vegetation colonizes and stabilises, particularly once trees become established. Thus, in their classic study Crocker and Major (1955) showed a decline in pH of 3.0 units in 48 years under alder. Rapid changes in pH can also result from species changes in non-forest vegetation. Thus, Grubb *et al* (1969) reported acidification following invasion of chalk grassland by Calluna.

In conclusion, in almost all the studies of recently planted stands, the impact of the trees is usually restricted to the top 20 to 25 cm, as suggested by Hallbacken and Tamm (1986). Thus while acid deposition may contribute to acidification in these near surface horizons, the main processes, particularly in rapidly growing forests, are likely to be base cation uptake and accumulation in the trees and forest floor materials. Below the main rooting zone acidic deposition is probably the main driver of soil acidification.

5.3.4 Synthesis of the UK Data

The published data from 10 European countries for forests or non-forest semi-natural habitats provide a general consensus that acidic deposition was a significant factor in the widespread acidification of soils detected in the second half of the twentieth century. The results from the UK regional studies covering periods between the 1950s and the 1990s are consistent with this general European pattern. In the studies by Billett *et al* (1988) and Farmer (1995), forest growth and accumulation of base cations in biomass was probably important, although even here these processes cannot fully explain the detected trends. The four other UK regional studies considered non-forest sites at which there was no significant change in vegetation and where uptake and accumulation of base cations in biomass was unlikely to be a significant factor.

In contrast to the European and UK regional data, results from the recent national studies, covering periods between the 1970s and mid to late 1990s show an increase in pH across a range of soil types. These studies, based on the NSI and the RSS, only considered soils under arable crops or intensively managed grassland and the increase in pH could, therefore, be due primarily to changes in management regimes. Garwood *et al* (1999), discussing the RSS, conclude that better targeted liming is a factor in the increase in the pH of arable soils and perhaps, on calcareous soils, deeper ploughing has introduced more readily weatherable base rich material into the surface soil; however, they also mention the possible contribution of reductions in acidic deposition. In the case of the grassland soils, the same authors report that the main increase in acidity was between 1969 and 1980, with the greatest increases recorded in Wales and the North. The ADAS lime model suggests that over this period when acidic inputs were at their maximum, lime loss was greater than annual lime applications. Although further analysis is needed it would seem that management factors were the dominant control of soil acidity in the arable and managed grass areas but with possible interactions with reductions in acidic deposition.

The CS2000 study included soils under semi-natural habitats as well as under arable and managed grassland. Elements of these data have, therefore, more in common with the regional studies discussed above. The increases in peat pH detected by CS2000 are unlikely to reflect land management so that a reduction in acidic deposition is a likely cause. It is interesting that the largest increases in peat pH are shown in the samples from the Pennines and the smallest from the Scottish Highlands. More detailed analysis of the full data set is required before we can make meaningful comparisons with the regional studies.

Acidic inputs peaked in the early 1980s and soil acidification would have been expected on sensitive soils between the 1950s and the 1980s or later, because of lag effects. This is consistent with the available field evidence. The recovery in pH of soils under semi-natural habitats found in the CS2000 study is unexpected; conceptually, a slower response would be expected. The difference in trends between the soils with initially lower pH and those with higher pH also needs further investigation. The effects of management on the more intensively managed soils are an important confounding factor in the NSI and RSS data sets. Further, more detailed analysis of these data is needed and a re-sampling of the upland soils in the NSI is required before firm conclusions can be drawn.

5.3.5 Nitrogen

There have been comparatively few studies that have monitored soil nitrogen contents over time. It is also very difficult to detect changes in soil N as one is generally trying to detect a small change in a large pool. Data on nitrogen contents are usually presented as percent N by volume, more rarely as N content per unit area or mass.

In the UK, the regional studies carried out by Billett *et al.* (1988 and 1990b) and by Farmer (1995) are probably the only re-sampling exercises on non-agricultural soils which considered N. The RSS considered N in agricultural soils.

In his study in Wytham Wood, Farmer (1995) reports an increase in percent N between 1974 and 1991 which is significant in both ancient (a mean increase from 0.24 to 0.36%) and recent woodland soils (a mean increase from 0.28 to 0.42%) and at all sampled soil depths. N deposition is likely to be high as the woodland is surrounded by agricultural land, a network of major roads and is close to the city of Oxford.

Billett *et al* (1990b) did not find an increase in soil N concentrations but an accumulation of N, linked to accumulation of soil carbon; a rate of N accumulation of 21.2 kg ha^{-1} y^{-1} was calculated. The authors also calculated that organic horizon thickness had increased by over 200% at the sites which had become more acid and postulated that this could be due to high annual litter inputs or a decrease in the rates of decomposition over time as soil pH declined.

Studies of soils close to an agricultural point source in North Yorkshire showed large differences in the exchangeable ammonium between woodlands upwind and downwind. There were also differences in soil acidity, exchangeable potassium and extractable nitrate (Figure 5.6, P Ineson *pers comm*).

			UPWIND Middle Lodge Wood	DOWNWIND The Willows
Needle chemistry		%K	0.82 ± 0.10	0.48 ± 0.06**
		%Mg	0.12 ± 0.02	0.15 ± 0.01
		%N	1.61 ± 0.06	1.63 ± 0.06
Root chemistry		%N	1.4 ± 0.3	1.8 ± 0.4*
Soil chemistry				
pH		Ah	5.1	4.0**
		AB	5.3	4.8
Exchangeables	NH$_4$	Ah	0.33 ± 0.13	5.35 ± 0.98**
(mg/100g)		AB	0.05 ± 0.02	0.16 ± 0.04
	K	Ah	6.68 ± 0.73	5.53 ± 1.02
		AB	0.56 ± 0.06	1.53 ± 0.25*
Extractable	NO$_3$	Ah	1.14 ± 0.25	5.03 ± 0.70**
		AB	0.80 ± 0.13	2.63 ± 0.25**

Figure 5.6 Comparison of soil chemistry upwind and downwind of a point source for ammonia emissions from an intensive pig farm, * indicate statistical significance, * = P < 0.05, ** = P < 0.01 (P Ineson *pers comm*).

Chronosequence studies

In the absence of long-term data, an alternative approach is to use a chronosequence of sites with common characteristics but at different stages of development, for example analysis of profiles of the same soil type but with different ages. This effectively substitutes space for time.

In a study of 20 forest and 5 moorland sites throughout Wales, Stevens *et al.*, (1994) were able to examine the interacting effects of forest age and nitrogen deposition. The study showed that soil water nitrate leaching fluxes exceeded nitrate inputs (estimated from the throughfall nitrate flux) at sites more than thirty years old (Figure 5.7, Emmett *et al.*, 1995). The onset of nitrate leaching was related to a decrease in biological sinks for nitrogen in combination with increased scavenging of nitrogen pollutants by the taller trees. Beyond the breakthrough point at which stands become net sources of nitrate (Figure 5.7), nitrate leaching was highly variable and linked to the fate of the incoming ammonium and soil type. In freely draining soils with organic horizons containing more than 1.7%-N, ammonium inputs stimulated nitrate production. Nitrate production did not increase in poorly drained soils where denitrification rates probably increased. Thus, two types of forest could be distinguished, those exhibiting no ability to retain incoming nitrate, but retaining all incoming ammonium, and those more nitrogen-rich sites, which responded to increased ammonium inputs with immediate increases in nitrate production and nitrate leaching losses.

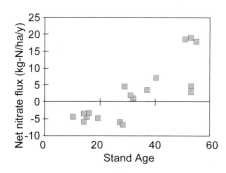

Figure 5.7 The net soil water nitrate flux (inputs-outputs) below the rooting zone of 20 Sitka spruce plantations in Wales. (Source: Emmett *et al.*, 1995).

5.4 Evidence of Change: Manipulation Experiments

For more than a decade, ecosystem scale manipulation experiments have been undertaken to investigate the chemical and biological responses of soils and freshwaters to changes in acidic atmospheric inputs (Jenkins *et al.*, 1995). These experiments have provided an opportunity to test our scientific understanding of the processes involved in acidification and recovery, thereby informing the development of predictive models whilst at the same time providing a baseline against which to assess model predictions in the absence of long-term data (Sullivan *et al.*, 1994). The experiments fall broadly into two categories a) those in which sulphate, nitrate and ammonium are added either singly or in combination to ambient rainfall to simulate increasing deposition inputs and b) those in which acid atmospheric inputs are removed from ambient rainfall usually via a roof structure to simulate the effects of reduced deposition. Both approaches are subject to criticisms that they introduce artefacts, for example by changing the micro-climate beneath a roof, are short-term compared with the anticipated rates of ecosystem response and are often un-replicated and site specific by virtue of size and cost. Notwithstanding this, they are essentially the only way to investigate ecosystem responses at anything like a meaningful spatial scale under realistic 'field' conditions. Most experiments are carefully designed to minimise artefacts with the careful use of control treatments and the importance of long-term experiments with realistic 'chronic' treatments has been recognised (Gundersen *et al.*, 1998a). New statistical techniques such as Randomised Intervention Analysis (Uddameri *et al.*, 1995) have been developed which provide a rigorous comparison between pre- and post-treatment results in non-replicated experiments such as catchment studies, provided there is a sufficiently long run of pre-treatment data. Extrapolation from site-specific studies has been achieved using multi-site networks across environmental gradients (e.g. NITREX and EXMAN; Wright and Rasmussen 1998) or by combining manipulation experiments with lower intensity surveys (e.g. Emmett *et al.*, 1995). The experimental results have provided many valuable insights into processes, potential interactions and feedbacks, which have led to improved understanding and enhanced predictive capabilities (Rasmussen and Wright, 1998).

5.4.1 Sulphur

In the early years of acid deposition research during the 1970s and early 1980s many experiments investigated the effects of acid deposition on soils using additions of sulphuric acid, ammonium sulphate or mixtures of sulphuric and nitric acids. These experiments were valuable for elucidating processes. The studies most commonly involved plot and lysimeter scale manipulations. Other studies used transfer of soil cores across deposition gradients. Indeed, one of the earliest relevant UK studies used core transplants to examine the impacts of acid inputs from a point source. This showed a reduction in pH from 4.9 to 3.9 over a 30 month period at a site 0.5 km downwind of a coking plant (Killham and Wainwright, 1984). Studies from Norway provide examples of plot and lysimeter scale studies (Abrahamsen *et al.*, 1989). A series of plot scale studies were established in the mid-1970's under Norway spruce, Scots pine, Lodgepole pine and silver birch (Abrahamsen *et al.*, 1976; Abrahamsen *et al.*, 1994), together with a series of field based soil monolith studies (Teigen *et al.*, 1976). The plots or lysimeters were irrigated with 'rainfall' ranging from ambient down to pH 2 for periods of up to 6 years. The results showed increased leaching of base cations and/or aluminium in response to the simulated acidic deposition but with the magnitude of the impact varying with soil type and the acid loading. Thus, in a podzolic soil leaching was in the following order Al>Na>Ca>Mg>K>H (Abrahamsen and Stuanes, 1986) but in a more fertile brown soil leaching was in the order Ca>Mg>Na=K>H>Al (Abrahamsen, 1985). The amount of the cations leached increased with acidity of the applied 'rainfall' but the order of leaching remained unchanged as the 'rainfall' pH was decreased from 6 to 3. The series of studies also showed that added sulphate was more effective in leaching the cations than nitrate, as most of the added nitrogen was retained in the system.

The acidic inputs also resulted in a reduction in soil pH plus a decrease in the stock of exchangeable base cations and in base saturation in the podzolic soil (Figure 5.8); the impact on soil pH was larger than that on base saturation. Again, the magnitude of the impacts varied with the acidity and volume of the added 'rainfall'; however, the impacts on base saturation were only significant when the added 'rainfall' had a pH less than 3 (Abrahamsen & Stuanes, 1986). Other studies have also reported that significant changes in leachates and soils were only found at the most acid of a series of treatments, for example Moore (1987) used additions of pH 5.5, 4 and 3 to a spruce lichen woodland in Canada and found increased leaching of base cations only with the pH 3 treatment.

In a UK study, Brown (1987) treated monolith lysimeters of a podzolic soil with simulated acidic rain adjusted to pH 3 with sulphuric acid or distilled water for 4.8 years. The sulphuric acid treatment gave an enormous addition, equivalent to 240 kg-S ha^{-1} y^{-1}, illustrating one of the difficulties of using a short-term experiment to simulate long-term changes. The treatment resulted in acidification of the soil to a depth of 80 cm with a reduction in pH of 0.8 units in the litter horizon and 0.2 units to a depth of 80 cm. Enhanced leaching of base cations from the litter and A horizon in the acid treatment resulted in a decrease of extractable Ca^{2+}, Mg$^+$ and Mn reserves by 70 to 80%. Below the A horizon, dissolution of Al was the main neutralisation process. There was an increase in both exchangeable Al and in Al leaching from lower horizons.

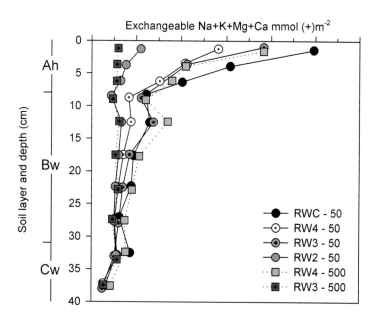

Figure 5.8 Exchangeable base cations in lysimeters with a Gleyic to Dystric Cambisol exposed to a total of 1250 mm (circles) or 12500 mm (squares) of rainwater of different acidities over a period of five years. RWC-50 means that rainwater control at 50 mm month^{-1} (control = pH 4.5) was added; RWC-500 means that rainwater pH 4 at 500 mm month^{-1} was added etc. (after Abrahamsen and Stuanes, 1986).

A plot scale study in the UK has explored the effects of acid mists applied to the canopy of 19 year old Sitka spruce growing on a brown earth in southern Scotland (Carreira *et al.*, 1997). Mixtures of sulphuric acid and ammonium nitrate at pH 2.5 were sprayed onto the trees twice per week for all or part of the growing season for four years. The treatment caused decreases in soil pH of the 0 to 5 cm soil layer of between 0.3 and 1.0 unit (from 5.09). The exchangeable content of all base cations also decreased in this layer but extractable Al, Fe and Mn increased; the increase in Al was particularly dramatic, from 0.65 meq 100g^{-1} to 4.23. Base saturation decreased from 89.9% to 30%. An added point of interest in the study was a detailed examination of P chemistry. There was a marked reduction in readily extractable and available P following the acid treatment; this mirrored an increase in P sorption capacity. The changes in nutrient availability were linked to a reduction in growth of the acid treated trees.

Plot and lysimeter scale manipulations have also been used to identify key processes controlling the response of soils to acidic deposition. Thus, a number of studies have shown the importance of sulphate adsorption. For example, David and Mitchell (1987) applied simulated acid rain to forest soil plots in the Adirondack Mountains of New York State and found that 70 and 99% respectively of the added ^{35}S was retained in their two treated plots. Lee and Weber (1982) found that sulphate adsorption prevented any change in base cation concentrations in leachates or soil for the first six months of additions of simulated acid rain treatments at pH 4.0, 3.5 or 3.0. After six months sulphate concentrations increased at 20 cm depth in the pH 3.0 treatment, and after 10 months and one year in the pH 3.5 and 4.0 treatments respectively. The pH of the solutions from 20 cm depth decreased and calcium and magnesium concentrations increased simultaneously with the increase in sulphate. No results of the acid additions were found at 1 m depth after 2.5 years of treatments. The study by Brown (1987) discussed above showed reversible sulphate adsorption in the lower horizons of the acid treated podzol.

The Norwegian plot studies referred to above (Abrahamsen et al., 1989 and 1994) are particularly interesting as they have been used to assess the recovery of the soils following the ending of the acid additions, in 1978, for some plots and in 1983, for others. The soils were sampled in 1978, 1981, 1984, 1988 and 1996 (Stuanes et al., 2000). In the plots where treatment ceased in 1978, the differences in pH induced by the acid treatments had disappeared by 1996 in all horizons and most horizons showed an increase in pH between 1988 and 1996. However, the forest floor pH had decreased between 1988 and 1996; the authors suggest this was probably due to forest growth. The trends in base saturation followed those for pH. In the studies where treatments ceased in 1981 or 1983, there were still significant differences in soil pH and base saturation between the former treatments. However, plots in the study under relatively young Scots pine showed an increase in forest floor pH between 1988 and 1996, which the authors ascribe to the impact of nutrient uptake and cycling. In contrast an old (>120 years) Scots pine stand showed no recovery and the authors suggest this is because current leaching is close to the weathering rate and the uptake of base cations by the old growth trees is small. These studies indicate the complex considerations that must be taken into account when assessing potential recovery.

Larger scale studies have involved manipulations of mini-catchments or large roofed plots. For example at Sogndal, an area of low ambient acid inputs in Norway, experimental acidification of two small catchments with loadings of approximately 100 meq-H^+ m^{-2} y^{-1} above ambient over 4 years showed only a very small increase in weathering rate (Frogner, 1990). The main contributor to the increased base cation flux in runoff was thought to be the exchangeable base cation pool although no statistically significant change in pool size could be identified from field sampling. Following the implementation of sulphur emission protocols, the experimental emphasis changed to reducing inputs to simulate recovery.

The soil acidification response to current and future planned reductions in sulphur deposition will depend on the magnitude and timing of sulphate desorption from the soil. The Solling roof experiment, where inputs of reduced and oxidised N, sulphur and hydrogen ions have been reduced respectively by 67%, 56% & 74% of ambient, provides experimental evidence for the effects of sulphate desorption on soil water chemistry (Bredemeier et al., 1998a). Within 1-2 years following the start of treatment and at a depth of 10 cm in the soil, sulphate concentrations decreased from an average of 8 mg-S l^{-1} to 2.5 mg-S l^{-1}, while Al concentrations decreased in parallel from 3.5 mg l^{-1} to about 2 mg l^{-1}. At 70 cm, a slower response in sulphate and Al concentrations was observed which was thought to be due to release of stored Al-S compounds (Alewell *et al.*, 1997). Drainage water nitrate concentrations at 70 cm decreased from 4 mg-N l^{-1} to less than 1 mg-N l^{-1} (equivalent to inputs). A seasonal pattern was established at 10 cm depth post treatment with winter peaks reaching the concentrations of inputs, and zero in summer.

In flux terms, the reduction in inputs turned the nitrate budget for the soil profile from surplus (1.2 keq ha^{-1}) to deficit (-0.8 keq ha^{-1}) within 1-2 years (Xu *et al.*, 1998). For sulphate and aluminium, the flux response was more complex with evidence of sulphate desorption from the increasingly large surpluses reflecting losses of stored sulphur from the mineral horizons (Alewell and Matzner, 1993; Table 5.3). Aluminium output fluxes remained large reflecting the loss of sulphate. From 1992 to 1994, the proton budget for the clean rain roof plot showed a deficit of 0.5 kg-H^+ ha^{-1} compared to a surplus of 2.4 and 2.2 kg-H^+ ha^{-1} in the ambient control and control roof plots.

Table 5.3 Sulphate and aluminium fluxes for the Solling roof experiment (from Xu *et al.*, 1998).

SO_4^{2-} (kg ha^{-1} y^{-1})			
Year	Input	Output	Budget
1991 pre-treatment	31.8	29.3	+2.5
1992	14.9	46.9	-32.0
1993	18.6	55.0	-6.4
1994	22.2	67.4	-45.2

Al (kg ha^{-1} y^{-1})			
Year	Input	Output	Budget
1991	0.7	23.8	-23.1
1992	0.1	35.8	-35.7
1993	0.2	30.4	-30.2
1994	0.2	35.1	-34.9

At Gårdsjön in southwest Sweden a roof placed beneath the tree canopy over a 0.63 ha mini-catchment has been used to reduce sulphate in incoming rain from 128 to 25 meq m^{-2} y^{-1} corresponding to a major reduction in acid rain. At the same time, nitrate was reduced from 63 to 4 meq m^{-2} y^{-1} and ammonium was removed entirely (formerly 31 meq m^{-2} y^{-1}). Soil solution sulphate concentrations responded within 4 to 6 months of treatment in the O and E horizons, with a 75% and 63% decrease respectively compared to average pre-treatment conditions. After the initial decrease, concentrations remained relatively constant at *ca* 200-250 µeq l^{-1} (Giesler *et al.*, 1998 and Figure 5.9). However, these concentrations are still larger than those in the incoming treated 'rain' solution. Even allowing for the effects of evaporative concentration in the soil waters, this may indicate that organic sulphur is being mineralised and released into solution. In the B horizon, soil water sulphate concentrations declined more slowly due to desorption from the large pool of sorbed sulphate. Indeed, sulphur isotope studies concluded that sorption processes in the B horizon were the main sulphur flux mechanism in the catchment (Torssander and Mörth, 1998). The reductions in sulphate were accompanied by decreases in Al and divalent base cation concentrations although part of the latter is probably due to a reduction in seasalt deposition at the site during the treatment period.

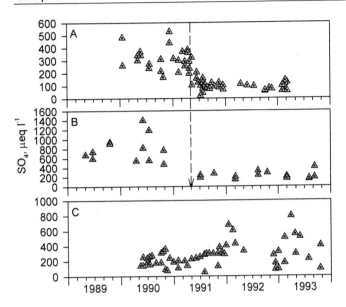

Figure 5.9 Sulphate concentrations in the soil solution from O and E horizons (0.05 – 0.10 m depth) sampled by a) lysimeter and b) by centrifugation from beneath the acid exclusion roof at Gårdsjön in Sweden and c) from the reference site receiving ambient inputs. (after Giesler *et al.*, 1998).

The Gårdsjön experiment also provides an assessment of the changes in soil chemistry following a reduction in acid inputs. Samples were collected prior to establishing the roof in 1990 and again after five years of acid exclusion. Following the reduction in inputs to the experimental catchment, there was an 87% increase in extractable carbon but significant decreases in soil pH and base saturation (Moldan, 1999). In the Bs horizon, extractable sulphur declined, but in the surface organic layers there was a significant increase in extractable S, possibly associated with the increase in carbon content. This supports the hypothesis of an increase in mineralisation rates following treatment. The work also highlighted an experimental artefact, in that part of the change in soil Ca^{2+} status could be attributed to the removal in the artificial rainfall of that part of the Ca^{2+} cycled as canopy leaching in throughfall and stemflow. Interestingly, in the control catchment where ambient sulphur inputs have also been declining, a decrease in extractable sulphur in the B horizon is the only significant effect on soil chemistry.

The Gårdsjön experiment provides unequivocal evidence that soil solution and drainage water recovery can proceed rapidly before soil recovery (signified by an increase in soil base saturation) and this confirms model predictions. However, there can be considerable spatial variability in the response in surface water and soil chemistry, for example an 18% reduction in the soil extractable sulphur pool in the control catchment was accompanied by only a 3% change in S outputs over four years, whereas a much larger (32%) decline in outputs was observed in the manipulated catchment for only a 10% change in the extractable sulphate pool. Thus input-output budgets may not always truly reflect the change in soil element pools.

There was a similar result at the RAIN experiment at Risdalsheia in Norway, where a roof was established over an entire 860 m^2 mini-catchment which received rain cleaned of acid pollutants (Wright *et al.*, 1988a). Input-output budgets for the clean roof catchment over an eight-year period showed net losses for sulphate (-119 meq m^{-2}), with outputs (300 meq m^{-2}) nearly twice as large as the inputs in the 'clean rain' (181 meq m^{-2}). However, there was no change in the soil pool of water-extractable sulphate (Figure 5.10a) even though the net loss of sulphate over the eight-year period was larger than the combined pool of water-extractable plus adsorbed sulphate (112 meq m^{-2}). This was taken as an indication that the pool of readily available sulphate was being replenished from the 30-fold larger pool of organically bound sulphur in the soil (Wright *et al.*, 1993). However, with the benefit of hindsight after a further three years of treatment it became clear that a new steady-state condition had been reached after seven years of treatment after which there was no net release of sulphate (Beier *et al.*, 1995). There was no significant change in the exchangeable base cation pool of the soils (Figure 5.10b) from the beginning of the experiment. This was attributed to noise in the data resulting from both year-to-year variability and a high degree of spatial heterogeneity.

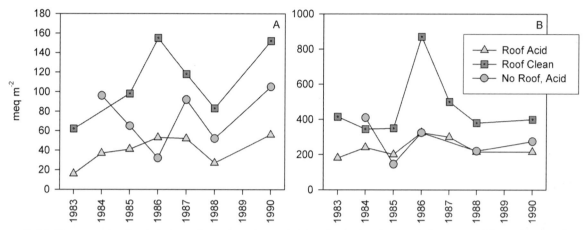

Figure 5.10 Changes in the total pool of a) water soluble plus adsorbed sulphate and b) exchangeable base cations in the soils of the Risdalsheia catchment in Norway over the period 1983 to 1990. No measurements were made in 1989. (after Wright *et al.*, 1993).

The rate of sulphur response can also be very variable between sites due to differences in soils, water-extractable sulphate pool and to a lesser extent, hydrology (Beier *et al.*, 1995). At Risdalsheia, where thin, organic soils with low sulphur content overly bedrock resulting in high runoff rates, a steady state was established in about 7 years as the soil pool of available sulphate was depleted. At Klosterhede, another sub-canopy roof experiment on sandy forest soils in Denmark, the sulphate pool is twice the size of that at Risdalsheia and runoff rates are slower. Sulphate release is slower, and the MAGIC model predicts steady-state conditions after 10-12 years of treatment (Beier *et al.*, 1995). The soils are podzolic with a well developed B horizon at Gårdsjön resulting in an available sulphate pool which is three times that at the Risdalsheia. The MAGIC model predicts that 15 years of treatment are required before sulphate outputs are at steady-state with inputs.

5.4.2 Nitrogen

The response of soil nitrogen processes to changes in atmospheric inputs is one of the key issues in assessing the future responses of acidified systems. This issue provided the impetus to the EU funded NITREX experiment in which nitrogen inputs to managed forest ecosystems were manipulated to simulate both increased (by low dose, chronic N additions) and reduced (by sub-canopy roofs) atmospheric inputs at a range of sites across a European nitrogen pollution gradient (Wright & Breemen, 1995). The results have shown that significant decreases in soil drainage water nitrate concentrations can be rapidly obtained by reducing N inputs to N saturated sites by 60 - 95% (Bredemeier *et al.*, 1998b). At one site, nitrate leaching continued in excess of inputs under the roof (Emmett *et al.*, 1998a), indicating that high rates of N mineralisation were continuing despite reduced inputs. This has the effect of lowering the N status of the site, although recovery of the drainage waters may be slow.

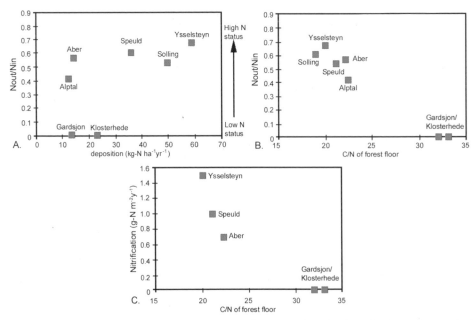

Figure 5.11 The relationship between the proportion of nitrate leached and A) ambient N deposition, B) the forest floor C/N ratio. C) The relationship between forest floor C/N ratio and annual forest floor nitrification rates. (Source: Emmett *et al.*, 1998b).

Strong relationships between N deposition fluxes and nitrification across a United States transect (McNulty *et al.*, 1996) and across a N deposition gradient in Sweden (Diekmann *et al.*, 1999) suggests there is a link between N inputs and accelerated nitrification rates if forests have experienced elevated N inputs over a prolonged period. Analysis of European data indicates that nitrification is more closely related to the C/N ratio of the forest floor material than N inputs (Gundersen *et al.*, 1998a) and also illustrates the importance of competition from other soil sinks even in the presence of large N inputs in the short term. The response to increased atmospheric nitrogen inputs thus depends on the N status of the site, which is a key factor determining its nitrogen retention capacity (Emmett *et al.*, 1998a). At N saturated sites (those where N inputs exceed biotic requirements), increasing N inputs resulted in large and rapid increases in N leaching (Figure 5.11a). At sites with a lower N status, the response to increased inputs was much smaller and delayed. Site N status is determined by site characteristics, deposition and management history and one of the most useful indices combining these factors is the forest floor C/N ratio (Gundersen *et al.*, 1998a). This ratio is closely related to nitrate leaching (Figure 5.11b) because it is a major control on soil nitrification rates; the nitrification rate increases as the C/N declines (Figure 5.11c) and thus the forest floor N retention efficiency also declines. Using ^{15}N, the NITREX study confirmed these observations (Tietma *et al.*, 1998), showing that the increase in nitrate leaching was a result of increased gross nitrification rates (Tietma, 1998), rather than a reduction in nitrate immobilisation by soil microbes as proposed by Stark and Hart (1997). If it is assumed that the initial primary source of nitrate leaching is atmospheric nitrate deposition (Durka *et al.*, 1994), such that output can be expressed as a proportion of inputs, then a simple relationship with forest floor C/N ratio can be plotted (Figure 5.12). Above a C/N of 24, nitrate leaching is low and accounts for less than 10% of nitrate inputs. Below 24, nitrate leaching increases and represents a larger proportion of nitrate inputs until at low ratios, nitrate outputs exceed nitrate inputs indicating that nitrification is active and/or that the sinks for deposited and internally generated nitrate have been reduced (Emmett *et al.*, 1998a). Several studies in a variety of different forest ecosystems have all observed a stimulation of nitrification rates when the N content of forest floor material increases above 1.4%-N (Wilson and Emmett, 1998) or at a C/N ratio less than 27 (Kriebitzsch, 1978).

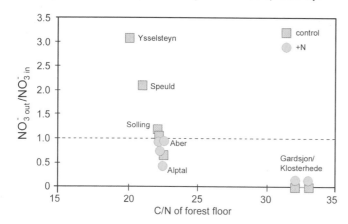

Figure 5.12 Nitrate leaching as a proportion of nitrate inputs in ambient and nitrogen addition plots (+N) relative to forest floor C/N ratio for the NITREX experimental sites. (Source: Emmett *et al.*, 1998b).

The timescale of change in C/N ratio in response to N deposition is crucial to predicting future nitrate leaching and acidification of forest ecosystems. Soil processes are often slow to change in manipulation experiments (Gundersen *et al.*, 1998a). One factor slowing the response of N transformations to chronic N additions may be the slow change in the quality of soil organic matter and the associated biotic community. Nitrogen can be retained either by direct complexation into organic matter or through cycling and accumulation of N-rich root and needle litter. Indeed, ^{15}N studies show that between 11 and 56% of incoming N is retained in the forest floor by either biotic or abiotic processes (Tietema, 1998 and Tietema *et al.*, 1998). Berg and Matzner (1997) have proposed that N storage will increase with N availability because of lower decomposition rates through the inhibitory effect of N on lignolytic enzyme production. However, this does not accord with the high mineralisation rates and small N pools observed at the high N status NITREX sites and more work is required to identify the balance between these opposing N processes.

The CORE project used a complimentary approach to NITREX by using soil core transplants to investigate the impacts of ammonium sulphate at six European forest sites with contrasting soils and pollution climate (Carnol *et al.*, 1997). At each site soil cores from all six sites were installed in the field. Cores received either ambient throughfall or were roofed and irrigated with ammonium sulphate at 75 kg-N ha^{-1} y^{-1}. Each treatment also had rooted and non-rooted sets of cores. The acidification responses of the soils to the ammonium sulphate additions were primarily related to soil pH, texture and the ability of the soils to nitrify the added ammonium. Two less acid, clay/clay loam soils showed almost total retention of the added ammonium whilst in the acid sandy soils almost 75% of the added ammonium was leached as nitrate. In those soils showing an increase in nitrate leaching in response to ammonium additions, Al was the dominant matching cation in the low base saturation, acidic soils. The presence of live roots significantly reduced nitrate, and linked cation leaching. The results underlined the need to allow for differences in N storage capacity and nitrification potential when assessing likely impacts of ammonium inputs on soils.

Currently, much of our understanding of the soil response to changing atmospheric N inputs is based on the results of studies on forest systems, such as NITREX and CORE. Although a large number of ecosystem scale N manipulation experiments have been performed in non-forest ecosystems (Green *et al.*, 1999), which are considered further in Chapter 7, relatively few of these have used chronic low dose additions to simulate increased atmospheric deposition. Rather, the majority of studies have used a single or perhaps two fertiliser applications in a year, often with very large doses, which is not considered appropriate for simulating the chronic effects of atmospheric nitrogen deposition (Johnson, 1992). Many of the experiments have been relatively short term (<5 years) with the main emphasis on the investigation of botanical and plant physiological responses with little information on soil water chemistry (Green *et al.*, 1999). Many studies have been undertaken on calcareous grasslands where soil acidification is not considered to be a problem and no N reduction experiments have been reported (Green *et al.*, 1999).

Notwithstanding these limitations a number of relevant experiments have been undertaken on a range of acidic and acid sensitive ecosystems both in the UK and abroad (Fisk and Schmidt, 1996; Yesmin *et al.*, 1996; Lee and Caporn, 1998; Kristensen and McCarty, 1999). At Pwllpeiran in mid-Wales which is located on acid grassland developed on acid peaty gley soils, leaching losses of nitrate from the surface organic horizons have increased, irrespective of grazing pressure, in response to sodium nitrate (20 kg-N ha^{-1} y^{-1}) but not to ammonium additions (10 and 20 kg-N ha^{-1} y^{-1}; Gordon *et al.*, 2001a). This indicates a greater retention efficiency for ammonium which is consistent with results from the NITREX study at Aber forest (Emmett *et al.*, 1998b). However, there is no measurable increase in any form of N in the mineral horizons which indicates that they are a nitrogen sink, possibly by adsorption of ammonium and/or denitrification. However, it is possible that lateral flow through the mineral horizons on this sloping site is diluting the signal. Of interest at Pwllpeiran is the net export of total dissolved N from the control plots, which represents 30-50% of the inputs. This unexpectedly low retention rate may be due to the short growing season, large rainfall inputs giving short soil water residence times or the relatively large N inputs (25-30 kg-N ha^{-1} y^{-1}) which probably exceed biotic and abiotic sinks (Gordon *et al.*, 2001a). Soil process studies are ongoing at Pwllpeiran and have not yet been reported. However at another acid grassland experiment in the Peak District, nitrogen additions of 35, 70 and 140 kg-N ha^{-1} y^{-1} above ambient have stimulated summer mineralisation rates, with no difference in rates between ammonium nitrate and ammonium sulphate treatments (both at 140 kg-N ha^{-1} y^{-1}) (Morecroft *et al.*, 1994). Soil pH has decreased in the ammonium sulphate treatment but not in the ammonium nitrate treatments.

At Ruabon in north Wales, seven years of ammonium nitrate addition to heather moorland at rates up to 200 kg-N ha^{-1} y^{-1} have resulted in significantly higher concentrations of NH_4^+ and NO_3^- in the litter layer; the C:N ratio of litter has also declined. In the summer, soil bacterial biomass was increased in the nitrogen treated plots accompanied by greater use of amino acids, amides and carbohydrates (Johnson *et al.*, 1996). Nitrogen additions increased soil phosphomonesterase (PME) activity in both the litter layer and the surface peat in the vicinity of roots, suggesting greater demand for P but there was little effect on this activity in deeper layers (Lee *et al.*, 2000d). The weight and total nitrogen content of Calluna litter also increased in response to 80, 120 and 200 kg-N ha^{-1} y^{-1} additions. Perhaps the most striking result from this study has been the very small proportion of the added N that has leaked out of the system. In 1999 only the equivalent of 4% of the year's N additions were leached from the soils (Lee *et al.,* 2000d), this after total additions equivalent to up to 2000 kg-N ha^{-1}.

At a lowland acid heath at Thursley Common, 45 km south west of London, there was no significant difference in nitrate, ammonium or base cation leaching between treated and control plots although soil pH decreased significantly in the surface 5 cm of the treated plots. In this experiment, four nitrogen treatments were applied (0, 7.7, 15.4, 0 or 15.4 alternating, kg-N ha^{-1} y^{-1} of ammonium sulphate) as a mist with 42 applications per year over seven years in addition to a background deposition of 19 kg-N ha^{-1} y^{-1} (Uren, 1992; Power et al., 1995).

5.5 Predicting the Impacts of Acid Deposition on UK Soils

In order to provide a scientific basis for negotiation of protocols aimed at reducing the impact of acid deposition on ecosystems under the auspices of the United Nations-Economic Commission on Europe (UN-ECE) Convention on Long Range Transboundary Air Pollution (CLRTAP) it was agreed that an effects-based approach should underpin international negotiations. This was possible because of the advances in the scientific understanding of the processes of acidification, which were sufficiently quantified to permit a targeted approach for controlling acidifying emissions. The favoured effects-based method was encapsulated in the concept of critical loads. A critical load can be generally defined as 'the highest deposition of acidifying compounds that will not cause chemical changes leading to long term harmful effects on ecosystem structure and function' (Nilsson and Grennfelt, 1988). By comparing critical load data with deposition, it is possible to show regions of the country where the critical load has and will be exceeded by the acid deposition inputs and, thus, changes to soil chemistry and the threat of ecosystem damage may occur.

Two approaches are available for the assessment of likely future impacts of changing acid deposition on soils. The first of these is to predict the spatial changes in steady state critical load exceedance in response to future acid deposition reduction scenarios and to compare these with exceedance calculations for a reference scenario. Such an approach may also be used to present historical snapshots of critical load exceedance over an extended time frame. It is important to remember, however, that steady state models can say nothing about the timescales required to achieve a response. Thus, whilst the area of exceedance may change with differing deposition, the amount of change observed in the soil will be related to the historical amount of deposition and the initial status of the soil. Only in those areas where there have been substantial inputs of acid pollutants over a significantly long period (i.e. decades) is it likely that severe soil acidification will have occurred. Conversely, a change in status from exceeded to non-exceeded as a consequence of reduced deposition does not imply immediate recovery.

An assessment of timescales requires a dynamic modelling approach and a number of models are available for the assessment of the impacts of deposition scenarios on soil chemistry, e.g. SAFE (Warfvinge et al., 1993), WHAM (Tipping, 1994), MAGIC (Cosby et al., 1985). Until recently these could only be applied at individual sites because of their large data requirements. However, recent developments now allow regional applications of acidification models to freshwaters and soils (Collins and Jenkins, 1998). The following section investigates what steady state and dynamic modelling have to say about the future response of soils to changes in acid deposition.

5.5.1 Steady-State Critical Loads

In the UK, empirical critical loads of acidity for soils have been assigned to the dominant soil in each 1 km square following the approach described in Hornung *et al.* (1995a). To provide a visual assessment of the predicted impact on UK soils of changing sulphur deposition over the period 1970 to the present day and into the future, these data have been used to produce maps of the exceedance of the empirical soil acidity critical load for 1970, 1983, 1995/97 and 2010 (Figure 5.13). The historic deposition scenarios are those predicted from past emissions data by the HARM model and mapped at 10 x 10 km square resolution. Those for 'present day' (1995-97) are modelled at 5 x 5 km resolution from measured data whilst future predictions, also mapped at 10 x 10 km resolution, are from HARM/FRAME utilising the Gothenburg emission scenario. The large emissions and hence deposition in 1970 result in the largest number of 1 km squares for which the empirical critical load for soils is exceeded, with correspondingly smaller numbers of exceeded squares in 1983 and 1995-97 as emissions of sulphur dioxide decline (Figure 5.13; Table 5.4). The predicted sulphur emissions to be achieved under the latest protocol (Gothenburg) show that by the year 2010 the proportion of 1 km squares containing soils at risk from acidification will be much reduced from 70% in 1970, to 62% in 1983, 46% for current day (1995-97) to 16% in 2010. For the same years, the proportion of land in which critical loads are exceeded by more than 1 keq ha^{-1} y^{-1} are respectively: 20%, 7%, 2% and <1% (Table 5.4).

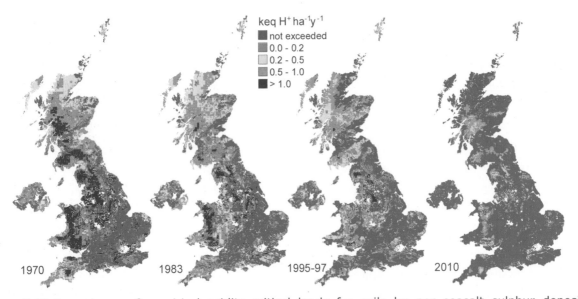

Figure 5.13 Exceedance of empirical acidity critical loads for soils by non-seasalt sulphur deposition predicted by HARM for 1970, 1983, 2010 (Gothenburg protocol, uses HARM and FRAME) and measured values for 1995-97.

Table 5.4 Exceedance of the empirical soil acidity critical load by non-seasalt sulphur deposition.

Year(s)	Number & percentage 1km squares in each exceedance class (class ranges in keq ha^{-1} y^{-1})					Total exceeded
	Not exceeded	< 0.2	0.2 – 0.5	0.5 – 1.0	> 1.0	
1970	71775	16032	39937	63521	47269	166759
	30.1%	6.7%	16.7%	26.6%	19.8%	69.9%
1983	90934	32434	50070	48124	16972	147600
	38.1%	13.6%	21.0%	20.2%	7.1%	61.9%
1995-1997	128768	37087	40675	27198	4732	109692
	54.0%	15.6%	17.1%	11.4%	2.0%	46.0%
2010	200580	24017	11758	1177	4	36956
	84.4%	10.1%	4.9%	0.5%	0.002%	15.6%

Within the UK, ecosystem specific critical loads for total acidity are calculated for coniferous and deciduous woodland using the simple mass balance calculation (see Appendix D). These critical loads are not calculated for other, non-woodland ecosystems because of uncertainties in the Ca^{2+}/Al critical ratio. The exceedance values have been calculated in two ways in order to demonstrate the potential acidifying effect of NH_x deposition on terrestrial ecosystems. Firstly it is assumed that NH_x deposition does not contribute to ecosystem acidification and secondly that each equivalent of NH_x deposition contributes one proton (see Section 5.1.4 and Figure 5.2). The resulting exceedance maps showing 1 km squares containing coniferous woodland under current day deposition (1995-97) and the 2010 scenario are shown in Figure 5.14.

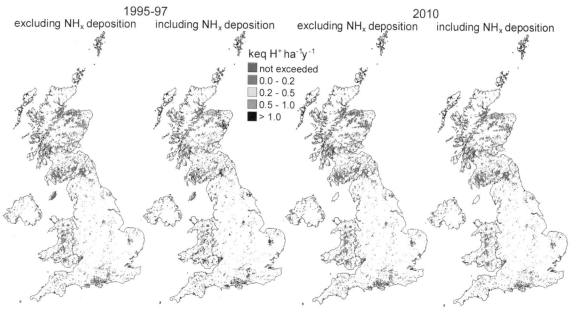

Figure 5.14 Exceedance of simple mass-balance critical loads of acidity for coniferous woodland by measured acid deposition for 1995-97 and predicted acid deposition for 2010 following implementation of the Gothenburg protocol.

For 1995/97, 5 km resolution deposition data based on field measurements have been used, whilst the 2010 scenario is derived from a combination of HARM model predictions for sulphur and NO_x and predictions from the FRAME model for NH_x. For 1995/97, including NH_x as an acidifying input increases the proportion of exceeded 1 km squares from 16% to 73% (Table 5.5). Under the Gothenburg protocol in 2010, the critical load of acidity is not exceeded in 95% of squares containing coniferous woodland if it is assumed the NH_x deposition has no long-term acidifying effect. However, 47% of squares are exceeded if NH_x deposition is allowed to contribute one proton to the acidification of the ecosystem. In terms of ecosystem area, this represents 38% of the area of coniferous woodland in the UK (Table 5.6). Key to the interpretation of these maps and statistics is the recognition that the critical loads and exceedances are calculated assuming long-term, steady state conditions. Given its potential importance, there is a pressing need to understand the extent to which NH_x deposition will contribute to acidification of terrestrial ecosystems and over what timescale. Crucial in this respect are the controls on nitrate leaching in response to the increasing nitrogen richness of the ecosystem. This will determine the timing of nitrate release and the associated acidification following continued atmospheric nitrogen inputs. Predicting the timescale for these effects requires the use of dynamic models that are discussed in the following Section.

Table 5.5 Exceedance of the SMB critical load for acidity for coniferous woodland.

Year	Number & percentage 1km squares in each exceedance class (class ranges in keq ha^{-1} y^{-1})					Total exceeded
	Not exceeded	< 0.2	0.2 – 0.5	0.5 – 1.0	> 1.0	
1995-97	24557	2316	1266	905	264	4751
(excluding NH$_x$)	83.8%	7.9%	4.3%	3.1%	0.9%	16.2%
1995-97	7827	1469	2971	5632	11409	21481
(including NH$_x$)	26.7%	5.0%	10.1%	19.2%	38.9%	73.3%
2010	27506	475	826	22	0	1323
(excluding NH$_x$)	95.4%	1.6%	2.9%	0.1%		4.6%
2010	15137	2088	2966	4538	4093	13685
(including NH$_x$)	52.5%	7.2%	10.3%	15.7%	14.2%	47.5%

Table 5.6 Area of coniferous woodland for which the critical loads of acidity are exceeded by sulphur, NO$_x$ and NH$_x$ deposition.

Year	Percentage area
1995-97	69.2%
2010	38.0%

5.5.2 Dynamic Modelling

Soil acidification

Dynamic models can provide predictions of both the magnitude and timing of soil and soil water chemical responses to changes in acidic deposition and/or land use. The models provide a test bed for our understanding of the processes involved in acidification and recovery. There have been relatively few soil specific dynamic modelling exercises in the UK although a number of dynamic model predictions of soil chemistry are available as an adjunct to catchment scale stream hydrochemical modelling using the MAGIC model. These often provide a very simplified assessment of the soil response because of the 'lumped' nature of the model and the requirement to achieve a mass balance of elements at the catchment scale rather than for the soil profile. In catchments with significant inputs of groundwater enriched in base cations from deep weathering sources, predicted 'catchment' weathering rates will often be much larger than those found in the soil profile.

The future response to nitrogen deposition is likely to be crucial to determining the rates of recovery of acidified soils. However, our understanding of key processes in effectively non-managed, acid sensitive, upland soils is limited. Adequate modelling of soil nitrogen dynamics in these soils, in relation to acidification, has yet to be undertaken in the UK. In view of the limited amount of dynamic soil acidification modelling in the UK and weaknesses in process understanding, especially for nitrogen, there has, for the time being, to be greater reliance on the results of experimental studies, such as those described in Section 5.4 to predict likely future changes in soil chemistry in response to changes in acid inputs. The following, however, give some examples of model applications to soils in the UK and Europe with an emphasis on identifying common responses amongst the contrasting ecosystems.

The SAFE model (Warfvinge et al., 1993) has been parameterised with data from the Rothamsted long-term experimental site and the model tested alongside the measured data (Sverdrup et al., 1995). The model study showed that the model reproduced the observed changes in soil chemistry over time without calibration. The model application suggested that deposition of sulphur and nitrogen from pollutant emissions has been the major cause of soil acidification in the Geescoft Wilderness over the last 110 years with a significant but smaller generation of acidity as a result of the natural development of woodland. The model results also suggested that the decrease in base saturation may be irreversible because of the slow rate of weathering of clay minerals.

Reynolds (1997) applied the SAFE model to acid stagnopodzols in mid-Wales. The model predicted acidification of the soil and soil waters following the increase in sulphate and nitrate deposition after the industrial revolution. Thus, base saturation of the B horizon was predicted to decline from *ca* 20% in the 1850s to *ca* 4% in the 1970s, and the B horizon soil water ANC from *ca* +33 µeq l^{-1} to −68 µeq l^{-1} over the same period (Figure 5.15). Recovery of ANC is predicted following the decline in emissions since the late 1970's and simulated ANC during the period 1986-1994 matches well with observed values in samples of soil water collected at Plynlimon. The model predicts a continuing increase in ANC in response to further planned reductions but the base saturation is only predicted to recover to *ca* 50% of its 1850 level by 2050, mainly due to the very low weathering rate.

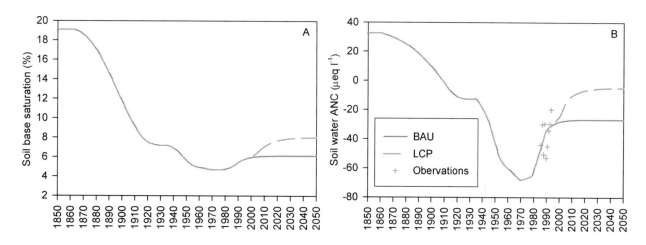

Figure 5.15 Time series of a) Bs horizon base saturation and b) Bs horizon soil water ANC predicted by the SAFE model for an acid moorland site in mid-Wales (BAU ≡ Business As Usual scenario, LCP ≡ scenario based possible controls of Large Combustion Plant).

Application of the SAFE model to three European sites (Birkenes, Stubbetorp and Solling) indicated that all three sites had become acidified with significant decreases in base saturation and soil solution Ca^{2+}/Al ratio, although there were distinct differences between sites reflecting the different soil mineralogy and acid inputs to the sites (Jönsson *et al.*, 1994). Cumulative accounting of base cation sources and sinks clearly illustrated the acidification process at the sites, as along with base cation deposition, depletion of base saturation was a major source of base cations, exceeding weathering at Birkenes. Base cation deposition was identified as one of the major sources of uncertainty in the model predictions.

Application of the '2-box' version of the MAGIC model to 21 sites of the UK Acid Waters Monitoring Network also predicted extensive acidification at all sites with an average depletion of base saturation by 14% from 1851 to 1997 (Helliwell *et al.*, 1998a). This model allows the soil to be partitioned into two layers that can be physically identified with the surface organic-rich layer and the mineral subsoil, although the soils are still lumped spatially within the catchment. At the AWMN sites, the surface organic horizon was identified as the most sensitive to change, responding rapidly to both an historic increase and future predicted decrease in acid inputs. Following implementation of the Second Sulphur (Oslo) Protocol, base saturation in the organic layers was predicted to increase across the sites by an average of 2% between 1997 and 2041. Little change or continuing deterioration was predicted over the same period for the mineral subsoil at all eight sites in England and Wales and two in Scotland. A subsequent application of the 2-box version of MAGIC to the Dargall Lane catchment in the Galloway region of Scotland (Heliwell pers comm) shows that the Gothenburg protocol results in little improvement in soil base saturation compared to the Oslo protocol (Figure 5.16a). At the same site, the model predicts a rapid decline in soil water ANC in the organic layer reaching a value of -87 µeq l^{-1} in the mid 1970s (Figure 5.16b). This is followed by an abrupt increase that continues over the next 30 years. A recovery to -20 µeq l^{-1} is predicted by 2040 under the Gothenburg emission reduction protocol. The mineral horizon responds more gradually to increasing acid emissions, with the lowest ANC values (-11 µeq l^{-1}) predicted in the mid to late 1990s, followed by a slow, steady increase to $+6$ µeq l^{-1} by 2041 following implementation of the Gothenburg protocol.

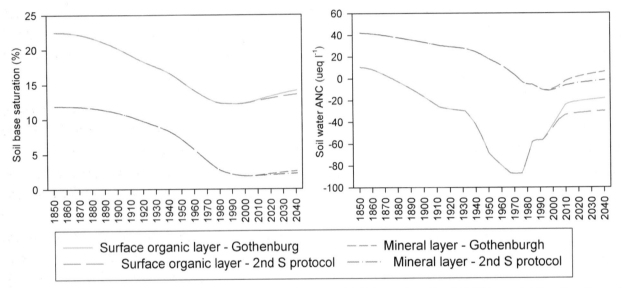

Figure 5.16 Predicted soil base saturation and soil water ANC for using the MAGIC model for the Dargall Lane catchment in Galloway, Scotland. (Gothenburg and 2nd S protocol refer to the emission control protocol scenarios, see Table 1.1, Source: MLURI, unpublished data).

The MAGIC model has been applied to the Aber forest nitrogen manipulation site to predict the changes in soil and soil water chemistry resulting from the combination of acid deposition and afforestation of acid upland soils with a Sitka spruce plantation (Wright *et al.*, 1998a). The model predicts a gradual increase in soil water base cation and sulphate concentrations and a decrease in soil water ANC during the period 1950-1980 in response to increased acid deposition and the growth of the forest from 1960 onwards. The model reproduces observed data reasonably well despite the large year-to-year variability. Soil base saturation declines steadily from *ca* 16% to 13% in the same period, but from 1980 onwards a much sharper decline is predicted with base saturation declining to about 8% in 2010 with deposition of nitrogen and non-seasalt sulphur held at 1995 levels. There is considerable scatter in the observed base saturation data reflecting variations in both time and space, since repeat samples cannot be collected from exactly the same place. The model simulation passes roughly through the centre of the observations, which gives some confidence in the predictions.

Nitrogen models

The increasing importance of nitrogen to acidification has necessitated the development of models with more sophisticated nitrogen dynamics than those included in earlier acidification models such as MAGIC. The development has focused on representing the dynamics of soil organic matter transformations within the context of nutrient cycling within the soil-plant system. However, in contrast to many models of nitrogen cycling, emphasis is place on the soil N leaching term as one of the key outputs (Emmett *et al.*, 1997). Examples of such models are NuCM (Liu *et al.*, 1992) developed in the United States as part of the Electric Power Research Institute's Integrated Forest Studies Programme (Johnson and Lindberg, 1992), MERLIN (Emmett *et al.*, 1997) which arose from the NITREX project, the Dutch models NUCSAM (Groenenberg *et al.*, 1998) and NICCCE (van Dam and van Breemen, 1995) and the American P-NET model (Aber and Federer, 1992). The European models specifically link the dynamics of nitrogen to those of carbon within several organic matter compartments. In the case of MERLIN and NICCCE these are conceptual whereas NUCSAM defines the compartments with respect to identifiable organic layers in the soil (litter, fermented layer and humus layer). This has the advantage that the model can be calibrated to measurable organic matter and nitrogen pools within these soil layers. Whilst MERLIN and NICCCE are specifically designed to model C and N dynamics, NUCSAM and NuCM include the inorganic soil reactions involved in acidification such as weathering, sulphate adsorption, cation exchange etc.

Applications of the MERLIN model to the Risdalsheia RAIN experiment (Wright *et al.*, 1998b) and the Aber NITREX site (Emmett *et al.*, 1997) successfully reproduced the results of the experimental manipulations. At Risdalsheia, the model results supported the concept of the soil as the major sink for nitrogen deposited from the atmosphere. As the molar C/N ratio in the labile organic pool (LOM) fell below 23, the model predicted a progressive decrease in the amount of N immobilised with a consequent increase in nitrate leaching. This again is consistent with the empirical concept of the C/N ratio as an index for the onset of nitrate leaching (Gundersen *et al.*, 1998b). At Aber, the model successfully reproduced the increase in nitrate leaching losses with forest age described by Stevens *et al* (1994) (see Section 5.3.5.1). Furthermore, the model also captured the increases in nitrate leaching and the changes in soil organic matter and tree nitrogen content observed at the site in response to the experimental nitrogen additions (Emmett *et al.*, 1997). The model was less successful when applied at a nitrogen limited site in Sweden (Wright *et al.*, 1998b) because of limitations of current understanding of key processes of nitrogen assimilation and carbon dynamics. Nevertheless, the model predicted increased nitrate leaching would occur as the C/N ratio in the LOM decreased below 28.

Summary of model findings

The dynamic models consistently predict soil acidification by depletion of base saturation in response to increasing acid deposition from the middle of the last century. Acidification generally became most severe in the 1970s and 1980s, although the exact timing and nature of the response is variable depending on site characteristics and soil horizon. The models predict more rapid chemical changes in the surface organic layer compared to the mineral subsoil. This is consistent with the field observations described in Section 5.3. Unfortunately there are no long-term records of soil solution chemistry in the UK covering the period of predicted soil acidification. However, there are examples where model predictions agree reasonably well over a period of several years with relatively recent field observations of soil water ANC. The models consistently predict slow recovery of base saturation but a more rapid response of soil water ANC. The results from the ecosystem-scale experimental manipulations described in Section 5.4 confirm these predictions. Even under the most stringent deposition reductions, it is likely that in many soils base saturation will not recover to the levels predicted to exist prior to the Industrial Revolution. Indeed, some soils may never recover beyond current day values. The slow and partial recovery of soil base saturation means that future land management strategies must be sympathetic to the acidified nature of these soils (Helliwell *et al.*, 1998a). It must be designed to prevent further deterioration of soil base status with the accompanying risk of damage to linked ecosystems such as freshwaters by leaching of acidified runoff.

The role of nitrogen in soil acidification remains an outstanding issue for research. Application of steady state models show that there is a large potential for soil acidification linked to the deposition of NH_x and leaching of nitrate. The exact timing of nitrogen breakthrough in systems continuing to receive chronic nitrogen deposition is unknown, although there is field evidence of nitrate leaching in excess of NO_y deposition in stands of mature coniferous forestry. Dynamic models have successfully predicted nitrogen breakthrough at experimental sites, but generally the models are too complex and data demanding to apply at less well characterised sites or at a regional scale. Thus there is an urgent need to develop simplified models of nitrogen dynamics to link to acidification models.

5.6 Conclusions

There is substantial evidence that acid deposition has resulted in the widespread acidification of acid sensitive soils in the UK and Europe. Despite the reduction in emissions over the last decade, there is little unequivocal evidence of recovery from soil acidification in the UK because there are few data collected from appropriate soil types. Most available data suggest continuing acidification of soils under semi-natural vegetation into the 1990s, but decreases in the acidity of arable and intensive grassland soils. The presence of potentially confounding management factors makes the interpretation of these data difficult. This review has highlighted the paucity of relevant long-term soil acidification data and points to the need for a nationally co-ordinated approach to the monitoring of soil acidification and recovery in line with the programmes for assessing long-term changes in deposition and stream water chemistry.

Experimental data and long-term model predictions indicate that soil water chemistry will respond relatively rapidly (up to 5 years) to decreases in acid deposition inputs and there is some limited, long-term field evidence to confirm this. However, in soils with a large pool of readily extractable sulphate, desorption of this sulphate will inhibit recovery of soil water ANC over a time scale of one to two decades. In soils with peaty surface horizons, episodic seasalt deposition will continue to result in temporary soil water acidification even where acid deposition inputs have been significantly reduced. The acidity of such organic soils will be buffered by organic acids.

The experimental and modelling data suggest that recovery of soils by increases in base saturation will take much longer (decades) than for soil water chemistry. The majority of long-term modelling suggests that the base saturation of most acidified soils will not recover to those levels believed to exist prior to the industrial revolution. The rate of recovery is dependent on base cation supply from weathering and atmospheric inputs. Soils where the base saturation has been depleted by acid deposition will remain 'acid sensitive' for a considerable period of time, as there will be little capacity to buffer acidity by cation exchange. This may have important implications for future land management. Land use practices that promote net base cation removal or acidification in some other way should be avoided.

The future role of nitrogen deposition in the acidification and recovery of soils remains an important area of research. Although it is clear that ecosystems have a considerable potential to retain incoming nitrogen, there is evidence from experimental manipulations and field studies that chronic nitrogen deposition can result in increased nitrate leaching and lowering of soil water ANC. For forest systems, this response depends on the nitrogen status of the site, which can be indexed by the C/N ratio of the forest floor. There is experimental evidence that a reduction in the amounts of deposited oxidised-N results in a decrease in soil water nitrate concentrations and an increase in soil water ANC. Much less is known about the controls on nitrate leaching in non-forest, natural and semi-natural ecosystems and this remains a topic of ongoing research.

Several dynamic biogeochemical models have been developed to predict future nitrate leaching trends in response to changes in nitrogen deposition. Those models containing a detailed process-representation of the nitrogen cycle and are generally too complex to be applied anywhere other than at well-instrumented research sites. In contrast, the more commonly used acidification models, which can be applied across a range of scales, contain very limited N dynamics that provide relatively poor predictions. Thus there is a continuing need for research to identify less complex ways of representing the key processes controlling the rate and timing of nitrate leaching particularly in non-forested, natural and semi-natural ecosystems, in response to changes in nitrogen deposition inputs.

Chapter 6: Effects on Freshwaters

> Acidification of freshwaters has been widespread across the uplands of the UK from the 1850s onwards.

> The main cause of surface water acidification is deposition of anthropogenic S, although N compounds contribute significantly in some areas.

> There is clear evidence of chemical changes that indicate the start of recovery from acidification in most areas since the 1970s, consistent with large reductions in S emission/deposition. This trend is important in indicating that target ecosystems are potentially recovering as a result of emission control.

> Since the mid-1980s S deposition has declined appreciably around source areas but very little in more remote areas. This is reflected in trends over the last 15 years, whereby SO_4^{2-} concentrations have decreased at sites across the UK. The spatial extent of this decline is not constant, however, and S concentration has decreased, with pH recovery, in 'near source' surface waters but with less change in remote areas, consistent with the observed changes in S deposition.

> There are indications of biological recovery from acidification but by contrast with the results from chemical assessments these are modest and restricted to a small number of locations. This might be because regional chemical trends have not yet been sustained or substantial enough to allow re-colonization, but for streams, limits imposed by continuing acid episodes cannot be ruled out.

> Predictions into the future show a continued chemical recovery if agreed emission reductions are achieved but significant time lags (decades) are likely.

> During the last 10 years, surface waters across the UK have shown a significant increase in the total organic carbon concentration (TOC). This is not thought to be related to decreased acidic deposition, but probably results from a change in the climatic regime with increased temperatures in recent years.

6.1 Introduction/Background

6.1.1 Historical Perspective

Direct chemical evidence documenting surface water acidification is rare in the UK, and indeed anywhere else in the world, since the recognition of the problem occurred as the emissions of pollutants to the atmosphere were beginning to decline. Consequently, even the longest data records were initiated too late to show the trend to increasing acidity. However, evidence for the acidification of surface waters can be obtained from pH reconstructions based on diatoms in lake sediment cores and this provides the key evidence linking historical emission of atmospheric pollutants with the acidification process (Figure 6.1). In the early 1980s this relationship was not universally accepted and a number of alternative explanations for surface water acidification were proposed. These included the possibilities that acidification was an entirely natural process (Pennington, 1981 & 1984) or that it was due to changes in catchment land-use and management (Rosenqvist, 1978).

A major palaeolimnological research programme was set up in the mid-1980s funded by the Surface Water Acidification Programme (SWAP) and by then UK DoE (Department of the Environment, now DEFRA) to evaluate these alternative hypotheses (Mason, 1990; Battarbee *et al.*, 1988 & 1990). SWAP was a collaborative project with Scandinavian scientists. Study sites were carefully selected in Norway, Sweden and the UK and sampling and analytical methods were harmonised between laboratories in the different countries. The results from diatom analysis, trace metal analysis and fly-ash particle analysis of dated lake sediment cores from these sites were combined with historical land-use and land management data for the lake catchments (Patrick *et al.*, 1990). The overall conclusion (Battarbee *et al.*, 1990; Renberg and Battarbee, 1990) was that acid deposition was the main cause of the surface water acidification problem, although long-term natural acidification processes had increased the sensitivity of many sites to acid deposition, and afforestation exacerbated acidification in areas of high acid deposition. The initial changes occurred in the mid to late nineteenth century and the extent of acidification is determined by the sensitivity of the lake relative to the amount of acidity deposited (DoE, 1995).

Decline and loss of fish populations have been reported in sensitive lakes and streams of most countries subject to high deposition of sulphur compounds. In some countries (e.g. Norway and Canada) up to 25% of all lakes have been reported to have damaged fisheries (Hesthagen *et al.*, 1999; Jeffries, 1997). Although most publicity has been devoted to changes in fish populations acidification causes changes to aquatic ecosystems at all trophic levels, including riparian populations of birds (Buckton *et al.*, 1998) and amphibians (Beebee *et al.*, 1990).

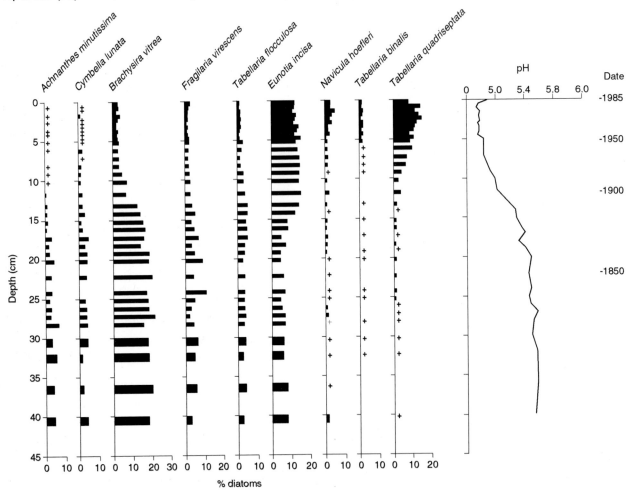

Figure 6.1 Diatom diagram for a sediment core from the Round Loch of Glenhead taken in 1985, showing a decline in species sensitive to acidification (e.g. *Brachysira vitrea*) and an increase in species tolerant of acidity (e.g. *Tabellaria quadriseptata*). The core has been dated using the ^{210}Pb radio-isotope method, and a diatom-pH transfer function has been used to reconstruct the pH history of the lake over the last 200 years (from Jones *et al.*, 1990).

Experimental studies have reinforced these observations. Increased acidic deposition to a whole catchment system in Norway proved the direct link between S and N deposition and surface water acidification (Wright *et al.*, 1994a) and lake manipulation experiments at the Experimental Lake Area in Canada have also documented biological decline and recovery in response to acidification and de-acidification (Schindler *et al.*, 1989 & 1991). Experimental studies in Scandinavia have also shown that the process is reversible and that recovery from acidification results after decreased deposition although the response is not necessarily linear (Wright *et al.*, 1993; Moldan *et al.*, 1995). Experimental manipulations of surface water chemistry reveal that some biological communities respond to improved water chemistry only slowly, and with even greater hysteresis or non-linearity (Rundle *et al.*, 1995).

6.1.2 Process of Acidification

The processes linking emissions of acidifying pollutants to the atmosphere, their transport and deposition and the subsequent acidification of soils and freshwaters are largely understood and documented. Since the terrestrial area of a river or lake catchment tends to be large relative to the surface area of open water, most atmospheric deposition is to land. The link, then, between soil and surface water chemistry is a function of flowpath and soil physico-chemistry. With S deposition, acidification of soils begins immediately as base cations are stripped from the ion-exchange complex and base saturation decreases. Soils generally have some capacity to adsorb SO_4^{2-} but in the young (post glaciation) and highly organic soils common in much of the upland UK, this is considered to be small relative to the flux of S deposited through time and is rapidly exhausted. If the rate of supply of base cations from primary weathering in the catchment is less than the incoming flux of strong acid anions, the base cation store in the soil becomes depleted and hydrogen ions and aluminium species will accompany acid anions into the surface water, promoting acidification.

Nitrogen deposition has the potential to cause a similar response but since N is utilised and cycled within the terrestrial ecosystem, not all N deposited leaks to surface water. Indeed, most of the deposited N is immobilised within the soil. If the vegetation is changed abruptly, such as through deforestation (Reynolds *et al.*, 1995), or if the ability of the soils to immobilise N is reduced through N saturation relative to C availability (Gundersen *et al.*, 1998c), then increased N leakage will occur. Since plants and microbes tend to assimilate the reduced form of N in preference to oxidised N, NH_4^+ deposition promotes surface water acidification only after it is cycled through the terrestrial ecosystem, immobilised in plants and soils and subsequently mineralised to NO_3^-. This then acts as a strong acid anion in the same way as SO_4^{2-}.

6.1.3 Impacts of Acidification

The impact of acidification on biota results partly from direct toxicity of increased H^+ concentration and increased mobilisation of toxic aluminium at lower pH and is manifest in alterations or loss of populations at all trophic levels. pH, Al and Ca^{2+} have long been recognised as the most important elements in determining the toxicity of acidic water to fish and other biota while the additional protection of dissolved organic matter has only recently been recognised (Roy and Campbell, 1997). Salmonids are the most sensitive fish species and for early life stages pH appears to be the main toxic agent but, for later stages, ionic forms of Al, Ca^{2+} and DOC (dissolved organic carbon) are more important in determining fish survival.

In addition to these direct effects, however, a range of indirect processes arise including altered rates of decomposition, and altered predator-prey interactions (UKAWRG, 1988). For example, the decline of some river birds along acid streams reflects changes in the availability of certain key prey rich in energy and Ca^{2+} (Tyler and Ormerod, 1991).

For many groups of organisms, acid/base status is significantly correlated with abundance and diversity, with many important organisms scarce and species-poor in acid streams. For this reason, acidification has represented a major negative impact on upland biodiversity across large areas. In Wales alone, for example, over 12,000 out of 24,000 km of river are impacted, with major consequences for primary producers, invertebrates, fish, and river birds (Stevens et al., 1997; Rimes et al., 1994).

6.1.4 Extent of Acidification

The extent of the problem of surface water acidification in the UK has been assessed using a sensitivity mapping approach (Edmunds and Kinniburgh, 1986; Hornung et al., 1995b) and by systematic water sampling (DoE, 1995). The former approach uses mapped soil and geological information, for example, to indicate base cation weathering and soil cation exchange characteristics whilst the latter involved sampling the most sensitive site from each square of a 10 km grid across the country. The chemistry database has formed the basis of the UK freshwater critical load assessment (DoE, 1995; Curtis et al., 2000). The most recent assessment using the FAB model (Henriksen and Posch 2001) to calculate critical loads indicates that of the sampled population of 1470 lakes and streams the critical load is currently exceeded in 29% (Curtis et al. 2000) and these sites are unlikely to recover in the future if this level of deposition is maintained (Figure 6.2).

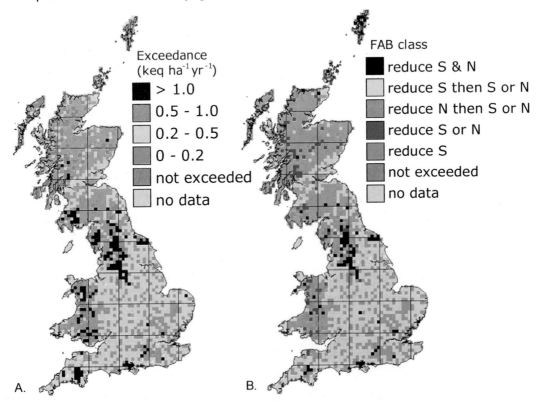

Figure 6.2 (a) Critical load exceedance calculated with the First-order Acidity Balance (FAB) model for UK freshwaters using ANCcrit = 0 μeq l^{-1} and 1995-97 deposition data. (b) Deposition reduction requirements from 1995-97 levels according to the FAB model for UK freshwaters using ANCcrit = 0 μeq l^{-1}.

In terms of the proportion of water bodies with critical load exceedance, Wales shows the largest effects, with 46% of sampled sites exceeded. Scotland and England have greater numbers of exceeded sites in absolute terms, but smaller proportions with 26% and 28% exceeded respectively. Note that these percentages refer to sampled sites, selected to be the most sensitive in their respective grid squares and not the whole population of water bodies in these countries. The results focus attention on the uplands of the UK including Dartmoor, the Pennines, mid and north Wales, the Lake District and most of Scotland (Figure 6.2).

In terms of biological damage there is now evidence that stream biota in Wales reflect current critical load exceedance. For example, in 1995 there were significant differences in trout density between exceeded and non-exceeded sites (Figure 6.3). For aquatic invertebrates, species richness was significantly lower at exceeded sites by comparison with non-exceeded sites (Figure 6.3). Critical loads, therefore, provide a tool for indicating potential damage (Ormerod *et al.,* unpublished data).

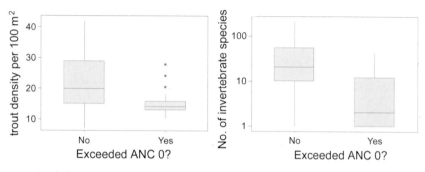

Figure 6.3 Differences in (a) trout density and (b) invertebrate species richness at sites in Wales where the critical load is exceeded or not, Henriksen model.

6.2 Acidification and Recovery Indicators

Acidification of surface waters is indicated by increased H^+ concentration and decreased pH but is also commonly defined as a reduction in the acid-neutralising capacity (ANC, see Chapter 5 for a full description). ANC can be defined as the difference in the sum of concentration (equivalents per litre) of base cations (Ca^{2+}, Mg^{2+}, K^+, Na^+) less the sum of concentrations of strong acid anions (SO_4^{2-}, NO_3^-, Cl^-) (Reuss and Johnson, 1986). From the ionic balance, ANC is also equal to the sum of concentrations of weak acid anions (HCO_3^-, OH^-, organic anions) less the sum of concentrations of acid cations (H^+ and inorganic Al species). Acidification, the decrease in ANC, may be manifest by an increase in SO_4^{2-} or NO_3^- as well as by increased H^+ and Al concentrations. By definition, reversibility is the increase in pH and ANC. The most common indicators of recovery (increases in ANC) are decreases in concentrations of SO_4^{2-}, NO_3^-, H^+ and inorganic Al species. ANC is a primary measure of sensitivity and recovery with the advantages that it is a pragmatic parameter, readily estimated, highly correlated to the biologically meaningful parameters (pH and inorganic Al) and reliably predicted in process-oriented models.

The most useful biological indicators of recovery are those that are representative of different trophic levels or different functional groups in aquatic ecosystems and that, in the absence of acidification, would otherwise be expected to be widespread in streams and lakes. In the UK diatoms (e.g. *Achnanthes minutissima*), aquatic macrophytes (e.g. *Myriophyllum alterniflorum*), benthic invertebrates (e.g. *Baetis rhodani*) and fish (e.g. brown trout, *Salmo trutta*) are used. Species groups and species diversity indices can also be used. Time-lags in biological recovery are expected to occur, however, depending on the proximity of refuge populations, the dispersal efficiency of different taxa and the presence or absence or dispersal barriers, for example.

There is now evidence from those sites where terrestrial liming experiments were undertaken in the mid-1980s that slow biological recovery at these de-acidifying sites reflects the effects of acid episodes rather than slow dispersal by acid-sensitive species. In Wales, roughly 80% of sensitive organisms have appeared at experimental sites in at least one year since liming. By contrast, their year-to-year persistence between years is reduced in years with low minimum pH. This pattern is consistent with the view that episodes prevent successful colonization of limed sites (Bradley and Ormerod, 2001).

The degree and rate of recovery of ANC and pH in response to decreased acidic inputs is also related to the supply of base cations from weathering and atmospheric deposition. During the acidification process, base cations are leached from exchange sites on soils and this process buffers the acidification in surface waters. Following reductions in acidic deposition, however, the deficit of soil base cations previously removed must be rebuilt before the complete restoration of surface water chemistry is possible. Replenishment of base cations on soils depends primarily on mineral weathering and is a slow process, especially on soils derived from siliceous parent material. Relative to the reversibility of SO_4^{2-} in surface water, base cation reversibility is often a slower process. Thus the initial response of freshwater systems to moderate decreases in acidic deposition is a decrease in SO_4^{2-} concentration and a decrease in base cation concentration as well, resulting in little change in ANC or pH. Sulphate adsorption within the terrestrial ecosystem and oxidation, especially in wetlands and peaty soils, can further delay the response to a decrease in S deposition, as the release through oxidation processes is slow.

6.3 Evidence for Recovery

6.3.1 Data Sources

Monitoring of surface water chemistry in the uplands of the UK began in earnest in the late 1970s following the recognition that surface water acidification presented a problem (Table 6.1). Few uninterrupted, long-term records exist, with the exception of sediment cores, with which to evaluate the recovery from acidification in response to the decrease in S emissions and deposition which began around 1970 (Chapters 2 & 3). Data collection has followed three methodologies: repeat sediment core analysis; sampling at specific sites through time and repeated synoptic surveys of wide areas at a single point in time, or over a short period of time. Specific site studies (e.g. Harriman *et al.*, 1995a; Tipping *et al.*, 1998) provide the most robust data with which to assess recovery through time especially when combined with sediment cores but extrapolation of the results to other sites nearby is problematic given the high degree of heterogeneity in the landscape. Repeated synoptic surveys also provide data describing recovery through time but for whole populations of lakes within a region (e.g. Wright *et al.*, 1994b). Here the problem lies in the question as to whether the single sample per year (or longer) is representative of the mean chemistry at the site since it is well known that surface water chemistry at any point in time is strongly influenced by rainfall and changes over relatively short timescales.

In response to the need to assess the success of emission reduction agreements, a formal network of sites was established in 1988 as the UK Acid Waters Monitoring Network. This comprises 22 sites, 11 lakes and 11 streams (Appendix B), and follows strict protocols for sampling and analysis to provide a unique and consistent long-term record to the present day. Stream sites are sampled for chemistry on a monthly basis and lakes on a quarterly basis given that their storage capability reduces the rainfall induced variation in chemistry. Biological determinands are sampled annually and include epilithic diatoms, aquatic macrophytes, aquatic macroinvertebrates and salmonid fish. This database provides for a unique assessment of trends in surface water chemistry and biology and detailed reviews of the period from 1988 to 2000 have recently been completed (Monteith and Evans 2000; Evans and Monteith, 2001).

Table 6.1 Data available for assessment of long term changes and spatial extent of surface water acidification in the UK (see text for details).

Region (Synoptic survey)	Number of sites sampled	Survey dates
Galloway	63	1979, 1988,1993, 1994, 1996, 1997, 1998
Wales	100	1984/85, 1995
Pennines	62	1998
Lake District	53	2000
Cairngorms	10, 39	1959, 1999
Sites (continuous monitoring)	Data record	Sampling frequency
Plynlimon	1980-present	Weekly
Llyn Brianne	1985-present	Monthly
UKAWMN	1988-present	Monthly (streams), Quarterly (lakes)
Tillingbourne	1977-82, 1998-2000	Weekly
Galloway Cluster	1992-present	Monthly
Loch Ard	1981-present	Monthly
Loch Dee Tributaries	1980-present	Weekly/Monthly
Balquhidder	1983-present	Weekly/Fortnightly
Allt a Mharcaidh	1985-present	Weekly
River Dee Tributaries	1983-present	Monthly
Lake District	1983-present	Monthly

6.3.2 Regional Assessment

Evidence for recovery from acidification is examined here region by region in accordance with the regional variation in present and historical S and N deposition (Chapter 3).

Galloway, SW Scotland

The first synoptic regional survey in the UK was undertaken in Galloway in 1979 (Wright and Henriksen, 1980) and demonstrated that lochs situated on the granite intrusion were extremely acidic relative to those on the surrounding sedimentary bedrock. A repeat survey of the same sites in 1988 (Wright et al., 1994b) shows a 42% decrease in SO_4^{2-} concentrations across the region resulting in a substantial increase in ANC and pH in the acidified lochs (Figure 6.4). Subsequent re-surveys have indicated improvement in the more acid lochs but at a much slower rate.

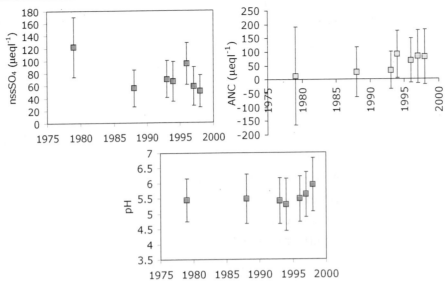

Figure 6.4 Surface water pH, ANC and non-seasalt SO_4^{2-} for 46 lochs re-sampled over the period 1979-1998 in the Galloway region of Scotland. The square shows the mean and the whiskers represent the extremes.

Chemical sampling of several high-elevation lochs on the granite intrusion was also started in 1978. Sampling prior to 1988 was at variable frequencies and thereafter on a monthly or three-monthly basis. Fish population surveys were made in 1978/79,1984 and 1994 involving systematic netting in lochs and quantitative electrofishing in streams. Time series data from these lochs reveal a marked decrease in non-seasalt SO_4^{2-} between 1978 and 1999 (Figure 6.5) although the reduction has not been linear. A steep decrease occurred between 1978 and 1990 followed by a stabilisation of concentration to 1997. The period 1997 to 1999 has shown a further marked decrease. This decrease in non-seasalt SO_4^{2-} concentration has promoted a recovery in pH that follows the same trend through time. In addition, the labile aluminium (toxic fraction) has also decreased significantly.

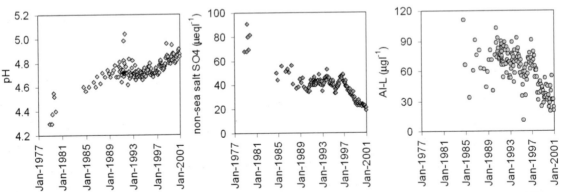

Figure 6.5 The observed changes in pH, non-seasalt SO_4^{2-} and labile (toxic) aluminium since 1978 at Loch Enoch, Galloway (after Harriman *et al.* 2001).

Of the three UKAWMN sites located in this region, Round Loch of Glenhead, Dargall Lane and Loch Grannoch, the former two show similar trends to those observed in the repeat surveys but also indicate a more rapid decline in non-seasalt SO_4^{2-} concentration over the last four years (Figure 6.6) and an improvement in pH (Evans and Monteith, 2001). Loch Grannoch, on the other hand, is the only site in the UKAWMN to show increased acidity over the last ten years. The reason for this is unclear since non-seasalt SO_4^{2-} follows the same pattern as Round Loch and Dargall Lane although calcium concentrations are also declining.

Galloway is also the region where sediment core analysis first showed evidence for acidification in the UK (Flower and Battarbee, 1983; Battarbee *et al.*, 1985; Jones *et al.*, 1986). Repeat coring here also showed signs of biological recovery related to S reductions in the early 1980s (Battarbee *et al.,* 1988; Allott *et al.*, 1992).

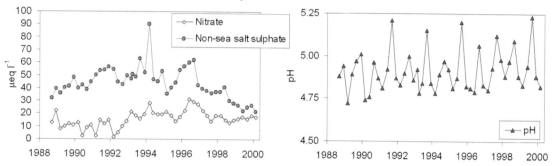

Figure 6.6 Observed changes in SO_4^{2-}, NO_3^- and pH since 1988 at Round Loch of Glenhead, an AWMN site in Galloway.

Despite these clear chemical changes, there is little evidence for biological recovery in Galloway lochs and streams for key indicators such as fish and invertebrates. The qualitative information available (angling records, *ad hoc* netting of lochs, survival of trout fry and experimental reintroduction of fish) indicates varying degrees of recovery. The 100 year angling catch records for lochs Riecawr and Macaterick in Galloway show greater numbers of fish (e.g. Harriman *et al.* 2001), with an associated reduction in average weight, while systematic netting of other lochs has revealed increasing numbers of trout in recent years. The successful reintroduction of trout into fishless Loch Enoch in 1995 (Collen *et al.*, 2000) also shows that recovery has proceeded to the point where only mortality at the most sensitive hatching and fry stage is preventing the establishment of a sustainable trout population.

Loch Ard, Central Scotland

The Loch Ard research area, at the headwaters of the River Forth, comprises a series of upland stream catchments selected during 1976 to investigate the effects of acidic deposition and conifer plantations on stream ecology (Harriman and Morrison, 1982; Harriman *et al.*, 1995a). A bulk deposition collector was established in 1972 and trend analysis revealed a significant decline in non-seasalt SO_4^{2-} averaging 2.0 µeq l^{-1} y^{-1} with a large decline in the early 1980s followed by a period of stability in the early to mid 1990s then by a further decline during the late 1990s. The response to this decrease in deposition of SO_4^{2-} is reflected in the chemistry of the Caorainn Achaidh Burn (Figure 6.7), where the non-seasalt SO_4^{2-} concentration declined from a mean of 115 µeq l^{-1} between 1979-1982 to 53 µeq l^{-1} between 1996-1998. Virtually the entire decline occurred prior to 1989 and non-seasalt SO_4^{2-} concentrations have been relatively constant for the past 10 years. There is, however, little evidence of an increase in pH or change in base cations. This maybe due to large, short-term episodic variation at this steep catchment.

Two AWMN sites, Loch Chon and Loch Tinker, are located in this region (Appendix B, Figure B3). Loch Chon shows improved conditions in biology (epilithic diatoms and macroinvertebrates) and chemistry (increased pH and alkalinity) over the period 1988 to 1998 (Figure 6.8). These trends are not observed in the nearby Loch Tinker since this loch is barely acidic with mean pH above 6.0.

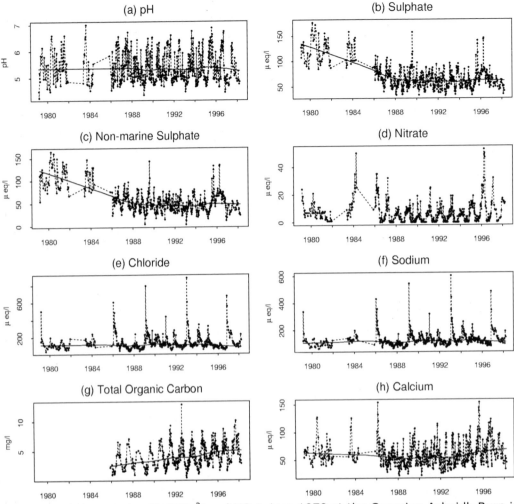

Figure 6.7 Observed changes in pH, *SO$_4^{2-}$ and NO$_3^-$ since 1979 at the Caorainn Achaidh Burn in the Loch Ard region of Central Scotland (Monteith and Evans, 2000).

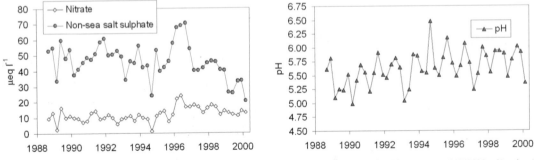

Figure 6.8 Observed changes in SO$_4^{2-}$, NO$_3^-$ and pH since 1988 at Loch Chon, an AWMN site in the Loch Ard region of central Scotland.

Cairngorms and Lochnagar

The Cairngorm Mountains in North East Scotland consist of a high plateau (*ca* 1200 m asl) underlain by granite bedrock. The plateau is remote from pollutant sources although it currently receives *ca* 10 kg-S ha^{-1} y^{-1} and *ca* 11 kg-N ha^{-1} y^{-1} deposition from the atmosphere. The lochs on the plateau provide unique indicators of the impact of atmospheric pollution. In 1953, 10 lochs on the plateau were sampled and analysed for major ion concentrations (Gorham, 1957). A repeat survey of 39 lochs in 1999 incorporated all of the lochs of the 1953 survey (Helliwell *et al.*, 2000 in press). Comparison of the data shows that pH has improved probably in response to decreased SO_4^{2-}. The decrease in SO_4^{2-} is in line with decreased S deposition since the mid 1970s.

Stream chemistry and macroinvertebrate ecology has been monitored in 10 streams draining the eastern Cairngorms since 1983 (Soulsby et al., 1997). All of these streams showed a decrease in SO_4^{2-} concentration and an increase in ANC over the period 1983 to 1994. In some of the streams, this change in chemistry coincided with an increase in the abundance of acid-sensitive mayflies but this was not the case in the most chronically acidified streams.

Two sites in the AWMN are located in this region: the Allt a Mharcaidh and Lochnagar. Data from Lochnagar indicate decreased non-seasalt SO_4^{2-} in the period 1988-1998 but an increase in NO_3^- over the same period has led to a further decline in pH and alkalinity (Figure 6.9). This trend of increased acidification was reflected in deterioration of the macroinvertebrate community although no significant trend is observed in epilithic diatoms until 1998. Since 1998, the elevated NO_3^- concentrations have declined substantially and the cause of the increased NO_3^- is not clear.

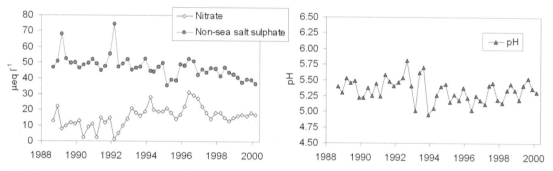

Figure 6.9 Observed changes in SO_4^{2-}, NO_3^- and pH since 1988 at Lochnagar, an AWMN site in the Cairngorms, NE Scotland.

Wales

In Wales, evidence for recent changesf comes from long-term data from Plynlimon, Llyn Brianne, Beddgelert, two acid waters surveys and four AWMN sites, the Afon Hafren, Afon Gwy, Llyn Cwm Mynach and Llyn Llagi. Long term monitoring at Plynlimon indicates only modest recovery (Figure 6.10). At the Afon Gwy, a moorland catchment, a decline in mean non-seasalt SO_4^{2-} is observed from 1980 to present but at the nearby-afforested Afon Hafren, no change in non-seasalt SO_4^{2-} concentration is detectable (Figure 6.10). This may well be attributable to the influence of the forest. At Llyn Brianne, pH in acid moorland streams has increased significantly from ca 5.0 to ca 5.3 from the mid 1980s to the present day.

Data from the Welsh Acid Waters Survey (WAWS) provide a regional context for site-specific assessments of trends at more intensively studied sites at Llyn Brianne, the UKAWMN, Plynlimon and Beddgelert. The stream data arise from monthly collections of chemical samples over one year at each of ca 100 sites in 1984, and again in 1995. These data in turn are accompanied by assessments of invertebrates, salmonid fish populations, and river bird distributions at 74 of the chemical sites. The conclusions from comparison of the data from the two surveys are set against a background of declining solute concentrations in rainfall over the same time period (Stevens et al., 1997). Sulphate concentrations decreased in surface waters between 1984 and 1995 by about 16% whilst base cation concentrations did not decline, instead increasing by ca 5% between 1984 and 1995. As a consequence, annual mean pH increased significantly across the Welsh region on average by 0.12 units. However, at 15 individual sites in the pH 5.2-5.5 range, pH increased by 0.4-0.8 pH units.

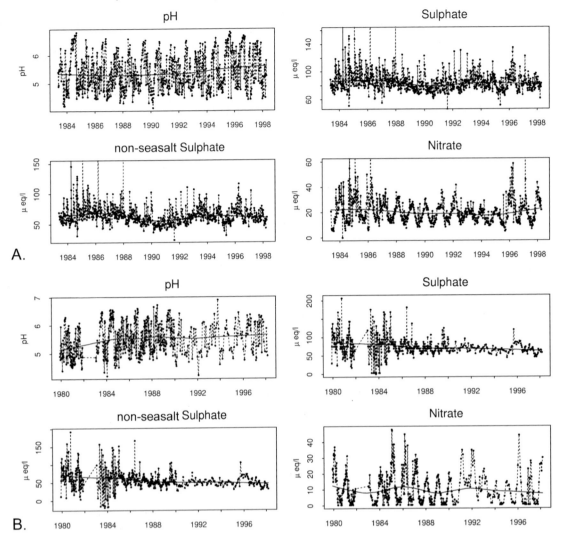

Figure 6.10 Observed changes in NO_3^-, non-seasalt SO_4^{2-} and pH since 1983 at the afforested Afon Hafren (a) and moorland Afon Gwy (b), Plynlimon, mid-Wales (Monteith and Evans 2000).

AWMN data at Llyn Llagi shows a clear chemical recovery with decreased non-seasalt SO_4^{2-} and increased pH (Figure 6.11). Both epilithic diatoms and macroinvertebrates are also showing improvement. A comparison of the diatom assemblage of sediment trap samples collected since 1991 and samples from a sediment core (taken in 1990) demonstrates that recent changes in the assemblage are approximately the reverse of those which occurred during the latter stages of acidification (Monteith and Evans, 2000).

Whereas the chemical data from Wales provide important evidence of chemical reversal in acidification, patterns in the biological data are not yet so marked. In Wales, the array of biological indicators of acidification used in survey work is comprehensive, and includes aquatic invertebrates, fish, macrophytes, river birds and, from 1995, stream diatoms. However, no biological indicator among invertebrates showed evidence of recovery from acidification between 1984 and 1995. Neither species richness, community composition, classification models nor indices of acid sensitivity changed systematically, changing instead within the range of natural variations which result from, for example, climatic effects. Furthermore, the data clearly show that invertebrates are affected by acid episodes, which might continue to limit recovery despite changes in average chemistry.

Among fish, salmon showed no increase in density between 1984 and 1995, while trout population densities across sites were lower than expected from habitat character, and were scarce or absent at sites with elevated acidity, Al, Zn and Mn. Rather than increasing between the years of the WAWS survey, there was a major and highly significant decline in density between 1984 and 1995, with few sites showing any increase.

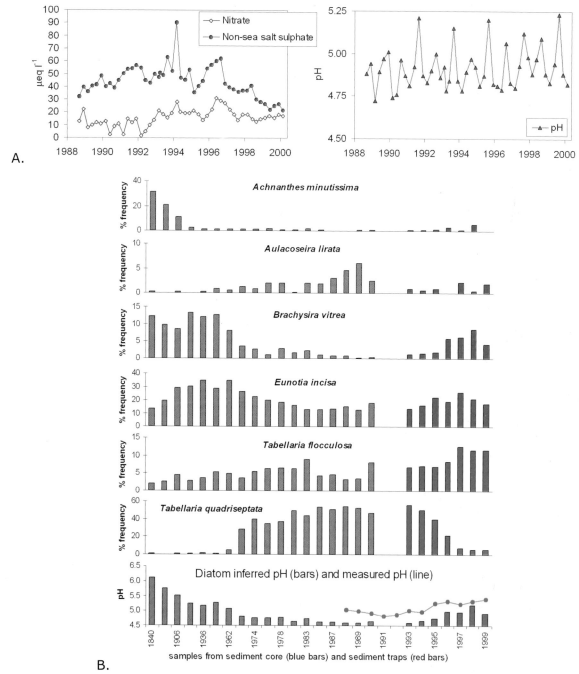

Figure 6.11 Recovery trends in AWMN data from Llyn Llagi; (a) water chemistry and (b) changes through time in the proportions of diatom species with pH change inferred from the diatom data. Samples from sediment cores (blue bars) and from sediment traps (red bars) (Monteith and Evans 2000).

Among river birds, dippers are known to be scarce at low pH. Surveys at the WAWS sites revealed birds at a near-identical proportion of sites in 1984 and 1995. However, there was a significant decline between the two surveys in the number of times per survey visit that birds were recorded per site. Geometric mean Al concentrations increased more at sites where bird records declined than where they increased.

Lake District

In the Lake District, long-term data are available from surveys undertaken by the Freshwater Biological Association and two AWMN sites, Scoat Tarn and Burnmoor Tarn. Samples of high altitude lakes in the Lake District during the 1950s and 1970s showed that there had been no significant changes in base cation concentrations and alkalinities (Sutcliffe *et al.*, 1982). The results of a further study (Tipping *et al.*, 1998) demonstrate clearly that the composition of five lakes (Levers Water, Devoke Water, Codale Tarn, Easedale Tarn and Stickle Tarn) have changed significantly during the period following the 1970s, with increases in pH in all cases, and in alkalinity in the four cases where measurements have been made (Table 6.2). For Devoke Water and Levers Water, decreases in non-seasalt SO_4^{2-} have occurred during a period in which atmospheric deposition of pollutant S has decreased and so it is reasonable to conclude that these changes are causally related. It is highly probable that there have also been decreases in non-seasalt SO_4^{2-} in Codale, Easedale and Stickle Tarns. The decrease in lakewater non-seasalt SO_4^{2-} must be the principal reason for the observed increases in pH and alkalinity and it can be concluded that the impacts of acidifying pollutants on the five water bodies are at least partially reversible (Figure 6.12). Indeed, in terms of pH, Devoke Water appears to have returned to its pre-industrial state on the evidence of diatom reconstruction, which indicates a pH of 6.5 to 7.0 during the 1850s (Atkinson and Howarth, 1990) although it must be stressed that this site has never been heavily acidified.

Table 6.2 Mean changes in pH and alkalinity between the 1970s and 1990s (Tipping *et al.*, 1998). The 'months' column shows the number of different months for which comparisons could be made.

	Months	Mean pH 1990s	Mean ΔpH	Months	Mean Alk 1990s	Mean Δalk
Codale Tarn	4	5.2	+0.26	4	-8	+24
Devoke Water	4	6.0	+0.84	1	42	+43
Easedale Tarn	3	5.7	+0.55	4	18	+16
Levers Water	12	4.8	+0.29	-	-	-
Stickle Tarn	2	6.1	+0.39	2	32	+14

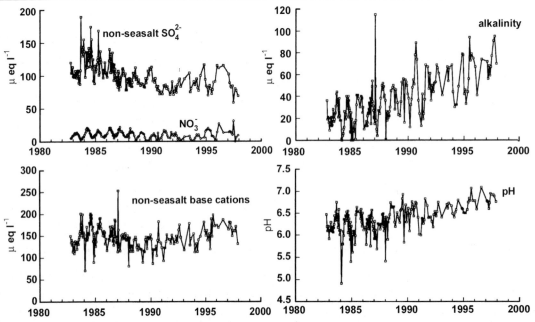

Figure 6.12 Time series from Lake District (Devoke Water).

The data also indicate that although there have been concurrent decreases in S deposition and lakewater non-seasalt SO_4^{2-} between the 1970s and 1990s, the latter has not responded quantitatively to the former. In the case of Levers Water, a decrease of *ca* 50% in S input resulted in only a *ca* 25% decrease in lakewater non-seasalt SO_4^{2-}. This may indicate that significant sulphate adsorption has occurred within the catchment soils and with reduced S input, reversible adsorption or mineralisation of organic sulphur has maintained lake SO_4^{2-} concentration and the catchment is currently a source of non-seasalt SO_4^{2-} to the lake. This may have a significant impact on the recovery of the lake, potentially delaying the improvement in pH and alkalinity.

A further important factor determining the response of catchments to changes in S deposition is the supply of base cations to percolating water, either from weathering or cation-exchange. If the rate of supply should decrease in response to decreased inputs of S then recovery of surface waters will be less likely although this would only be expected in the well buffered, higher alkalinity systems. There is no evidence of a long-term trend in the supply of base cations to either Devoke Water or Levers Water, despite the decreases in input acidity which indicates that the SO_4^{2-} and base cation chemistry is de-coupled (i.e. changes in SO_4^{2-} are not associated with changes in base cations and base cation supply is dominated by weathering rather than ion exchange in the soil) and yet in the case of Devoke Water, pH is above 6.0.

In terms of biological response to these observed chemistry changes, stream invertebrates and lake diatoms have shown a trend towards recovery at a number of sites (Tipping *et al.*, 1999 & 2000). These changes, however, are not consistent at all sites.

Of the AWMN sites, Scoat Tarn is chronically acidic with mean pH of 5.0 and non-seasalt SO_4^{2-} concentrations have been relatively stable since 1988 (Monteith and Evans, 2000). Nitrate is a more important contributor to acidity at this site than at any other site in the AMWN and NO_3^- concentrations frequently exceed non-seasalt SO_4^{2-} concentrations during Spring. At Burnmoor Tarn, non-seasalt SO_4^{2-} concentrations since 1988 are also relatively constant. No consistent trends in biological parameters have been detected at either site.

Pennines

The South Pennine uplands lie close to large industrial areas in the UK. Historically, the region has experienced severe levels of acid deposition, and although emissions have declined in recent years, total deposition of non-seasalt sulphur in 1992-94 remained above 30 kg-S ha^{-1} y^{-1}, and the total nitrogen in the range 18-30 kg-N ha^{-1} y^{-1} over the same period (RGAR, 1997). These values are among the highest recorded for either pollutant anywhere in the UK. Combined with the low buffering capacity of the underlying Millstone Grits, this has led to exceedance of critical loads of acidity by at least a factor of two throughout the region (DoE, 1995). Available surface water chemistry data reflect this sensitivity. A regional survey of lakes and reservoirs in 1998 (Evans *et al.*, 2000) showed a very high proportion of reservoirs were acidic; 27 out of 62 had a negative ANC, and 28 had a pH below 5.0. SO_4^{2-} is present in surface waters at very high concentrations, most of which is derived from non-seasalt sources. On an equivalent basis NO_3^- is less significant than SO_4^{2-} but is nevertheless present at considerably higher concentrations than in other acid-sensitive regions with median concentrations of 46 μeq l^{-1}, and a minimum of 16 μeq l^{-1}.

Time series data for a number of reservoirs in the region collected over the period 1980-98 by Yorkshire Water and North West Water (e.g. Tipping and Smith 2000) has enabled the assessment of long-term changes in surface water acidity (Figure 6.13). Robust statistical analyses have identified significant pH recovery at seven out of eight sites, covering a range of locations, soils and land-use (Evans and Jenkins, 2000). The period of recovery appears to extend back at least to 1980 and may have begun some time prior to this.

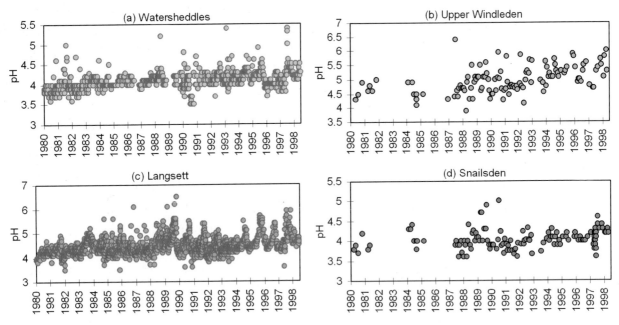

Figure 6.13 Long-term pH data for four Yorkshire Water reservoirs, South Pennines.

At the River Etherow AMMN site, there has been a clear reduction in non-seasalt SO_4^{2-} concentrations of 25-30% since 1988 (Figure 6.14). As yet there is no clear evidence of recovery in pH or alkalinity. In part this may be due to the considerable flow-dependant temporal variability at this site where pH at low flows can reach 7.0 and fall as low as 3.8 during high flows. It is also apparent, however, that NO_3^- concentrations have risen significantly over the same period. There is as yet no evidence of biological change at the site.

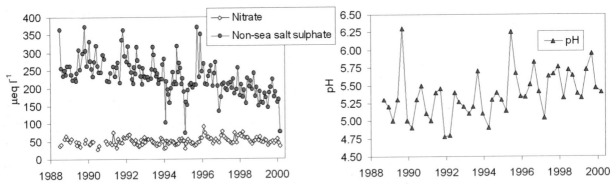

Figure 6.14 Observed changes in SO_4^{2-}, NO_3^- and pH since 1988 at the River Etherow, an AWMN site in the Pennines.

These data confirm that in the South Pennines, an area with a history of severe atmospheric pollution, significant improvement in surface water chemistry has taken place over the last two decades. With acid deposition still relatively high in the region, however, many surface waters remain acidic (ANC<0) and are unlikely to be able to support fish or other acid-sensitive aquatic species in their present state.

Southern England

Several areas of Southern England were identified as acid sensitive from the survey undertaken by the Critical Loads Advisory Group (CLAG) including streams in the Ashdown Forest, Kent and more extensively on Dartmoor (DoE, 1995). Two AWMN sites have been established to represent these areas, Old Lodge and Narrator Brook, respectively. Old Lodge is severely acidified but has experienced a large decline in non-seasalt SO_4^{2-} concentrations since 1988 (Figure 6.15a). There is little evidence of an accompanying change in acid status over the period, largely as a result of a concurrent decline in Ca^{2+} concentrations and an increase in NO_3^-. In addition, however, a general improvement in trout density and condition factor has been recorded but similar recovery has not been identified for other biological groups (Figure 6.15b).

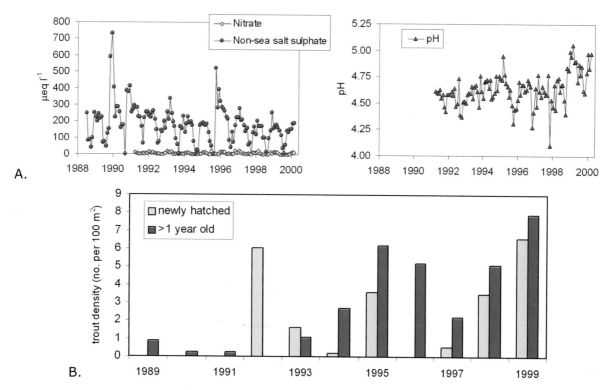

Figure 6.15 Trends in (a) water chemistry and (b) density of newly hatched trout (less than 1 year old) and older trout, at the AWMN Old Lodge site.

These data are supported by observations at the Tillingbourne catchment near Dorking, Surrey. Here, chemistry data collected over two periods, 1977-1982 and 1998-2000, indicate strong evidence of recovery from acidification (Hill *et al.* 2000). In response to a 61% decrease in volume weighted concentration of SO_4^{2-} in precipitation, streamwater SO_4^{2-} concentration has decreased from 18.0 to 16.0 mg l^{-1} and pH has increased from 4.2 to 4.5. In contrast, whilst N concentration in precipitation has decreased (37%), NO_3^- concentrations in the stream have increased from 0.7 to 2.5 mg l^{-1}.

At Narrator Brook in SW England, non-seasalt SO_4^{2-} concentrations have increased since 1991 but pH and alkalinity have also increased indicating variability induced by seasalt deposition.

Northern Ireland

The CLAG national survey carried out in 1992 (DoE, 1995) identified two acid sensitive regions in the Province characterised by low critical loads and current exceedances - the Mourne

Mountains and the Sperrin Mountains. Sediment core analysis of Blue Lough in the Mournes shows that recent acidification has taken place as for similar sites in Galloway, the Lake District and Wales. Four sites are included in the AWMN; the Blue Lough, Bencrom River, Coneyglen Burn and Beaghs Burn.

The Mourne Mountains in south-eastern Northern Ireland are underlain by tertiary granites which give rise to acid soils, mainly podzols and rankers. Surface water pH in the region is in the range 4.5-5.5 with mean nitrate concentrations of *ca* 20 μeq l^{-1} (Jordan and Enlander, 1990). The two AWMN sites in this region, the Bencrom River and Blue Lough, are chronically acidified with mean pH of 5.2 and 4.7, respectively, in response to high levels of S deposition. The last 10 years have seen a decline in non-seasalt SO_4^{2-} concentration at Blue Lough but, as yet, no observable trend in pH (Figure 6.16). Both sites also exhibit very high NO_3^- concentrations although there is no evidence of a consistent increasing trend over the last 10 years (Monteith and Evans 2000).

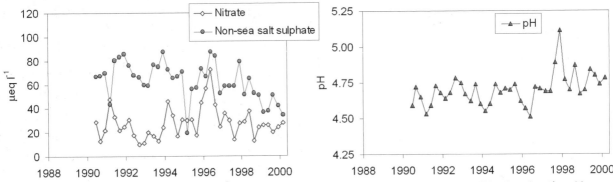

Figure 6.16 Observed changes in SO_4^{2-}, NO_3^- and pH at Blue Lough, an AWMN site in the Mourne Mountains, N Ireland.

6.4 Chemical and Biological Recovery

Since the late 1970s, SO_4^{2-} concentrations have decreased in surface waters in Galloway, Central Scotland and the Lake District. This is in line with large reductions in S deposition in these areas up to the mid-1980s. The decline in SO_4^{2-} concentration has led to a documented improvement in pH and ANC. In other regions, long-term data are not available but it is likely that similar reductions in SO_4 and, consequently, improvements in acid status have occurred.

From the mid 1980s to the mid 1990s streamwater non-seasalt SO_4^{2-} concentrations across the whole of the UK were essentially constant. Concentrations of all ions were, however, extremely variable through this period as a result of influences of other factors such as seasalt deposition and climate. Since the mid 1990s, large declines in non-seasalt SO_4^{2-} concentrations have been recorded at sites in areas that are relatively close to emission sources, i.e. Old Lodge, south-east England (Figure 6.15) and the River Etherow, Pennines (Figure 6.14). Smaller, but still significant declines in concentration have occurred at many upland sites throughout the UK (e.g. Figures 6.4 and 6.6). This most recent decrease is accompanied by decreased acidity and labile aluminium at these sites and indicates further widespread recovery from acidification across the UK (Evans and Monteith, 2000). The present situation in the UK surface waters, therefore, is characterised by the lowest documented concentrations of non-seasalt SO_4^{2-} ever observed, with the exception perhaps of the extreme NW and SW of the mainland UK where anthropogenic S deposition is low.

In addition, changes in acid/base status reflected by ANC or alkalinity have broadly followed the changes in non-seasalt SO_4^{2-} in a linear response. For pH, the picture is not so clear as at some sites the pH has not changed in response to quite large reductions in non-seasalt SO_4^{2-}. The controls on this are at present unknown but seasalt deposition and climate influences are the likely confounding factors.

Given that the reductions in non-seasalt SO_4^{2-} are most dramatic at heavily impacted sites and that these reductions have not yet provided improvements in chemical acidity status to the levels required to support biological "recovery", widespread biological changes should not be anticipated. Nevertheless, at the lowest trophic level, i.e. epilithic diatoms, species changes indicative of an increase in pH are observed at most lake sites which show significant trends in pH, for example at Llyn Llagi (Figure 6.11). For the streams, there is strong, although indirect, evidence from rainfall data and flow/pH relationships, that the diatom community reflects mean summer acidity. At sites such as the River Etherow that undergo large variation in pH as hydrological pathways change in response to rainfall, substantial improvements in pH at high flow will be necessary before effects are likely to be detectable in diatom time series. The other primary producer group, the aquatic macrophytes, provide no indication of response to temporal change in pH. For invertebrates, there is little evidence of improvement with the exceptions of Llyn Llagi and Loch Chon. For trout, only Old Lodge indicates an improvement (Figure 6.15b). Overall, the year to year variability in population data, the expected time lags involved between chemistry changes and biological changes and the influence of other factors such as flow variation, have so far precluded a clear observation of biological improvement.

6.5 Confounding Factors

The lack of consistent trends across the UK is to be expected given the spatial variation in soils, geology, climate and acidic deposition. Different physico-chemical characteristics within catchments will promote different rates of recovery, which are likely to be non-linear. This problem of non-linearity will also be pronounced in the link between surface water chemistry and biological recovery since other factors contribute to ecological responses such as energy inputs, physical barriers, species mobility, etc.

Detection of trends in time-series water quality data in response to changes in the deposition of S and N from the atmosphere is also hampered by changes in other ecosystem driving variables such as land-use and climate. These confounding factors impart a signal in the water chemistry record that can mask the impact of decreased deposition. In addition, the strong correlation between flow and water chemistry at stream sites and the rapid flow response to rainfall in upland areas imparts noise into the long-term signal since samples are taken at best monthly and flow changes can occur over a period of hours.

6.5.1 Climate

Recent analysis of UKAWMN data (Monteith *et al.* 2000, 2001) has established several potential links between change in chemical and biological variables and the North Atlantic Oscillation Index (NAOI, see Appendix A). The NAOI represents the oscillating air pressure difference between the Iberian peninsula Azores region and the Icelandic region of the North Atlantic and has been shown to exert a dominant effect over weather in the UK, particularly during winter. High NAOI values during winter correspond to periods of frontally dominated weather, characterised by strong westerly winds, high rainfall and relatively mild air temperatures. Negative values imply the presence of high-pressure system over the Icelandic region and this results in cold and relatively dry weather dominated by north-easterly winds.

At 19 of the 22 sites in the UKAWMN, significant rising trends in DOC have been observed over the last 10 years. This change could potentially increase ANC concentration. It is not currently possible to identify the mechanism for these increases or, therefore, to predict whether they will continue into the future. It is unlikely that this is linked to observed changes in sulphur because of the widespread regional occurrence. The most likely hypothesis is considered to be increased microbial decomposition of soil organic matter resulting from increased summer temperatures. The biological impacts of these increases are likely to be varied, including: reduced light penetration due to increased water colour which could restrict the depth of plant growth; reduced penetration of potentially damaging UV-B radiation; reduced fish toxicity under acidic conditions due to organic complexation of aluminium.

6.5.2 Sea-Salts

Whilst Cl^- deposited in the catchment is considered to be conservative, accompanying cations have been shown to undergo chemical reactions through the 'seasalt effect' (Wright et al., 1988b). High soil water concentrations of seasalt cations, primarily Na^+ and Mg^{2+}, cause displacement of other cations held on the soil exchange complex which are then leached to surface waters. Na^+ and Mg^{2+} are in turn displaced as soil water concentrations return to pre-event levels giving no overall change in either soil or surface water composition. The seasalt effect is generally considered as a short-term process focusing on episodic acidification due to H^+ displacement from ion exchange sites.

Inter-annual variability in levels of seasalt deposition has been identified as a cause of chemical variation in the UKAWMN dataset (Evans and Monteith 2001). The majority of UKAWMN sites lie within 50 km of western or southern coasts and receive large seasalt inputs during westerly or south-westerly frontal storms. The frequency of these storms has been shown to vary substantially from year to year, with maxima associated with high winter values of the NAOI.

Seasalt ion concentrations at near-coastal sites have consequently shown highly consistent cyclical variations, with a major peak during the high NAOI 1989-1991 period. Through cation exchange processes associated with the seasalt effect, cyclical variations have also been observed in non-seasalt cations, including H^+ and labile Al, generating more acidic conditions during high seasalt years. Alkalinity and pH are also likely to be depressed by higher than average rainfall during stormy, high NAOI periods. It is possible that a parallel process of SO_4^{2-} adsorption and desorption may also operate, leading to cyclical fluctuations in calculated non-seasalt SO_4^{2-} that are unrelated to variations in pollutant S inputs.

6.5.3 Nitrogen Breakthrough

In areas of low N deposition, nitrogen is cycled fairly tightly within the terrestrial ecosystem and the major out-flow is gaseous emissions of N from denitrification, mainly as N_2 but also N_2O. Concentrations in surface waters tend to be very low or zero during the summer when plant uptake requirement is high and more pronounced in the winter when plant uptake is reduced to near zero. When N deposition is increased, plant uptake requirement may increase slightly but soil immobilisation increases to maintain a low loss of N in surface waters. As high N deposition continues, soil C:N ratio decreases and the soil microbial population becomes less able to sustain the higher rate of immobilisation and as a result, NO_3^- leakage to surface waters increases. This process has been termed N-saturation and breakthrough (Aber *et al.*, 1989). N saturation has been described as occurring in a series of stages (Stoddard, 1994) that reflect the temporal trend in surface water NO_3^- concentrations on an annual basis. Sites in the UK demonstrate stage 0, 1 and 2 of N-saturation (Figure 6.17) but the cause of observed increases in NO_3^- concentration over the last 10 years at Lochnagar, Round Loch of Glenhead, Loch Chon and the River Etherow is not known and could be linked to climatic variation rather than N saturation. At Lochnagar, for example, (Figure 6.9) NO_3^- increased in the mid 1990s at the same time as non-seasalt SO_4^{2-} decreased promoting a net trend towards further acidification (decreasing pH). Since the mid 1990s, NO_3^- concentration has decreased and with continued non-seasalt SO_4^{2-} decline, pH has recently increased. At other sites, however, if this increased NO_3^- is the result of N-saturation in the soil, the increasing trend would be expected to continue with further decreased pH resulting.

Nitrate variability is also linked to climate and UKAWMN data show a link between the magnitude of annual peaks in NO_3^- concentration, normally observed in early spring, and the NAOI over the preceding winter months (Monteith *et al.* 2001, in press). The largest concentrations occur following low NAOI period and are, therefore, associated with the coldest, driest winters. For example, climatic variation may have promoted the increased NO_3^- at Lochnagar. Nevertheless, at areas of high N deposition, the possibility of increased NO_3^- leakage as a result of soil saturation cannot be excluded.

6.5.4 Forestry

The debate over the link between afforestation and surface water acidification was a key issue through the 1970s and '80s which prompted the initiation of a number of paired catchment studies and comparisons, e.g. Llyn Brianne, Plynlimon, Galloway etc. The effects and relationships are now well known; afforestation results in lower pH and increased aluminium concentrations in streams draining heavily afforested catchments in areas receiving acid deposition (Ormerod *et al.*, 1989). There are also effects on other solutes, such as nitrate (Reynolds *et al.*, 1994). Sulphate and aluminium concentrations are elevated in soil waters beneath mature forest canopies, in turn explaining increased aluminium at forest sites. The effect is due largely to increased S and N deposition onto the forest canopy at high altitude, coupled possibly with decreased dilution from increased evapotranspiration and increased uptake of base cations (Cosby *et al.*, 1990). Short-term effects on N release following felling, and additional effects on Cl^- deposition and hence acid episodes, are also possible (Neal and Reynolds, 1999).

6.6 Future Predictions

Given the existing evidence which confirms that the impacts of atmospheric S deposition are, at least partially, reversible in terms of surface water chemistry, the key question that remains is the degree of recovery we might expect in the future in response to the most recently agreed emission reduction targets under the Gothenburg Protocol. This has been assessed to a degree by comparing the critical load exceedance for freshwaters with the predicted deposition in 2010 assuming the emission reductions are achieved.

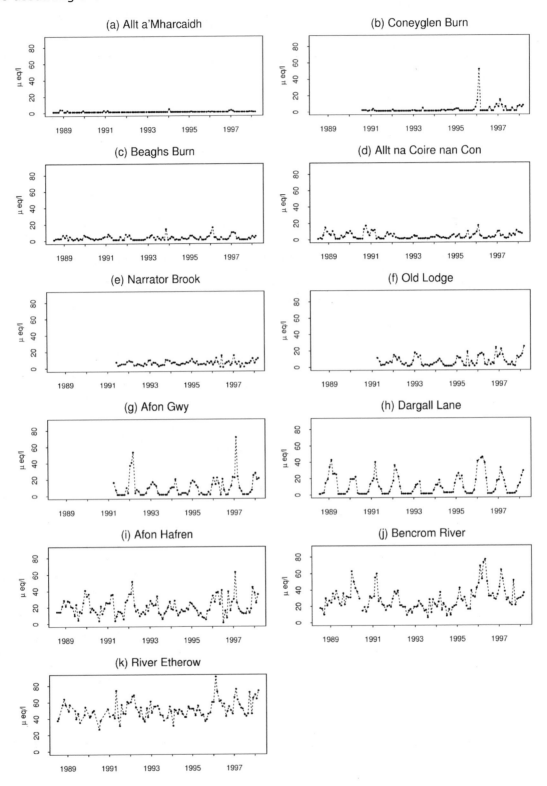

Figure 6.17 Nitrate time series for UKAWMN stream sites.

Using modelled deposition data for 2010 (HARM/FRAME; see Chapter 4) changes in critical load exceedance have been assessed for freshwater sites (CLAG) in Britain (Curtis *et al.*, 1999). Under the Gothenburg Protocol scenario, only 18% of sampled sites would be exceeding their critical loads in 2010 (Figure 6.18). It must be stressed, however, that non-exceedance of the critical load does not imply either chemical or biological recovery at the time that is achieved. The FAB model calculates a steady-state critical load with no indication of recovery time. This implied recovery must also be interpreted with caution given uncertainty in predicted deposition to these small upland catchments. In addition, the model calculations are based on the assumption that ANC = 0 is an appropriate threshold for the presence/absence of a Brown Trout population. The biological relevance of achieving ANC = 0 is questionable, particularly in cases where species are damaged by acidic pulses. These episodes may persist even after a mean annual ANC of zero is achieved such that the biota do not recover. There are also other factors that will affect the rate of biological recovery at a site.

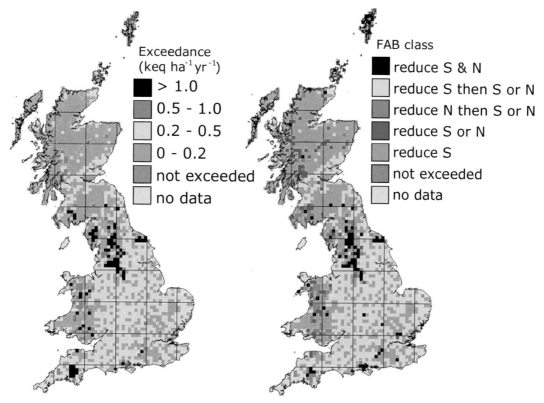

Figure 6.18 (a) Critical load exceedance calculated with the First-order Acidity Balance (FAB) model for UK freshwaters using ANCcrit = 0 μeq/l and Gothenburg Protocol (2010) deposition data. (b): Deposition reduction requirements from 2010 (Gothenburg Protocol) levels according to the FAB model for UK freshwaters using ANCcrit = 0 μeq l^{-1}.

It is often assumed that by achieving the critical load for freshwater the system has been protected. This is certainly the case over a long time period but, in order to estimate the potential time lags in recovery, a dynamic modelling approach must be used. In the UK the Model of Acidification of Groundwaters In Catchments (MAGIC) model has been used extensively to assess the expected time-scale of recovery for a range of emission/deposition scenarios (Jenkins *et al.*, 1998; Evans *et al.*, 1998; Sefton and Jenkins, 1998; Helliwell *et al.*, 1998b). Most recently, the calibrated models for Wales (Collins and Jenkins, 1998) and the Pennines have been used to assess the impact of the agreed emissions reduction under the Gothenburg Protocol.

Assuming that the required emission reductions are achieved linearly by 2010, the model predicts that 94% of lakes/reservoirs in the Pennines will have ANC concentrations above zero by 2050 (Figure 6.19). In Wales, all modelled lakes achieve ANC greater than zero by 2050 (Figure 6.20). The fact that these results represent the percentage of 'lakes modelled' must be stressed since not all surface waters in these regions were sampled and those sampled do not necessarily reflect a statistically representative population of all streams and lakes. Nevertheless, the predictions are encouraging and demonstrate that the agreed emission reductions are likely to promote significant chemical recovery. The model also indicates, however, that at the most acidified sites, time-lags of the order of several decades are likely between achieving the critical load and 'recovery' of surface water chemistry above zero ANC.

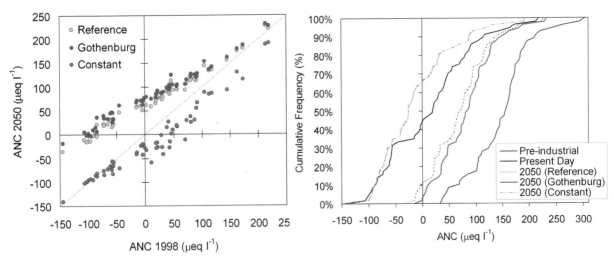

Figure 6.19 Cumulative frequency distributions of ANC for present day (surveyed 1998) and modelled pre-industrial using MAGIC in the south Pennines. Future predictions, also using MAGIC, are for 2050 under three deposition scenarios; constant at 1990 levels; the 2nd Sulphur Protocol (Reference) scenario; and the Gothenburg Protocol. Future deposition scenarios are derived from emissions projections using the HARM model.

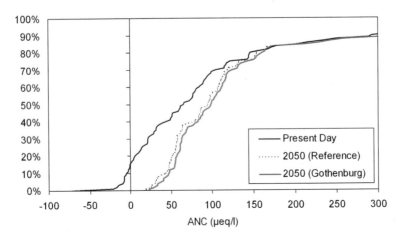

Figure 6.20 Cumulative ANC frequency distribution for surface waters in Wales from MAGIC simulations for present day (1995) and for 2050 under the 2nd Sulphur Protocol (Reference) and Gothenburg Protocol (Gothenburg). The scenario assumes the emission reductions are achieved by 2010 and held constant at that level thereafter.

At sites where diatom, present day and modelled future chemistry data exist the recovery from acidification over the last *ca* 20 years can be seen to be rather small in relation to the overall acidification (Figure 6.21). It is predicted, however, that significant improvements in water chemistry will occur if current international agreements are achieved within the agreed timescale but a return to pre-acidification conditions will require greater reductions and will take many decades.

Interpretation of the dynamic model output at any site must, however, be undertaken cautiously since the controls on the behaviour of N in catchment systems is still not well understood. Further development of the MAGIC model is required to better predict N retention in catchments and N release to surface waters. In addition, a technique must be developed to couple predictions of mean annual water chemistry with estimates of episodic acidity extremes since this is likely to be the main influence on biological recovery (particularly brown trout) in both lakes and streams.

Given the potential time-lags in biological recovery, relative to water chemistry, the full re-establishment of pre-acidification biological communities may be significantly delayed. Species already present in reduced abundance should be able to respond rapidly to ameliorating conditions, whereas the re-colonization rate of species that have been entirely lost from a water body will depend on many factors, especially the proximity of refuge populations and their dispersal efficiency. Predicting the timing of biological responses is not yet possible since the dynamic elements of these biological processes are not well understood. Current research is at a stage of identifying reference sites, principally in north-west Scotland, to define the structure and functioning of non-acidified streams. Data from these sites will then be used to define biological targets for the recovery of acidified streams and lakes in other parts of the country. These data would be added to chemical/biological databases to improve assessments of the probable responses of biota to chemical change.

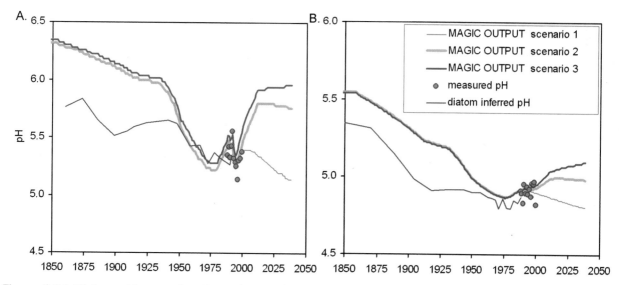

Figure 6.21 Diatom pH reconstruction, observed AWMN data and MAGIC reconstruction and prediction for Lochnagar (a) and Round Loch of Glenhead (b). Scenario 1 represents no further deposition requirement above present day level: Scenario 2 represents the Gothenburg Protocol with a 'worst case' assumption regarding NO_3^- leaching, and, Scenario 3 represents the Gothenburg Protocol with a 'best curve' assumption regarding NO_3^- leaching.

Chapter 7: Effects on Vegetation

> - Decreases in SO_2 concentrations over the past two to three decades have had detectable effects on vegetation, including substantial increases in the distribution of many lichen species, improved tree growth in certain areas and increased likelihood of sulphur deficiency in crops.

> - Instances of change in vegetation composition observed throughout the UK are consistent with effects of nitrogen deposition. Community composition in several nutrient poor habitats is changing towards species associated with higher nitrogen availability. Effects of habitat management are also implicated in these changes.

> - There is no field evidence of recovery of vegetation composition in the UK in response to reduced N deposition, and such responses are expected to lag by several decades. Simple reversal of change may not be possible, and active site management may be needed to promote recovery.

> - Current O_3 concentrations in the UK have been shown experimentally to reduce tree growth, cause visible leaf injury, reduce crop yield and affect semi-natural vegetation. Peak concentrations are falling but the implications of this for vegetation are uncertain.

> - The AOT40 exposure index currently used for O_3 risk assessment in Europe has several limitations, most notably the fact that data from the experimental conditions in which it was derived are not directly applicable in field conditions.

> - Surveys of tree condition since 1987 have not identified a chronic deterioration in the UK, related to air pollution. However, there is clear evidence of the effects of drought, and insect and fungal attack on some species in specific areas, and air pollution may play a role in predisposing trees to such effects.

> - By 2010, most of the country will be protected from the direct adverse effects of SO_2. However, ozone and nitrogen deposition are likely to still pose a major threat to vegetation in the UK.

> - The empirical critical loads for nutrient nitrogen which are currently used for UK mapping may be too high to reflect adverse ecological change in some ecosystems, and need to be reviewed.

> - Critical levels of SO_2 and NO_x may be exceeded close to some major roads, industrial works and urban areas, and the implications of such exceedances on sites of high nature conservation value in such locations need to be examined in more detail.

> - More sophisticated methods of ecological risk assessment need to be developed to provide a closer link between critical loads and levels and actual impacts on vegetation, taking into account factors such as land management, climate, soil water and nutrient status and initial species composition.

7.1 Background

The aim of this chapter is to critically assess the evidence that current levels of air pollution affect vegetation in the UK. The chapter also considers the evidence that changes in pollution levels over the past 20-30 years, and in particular decreases in SO_2 concentrations and sulphur deposition, have caused detectable changes in vegetation, and assesses the likely implications of future changes in air pollution concentrations.

This chapter does not aim to be comprehensive; rather, it focuses on key issues and key evidence, and also identifies important knowledge gaps. It builds on assessments of the impacts of air pollution on vegetation in the UK provided in previous DETR reports, especially those of the Critical Loads Advisory Group on critical levels and loads, those of the Photo-oxidant Review Group on the impacts of ozone, and two reports from the early 1990s on the impacts of nitrogen deposition (INDITE) and on the link between air pollution and tree health. For a more general overview of air pollution impacts on vegetation, there are many useful review articles. Several excellent reviews of the effects of N deposition on vegetation have recently been published; (Lee & Caporn, 1998, Aerts & Bobbink, 1999), and there are also a number of journal special issues covering this topic (New Phytologist 139(1); Environmental Pollution 102(S1); Forest Ecology and Management 101).

This chapter considers the impacts of different pollutants in turn, evaluating effects on agriculture, forestry and semi-natural vegetation, as appropriate. In many cases, especially for the impacts of acid deposition and nitrogen deposition on forestry or semi-natural vegetation, effects on vegetation need to be considered alongside those on soils that were assessed in Chapter 5. In particular, when considering the dynamics of vegetation responses to air pollution, it is useful to distinguish between direct effects of the pollutants on the plant and indirect effects mediated through changes in soil chemistry, for which the speed of change in response to reductions in deposition may be much slower. References to the links between vegetation responses and those of soils that were described in a previous chapter will be provided at appropriate points.

7.1.1 Nature of Evidence

It is useful firstly to review the nature of the evidence that is available to us, and the constraints this places on our ability to make statements about impacts of air pollution in the UK. Essentially three major types of evidence are available, which can be placed along two contrasting gradients of increasing certainty of ascribing cause-effect relationships and increasing relevance to field conditions.

Field observations provide evidence for changes in plant performance or species composition; however, such changes may be due to many causes apart from air pollution (and indeed to interactions between causal factors, including air pollution). Spatial associations between pollutant exposure and vegetation response may be readily demonstrated around point sources, where the large gradients in pollutant exposure are the dominant causal factor, but are more difficult to demonstrate on a regional scale. Temporal associations provide an even greater challenge in terms of separating the effects of air pollution from those of other variables, especially climate and management, particularly given the lagged responses of vegetation to many stress factors. Space/time associations, especially when there are good baseline data, provide the strongest test of field associations. However, although UK vegetation has been extensively surveyed over the years, very few, if any, appropriate UK data exist for such analyses, as the data have not normally been collected for the purpose of elucidating the impacts of air pollution.

Field experiments allow manipulation of pollution inputs under field conditions, and the study of ecosystem response. However, there are a number of important limitations to such studies

(Green *et al.*, 1997). Pollution inputs often do not simulate the patterns of field exposures, and experiments cannot normally deal with reductions, as opposed to increases, in pollutant deposition. Experiments may not be continued for the length of time required to show effects; use of very high pollutant exposures can reduce the response time, but there is no certainty that responses to an experimental pollutant dose given as a short-term high exposure are comparable to those to the same dose given as a longer-term low exposure. Plot size and replication are often a problem, and extrapolation from a single field experiment at a specific site to the wider countryside raises significant problems.

Laboratory or field chamber experiments allow more controlled manipulation of a range of pollutant concentrations. Such experiments usually involve isolated plants in artificial rooting environment – often well supplied with nutrients and water. Chamber environments provide artificial growth conditions compared with the field, and extrapolation to field conditions is problematic. Such experiments are usually of limited duration, and their interpretation in terms of long-term effects of air pollutants is difficult. The limitations of experimental approaches are least for annual crops, and greatest for long-lived mixed-species forest stands.

Models are also a possible method of assessing pollutant impacts. Such models, especially when they have a mechanistic basis, can allow the long-term implications of experimental or field data for vegetation response to be assessed. There is increasing international interest in modelling approaches as tools to assess, for example, long-term effects on forest growth, but there has been little application of this approach in the UK to date.

7.2 Evidence of Change from Field Surveys and Observations

As noted in the previous section, field observations provide an important source of evidence of changes in species distributions, or of vitality and growth, which may be caused by air pollution. However, in the UK relatively few such studies have been designed specifically to capture the impact of air pollution; in other cases, national or local datasets obtained for other reasons have been analysed in the context of air pollution. In this section, we consider some of the key evidence, assessing the extent to which it may be possible to link the observed changes to concurrent changes in air pollutant concentrations or deposition.

7.2.1 Forestry

As a result of concerns over the health of the nation's woodlands, the UK tree health survey was initiated in 1986 and since that date, has assessed the health of five major forestry species (oak, beech, Sitka spruce, Norway spruce, Scots pine) at over 300 sites on an annual basis. Forest condition is estimated from the degree of transparency of 24 trees in each plot. Crown transparency or crown density is affected by a number of factors including leaf or needle senescence and fall, defoliation resulting from insects or fungal pathogens, tree age, recent storms and the extent of coning or seed production in conifers and broadleaves, respectively. High crown transparency is indicative of poor forest condition, and other indices such as foliar discolouration, flowering and insect or fungal damage are also recorded.

The results are reported annually as Forestry Commission Information notes, with data up to 1999 given in Figure 7.1 (Redfern *et al.*, 2000). There has been little change observed in Scots pine or Norway spruce, but a gradual improvement in Sitka spruce. The inter-annual variations in this species partly coincide with *Elatobium abietinum* (green spruce aphid) infestation reducing crown density. There have been large inter-annual changes in the crown condition of beech corresponding to either summer droughts (e.g. 1993), or significant preceding 'mast' (seed) years, although no overall trend is evident. Initial analyses of the trends in crown density suggest that there may have been a significant deterioration in the condition of oak since 1987. However, the data require further analysis before these trends can be confirmed (Redfern *et al.*, 2000).

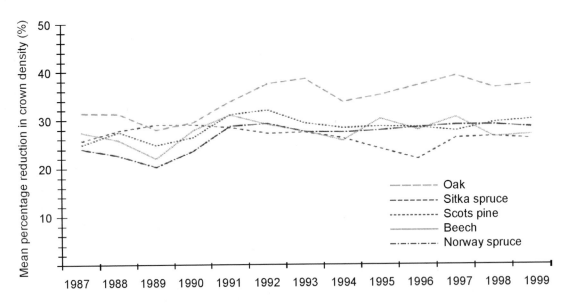

Figure 7.1 Crown condition from 1987 to 1999 for the ~300 National Forest Health Monitoring Plots (Redfern *et al.*, 2000, reproduced with permission of the Forestry Commission ©Crown Copyright 2000).

This survey work has led to more detailed diagnostic work on a number of sites over the years. For oak, damage from the winter moths *Operophtera brumata* and *Erannis defoliaria* has accounted for poor crown density, while the blight fungus *Cucurbitaria piceae* was important in 1999. Furthermore, there is widespread concern in Europe over the role of root *Phytophthora spp.* in oak decline. However, there is no convincing evidence that there is widespread chronic damage to UK forests as a result of acid deposition or air pollution – it is most likely that any impacts of air pollution are mediated through a heightened predisposition to natural injury resulting from climate effects (Mather *et al.*,1995), particularly drought, or pathogen and insect attack. These observations should also be placed in the context of a changing global climate, where direct effects on forest condition are likely together with indirect effects acting through changing selection pressures on pest, pathogen and insect populations (Straw, 1995; Evans et., 1996; Brasier, 1999).

A sub-set of ninety of the 300+ national tree health plots are also part of a pan-European monitoring programme across 19 countries and 5700 plots (UN/ECE ICP Forests Level I network). Of the six species assessed in detail, a widespread deterioration of holm oak and maritime pine is the most noticeable trend (Figure. 7.2; Fischer *et al.*, 2000). There has also been some decline in crown condition of European oak, in line with UK observations. In addition to crown condition, increment is measured (five yearly), and foliar chemical composition (five yearly), soil description (single measurement) and soil chemical composition (ten yearly) assessments have also been made.

The crown condition assessment involves more detailed measurements than the national tree health survey, including needle retention, and an initial analysis of UK data has revealed that poor needle retention in Scots pine is associated with larger total nitrogen deposition (Figure 7.3; Kennedy and Freer-Smith, 2000).

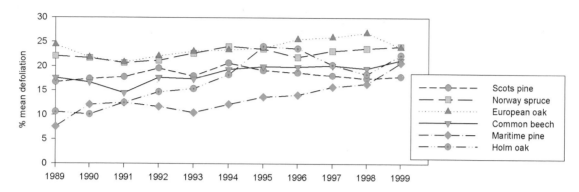

Figure 7.2 Crown condition recorded in 5700 UN/ECE Level I Forest Health Monitoring Plots from 1989 to 1999 (Fischer *et al.*, 2000).

Further analysis of this level I dataset has indicated a significant relationship between total nitrogen deposition and the frequency of insect damaged trees (Figure. 7.4; Kennedy and Freer-Smith, 2000). The correlation between climatic factors, such as temperature, and both needle retention and insect damage is much weaker than that with nitrogen deposition, suggesting a cause-effect relationship between nitrogen deposition and crown condition. Further work relating forest condition to soil critical loads is currently underway.

These national evaluations are still at an early stage, and it may be that other relationships become evident in time. A further sub-set of ten of the ninety 'Level I' sites have been designated 'Level II - Intensive Monitoring Plots' (UK plots set up in 1994/5) including measurements of pollutant input (throughfall), meteorology, biannual foliar chemical analysis, phenology, ground vegetation, leaf area (at selected sites - litter traps) and soil water analysis (lysimeters) in addition to the standard 'Level I' measurements. No national evaluations have been possible to date.

The large number of plots available in the pan-European studies enables a more thorough and far-reaching statistical analysis to be undertaken across a wider range of climatic and air pollution environments (Klap *et al.*, 1997), indicating which drivers of forest condition may be of most influence. This analysis has indicated that, particularly in the case of beech, the inclusion of terms for ozone exposure (AOT60), NO_2 and SO_2 concentration increases the variation in crown condition that can be explained by the defined models.

Yield data are also available both within the UK and across Europe, which indicate changes in growth rate, but do not necessarily identify changes in forest condition. In an analysis of 22 studies across Europe, Spiecker *et al.* (1996) demonstrated a significant increase in site index commonly by 20-50% (Figure 7.5). This was also true for most conifer plantations in northern Britain, which increased in General Yield Class by a mean of about 1 m^3 ha^{-1} y^{-1} per decade (Cannell *et al.*, 1998). A part of this increase can be attributed to improved silvicultural practices and to the fact that many European forests grow on sites recovering from previous nutrient depletion by centuries of litter removal ('litter raking') and/or agriculture. It has also been demonstrated that much of the rise in productivity of UK forests can be explained by the changing age structure of the national forest estate (Worrell, 1987; Worrell and Malcolm, 1990).

However, substantial evidence from observations, experiments and models suggests that nitrogen deposition, combined with increasing atmospheric CO_2 levels and temperatures have promoted, and may still be benefiting, European forest growth (Cannell, 1999).

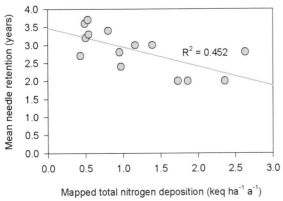

Figure 7.3 Relationship between mean needle retention and mapped total nitrogen deposition for Level 1 Scots pine plots; data are for 1996 (after Kennedy and Freer-Smith, 2000).

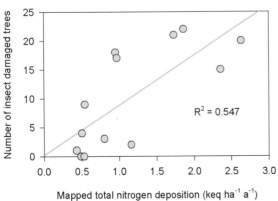

Figure 7.4 Relationship between observed number of insect damaged trees and mapped total nitrogen deposition for Level 1 Scots pine plots; data are for 1996 (after Kennedy and Freer-Smith, 2000).

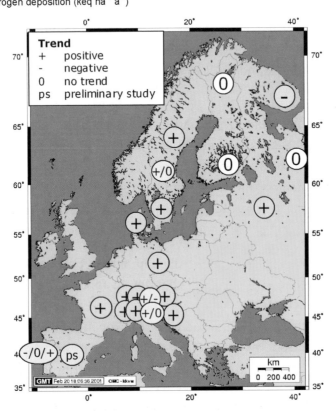

Figure 7.5 An assessment of European forest plots where site indices were demonstrated to have increased. (after Spiecker et al., 1996, NB the political boundaries do not show changes post 1989).

7.2.2 Semi-Natural Vegetation

There is no systematic assessment of air pollution impacts on vegetation comparable with the national tree health surveys. The Statutory Conservation Agencies (i.e. English Nature, Countryside Council for Wales, Scottish Natural Heritage and the Joint Nature Conservation Committee) do not currently undertake systematic monitoring or assessment of air pollution impacts upon habitat health. Nevertheless, there is a national survey of vegetation composition in Great Britain, the Countryside Survey, which was carried out in 1978, 1990 and 1998. This was based initially on 256 1 km squares, within which fixed recording plots were established within each land cover type. The Countryside Survey can detect patterns of change over time in species composition, rather than in the health of individual plants. To elucidate possible causes of change in vegetation composition, including both pollution and changing patterns of land use management, use was made of the Ellenberg classification which assigns a value to each species in terms of its optimal soil pH, moisture, fertility and light (Hill *et al.*, 1999).

The clearest pointer to the influence of pollutants is a widespread tendency for changes in species composition to favour those plants more suited to fertile conditions, which is accompanied by deleterious change in species richness in several habitats (Firbank *et al.*, 2000; Haines-Young *et al.*, 2000). Figure 7.6 shows the results for change over the period 1990-1998 for eight broad habitats for three types of plot. There was a consistent small increase in the fertility index in all three types of plot in infertile grassland, upland wooded, moorland grass and heath/bog, although the effects were not statistically significant in every case. In contrast, fertile grassland did not show any change, while the index for crops and weeds showed a decrease in fertility index. Thus the increases in fertility index were concentrated in the habitats of lower nutrient status, as might be expected if nitrogen deposition was a contributing cause.

There is some evidence that these changes across the country are due at least in part to nitrogen deposition rather than to change in land use practice (effects of nitrogen deposition on vegetation are discussed in detail in Section 7.5) (Firbank *et al.*, 2000). In contrast, Ellenberg indices for pH showed no evidence of shifts towards vegetation with a preference for acidic conditions. In fact, in some habitats there are small increases in species preferring *less* acidic conditions, concomitant with an apparent increase in soil pH (Haines-Young *et al.*, 2000). These findings suggest that nitrogen deposition is posing a continued threat to semi-natural vegetation in Britain, but that acidification is not currently causing detectable change.

7.3 Sulphur Dioxide and Nitrogen Oxides

7.3.1 Responses to Falling SO$_2$ Levels

The UK has one of the most diverse lichen flora in the world. The British Lichen Society has maintained a national database of lichen observations, which records the presence of individual lichen species within a 10 km square. Historical records and field observations clearly document the widespread loss of lichen species across many areas of England from the last century, with air pollution levels and changes in land use being the most likely causes. There were large differences in the extent of the loss of different species, largely reflecting their sensitivity to sulphur dioxide; indeed, methods were developed of mapping SO_2 concentrations using the range of lichen species found at different sites (Hawksworth & Rose, 1970). The patterns of re-invasion since then can provide important insights into the processes and timescales of biological recovery in response to falling pollution levels. As described in Chapter 2, low-level emissions of SO_2 have fallen by an order of magnitude from their peak in 1970 to the present. The national database provides a valuable picture of the recovery in the distributions of different lichen species that have occurred over this period in response to the dramatic decline in SO_2 concentrations. A key feature of the data is the large difference in the rate of recovery between species, which are illustrated in Figure 7.7.

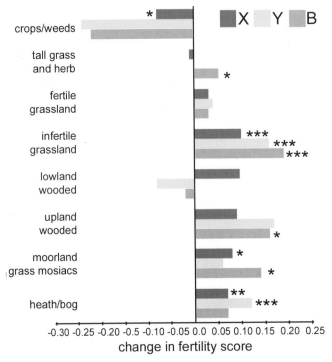

Figure 7.6 Changes in the mean fertility score for main (X), boundary (B) and targeted plots (Y) in Great Britain 1990-98. Plots are classified according to the vegetation type present in 1990. Main (X) refers to randomly selected plots in 1 km x 1 km survey squares, boundary (B) plots are located on the boundary of main plots and targeted (Y) are selected to sample the least abundant habitats in the survey square (Haines-Young *et al.,* 2000). Statistically significant changes are indicated as * P<0.05; ** P<0.01; *** P<0.001. (after Haines-Young *et al.,* 2000).

The blue squares in Figure 7.7 represent records of the species made since 1963, while the red squares represent new records made since 1980. The grey squares represent records from the 19th century in squares for which no 20th century record exists, and serve to confirm that the species did historically occur at sites at which it was no longer found in the latter half of the 20th century. The black line on the maps represents an estimate of the areas where the SO_2 concentrations around 1970 exceeded the threshold for effects on the most sensitive lichen species, while the yellow area represents the potential distribution of the species, based primarily on climatic variables.

For *Lobaria pulmonaria*, the most SO_2-sensitive species illustrated in Figure 7.7, there have been almost no new records since 1980 in the zone of historically elevated SO_2 levels. The same is true for *Physica aipolia*, despite the greater number of records between 1963 and 1980 in the affected zone. Hence, both these species have shown very little recovery in response to falling SO_2 levels. In contrast, *Xanthoria polycarpa* shows large numbers of new records, i.e. a rapid recovery, since 1980 over the historically affected zone. It is also noticeable in Figure 7.7 that there are substantial numbers of new records for *Xanthoria polycarpa* and *Physica aipolia* in areas such as Devon and mid-Wales which historically had low SO$_2$ concentrations; it is possible that this may reflect an impact of increased nitrogen deposition.

Seaward (1998) provides a more detailed analysis of the changes in distribution of lichen species between 1992 and 1997 over an area where the impacts of air pollution on sensitive lichen species were significant historically. The results confirm two key points illustrated by Figure 7.7. Firstly, even over a limited period of 5 years, there have been substantial numbers of new records for certain species. Secondly, there are large variations in response between species; while some species, such as *Hypogymnia tubulosa*, *Lecanora expellans* and *Evernia prunasti*, have shown considerable increases in the numbers of squares for which there are new records, other species with comparable initial frequency have shown relatively small changes. These differences in the rates of recovery between species may reflect the operation of a range of ecological factors, as discussed further below.

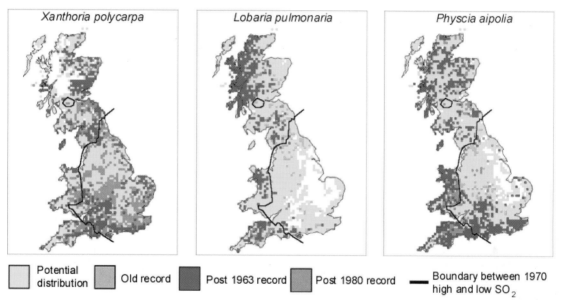

Figure 7.7 Maps to illustrate the recent changes in the national distributions of three lichen species. For further explanation of symbols, see text. Source: Beaudin, Headley, Ashmore & Seaward, unpublished data.

The interpretation of such a national database is difficult, because the appearance of a new record in a given square may be due to many causes, including new surveys of sites that had not been investigated in the past. Convincing complementary evidence comes from the resurvey of specific sites in areas where pollutant concentrations have decreased significantly. Several studies in the UK over the past 30 years have clearly demonstrated that extensive recolonization has occurred in and around urban areas. These studies, which have focussed primarily on epiphytic species, are summarised in Table 7.1 (based on Batty, 1997).

Rose & Hawksworth (1981) examined lichen populations in north and west London, and found several species, such as *Evernia prunasti*, *Parmelia caperata*, *Parmelia subaurifera* and *Usnea subfloridana*, that were rare or extinct in the area prior to 1970. A later study by Hawksworth & McManus (1989) showed evidence of further recolonization; for example, *Parmelia caparata* was found at 12 sites, compared with one in 1980, and several species had reached parks in central London. Of particular interest was the lack of any significant correlation between distance from London and species numbers, as would be expected if pollutant concentrations were a major determinant of the lichen species survival. The hypothesis proposed to account for this observation was that SO_2 sensitivity was not the primary determinant of recolonization. Rather, the dispersal efficiency of the lichens appeared to be a major factor; Hawksworth and McManus (1989) coined the phrase 'zone skippers' to describe SO_2-sensitive lichens which were able to recolonize historically more polluted sites ahead of more tolerant species with lower dispersal rates.

Table 7.1 Summary of the recolonization studies, from Batty (1997).

Reference	Area	Found
Rose and Hawksworth, 1981	North and West of Greater London	1970-1981. Many species which had not been recorded since the 1800's, e.g. *Evernia prunastri*. *Parmelia caperata* had re-established by 1981.
Hawksworth & McManus, 1989	Re-examined N and W London sites, and further sites	49 epiphytes, of which, 25 had not been found within 16 km of the centre of London this century. e.g. *Evernia prunastri, Ramalina farinacea*. *Parmelia caperata* found at 12 sites compared with only one site from the 1980 study.
Guest, 1989	Cheshire	Recolonization is habitat-dependent, occurring first on willow carr, then spreading to the base of ash and sycamore. Evidence of recolonization on young but not mature oaks.
Hawksworth and McManus, 1992	Epping Forest, NE of London	1989/91: 41 species found. This accounted for a 51% increase in number of species since 1968/70. Recolonization possibly began between 1982-5 and is habitat-dependent: occurring on trees with a nutrient-rich bark and high pH: young trees and branches under 15cm in diameter with rough bark e.g. *Quercus.*
Boreham, 1993	Epping Forest, NE of London	1987-1991 *Cladonia coniocraea* and *Hypogymnia physodes* showed some degree of expansion on *Betula pendula*.
Cook *et al.*, 1990	Transect from Liverpool to North Wales	1973-1986 Slight increase in species diversity.
Bates *et al.*, 1990	Transect stretching 70 km SSW from London	1979-1990 No evidence for recolonization on oak.

In contrast to these findings, Bates *et al.* (1990) found little evidence of recolonization along a transect running about 70 km SSW from central London over the period 1979-1990. At the end of this period Bates *et al.* (1990) found no lichen species in Kensington Gardens, whereas Hawksworth & McManus found 12 species in the adjoining Hyde Park. A key difference between these two studies is that the study of Bates *et al.* examined only mature oak, whereas Hawksworth & McManus surveyed all tree species in an area. It was hypothesised that bark of oak, which acidified under high concentrations of SO_2 remained acid when these concentrations fell. A more detailed ordination analysis of the data for oak by Batty (1997) confirmed that bark pH was a major determinant of lichen densities.

Guest (1989) also noted the importance of micro-habitat for the recolonization of epiphytic species in Cheshire. Bases of trees, which are more favourable habitats for lichen growth, tended to be colonized first. Willow species were recolonized first, an observation also made by Rose & Hawksworth (1981), being followed by ash, sycamore and beech; there was also some colonization of young oak trees, but not of mature oak. Hawksworth & McManus (1992), who resurveyed the lichen flora of Epping Forest, NE of London, and compared it with that in a survey in 1968-70, also identified the importance of micro-habitat for recolonization. 21 new species were recorded, but these tended to be restricted to nutrient-rich trees with high bark pH, to young trees, and to branches with diameters below 15 cm.

These studies in and around the London area identify the main features of the observed patterns of recolonization; studies in other parts of the country, summarised in Table 7.1, provide similar patterns. In summary, there is considerable field evidence of a substantial recolonization of areas previously polluted by SO_2. However, a number of factors, including dispersal rates, substrate chemistry and micrometeorology, and possibly other air pollutants, influence the dynamics of recolonization by individual lichen species. This dynamic and complex situation illustrates the difficulty of predicting the scale and rate of biological recovery in response to falling atmospheric concentrations.

While the lichen data provide the most detailed evidence of the impacts of declining concentrations of SO_2, there is other evidence of changing impacts on vegetation. It has long been recognised that certain fungal pathogens are eliminated in areas of high SO_2, and indeed their prevalence has been used, as with sensitive lichen species, as a biomonitor of SO_2 concentrations. In the UK, the impact of SO_2 in urban areas was first established by Saunders (1966), who was able to demonstrate that the absence of blackspot of roses (*Diplocarpon rosae*) was associated with high SO_2 concentrations. The absence of a second species, tar-spot of sycamore (*Rhytisma acerinum*), has also been established as an indicator of high SO_2 concentrations. The dynamics of recolonization of urban areas by tar-spot and blackspot has not been investigated in the same detail as that of lichens. However, a recent re-survey of sites where these species were absent in the 1970s shows almost complete recolonization and no significant association between current-day SO_2 levels and the infection indices of these pathogens, indicating that current concentrations no longer affect these sensitive organisms (Jarrauld, 2000). The exception was central London, where experimental saplings exposed to inoculum also failed to be infected, suggesting that an additional factor, such as the high NO_x concentrations in this area, may be significant

Studies in urban and polluted rural areas demonstrated significant effects of ambient air pollution on the growth of grass and clover species in the 1970s (e.g. Crittenden & Read, 1978). There is little concrete evidence to show the loss of these impacts, but one indicator of the potential for changes in plant performance in response to changing SO_2 concentrations is changes in the tolerance of plant populations in the field. The most interesting UK study is that of Wilson & Bell (1985) who studied changes in tolerance to sulphur dioxide in five grass species in plots established in suburban Manchester in 1975. The study showed that within 4-5 years, increased tolerance to SO_2 had developed in three of the five species. However, this tolerance was then lost again within a further 2-3 years, an effect that Wilson & Bell (1985) ascribed to the rapid fall in SO_2 concentration at the experimental site. This observation implies that the tolerant ecotypes are at a selective disadvantage at low SO_2 concentrations, an inference which is supported by experimental studies (e.g. Ayazloo & Bell, 1981). Since evolution and loss of tolerance can be interpreted as evidence of significant selection pressure, the data suggest that changes in SO_2 concentrations over this period were significantly affecting urban grass populations.

Historically, tree growth was poor in certain areas of the UK, particularly the southern Pennines where mean concentrations of sulphur dioxide were approximately 150-200 $\mu g\ m^{-3}$ in the

1950s. This area is surrounded by industrial towns, with the result that pollution loads were high when the wind blew from any direction. A series of species and seed origin trials were initiated in 1951 (Lines, 1984; 1985), which demonstrated that the establishment and growth of many species was significantly suppressed in comparison with sites subject to lower acid deposition. However, both lodgepole and Corsican pine (*Pinus contorta* and *Pinus nigra*) did appear relatively resistant. It is uncertain whether these observations resulted from the direct impacts of sulphur dioxide, or whether the effects were mediated through soil acidification and the consequent mobilisation of aluminium ions. Sulphur dioxide concentrations have fallen since this time, and poor growth as a result of sulphur deposition is no longer considered a problem in the area.

7.3.2 Sulphur Deficiency in Crops

Sulphur is often referred to as the fourth major nutrient needed for plant growth and development. The sulphur required by crops can be supplied from soil pools, through fertiliser application and through atmospheric deposition. Over the past four decades, traditional S-containing fertilisers, such as ammonium sulphate and superphosphate, have been replaced with those, such as ammonium nitrate and urea, which contain almost no sulphur. During the same period, atmospheric deposition of sulphur has decreased greatly, and there is experimental evidence that moderate exposures to sulphur dioxide can stimulate the growth of crops grown in sulphur-deficient soil. It has been claimed that these changes in fertiliser application and pollutant concentrations have resulted in an increased incidence of sulphur deficiency, especially in crops, such as oilseed rape, which have a high sulphur demand.

An assessment of changes in grain S content of wheat between the early 1980s and early 1990s is provided by Zhao *et al.* (1995). In this species, sulphur deficiency can reduce the bread making quality of flour, as well as affecting total yield. Data from surveys conducted in 1992 and 1993 were compared with earlier surveys in 1981 and 1982. The fact that two consecutive years were sampled in each decade means that there is greater confidence that these are real changes. The results, shown in Figure 7.8, indicate that S contents, but not N contents, were lower in both 1992 and 1993 than in 1981 and 1982. Geographical analysis of the data suggests that higher grain S contents are associated with higher levels of S deposition, with the effect being stronger in the 1981/82 data than in the 1992/93 data.

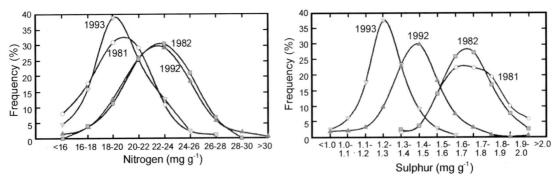

Figure 7.8 Frequency distribution of (a) grain N and (b) grain S in 1981,1982, 1992 and 1993 (from Zhao *et al.*, 1995).

It is important to note, in interpreting Figure 7.8, that the sulphur deficiency level for wheat is set at 1.2 mg kg^{-1}. None of the samples in 1981 or 1982 had values below this level; in contrast, 7% of samples in 1992 and 26% of the samples in 1993 had values below the deficiency level. Zhao *et al.* (1995) consider several alternative explanations of these changes, such as growth dilution due to increased yields and changes in the varieties used, but conclude that their results strongly suggest that reductions in S deposition over this period have contributed significantly to the observed reduction in grain S content.

The impacts of further reductions in S deposition were assessed by McGrath & Zhao (1995) using a risk assessment model based on soil properties that influence sulphate leaching and atmospheric deposition. The analysis was based on 1990 deposition estimates (RGAR, 1990) and applying a scenario of a 60% reduction in non-seasalt S deposition from 1980 levels by 2003. The model predictions are shown in Figure 7.9. The areas of high risk in the early 1990s are broadly consistent with areas where S deficiency has been most commonly reported; these areas have relatively low S deposition, and light soils with low organic matter. The predicted areas of high risk increase greatly in the 2003 scenario, from 11% to 23%. However, it is important to emphasise that changes in fertiliser application practice would greatly reduce the actual risk of sulphur deficiency in these areas. There is evidence that sulphur content of commercial fertilisers is being increased to meet this increased demand from the soil, although this does increase the cost.

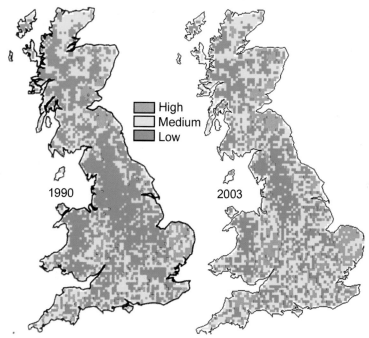

Figure 7.9 (a) current (1990) risk of sulphur deficiency in cereals and (b) risk of sulphur deficiency in cereals 2003 (from McGrath & Zhao, 1995, provided by IACR-Rothamsted, © Lawes Agricultural Trust).

7.3.3 Nitrogen Oxides

It is likely that the strongest effect of emissions of nitrogen oxides across the UK is through their contribution to total nitrogen deposition, which is considered in Section 7.5. However, direct effects of gaseous nitrogen oxides, and ammonia, may also be important, especially in areas close to source.

Experimental evidence suggests that moderate concentrations of NO_x may produce both positive and negative growth responses, with the potential for synergistic interactions with SO_2 being very important. There is substantial evidence to suggest that the effects of NO_2 are much more likely to be negative in the presence of equivalent concentrations of SO_2. The ratio of SO_2 to NO_2 has decreased greatly in urban areas of the UK over the past 30 years. Unfortunately, very few experimental studies have examined the effect of different proportions of the two pollutants on vegetation, and the implications of these falling SO_2/NO_x ratios for plant response are very uncertain. It is also important to note that NO may also have significant effects on vegetation, but there remains a paucity of data on plant response to this pollutant at the concentrations currently found in UK urban areas.

One important effect of NO_x may be its influence on insect populations; there is evidence of improved performance of insect pests on plants grown in moderate concentrations of NO_2, and of SO_2. Dohmen *et al.* (1984) showed the importance of this phenomenon in the urban air pollution climate of the 1980s; bean plants grown in ambient air had 60% more aphids than those grown in filtered air. High insect populations have also been identified along UK motorways and ascribed to the increased NO_x concentrations. The significance of NO_2 or NO_x in increasing insect pest problems in areas with more moderate concentrations is uncertain. However, a study by Houlden *et al.*, described by Bell *et al.* (1993) (Figure 7.10), along a transect west of central London, clearly indicates a large change in the growth rates of aphids on barley between central London, with an NO_2 concentration of 30 ppb, and sites in the suburban fringe with concentrations in the range 10-15 ppb. However, the confounding effect of other pollutants on these observations cannot be ignored.

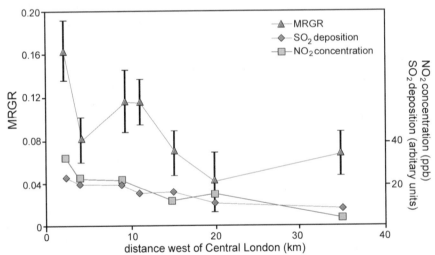

Figure 7.10 Four-day mean relative growth rate (MRGR) (with 95% confidence limits) of the aphid *Metapolophium dirhodum* on barley grown for 6 weeks along an air pollution gradient westwards from Central London (from Bell *et al.*, 1993).

7.4 Biological Effects of Soil Acidification

7.4.1 Direct Effects of Acid Mist

The form of pollutants in which the majority of long-range transport occurs is the aerosol phase. For sulphur and nitrogen the pollutants are transported largely as SO_4^{2-}, NO_3^-, and NH_4^+ in aerosols whose sizes range from 0.1 to 1.0 μm (diameter). Such small particles (or droplets) do not deposit rapidly to terrestrial surfaces and in the absence of rain they are removed from the boundary layer only slowly. If, however, these aerosols are forced to rise in a moist atmosphere, the decrease in temperature and increase in relative humidity readily leads to activation of the droplets and formation of cloud droplets. The droplet size depends on the height above cloud base, but typically the 0.5 μm diameter aerosol particles would be converted to 4 or 5 μm droplets by the time they reach 100 m above cloud base. The cloud droplets are now sufficiently large to deposit rapidly onto vegetation, especially aerodynamically rough vegetation such as forest.

The uplands of the UK present large areas of land that experience hill (orographic) cloud frequently (500 to 2000 hours per year) and which as a result receive large inputs of the major pollutants. Experimental studies have shown that hill cloud contains much larger concentrations of pollutants than precipitation (typically by a factor of 4 to 10) and these concentrations have been shown to cause direct effects on the physiology and frost sensitivity of a variety of tree species (Fowler *et al.,* 1989; Cape *et al.,* 1991). The work on effects of 'acid mist' on forests has been used to develop a critical level for forest trees (Cape, 1993), which provides a means of assessing exceedance. The concentration of SO_4^{2-} present as aerosol set as the critical level was 1 μg-S m^{-3} and substantial areas of the UK uplands were subject to concentrations in excess of this value in 1991 (Cape, 1993). The upland areas in exceedance included the Scottish borders, the Pennine hills and the Welsh uplands. The Scottish highlands were largely unaffected, but the area of the UK in exceedance amounted to approximately 4% of the total area.

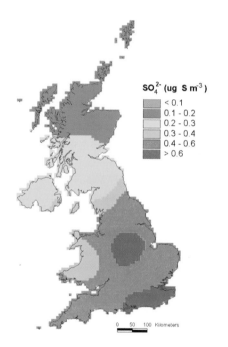

Figure 7.11 Concentrations of sulphate aerosol in the UK, interpolated from network measurements (Sept. 1999 to Aug. 2001 average).

SO_4^{2-} (ug S m^{-3})

	< 0.1
	0.1 - 0.2
	0.2 - 0.3
	0.3 - 0.4
	0.4 - 0.6
	> 0.6

The substantial reductions in emissions of sulphur throughout Europe have reduced the concentrations of SO_4^{2-} in precipitation (see Chapter 3) and especially in the high concentration areas of the Midlands. The concentrations of aerosol SO_4^{2-} have only been monitored at a network of sites throughout the UK within the last two years, but these measurements (Figure 7.11) show that no areas of the UK are currently in exceedance of the critical level. The reduction in aerosol SO_4^{2-} concentrations therefore represents an important component of the recovery to date, provided that extended monitoring of the aerosol SO_4^{2-} concentrations confirm the values in Figure 7.11.

The concentrations of NO_3^- and NH_4^+ in hill cloud remain large and represent an important pathway for N deposition at high elevation sites. However, the direct toxic effects of SO_4^{2-} and acidity on trees have not been shown with NO_3^- or NH_4^+.

7.4.2 Soil Acidification

The effects of sulphur and nitrogen deposition on soil acidity, and other chemical indicators, were reviewed in Chapter 5, which also considered effects on soil microbial processes. In this section, we briefly consider the evidence for effects of soil acidification on species composition, on forest vitality and on animal populations.

Soil acidification as a result of nitrogen deposition has been suggested to have caused the loss of many characteristic forbs in acid grasslands in the Netherlands (reviewed by Aerts & Bobbink, 1999). It is likely that it is the increased soil Al/Ca^{2+} and/or NH_4^+/NO_3^- ratios that occur at low pH which are associated with the loss of individual species. Brunet et al. (1998) showed that the field layer vegetation composition of deciduous forests in southern Sweden was primarily controlled by gradients of soil acidity and nitrogen supply, and that both nitrophilous and acid-tolerant species were increasing in frequency, in an area where extensive soil acidification has taken place.

In the UK, there is little field evidence of such recent changes in species composition. Soil pH currently appears to be increasing in the UK (see Chapter 5) and national vegetation change in the Countryside Survey appears to be related more strongly to eutrophication than to acidification (Firbank et al., 2000; Haines-Young et al., 2000).

However, longer-term studies at high deposition inputs do provide clearer evidence of the potential effect of acidification. One of the longest experimental studies of the effects of changing soil acidity and nutrient levels is the 150 year Park Grass experiment at the Rothamsted station (Goulding et al., 1998). Addition of sodium nitrate at 48 kg-N ha^{-1} y^{-1}, had little effect on soil pH, but caused a rapid loss of about 15 species, primarily legumes, when it was first applied in 1856. This difference between nitrate fertilised and unfertilised plots was maintained over the next 140 years, although species numbers in both treatments declined gradually, an effect which Goulding et al. (1998) attribute to increasing atmospheric N deposition (from ca 10 kg-N ha^{-1} y^{-1} in the 1850s to 45 kg-N ha^{-1} y^{-1} today). An ammonium sulphate treatment, also at 48 kg-N ha^{-1} y^{-1}, had an additional acidification effect, reducing soil pH from an original value of 5.8 to 3.5 in the 1990s. This caused the loss of an additional group of about 20 species over the first two decades of treatment. Interestingly, the addition of lime to this treatment from 1903 has had a much slower effect in terms of recovery of species numbers, with only about 5 additional species being found after 50 years of liming. While the deposition loads represented by these fertiliser treatments are considerably higher than the deposition of nitrate or ammonium to grasslands over most of the UK, the data demonstrate the potential for significant species loss from both eutrophication and acidification.

Although pot experiments with very high levels of acid input have shown adverse effects on tree seedlings, there is little direct evidence that soil acidification is associated with adverse effects on tree vitality or production in the field in the UK. Few studies have included detailed examination of root systems, where the most immediate impacts might be found, although Power & Ashmore (1996) showed that poor crown condition in beech in southern Britain was associated with lower root vitality and lower soil Ca^{2+}/Al ratios on acidic sites. It should be emphasised that this study examined between-tree variation and not acidification itself. Such associations between root vitality and soil acidity have been reported in areas of central Europe and North America with greater acid deposition.

The longer-term impacts of acid deposition on forest health may be primarily through base cation deficiencies caused by increased base cation leaching, rather than through root toxicity. North American studies have demonstrated the long-term effects on base cation status over periods of 30 years (Mclaughlin & Percy, 1999). However, in the short-term, experimental acidification may increase base cation availability and hence increase tree growth, for reasons explained in Chapter 5. For example, in a large scale field experiment in which a 20 year old Sitka spruce plantation on blanket peat was subjected to simulated acidified and N enriched treatments, the treatments with additional nitrogen, in the absence of sulphur and acidity, had no effect on litterfall (Sheppard and Crossley, 2000). The treatments with acidity and sulphur increased stemwood increment and litterfall and were associated with larger base cation concentrations in throughfall and soil water. The results are consistent with forest growth at this site being limited much more by base cation supply than by available nitrogen. The acid, but not the N-enriched treatments, showed direct toxic effects on terrestrial mosses at an early stage of the treatments; this was later exacerbated by the increased litterfall in the acid treatment.

Although most of the effects of acid deposition on animals have focussed on aquatic ecosystems, real and potential effects on terrestrial animals are increasingly recognised. Part of the impetus has come from evidence that terrestrial birds in the Netherlands might be impacted negatively at acidified sites where calcium-rich prey become scarce (Graveland *et al.*, 1994). Although the exact mechanisms are still debated (reviewed by Ormerod & Rundle, 1998), and effects are often weak, there is now sufficient empirical evidence from the UK to raise questions about how deposition might be linked with the breeding performance of some terrestrial birds (Green 1998; Chamberlain *et al.*, 2000).

Other work has focussed directly on animals at other trophic levels, and in other groups, especially soil invertebrates (Haddad *et al.* 2000). This work has addressed not only direct and indirect effects from the deposition of acidity and nitrogen, but also the effects of measures aimed to combat acidification such as liming (Buckton & Ormerod, 1997). So far, the bulk of the available literature has arisen outside the UK, at relatively high deposition rates, or in experimental manipulations. At present, therefore, our understanding of any similar effects of acid deposition on terrestrial animals in the UK is limited.

7.5 Nitrogen Deposition

7.5.1 What are the problems of nitrogen deposition for vegetation?

All plants require N for growth; farmers apply N fertilisers to maximise crop yield, and in many ecosystems low availability of N limits productivity. However, the plant species within these ecosystems are adapted to low N supply, and so an increase in N availability can change the character of the vegetation. Although both oxidised and reduced N can contribute to soil acidification, as described in Chapter 5, the greatest concern is the "nutrient effect", or eutrophication of ecosystems caused by N deposition; this section focuses on this problem.

Vegetation types differ greatly in their sensitivity to N deposition. Even the highest rates of total N deposition in the UK, occurring around point sources, are only approximately one third of those that might be applied in fertiliser to agricultural land. Thus crops and fertilised grasslands will not be affected by atmospheric N inputs, neither will any natural or semi-natural vegetation growing in conditions where nutrient supply is naturally sufficiently high that nitrogen is not limiting. However, in many natural and semi-natural ecosystems nitrogen is limiting; the ecosystems most sensitive to N deposition are thus those that naturally have the lowest N availability, such as heaths, moors, blanket bogs and semi-natural grasslands. Atmospheric N inputs may have direct effects on the growth and tissue chemistry of individual species within such systems. These in turn result in many indirect effects of N deposition, such as changes in the outcome of competitive interactions and altered sensitivity to climatic events and insect attack. Very important indirect effects are the stimulation of decomposition and mineralisation rates (see Chapter 5) which act as positive feedbacks, increasing the potential of the soil to supply nitrogen to the vegetation and thus enhancing the nutrient effect of N deposition.

The actual mechanisms of the effect of N deposition on the species composition of an ecosystem are difficult to distinguish due to all these interactions. A further complicating factor is that most vegetation in Britain is considered "semi-natural" rather than natural, meaning that it is subject to at least some human influence such as grazing, maintenance of high deer densities, or burning for grouse or grazing management. All these management practices could affect the response of the ecosystem to N deposition. In addition, the ways in which particular areas of land have been managed (particularly grazing densities) have changed during the time over which N deposition has increased. This makes it difficult to attribute the cause(s) of observed long term changes in vegetation, which are probably due at least in part to atmospheric N inputs.

7.5.2 Evidence of Effects: Foliar N

The foliar N concentration of several lower and higher plant species has been shown by survey and by transplantation experiments to be closely related to N deposition. Ectohydric mosses have been most commonly studied as their reliance on atmospheric nutrient supply and absorbance of nutrients over their entire surface area means that their foliar N concentration is particularly tightly coupled with deposition. At lower deposition rates (0-30 kg-N ha^{-1} a^{-1}) the relationship tends to be linear, with reported increases in tissue N per 1 kg ha^{-1} a^{-1} increase in N deposition of 0.01-0.04% dry weight for mosses and 0.04-1.15 % dry weight for a range of upland higher plant species (Hicks *et al.,* 2000, Pitcairn *et al.,* 1995, Pitcairn *et al.*, 2001, Woodin & Choy, unpublished data).

Such relationships have been demonstrated at a range of spatial scales, and thus foliar N may be a useful indicator of N inputs, particularly in terrain where actual deposition monitoring is difficult. It has been shown that patterns of N deposition are reflected in foliar N concentrations across wide geographic areas. This is true of Calluna and ectohydric mosses across the whole of Britain (Pitcairn *et al.,* 1995), *Sphagnum* throughout Wales (Woodin & Farmer, 1993), *Racomitrium* throughout northern Britain (Baddeley *et al.,* 1994), *Hylocomium* and *Pleurozium* throughout Britain (Woodin & Choy, unpublished data)*,* and a lichen *Cladonia portentosa* on heaths and moors, throughout Britain (Hyvärinen & Crittenden, 1998). More locally, altitudinal increases in tissue N, reflecting deposition rates, have been shown for *Racomitrium*, Calluna, *Nardus, Deschampsia, Erica* and *Hylocomium* in Scotland and northern England (Baddeley *et al.*, 1994, Pitcairn *et al.*, 1995, Hicks *et al.*, 2000) illustrating the potential for very significant effects of N deposition in the most sensitive, high altitude, ecosystems.

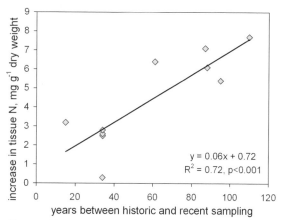

Figure 7.12 Increase in moss tissue N over time. Each data point represents the increase in tissue N in moss at a single site over a period of years between two sampling dates, the recent sampling at each site having been in 1989 or 1993.

An elegant use of the close relationship between moss foliar N and N deposition has been the demonstration of historical increases in N inputs by analysis of dated herbarium specimens from known locations and comparison with current material from the same sites (Woolgrove & Woodin, 1996; Baddeley *et al.*, 1994; Pitcairn *et al.*, 1995). In Figure 7.12, each data point represents a single site, all sites being within Scotland and northern England. The data show a linear tissue nitrogen increase of 0.06% per decade throughout the past century which, based on the relationships described at the beginning of this section, represents an average increase in deposition of at least 1.5 kg-N ha^{-1} decade^{-1}.

Increased foliar N itself is not a direct measure of plant health, but for many species it will be coupled with increased growth, whilst in sensitive bryophytes it often causes reduced growth. The biochemical changes to plant tissue may also result in increased frost sensitivity and susceptibility to herbivory. There are important effects of decreased foliar C:N ratio for ecosystem processes, as the changed quality of plant litter will result in changes in decomposition and subsequently other nutrient cycling processes. Thus the demonstration that foliar N has increased as a result of increased N deposition does provide an indicator that N deposition is affecting the functioning of the ecosystem.

7.5.3 Mechanisms of Effect of N Deposition on Species Composition

Atmospheric N deposition can alter species composition by a complex variety of mechanisms, of which a simplified summary is given in Figure 7.13. In studies that look for correlative evidence of relationships between species composition and spatial or temporal variation in N deposition, the specific mechanisms of effect are usually not identified. However, field manipulation experiments have sometimes enabled identification of the mechanisms by which added N causes change in species composition, and some pot experiments have aided interpretation of field survey observations. Understanding of these mechanisms is crucial to assessment of the possible role of nitrogen deposition in long-term changes in vegetation composition in the field.

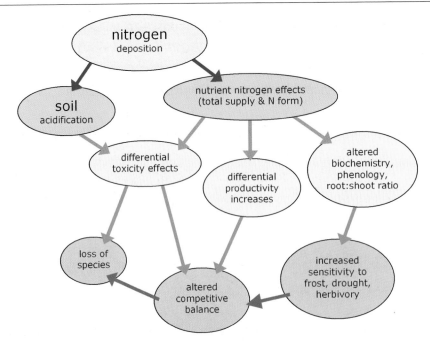

Figure 7.13 Simplified schematic of the mechanisms of effect of nitrogen deposition on vegetation.

Toxicity

High rates of N deposition have been found to be directly toxic to some species, particularly ectohydric mosses and lichens within heathlands (e.g. Press *et al.*, 1986; Gordon *et al.*, 2001b; Jones & Ashenden, 2000). Decreased higher plant diversity of grasslands has also been attributed to "toxicity" because it occurred despite reduced total plant cover, indicating that competition could not be becoming more intense (Lee & Caporn, 1999).

Competition

In some N addition experiments, decline in mosses and other understorey species has been attributed to increased competition for light caused by increased productivity of canopy species and consequent increase in shading by the canopy and/or by increased litter production (Lee & Caporn, 1998, Jonasson, 1992). Interestingly, in an upland heath fertilisation experiment, an initial loss of mosses and lichens beneath Calluna, which had increased shoot growth, was reversed a decade later due to more rapid ageing and degeneration of the N treated Calluna, alleviating light competition (Lee *et al.*, 2000e). High nitrogen inputs may also directly affect the competitive interactions between the dominant species which form the canopy, for example leading to the replacement of *Erica* by *Molinia* in wet heaths in the Netherlands (reviewed by Aerts & Bobbink, 1999), and increasing the ability of Calluna to compete with *Pteridium* below ground (Gordon, 1998). However, the effects of N on competition are often mediated by other factors. The best known example is that of competition between Calluna and grasses, in which Calluna is able to maintain dominance under high N inputs unless its canopy is opened due to stress or disturbance (Aerts & Bobbink, 1999; Hartley, 1997). Thus high N inputs are more likely to result in a loss of Calluna in grazed than in ungrazed systems (see below). In some instances the N input itself triggers the mechanism for canopy opening by causing increased susceptibility of Calluna to frost, drought and/or heather beetle attack as described below.

7.5.4 Interactive Effects of N and Other Biotic and Abiotic Factors

Invertebrate herbivory

Increased foliar N concentration improves invertebrate herbivore performance and so increases the likelihood and severity of insect "outbreaks". This has been shown to be true for roadside insects (Port & Thompson, 1980), for heather beetle outbreaks (Aerts & Bobbink, 1999; Power et al., 1998a), for winter moth that has caused major localised destruction of Calluna in Scotland in recent years (Kerslake et al., 1998), and for aphid infestation of trees (Flückiger & Braun, 1999).

Grazing, Mowing and Burning

Effects of livestock grazing are also interactive with effects of nitrogen deposition on vegetation, and in many cases grazing is suggested to be the overriding influence. In a recent experiment on upland acid grassland at Pwllpeiran, mid Wales, the vegetation showed more response to nitrogen addition under a light grazing than under a heavy grazing regime. The suggested explanation is that heavy grazing is the limiting factor on the vegetation, and has already driven it towards unpalatable grasses and reduced diversity, such that added nitrogen has no further effect (Gordon et al., 2001a). In a parallel mesocosm study, clipping of the higher plant sward enabled the moss Racomitrium to tolerate higher N inputs (Jones & Ashenden, 2000). Grazing is also suggested to be the controlling factor for Scottish moorland. A combination of field, turf and pot experiments showed that nitrogen addition to this vegetation will only result in transition from Calluna to a grass dominated sward where the heather canopy is opened by grazing (Hartley, 1997; Alonso & Hartley, 1998; Alonso et al., 2001). Appropriate grazing management has also been shown to be a much bigger influence than nitrogen addition on species diversity in lowland calcareous grassland and dune grasslands (Wilson et al., 1995; Ten Harkel & Van der Meulen, 1995). The spread of false brome grass, Brachypodium pinnatum in calcareous grasslands in the Netherlands, and on some sites in southern Britain, was initially attributed to nitrogen deposition, but for the British sites change in grazing management is now recognised to have been a very important factor (e.g. Baxter & Farmer, 1993). The most important active management methods of maintaining Calluna dominance on lowland heath and upland moors are mowing and burning respectively. These may also show important interactions with nitrogen deposition, but there is little experimental evidence on which to base an assessment.

Frost

There is evidence that high N deposition may cause increased susceptibility of Calluna to frost damage, particularly in spring and possibly due to advanced onset of shoot growth (Lee & Caporn, 1998; Power et al., 1998a; Caporn et al., 1994; reviewed by Aerts & Bobbink, 1999), although effects have differed between experiments and varied with duration of experiments. In arctic heath (analogous to montane dwarf shrub heath), damage to shrubs caused by ice encasement was more severe in N treated plots (Robinson et al., 1998; Woodin & Alexander, unpublished data). "Winter browning" has also been observed in N treated Calluna (Carroll et al., 1999; Gordon et al., 1999), with the severity being greatest in plots which had been experimentally droughted during the previous summer (Gordon et al., 1999). This symptom, which is sometimes attributed to frost damage, appears to be a result of physiological drought due to the combination of frozen soil and low humidity (Watson *et al.*, 1966).

Climatic warming

Effects of nitrogen are interactive with those of temperature, but the outcome of the interaction is difficult to predict since it varies between species and environments (e.g. Jonasson *et al.,* 1999), and can depend on extreme climatic events. For example, in a large scale manipulation experiment, temperature enhancement and nitrogen addition had a positive synergistic effect on the performance of Calluna, but a negative effect on *Pteridium* (Gordon *et al.*, 1999). This negative effect was due to a synergistic reduction in cold hardening, resulting in increased damage to the rhizome during an extreme cold spell in winter.

Drought

Vegetation which has increased above-ground productivity and decreased root:shoot ratio in response to increased N input is likely to be more severely damaged by drought due to the combination of increase in transpiring surface and decrease in water absorbing surface. This has been shown at a species level for Calluna (Gordon *et al.*, 1999; Berdowski, 1993) and at a community level where N addition had shifted prairie vegetation composition to species with greater water demand and lower resistance to drought (Tilman & Downing, 1994). In N-enriched heaths in the Netherlands, drought damage has been reported to trigger the breakdown of heather canopy, leading to invasion of grasses (Prins *et al.*, 1991).

Fungal communities

Due to their importance in the life, and death, of plants, the effects of N deposition on fungi may have significant consequences for the entire vegetation community. Changes in fungal communities in response to nitrogen enrichment have been particularly well documented in the Netherlands. The overall pattern is for an increase in fruit bodies of saprotrophic and parasitic fungi, and a reduction in number and diversity of fruit bodies of mycorrhizal fungi, which form mutually beneficial associations with plant roots (reviewed by van der Eerden *et al.,* 1998). The effects of nitrogen on mycorrhizal infection of roots differ between mycorrhizal types, tending to be negative for ectomycorrhizas, but much more variable for VA (vesicular arbuscular) and ericoid mycorrhizas (Aerts & Bobbink, 1999). Within Britain, there has been little consistent effect of nitrogen on ericoid mycorrhizal infection of Calluna in an experiment on moorland in North Wales, or in associated pot experiments (Caporn *et al.*, 1995, Lee *et al.*, 2000e). Other workers have shown a decrease in infection of fertilised Calluna and *Nardus* (Hartley & Amos, 1999). Experimental nitrogen addition (48 kg-N ha^{-1} y^{-1}) to a 10 year old sitka spruce plantation in southern Scotland also had no effect on mycorrhizal infection of the tree roots, despite a reduction in mycorrhizal fruit body production (Sheppard, pers. comm.). This may be explained by a shift in mycorrhizal community composition as observed in several other studies (e.g. Wallenda & Kottke, 1998; Warburton & Allen, 2000). The effect of nitrogen deposition on the fungal mycelium in the soil, and its resource capture efficiency, require study (Wallenda & Kottke, 1998).

P availability

Prolonged N deposition to low nutrient ecosystems can result in P limitation. In ombrotrophic bogs increased N deposition eventually leads to a shift from N to P limitation, such that further response to N is limited by P availability (reviewed by Aerts & Bobbink, 1999). In upland grasslands, N addition alters P mineralisation and plant P demand increases, indicating that the system has become P limited, and the effects of N are lost (Lee *et al.,* 2000e). Phosphorus limitation in lowland chalk grasslands in the UK is suggested to prevent N accumulation by the vegetation (*cf.* Wilson *et al.,* 1995). In lowland calcareous grassland in the Netherlands the spread of *Brachypodium* is suggested to be due to the fact that with alleviation of N limitation, other grass species become P limited but *Brachypodium* does not (reviewed by Aerts & Bobbink, 1999). Also in the Netherlands, the effects of nitrogen deposition on the dominance of grasses in dune vegetation is greater where phosphorus is not limiting than where nitrogen and phosphorus are co-limiting (Kooijman *et al.,* 1998). Vegetation response to nitrogen in arctic heath is also dependent on phosphorus status, with the two nutrients apparently being co-limiting and addition of both being required to measurably alter species composition (Gordon *et al.,* 2001b).

7.5.5 Field Evidence of the Impacts of Nutrient Nitrogen in Britain

The fact that the increase in nitrogen deposition has affected vegetation in Britain during this century is shown quite clearly in the historical data for tissue nitrogen in mosses. The effects of nitrogen deposition close to point sources (particularly of ammonia) are also clearly demonstrable (e.g. Pitcairn *et al.,* 1998). However, evidence for vegetation change caused by excess nitrogen deposition away from local sources is less clear. In some habitats there have been changes in the vegetation over the past few decades that are entirely consistent with changes that would be expected as a result of excess nutrient nitrogen deposition. Examples include:

- a shift from Calluna to grass dominance in Breckland heaths (Pitcairn *et al.,* 1991),

- increased abundance of grasses in heather moor in NE Scotland (Alonso & Hartley, 1998),

- reduction in bryophyte cover and increased grassiness of *Racomitrium* heath in northern England and parts of Scotland (Thompson & Baddeley, 1991),

- a loss of lower plants from upland grassland at Moor House, northern Pennines (Pitcairn *et al.,* 1991),

- spread of *Brachypodium* in some chalk grasslands in southern England (Baxter & Farmer, 1993)

- failure of bryophytes to re-establish in the southern Pennines despite major reduction in sulphur pollution (Press *et al.,* 1986),

- increased incidence of winter moth attack on heather, leading to increased grass dominance, on Scottish moors (Kerslake *et al.,*1998).

In none of these examples can changes in land management practice be ruled out as contributory factors. Indeed in some cases, perhaps most notably that of *Racomitrium* heath, changes in land management have been shown to be important, and may have acted in concert with high nitrogen inputs to cause the observed vegetation change (e.g. Thompson &

Baddeley, 1991). The spread of *Brachypodium* on chalk grasslands is now thought to be due almost entirely to change in grazing management (e.g. Wilson *et al.,* 1995), and it is suggested that better moorland management would help preserve heather even in the face of high nitrogen deposition (Alonso & Hartley, 1998).

Despite this note of caution, it seems certain that nitrogen deposition has at least contributed to changes in vegetation composition in a range of habitats over a wide geographical range of the UK. It is likely that vegetation mediated changes in nutrient cycling, which are much less visible but no less ecologically important, are even more widespread. The need remains to identify sensitive and clear indicators of the regional scale impacts of nutrient nitrogen deposition.

One approach is to identify groups of native species found to increase or decline with increased N deposition, in both experiments and surveys, and then to investigate whether such species changes are actually taking place in the field within the UK. Here we examine data from the UK, and from some comparable ecosystems in northern Europe, on species changes which have occurred in N addition experiments or which have occurred in the field and been demonstrated conclusively to be due to N deposition (Table 7.2).

The most obvious feature of the species lists in Table 7.2 is that across all habitats, grasses are more frequently observed to increase in response to nitrogen enrichment than any other group, and mosses and lichens are most frequently observed to decline, as illustrated in Figure 7.14. This same pattern emerges from the examples of vegetation change listed above, confirming that nitrogen is a likely causal factor.

The average Ellenberg nitrogen score (a score indicating the relative nutrient requirement of a species) of the higher plant species that increase in abundance with increased nitrogen deposition is significantly greater than the average score of those species that decline (Figure. 7.15). This does not mean that in vegetation impacted by high nitrogen deposition only species with high Ellenberg scores will increase, and only those with low scores will decrease (see for example Wilson *et al.,* 1995), but rather that the average score for the whole vegetation community can be expected to increase.

Such a trend towards higher Ellenberg nitrogen scores has recently been detected in the Countryside Survey of Britain (Haines-Young *et al.,* 2000). Between 1990 and 1998 the overall condition of vegetation in Great Britain showed very marked trends towards increasing levels of nutrient availability. Average Ellenberg nitrogen scores increased by small but significant amounts in infertile grassland, moorland, heath and bog, and upland woodland. These changes are generally greater in England and Wales than in Scotland, and are occurring due to decreases in species typical of these nutrient poor habitats, and increased occurrence of species more typical of lowland semi-improved grasslands. Similar signals were also found in the period 1978-1990, with increasing Ellenberg fertility scores in infertile grassland, and in heaths and bogs (Firbank *et al.,* 2000).

The species changes summarised in Table 7.2 confirm that nitrogen deposition is influencing species composition by eutrophication rather than by acidification of the soil. The species increasing in response to nitrogen have significantly higher Ellenberg scores for soil pH (indicating a preference for less acid soil) than do those species that decrease (Figure. 7.15).

Table 7.2 Species shown to increase and decrease in response to excess nitrogen deposition to major habitat types. The general descriptors "mosses" and "lichens" have been included since many studies have not identified these to species level, but they represent an important component of the vegetation response. M = mosses & lichens, F = ferns and club mosses, G = grasses (includes one sedge), H = herbs, S = shrubs. Sources of reference at foot of table.

Habitat	Species increasing	M	F	G	H	S	Species decreasing	M	F	G	H	S
Woodland	Dryopteris carthusiana		•				Plagiothecium undulatum	•				
	Dryopteris dilitata		•				Polytrichum commune	•				
	Agrostis capillaris			•			Pseudoscleropodium purum	•				
	Carex pilulifera			•			Lichens	•				
	Deschampsia cespitosa			•			Mosses	•				
	Deschampsia flexuosa			•			Dryopteris dilitata		•			
	Holcus lanatus			•			Poa nemoralis			•		
	Lolium perenne			•			Galium odoratum				•	
	Ceratocapnos claviculata				•		Melampyrum pratense				•	
	Chamaenerion angustifolium				•		Oxalis acetosella				•	
	Rumex acetosella				•		Potentilla erecta				•	
	Stellaria media				•		Solidago virgaurea				•	
	Trientalis europaea				•		Viola riviniana				•	
	Rubus fructicosus					•	Calluna vulgaris					•
	Rubus idaeus				•		Erica tetralix					•
	Vaccinium myrtillus				•							
Moorland & Heathland	Agrostis capillaris			•			Hylocomium splendens	•				
	Agrostis stolonifera			•			Lichens	•				
	Danthonia decumbens			•			Mosses	•				
	Deschampsia cespitosa			•			Lycopodium annotinum		•			
	Deschampsia flexuosa			•			Lycopodium clavatum		•			
	Festuca ovina			•			Eriophorum angustifolium			•		
	Festuca rubra			•			Cuscuta epithymum				•	
	Molinia caerulea			•			Scorzonera humilis				•	
	Nardus stricta			•			Calluna vulgaris					•
	Cerastium fontanum				•		Erica tetralix					•
	Calluna vulgaris					•	Vaccinium myrtillus					•
							Vaccinium vitis-idaea					•
Acid Grassland	Anthoxanthum odoratum			•			Hylocomium splendens	•				
	Nardus stricta			•			Hypnum jutlandicum	•				
	Galium saxatile				•		Pleurozium schreberi	•				
	Hypochaeris radicata				•		Racomitrium lanuginosum	•				
	Polygala serpyllifolia				•		Rhytidiadelphus squarrosus	•				
							Lycopodiella inundata		•			
							Agrostis vinealis			•		
							Antennaria dioica				•	
							Dactylorhiza maculata				•	
							Gentiana pneumonanthe				•	
							Narthecium ossifragum				•	
							Pedicularis sylvatica				•	
							Polygala serpyllifolia				•	
							Potentilla erecta				•	
							Thymus serpyllum				•	
							Vaccinium myrtillus					•
Calcareous Grassland	Brachypodium pinnatum			•			mosses	•				
	Bromus hordeaceous			•			Cirsium dissectum				•	
	Danthonia decumbens			•			Euphrasia officianalis				•	
	Festuca ovina			•			Gentianella amarella				•	
	Holcus lanatus			•			Lotus corniculatus				•	
	Lolium perenne			•			Lotus pedunculatus				•	
	Filipendula vulgaris				•		Lychnis flos-cuculi				•	
	Hypochaeris radicata				•		Ranunculus bulbosus				•	
	Scabiosa columbaria				•		Thymus polytrichus				•	
	Thymus polytrichus				•							

Aerts & Bobbink (1999), Boxman et al. (1998), Emmett et al. (1999), Falkengren-Grerup (1993), Gordon et al. (2001a), Hallbäcken & Zhang (1998), Hartley & Mitchell pers. comm., Kellner & Mårshagen (1991), Lee & Caporn (1998), Lee & Caporn (1999), Pitcairn et al. (1998), van der Eerden et al. (1998), van Dobben et al. (1999), Wilson et al. (1995)

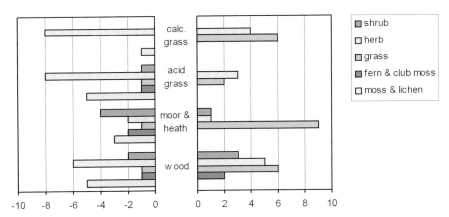

Figure 7.14 Number of reported increases and decreases in abundance of plant species, grouped by life form, in the UK and European nitrogen deposition studies summarised in Table 7.2.

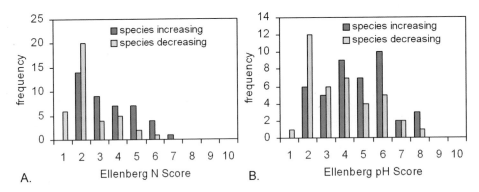

Figure 7.15 Frequency distributions of (a) Ellenberg N scores and (b) Ellenberg pH scores of plant species shown to increase and decrease in abundance in response to excess N deposition in the UK and European studies summarised in Table 7.2. In both (a) and (b) the difference between the distributions of the two groups of species is statistically significant.

This trend is also evident in the British countryside; there have been shifts towards species associated with less acid soils in acid grassland and bog (Firbank *et al.*, 2000). So, overall, we have clear evidence that eutrophication may have caused vegetation change in several sensitive habitats across the countryside during the past decade, although clearly a more detailed analysis of these changes in relation to known deposition patterns would strengthen this conclusion.

7.5.6 Potential for Recovery

Attention now needs to be turned to the potential for ecosystem recovery. Ecosystems of naturally low nutrient availability have very conservative nutrient cycling, such that added nitrogen is likely to be tightly retained within the system. Very little nitrogen was lost by leaching from a lowland heath in southern England receiving additions of 8 and 15 kg-N ha^{-1} y^{-1} over a seven-year period, with most of the added nitrogen being accumulated in the soil compartment (Power *et al.*, 1998a). Measurements made four years after these treatments ceased showed a significant effect of the previous nitrogen addition in increasing the growth rate of Calluna seedlings (Power *et al.*, unpublished data). In an upland heath in North Wales receiving additions of 40, 80 and 120 kg-N ha^{-1} y^{-1} continuously since 1989, virtually all the added N is still held within the system (Lee *et al.*, 2000e). It is likely that the accumulated nitrogen within these systems would be retained for a very long time after the cessation of nitrogen inputs, particularly as nitrogen is not being leached from the system. It is partly the accumulated nitrogen that drives vegetation change in lowland heaths and attempts at heathland restoration in the Netherlands have involved complete turf stripping to remove this nitrogen pool (DeGraaf *et al.*, 1998). In Britain, reduction of the soil pool of nitrogen is required for lowland heaths to realise the benefit of reduced atmospheric nitrogen deposition. For upland heath, it remains to be determined whether the retained nitrogen is primarily in the vegetation and litter or the soil, but removal of the vegetation/litter pool by traditional burning practice may promote recovery.

Some evidence of the slowness of recovery comes from experiments in which treatments were abandoned some time ago. Nitrogen (10 and 50 kg-N ha^{-1} y^{-1}) was added to high arctic dwarf shrub heath in three consecutive years, and after five-six further years without treatment the mosses were still showing identical responses to those in plots which had continued receiving annual treatment (Gordon *et al.*, 2001b). Lee & Caporn (1998) suggest that stimulation of nitrogen mineralisation by atmospheric nitrogen deposition may be sustained for decades by enhanced nitrogen deposition, and persist for similar periods after deposition is reduced. Twenty years after the cessation of fertilisation (50 kg-N ha^{-1} y^{-1} for four years) of short-grass steppe, effects on plant tissue C:N ratio were still apparent and an introduced annual species was abundant in fertilised but not in control plots (Vinton & Burke, 1995). Soil under this species had higher rates of C and N mineralisation than under other species and a positive feedback between plant persistence and soil nutrient status is suggested. Thus once increased nitrogen input has allowed the establishment of the new species, the situation becomes self perpetuating even in the absence of further fertilisation. It is notable in this context that the litter produced by grass species has a higher mineralisation rate than that produced by the ericaceous shrubs that they out compete in heathlands (van Vuuren *et al.*, 1992).

In a unique "pot" scale study of recovery, mesocosms of acid and calcareous grassland were removed in 1997 from sites in Wales and the Peak District receiving more than 20 kg-N ha^{-1} y^{-1} and given nitrogen inputs of 2, 10, 20 and 55 kg-N ha^{-1} y^{-1} (Jones & Ashenden, 2000). With reduced deposition, three moss species showed signs of recovery in turfs that were clipped to represent heavy grazing. The same trend was not observed in unclipped turfs, indicating the potential importance of vegetation grazing management in the process of recovery.

Together these studies suggest that significant recovery of vegetation composition will only occur on a timescale of decades or more. Change will be slowest in systems which are accumulating all deposited nitrogen and not losing it through leaching and/or denitrification. Some changes that have occurred in community composition may turn out to be permanent as a result of individual species effects on nutrient cycling. The switch from nitrogen to phosphorus limitation that has occurred in some habitats may affect the potential for, and pathway of, recovery. Finally, grazing, burning and other forms of land management will obviously influence recovery through their effects on species composition, nitrogen pools within the system and nitrogen cycling. Understanding of the changes in ecosystem processes caused by nitrogen deposition should enable the identification of land management practices most likely to enhance recovery once nitrogen deposition is reduced.

7.6 Ozone

7.6.1 Introduction

The last report of the Photo-oxidant Review Group (PORG, 1998) provided a detailed analysis of the possible impacts of ozone in the UK, based on the critical level approach. This analysis clearly indicates that most areas of the UK have exceedance of the critical level for crops and semi-natural vegetation, and significant areas of southern Britain show exceedance of the critical level for forests. However, there is substantial variation from year to year in both the absolute concentrations of ozone and their spatial variation; furthermore, patterns of exposure to ozone during the growing season may vary greatly from year to year. It is also important to emphasise that there is limited field evidence of the impacts of ozone in the UK, apart from the demonstration of symptoms of visible leaf injury, and that assessment of the risk of damage to vegetation is based primarily on experimental chamber studies in which either ozone has been added or ambient ozone has been filtered. The use of these experimental results to assess field effects is thus a central issue in ozone risk assessment in the UK

The large variation from year to year in ozone concentrations means that it is difficult to identify with great confidence any temporal trends. However, both observations and models suggest that peak concentrations of ozone have fallen since the 1970s, but that annual or summer mean ozone concentrations have increased over the same period, mainly as a result of changes in the global background tropospheric concentrations. Models also suggest that these trends are likely to continue over the next 20-30 years. Over this period, atmospheric CO_2 concentrations will increase further, and climatic conditions are likely to change; furthermore, land-use patterns across the UK are already changing significantly. All these factors will be significant when considering future impacts of ozone and the impact of measures to reduce precursor emissions.

7.6.2 Exposure Index Approaches to Ozone Risk Assessment

The current approach used to assess the risk of ozone damage to vegetation in Europe is based on a single seasonal exposure index, the accumulated exposure above 40 ppb (AOT40), which experimental evidence suggests is closely related to plant response in terms of growth and yield. However, it is important to realise the limitations of applying this exposure index under field conditions. Figure 7.16 shows the relationship between AOT40 and yield reduction for spring wheat, derived from synthesis of data from open-top chamber experiments in central and northern Europe; further background to this analysis is given by Fuhrer *et al.* (1997). However, it is essential to emphasise that this exposure-response relationship, obtained under well-watered conditions and high atmospheric turbulence, cannot be used to quantify yield losses under field conditions, and to evaluate the benefits of policies to reduce ozone exposure across locations with different climates (Fuhrer & Ashmore, 2000). This is particularly the case because, unlike under the experimental conditions used to derive the relationship in Figure 7.16, the spatial and temporal variation in ozone concentrations in the field is not independent of climatic variations.

A further important limitation of the AOT40 approach is the existence of the cut-off threshold of 40 ppb. It is important to note that the use of this threshold represents a simplification of more complex ozone exposure-response relationships. In regions where concentrations are generally low, and hence close to the threshold value, small differences in absolute ozone concentrations can have large effects on the estimated AOT40 value (Simpson *et al.*, 1998). This is important when considering the gradients in ozone concentration from a measurement point above a canopy through to the ground. For example, Figure 7.17 shows ozone concentration gradients above a moorland canopy in Scotland in four successive years. The differences between seasonal mean concentration measured at a standard height of 2-3 m and at the top of the canopy were considerable, of the order of 3 ppb. Such variations can lead to substantial differences in estimated values of seasonal AOT40.

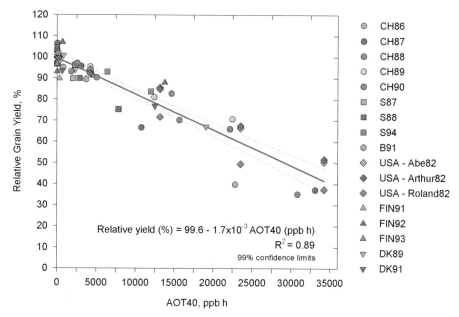

Figure 7.16 Relationship between wheat grain yield, expressed relative to a control treatment, and seasonal ozone exposure, derived from seventeen experiments in six countries; the codes refer to the country and year of experiment. After Fuhrer, 1996.

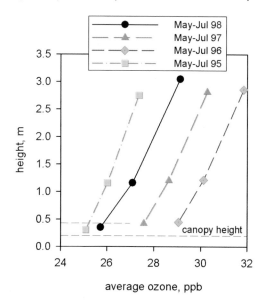

Figure 7.17 Ozone concentrations measured at 3 heights above a moorland canopy, averages for May to July 1995 to 1998 are plotted.

An important additional limitation of the AOT40 index is that the same seasonal exposure value may arise in several different ways – for example, a seasonal value of 10 ppm h over six months could be provided by the following days with 10 h of elevated ozone: 5 days at 240 ppb; 10 days at 140 ppb; 20 days at 90 ppb; 40 days at 65 ppb; or 100 days at 50 ppb. Although good exposure-response relationships have been obtained using the AOT40 index, it should not be assumed that these different exposure patterns will all have the same biological effect. For example, Krupa *et al.*, (1995) present evidence from statistical analysis of filtration experiments in the U.S. that, in ambient air, it is concentrations in the mid-range (i.e. 50-90 ppb) that are most significant. This is not because of a non-linearity in response to ozone. Rather, the key factor, as demonstrated by Grünhage *et al.*, (1997), is that the highest ozone concentrations tend to occur under meteorological conditions which limit the flux of ozone to the plant, both because of high resistance to ozone flux across the atmospheric boundary layer to the vegetation, and because such concentrations tend to occur with high vapour pressure deficits, which lead to low values of stomatal conductance.

7.6.3 Flux-Based Approaches

One approach which would improve the assessment of ozone impacts, taking into account the influence of climatic conditions, and other ontogenetic and environmental factors, is to base the assessment on the flux of ozone into the leaf rather than on the external ozone exposure, as both empirical evidence and *a priori* reasoning suggest that flux should be more closely related to effects than exposure. This involves modelling the pathway of ozone from the atmospheric surface layer through to the sites of damage in the leaf mesophyll, taking into account other ozone resistances in the canopy, connected with external plant surfaces, the canopy air, and the soil (Figure 7.18). In the U.S., the importance of such an approach has been recognised (e.g. Massmann *et al.*, 2000), but there has been little actual model development and application. However, in Europe, some progress has been made in developing this approach in the last few years.

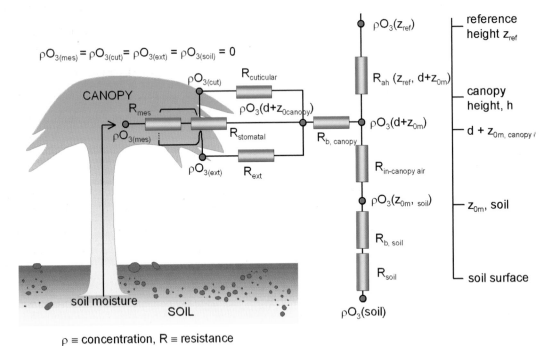

$\rho \equiv$ concentration, $R \equiv$ resistance

Figure 7.18 A resistance analogue of ozone transfer between the atmospheric surface layer and terrestrial ecosystems following the *dual source* concept (after Emberson *et al.*, (2000)).

Grünhage *et al.*, (1997) developed a soil-vegetation-atmosphere transfer model for ozone and used it to calculate an 'effective' AOT40 in the canopy, taking into account the effects of atmospheric and boundary layer resistances, stomatal resistance, and the phenological stages at which ozone uptake was limited by leaf senescence. The results for wheat calculated for the

German province of Hesse, using ozone and meteorological data over a 12-year period, show the large differences between the 'effective' AOT40 and that measured at a reference height above the canopy, demonstrating that actual impacts on wheat yield would be substantially lower than the use of AOT40 values above the canopy, i.e. at standard measurement height, would indicate (Figure 7.19).

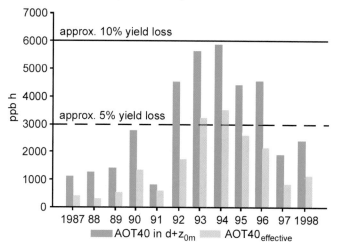

Figure 7.19 Yearly variation in May to June AOT40 at the top of an agricultural crop canopy (after Grünhage *et al.*, 1997).

The work of Emberson *et al.* (2000) has concentrated on the application of this approach on a European scale, using a more detailed stomatal model, which has been parameterised for a range of species, and linking this directly to the EMEP ozone model. Figure 7.20 compares the AOT40 values predicted in June 1994 by the EMEP model with the mean stomatal flux values calculated using this model for wheat and beech. It can be seen that the spatial patterns based on modelled flux are quite different from those based on AOT40; the modelled flux for wheat, for example, in this month in southern Europe was lower because of the higher VPD and the more advanced phenology of the crop. Table 7.3 provides more explicit comparisons of seasonal AOT40 values with modelled fluxes (assuming no threshold or one of 1.5 nmol m^{-2} s^{-1}) for four specific EMEP grid squares for both wheat and beech. Although there is a strong contrast between the AOT40 values in the four squares, there is little difference in the cumulative ozone dose, while the cumulative dose above a threshold is actually lowest in the square with the highest AOT40 value.

Table 7.3 Calculated total (CUO_3) and threshold ($TCUO_3$) cumulative ozone uptake values for beech and wheat over the 1994 growing season compared to equivalent values of AOT40 (Emberson *et al.*, 2000).

Location	CUO_3 (mmol m^{-2})	$TCUO_3$ (mmol m^{-2})	AOT40[a] (ppb h)
Wheat			
Sweden	7.35	3.33	4714
UK	6.54	3.23	4407
Czech Republic	6.43	2.44	8730
Spain	6.65	4.48	2283
Beech			
Sweden	6.55	1.24	4514
UK	6.68	0.96	4896
Czech Republic	7.03	0.62	15249
Spain	6.93	1.46	3856

a. AOT 40 is calculated over the modelled growing season and not for the fixed 3 or 6 month period currently used for Level 1 evaluations for agricultural crops and forest trees, respectively.

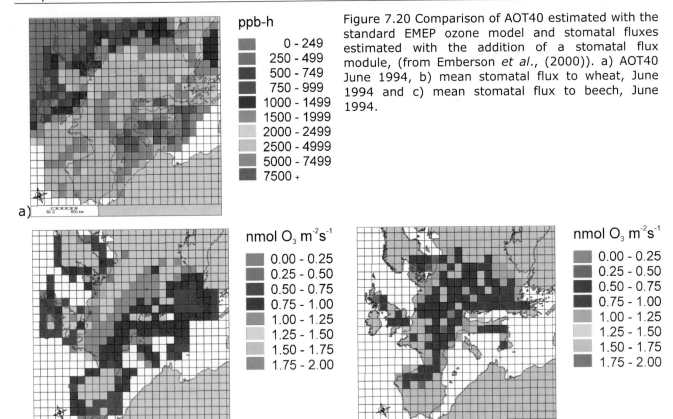

ppb-h

0 - 249
250 - 499
500 - 749
750 - 999
1000 - 1499
1500 - 1999
2000 - 2499
2500 - 4999
5000 - 7499
7500 +

nmol O_3 m^{-2}s^{-1}

0.00 - 0.25
0.25 - 0.50
0.50 - 0.75
0.75 - 1.00
1.00 - 1.25
1.25 - 1.50
1.50 - 1.75
1.75 - 2.00

nmol O_3 m^{-2}s^{-1}

0.00 - 0.25
0.25 - 0.50
0.50 - 0.75
0.75 - 1.00
1.00 - 1.25
1.25 - 1.50
1.50 - 1.75
1.75 - 2.00

Figure 7.20 Comparison of AOT40 estimated with the standard EMEP ozone model and stomatal fluxes estimated with the addition of a stomatal flux module, (from Emberson *et al*., (2000)). a) AOT40 June 1994, b) mean stomatal flux to wheat, June 1994 and c) mean stomatal flux to beech, June 1994.

These flux-based approaches clearly need further development and testing before they can be applied in ozone impact assessment and policy analysis. However, it is clear from the examples presented here that, whereas the AOT40 index has provided a valuable precautionary approach to assessing the need for measures to control ozone precursors, its application in quantifying ozone impacts may lead to misleading results which may distort policy assessments. It is also important to note that, although the flux approach provides a more mechanistic approach to assessing ozone impacts, there are many other crucial processes which need to be considered, such as the detoxification of the incoming ozone flux in the cell wall (e.g. Plöchl *et al*., 2000) and effects on carbon allocation patterns, which may be critical in trees and herbaceous wild plants.

The distribution of AOT40 shown in Figure 7.20, and in Chapter 8, implies that the impacts of ozone in the UK are small relative to those in central Europe. In contrast, assessments based on the flux approach suggest the differences in impact of ozone between central and northern Europe are smaller. This conclusion is also supported by coordinated studies with sensitive clover clones, which are discussed in more detail in Chapter 8.

7.6.4 Crops

Economic impacts of ozone on crops can occur both through visible injury and reductions in yield. The presence of characteristic visible symptoms has also been used to demonstrate the presence of ozone at concentrations that are potentially damaging to plants. The tobacco cultivar Bel W3 continues to be used for this purpose, for example in current projects in Edinburgh and Sheffield. UK sites also form part of a wider European biomonitoring programme, which involves assessing visible injury and growth of two clover clones, which differ in their sensitivity to ozone; further details of this study are given in Chapter 8.

An economic evaluation of the benefits of measures to reduce ozone concentrations has been carried out by the EU in connection with proposals for a daughter Directive relating to ozone in ambient air. These indicate that the direct economic benefits of reducing the gap between current ozone exposures and an AOT40 of 3 ppm h would be about 2000 million ECU across Europe, with that in the UK being 130 million ECU (Holland *et al.*, 1999). These benefits were of the same order of magnitude as the estimated health benefits, and significantly affect the results of any cost-benefit analysis of policy options.

However, it is important to consider the limitations, which were recognised by the authors of this exercise. Firstly, the method relies on assigning each crop to a specific sensitivity class to which generic exposure-response relationships are assigned. In the EU study, this classification was rather subjective, but a recent rigorous analysis under the auspices of ICP Vegetation (Mills *et al.*, 2000a) has provided a sounder basis for such a classification. The study reviewed all papers on exposure-response experiments on the most commonly grown crops in Europe, using either field or open-top chamber exposures, in both the US and Europe, applying rigorous quality control methods to select data for further analysis. The exposure-response analysis used both the AOT40 index and the 7h mean seasonal concentration employed in the US; the results for six crops illustrated in Figure 7.21 use the 7h mean concentration.

There were three important conclusions from this study. Firstly, there were no significant differences for individual crops between results for Europe and the US, allowing the results to be combined for analysis. Secondly, there was a clear distinction in sensitivity between three groups, with wheat and soybean being of highest sensitivity, potato, rape and maize being of intermediate sensitivity, and barley and oats showing no significant response to ozone. These two findings provide a robust basis for further assessments of yield losses across Europe, taking account of modifying factors such as soil moisture deficit and phenology. However, the third conclusion, that there were no usable exposure-response data for important crops such as sunflower and rye, provides an important limitation to any comprehensive analysis of yield loss.

Some of the limitations of using an AOT40, rather than a flux, approach are illustrated by the recent analysis of experimental data collected over several successive seasons in southern Sweden by Pleijel *et al.* (2000). The yield data were related to the ozone exposure over the period of grain-filling, which is the most sensitive stage in cereals. Figure 7.22a shows the relationship between yield and AOT40 in six seasons, illustrating that a 10% yield loss might be predicted at AOT40 values that differ by an order of magnitude over the different seasons. Figure. 7.22b shows the results plotted against the modelled absorbed dose of ozone over the same period, derived using a model comparable to that of Emberson *et al.* (2000). Five of the six experiments now appear to lie on a common response line, indicating that by incorporating the effects of irradiance, temperature and vapour pressure deficit, in modifying the ozone uptake, a stronger mechanistic relationship to yield is obtained. Analogously, within the same year, one might expect the range of growth conditions for wheat to vary across Europe to an extent which might provide similar differences in yield-response relationship as is indicated in Figure 7.22.

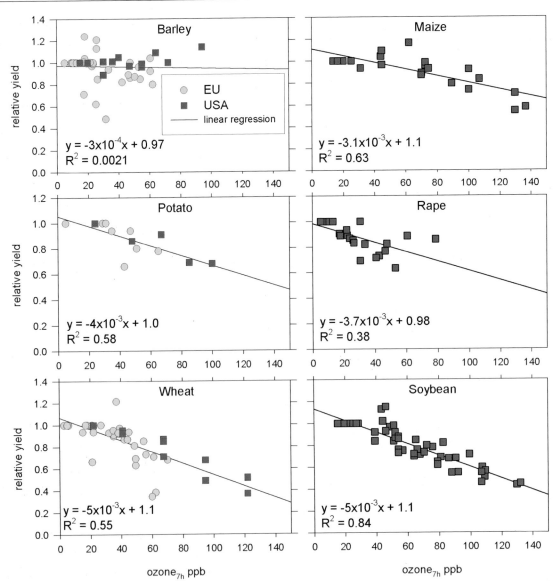

Figure 7.21 Yield response functions plotted from data presented in the literature on the response of yield of various crop species to ozone. Data from experiments in the USA and EU are presented separately on the figures, with the linear regression being through all data points.

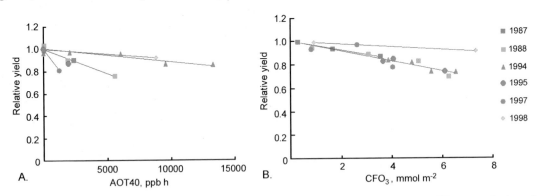

Figure 7.22 a) Linear regression of relative yield and AOT40 during the grain filling period and b) linear regression of relative yield and cumulative ozone uptake by flag leaves (with no flux threshold during grain filling) (from Pleijel *et al.* 2000).

Figure 7.22b shows a clear outlier exposure-response relationship, for the 1998 season. In this year, the crop grown was winter wheat, in contrast to the spring wheat cultivars used in all the previous years. Since only one winter wheat cultivar was used, and there is known to be very considerable variation in ozone sensitivity between cultivars of both winter and spring wheat, it is not possible to conclude that winter wheat in general is less sensitive that spring wheat. Nevertheless, this is an important observation, since the vast bulk of wheat grown in the UK is winter wheat, but the relationship in Figure 7.16 used to derive the AOT40 critical level for crops is based on spring wheat. This clearly illustrates the limitations of using generic exposure-response relationships to predict the yield response of specific crops, as in the EU assessment.

A further important factor is the economic significance of effects on crop quality. Oilseed rape has become a major component of UK arable agriculture over the past 10 years. Ollerenshaw *et al.* (1999) recently used a field fumigation facility at a site west of Newcastle to assess the impacts of ozone both in August/September of the year the crop was sown, and in May/June of the year it was harvested, with an overall AOT40 of 9 ppm h. The observed reduction in seed yield was 14%, a yield response somewhat greater than predicted by the analysis of Mills *et al.* (2000b). However, an important additional effect was observed on the oil content of the harvested seeds, which showed a small (5%) but statistically significant decrease in the ozone treatment. Since contract price in the UK is based on oil content, this would provide an important additional economic loss to the producer. Although the potential impacts of air pollution on crop quality have been recognised for three decades, there are very few good studies of the impact of ozone on this important factor.

In general, the impacts of ozone on horticulture have received much less attention than those on arable crops, despite the fact that many such crops are known to be sensitive to ozone. One issue that has received recent attention in the UK is the impact of ozone on high-value glasshouse crops. On days of high ozone concentrations, the glasshouse vents are likely to be open, allowing the ingress of ambient ozone, while the high humidity within such glasshouses would tend to increase the impacts of ozone that enters. Gillespie and Barnes (pers. comm.) have established in field studies on the south coast of England that concentrations within commercial glasshouses can be as high as those outside, and can cause significant visible injury to a range of horticultural crops and herb species. However, a further important factor was involved – the high levels of added CO_2 within the glasshouse, which are used to increase crop growth rates. When the effects of ozone in the presence of elevated CO_2 were compared to those in glasshouses without added CO_2, they found almost complete protection was provided by the CO_2.

Other experimental studies of the interaction between CO_2 and ozone suggest that the elevated ambient CO_2 concentrations expected by the end of the next century may provide some, but not complete, protection against the effect of ozone. For example, McKee *et al.* (1997) found that growth in elevated CO_2 prevented any adverse effect of ozone on the vegetative growth stages of winter wheat; however, there was an additional effect of ozone in the reproductive stages on which CO_2 appeared to have no effect.

7.6.5 Forests

The most extensive UK study of ozone impacts on trees has been the Forestry Commission open top chamber (OTC) research programme, which ran from 1986 to 1993. A total of five species were exposed to either ambient air, or air with reduced pollution inputs through the use of charcoal filters at three sites in the UK. Headley in Hampshire (beech, Norway spruce and Scots pine) represented a high ozone exposure, Chatsworth in the English Midlands (beech, Scots pine, Sitka spruce) historically had a high NO_x and SO_2 input, whilst Glendevon in the Scottish uplands (Scots pine, Norway spruce, Sitka spruce) was assumed to have a low pollution load.

Initially, beech and Norway spruce grew significantly better in the filtered treatments at Headley (Figure 7.23) with height growth enhanced by approximately 20% in both species, and biomass production of Norway spruce by up to 49% after 3 years exposure (Durrant et al., 1992). However, by the end of the experiment (when tree numbers were greatly reduced), only the growth of beech was significantly reduced by ambient air pollution at Headley; this enhancement of growth in filtered air was accompanied by improved needle retention in Scots pine (Figure 7.24) (Durrant et al., 1992).

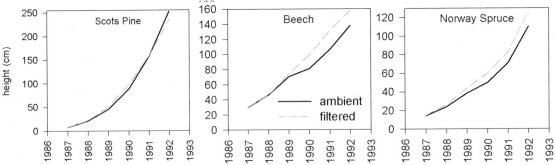

Figure 7.23 Height growth of Scots pine, beech and Norway spruce after 6 years growth in ambient or charcoal filtered open top chambers at Headley in Hampshire. (Durrant et al., 1992).

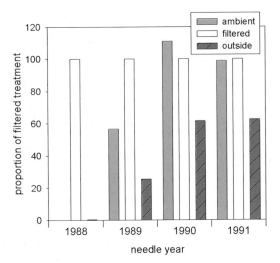

Figure 7.24 The effect of ambient air pollution on needle retention in Scots pine in the open-top chamber experiment at Headley (Durrant et al., 1992).

There was no enhancement of growth in filtered air at the other two sites, and most species grew better in ambient air at those sites, possibly indicating a lower N input in the charcoal filtered treatments leading to the development of sub-optimal nitrogen levels. The overall conclusion from this long-running experiment is thus that ambient air pollution did not affect the growth of the production forestry species investigated, except for beech in southern England, a region exposed to an ozone dose (AOT40 = 2-8 ppm h; 1986-1993), which although higher than at the other sites, is below the critical level set for forests (cf. Section 7.7.2.2). This experiment was superseded by a factorial investigation of the interactions between ozone pollution, elevated atmospheric CO_2 and water supply in 1993 (see Broadmeadow & Jackson, 2000), which provides further support for the approach of modelling ozone exposure as a physiologically effective dose or flux (Figure 7.25).

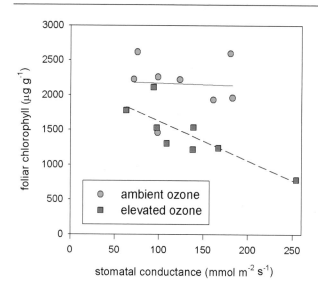

Figure 7.25 The effect of stomatal conductance (mean of measurements made on seven days during the 1996 growing season) on foliar chlorophyll content measured on 7 September for ambient and elevated ozone grown plants. Variation in stomatal conductance resulted from imposed CO_2 concentration and water supply treatments in this factorial experiment (Broadmeadow and Jackson, 2000).

These experimental studies relate to the effects on young trees, and it is clear that it is essential to also assess the longer-term effects of ozone on mature forest trees, if the impact of current and future ozone levels is to be assessed. Little research focussed on this objective has been carried out to date in the UK. However, work in Europe and the U.S. provides some useful indications of possible approaches. Firstly, it may be possible to use temporal and spatial gradients in ozone exposure to identify exposure-response relationships in mature trees in the field. Variation in annual growth is difficult to use, except where ozone is a dominant growth determinant, because of its close association with climatic factors, although Stribley & Ashmore (in press) did find evidence of a negative association between ozone exposure and twig growth patterns of beech over a period of 10 years at Whytham Wood, Oxfordshire, in addition to a strong effect of soil moisture deficit. The examination of shorter-term variations in growth might be more informative. For example, Mclaughlin & Downing (1995) made short-term measurements of stem growth on loblolly pine in the eastern United States, using a sensitive dendrometer, over a period of five years, relating these to weekly records of climate and of air pollution concentrations. The results showed that the strongest predictor of short-term radial growth was the interaction between ozone and soil moisture, with the short-term effect of ozone being greater in a moist year than a dry year. Radial growth showed a significant relationship with AOT40, with short-term decreases in growth being associated with daily mean values of 300 ppb h.

The analysis of spatial variations in growth rates may also prove informative, as demonstrated by Braun et al. (1999), who compared diameter growth in mature beech trees over a 4-year period at 57 plots across Switzerland with a range of site factors, and climate and pollution variables. A number of variables, including tree size, position in the stand, crown transparency, soil base saturation and nitrogen deposition showed significant relationships with growth. In addition a significant negative association with ozone, expressed as highest annual or four-year mean AOT40 was evident (Figure. 7.26); the slope of the fitted line indicated a reduction in 4-year stem increment of 22% for a 10 ppm h increase in AOT40.

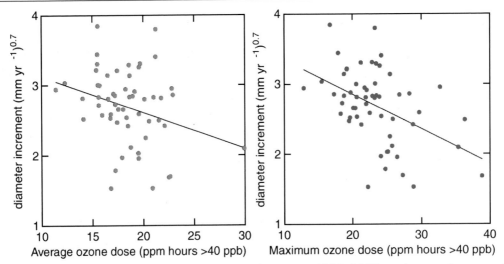

Figure 7.26 Correlation between diameter increment between 1992-1995 and annual ozone dose (both correlations are statistically significant at the p<0.001 level) from Braun *et al.* (1999).

Direct experimental comparisons have been made of the responses of seedlings and branches of mature trees of several tree species, with variable results. However, such comparisons cannot assess the longer-term effects on growth patterns and the allocation of resources to roots and stem tissue. The use of mathematical models for this purpose may offer a valuable route forward, especially as several existing physiologically-based tree growth models can readily be adapted to assess the effect of ozone. Weinstein *et al.* (1998) used such a model to compare the response of seedlings and mature trees of the American species, red oak, based on a three-year experimental study. In this case, the mature trees were more sensitive, primarily because of their higher stomatal conductance and hence ozone flux; and the model predicted that this would result in very much bigger effects on root growth in mature trees. Ollinger *et al.* (1997) used a different model, parameterised for American hardwood forests, using ozone and climatic data for the north-eastern U.S. The results (Figure 7.27) show a close empirical relationship with seasonal ozone exposure, but that the soil water-holding capacity had a strong influence on model predictions. These two model studies, taken together, indicate the need for further information on root allocation responses and their effects on interactions between ozone and the high soil moisture deficit which often accompanies high ozone years.

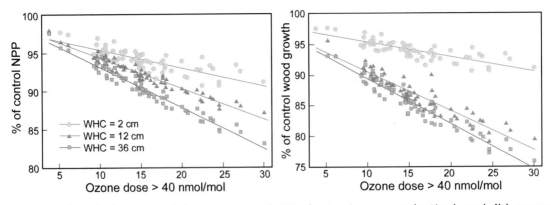

Figure 7.27 Predicted change in (a) mean annual NPP (net primary production) and (b) mean annual wood production, at 64 sites across a study region, in response to 1987 to 1992 mean ozone levels. Predictions are shown for three levels of soil water holding capacity (WHC), from well-watered (WHC=36) to severe drought (WHC=2) (after Weinstein *et al.,* 1998).

7.6.6 Semi-Natural Vegetation

The effects of ozone on over 100 wild species native to the UK have now been assessed, albeit mainly through short-term experiments with individual pot-grown plants. These studies show that many of these species are at least as sensitive as the most sensitive crop species, and it is on this basis that a critical level for semi-natural vegetation has been adopted which is the same as that for crops (Ashmore & Davison, 1996). However, as for crops and forests, this AOT40 critical level can only provide an indication of the potential for adverse effects on vegetation. In considering the effects on semi-natural vegetation, however, there are a number of additional factors to be considered in addition to those factors (such as the influence of climatic and edaphic conditions and the difficulty of assessing long-term effects on perennial species), which have been considered in the context of crops and forests in the previous sections.

Firstly, the sensitivity of plants grown from the seed sources used in these experiments may be quite different from the actual populations found in the field. Furthermore, these differences may relate to the actual ozone exposure in the field, as shown by Reiling & Davison (1992) for the annual *Plantago major*. This relationship has subsequently been extended by the inclusion of continental populations (Lyons *et al.*, 1997), which provide a more comprehensive dataset showing a positive correlation between the AOT40 index at the site of exposure and ozone resistance of the population (Figure. 7.28). There is also evidence that the ozone resistance of populations collected after years with high ozone concentrations is greater than that collected after years with relatively low concentrations. All this suggests the potential for rapid evolution of ozone tolerance in the field, at least in this species, although the spatial and temporal associations between high ozone levels and climate mean this hypothesis cannot be proved from the field data.

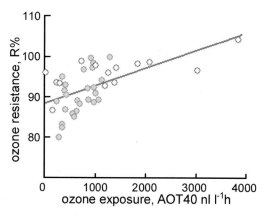

Figure 7.28 Ozone resistance of seed-grown *Plantago major* populations against AOT40 at the collection sites (filled yellow dots = UK, open green dots = continental Europe). Resistance = 88.7 + 0.00043.AOT40, r = 0.538, P < 0.0001 (from Lyons *et al.* 1997). R% is the percentage ratio of relative growth rate in ozone fumigated populations to those grown in filtered air ($R_{O3}/R_{filtered}$) where R = $(\ln(w_2) - \ln(w_1))/(t_2-t_1)$, w = dry weight, t = time in weeks and the number subscript denotes harvest date.

Secondly, the sheer range of species involved, in addition to the range of intra-specific tolerance, creates practical problems in assessing the impacts of ozone across a range of habitats. Some attention has been paid in recent years to identifying species characteristics that might be associated with high ozone sensitivity. Application of such an analysis to national datasets, such as the Countryside Survey, might then be used to test whether there are trends in species distribution which are consistent with an impact of ozone. Unfortunately, most such analyses, including that of Franzaring *et al.* (1999) who used a comprehensive database of 131 European species, show no association between ozone sensitivity and either Grime's CSR strategy or Ellenberg's ecological indicator approach. In contrast, weak associations were found with physiological characteristics, such as relative growth rate.

Two important constraints on any such analysis based on short-term experimental responses of individual species need to be identified. Firstly, these experiments generally record only vegetative growth or visible injury. However, these may not be the criteria that are most important for the actual survival of the species. For example, seed production is the most important factor for annual species, while for perennial stress-tolerant species a range of factors may be significant. This is important because plants may switch their resource allocation under ozone stress. For example, Bergmann *et al.* (1995) studied effects of ozone on 17 wild annual species (Figure 7.29); of these, 12 showed comparable effects on vegetative and reproductive growth, but five species were outliers, switching resource allocation to or from flowering under ozone stress. Hence, effects on vegetative growth may not be reliable indicators of the response to ozone of the most ecologically significant parameter.

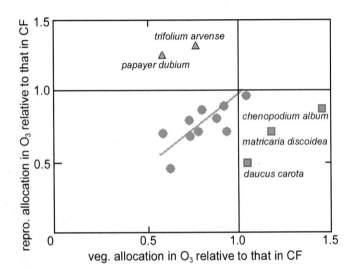

Figure 7.29 The effects of ozone on relative allocation of resources to vegetative and reproductive organs of herbaceous species exposed, from the seedling stage to flowering, to two different ozone regimes: CF (Charcoal Filtered) + 70 ppb for 8 hours per day and CF + 60% ambient + 30 ppb. Allocation is expressed as the ratio of that in ozone to that in CF-air (from Davison & Barnes, 1998; redrawn from Bergmann *et al.*, 1995; veg. = vegetative, repro. = reproductive).

Secondly, the responses of individual species within a plant community, where they are competing for light, water, nutrients etc. may be quite different from individual pot-grown plants. Where artificial communities have been constructed by planting a limited number of species together, the responses have been consistent with the response to ozone of the individual species when grown alone. However, the only two studies that have examined the effects of ozone on real communities in the UK have shown very different results. Evans & Ashmore (1992) placed open-top chambers over an acid grassland community, and found that ambient air reduced the cover of the dominant, but less ozone-sensitive, grass species and increased that of the more sensitive clover, suggesting that the release from competition for light was more important in its response than its innate ozone sensitivity. Thwaites (1996), who transplanted chalk grassland communities from Twyford Down into open-top chambers, found a similar effect, in that ozone exposure over three years reduced the dominant grass cover, but also increased that of some sub-dominant forb species.

In terms of biodiversity and conservation, effects of ozone on rare plant species may be of as great a concern as shifts in species composition within more common communities. Few experiments have been carried out on such species; however, Thwaites (1996) investigated 9 such UK species in short-term fumigations at 80 ppb ozone, and found that several had significant growth reductions. Clearly, this is an issue which requires further investigation.

The effect of ozone on bryophytes and lichens is less certain. Upland bryophyte communities may be exposed to relatively high ozone concentrations, and Gagnon & Karnosky (1992) found that chronic ozone exposure caused significant declines in the growth, photosynthesis and chlorophyll content of three *Sphagnum* species. However, these experiments were conducted under high temperatures that are untypical of the British uplands, and both Potter *et al.* (1996) and Foot (1996) suggest that current ozone concentrations are unlikely to have long-term effects on bryophyte populations in the UK uplands.

7.7 Critical Loads and Levels

7.7.1 Introduction

The concept of a critical load (or critical level when considering direct effects of gaseous air pollutants on vegetation) has provided an important basis for assessing those areas in the UK, and in Europe, where pollutant exposures are above those at which adverse effects on vegetation may occur. They are also employed in assessing the implications of planned changes in pollutant emissions.

The critical levels and loads currently used in ecological risk assessment for vegetation within UN/ECE are summarised in Table 7.4 and Table 7.5. The values were subsequently adopted, at least in part, as revised Air Quality Guidelines for Europe by WHO (2000), and in EU Directives. The derivation of critical levels and loads for vegetation is mainly based on a 'black box' or empirical approach, with little mechanistic analysis.

When interpreting the evidence of vegetation response to air pollution levels in the UK in the context of critical loads and levels, it is important to understand that different sources of information were used to set different critical level or critical load values. For SO_2, the values were primarily derived from field observation, while for O_3, the primary source was exposure-response studies in field chambers and for NO_x and NH_3 the primary source was experimental studies, but with no formal exposure-response analysis possible. The empirical critical loads of total N deposition for vegetation were derived primarily from field experiments and observations. It is important to note that there is uncertainty attached to all these values, which has implications for interpretation of maps showing areas where they are exceeded.

It is also important to appreciate that the empirical critical loads for N are set at the lowest deposition at which real change in community composition has been observed, based on studies up to 1995. In contrast, the mass balance calculations of critical loads of acidity for soils, described in Chapter 5, are based on criteria that are related to root growth rates and not to the threshold for major ecological change. Thus, although mass balance critical loads for acidification may be lower than the empirical critical loads for vegetation change, and hence the extent of exceedance may be higher, this does not mean that the ecological impact of N on soil acidification is greater than that of eutrophication. In fact, all the available field evidence in the UK suggests that the reverse is the case, and that the eutrophying effects of N on low-nutrient plant communities are far more significant than the acidifying effects.

Table 7.4 Summary of air quality guidelines, limit values and critical levels applied in Europe.

	Ozone	Sulphur dioxide	Nitrogen oxides
Nature of index	Cumulative exposure over growing season (ppb h)	Annual or winter mean (μg m^{-3})	Annual mean of sum of NO and NO$_2$ concentrations (ppb), expressed as μg m^{-3} based on conversion for NO$_2$
UNECE	3000 ppb h in daylight hours over 3 months (agricultural crops and natural vegetation) 10,000ppb.h in daylight hours over 6 months (forests)	30 (agricultural crops) 20 (forests) 15 (forests in harsh climates) 10 (lichens)	30 (all vegetation)
WHO	As for UNECE	As for UNECE	As for UNECE
EU	-	20 (all ecosystems away from vicinity of sources)	30 (all ecosystems away from vicinity of sources)

Table 7.5 Summary of proposed critical loads (kg-N ha^{-1} y^{-1}) for effects of nitrogen deposition on selected classes of vegetation.

Ecosystem	Critical load	Effect of exceedance
Forests		
Acidic coniferous forests	7-20 ***	Changes in ground flora and mycorrhizae
Acidic deciduous forests	10-20 **	Changes in ground flora and mycorrhizae
Calcareous forests	15-20 *	Changes in ground flora
Forests in humid climates	5-10 *	Decline in lichens
Heathlands		
Lowland dry heaths	15-20 ***	Transition from heather to grass
Lowland wet heaths	17-22 **	Transition from heather to grass
Upland Calluna heaths	10-20 *	Decline in heather and moss dominance
Arctic and alpine heaths	5-15 *	Decline in lichens, mosses and evergreen dwarf shrubs
Grasslands and wetlands		
Calcareous grasslands	15-35 **	Increase in tall grasses, altered diversity
Acid/neutral grasslands	20-30 *	Increase in tall grasses, altered diversity
Montane grasslands	10-15 *	Increase in tall grasses, altered diversity
Ombrotrophic bogs	5-10 **	Decline in typical mosses, increase in tall grasses

Quality of evidence supporting the proposed critical load:
*** reliable
** quite reliable
* uncertain

7.7.2 Application of Critical Levels

Sulphur dioxide and nitrogen oxides

The critical levels established for sulphur dioxide and nitrogen oxides, which are summarised in Table 7.4, have now been adopted as objectives within the National Air Quality Strategy for England, Scotland, Wales and Northern Ireland (AQS), based on the application of the first EU Air Quality Daughter Directive. In this section, we consider critically the application of these critical levels within the AQS, and compare the critical levels with current and predicted concentration fields.

It is important firstly to consider which values have been selected for application within AQS. For NO_x, there is only a single critical level value to be applied to all types of vegetation, and this has been adopted as the UK objective. For SO_2, however, the situation is more complex as four critical level values are available, for different receptors and/or climates. The AQS has adopted the critical level of 20 μg m^{-3}, as an annual or winter mean. This critical level aims to protect forests and natural vegetation. However, two lower critical level values are ignored. The first, at 15 μg m^{-3}, is for application in harsh climates, and there is a recommendation (not detailed in Table 7.5) as to the cumulative temperature at which this critical level should be applied. Analysis of UK data by CLAG (1996) indicated that there were only a very few 10 km squares in which the temperature criteria for application of the 15 μg m^{-3} value were met and this concentration was exceeded, and reductions in S emissions since this analysis was carried out in the mid-1990s are likely to have reduced this number further. Thus there is a strong justification for not applying this critical level in the UK. The second critical level which is not applied as a national objective is that of 10 μg m^{-3} to protect sensitive lichen species; the implications of this omission are that there may be a constraint to recolonization by some sensitive lichen species of areas meeting the national objective of 20 μg m^{-3}.

Figure 7.30 provides an indication of areas in the UK where the critical levels for the protection of semi-natural vegetation and forestry are exceeded (30 μg m^{-3} for NO_x, 20 μg m^{-3} annual and 20 μg m^{-3} winter means for SO_2 effects on forestry and semi-natural vegetation and 10 μg m^{-3} for SO_2 effects on lichens) Figure 7.30b shows that there are only isolated areas of exceedance of 20 μg m^{-3} SO_2, but that the 10 μg m^{-3} value is exceeded over significant areas of central and southern England. The 30 μg m^{-3} value of NO_x is exceeded around most urban areas and major roads.

However, it is also important to consider these maps in the context of statements within AQS, based on an interpretation of the EU Air Quality Daughter Directive, as to where these critical levels/air quality objectives are not to be applied. This indicates that the air quality objectives should not be applied: less than 20 km from an area with population above 250,000; and less than 5 km from Part A industrial processes, motorways and areas with a population above 5000. Figure 7.31 provides a modification of Figure 7.30 to which a mask excluding such areas is applied. These exclusions mean that the air quality objectives will not be applied in many areas with high concentrations of the two pollutants. While this chapter is focussed on regional issues, it is very important to point out the conservation value of many areas of high biological diversity close to urban areas and to motorways.

The implications of these exclusions for the protection of sensitive ecosystems need to be carefully considered, particularly as the areas concerned may include many sites of high conservation value. These include sites designated as Special Areas of Conservation (SACs) and Special Protection Area (SPAs) under the EU Habitats and Birds Directives. The Directive requires that these areas must be protected from habitat deterioration or damage, and maintained or restored to favourable conservation status (Article 6(1) 92/43/EEC) from any cause, including air pollution. A full assessment of the significance of this issue would require a detailed geographical overlay of SAC locations with current and future SO_2 and NO_x concentrations and with the 'exclusion zone' superimposed; such an analysis is outside the scope of this report. However, we would suggest that this issue needs further evaluation, and propose the following as a basis for further discussion. The AQS approach envisages a single area of 'exclusion' formed by combining areas close to industrial works, close to motorways and close to urban areas. In practice, each of these sources raises different issues and hence might be better considered independently. Behind our proposed approach is the concept that exceedance of a critical level indicates only that ecological effects may occur. A more detailed assessment will be required to investigate the relationship between critical level exceedance and the conservation status of individual features of SPA/SACs.

Figure 7.30 Exceedance of critical levels for a. NO_x b. SO_2 agriculture c. SO_2 forests and semi-natural vegetation and d. SO_2 lichens, based on 1996 NO_x and SO_2 concentrations.

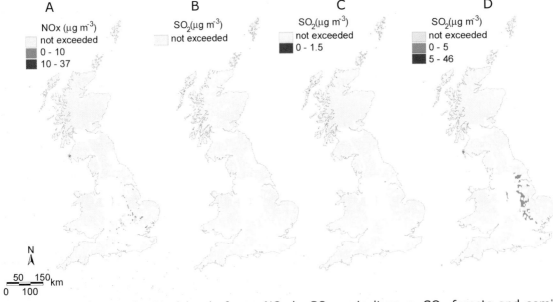

Figure 7.31 Exceedance of critical levels for a. NO_x b. SO_2 agriculture c. SO_2 forests and semi-natural vegetation and d. SO_2 lichens, based on 1996 NO_x and SO_2 concentrations, with regions less than 20 km from an area with population above 250,000; and less than 5 km from Part A industrial processes, motorways and areas with a population above 5000 excluded.

In terms of motorways/major trunk roads, the issues will be very location specific, with the greatest concern being the impact of elevated NO_x levels within a few hundred metres of the road. In this case, it seems preferable to develop simple assessment tools, based on traffic volume, average traffic speed and distance to assess the area where exceedance of the critical level is of concern (Vogel *et al.,* 2000). An example of the application of such an approach, in terms of species composition change in heathlands, is the study of Angold (1997). In terms of industrial processes, the evaluation again will be highly site specific, but the principle remains that the specific implications of exceedance of the critical levels at sites of high conservation value need to examined in relation to the sites' conservation objectives wherever local assessment indicates that exceedance will occur.

In the zones around urban areas, such site-specific evaluations are not relevant, and there is no obvious justification for excluding them from an air quality management plan. The zones around urban areas constitute a substantial land area; sites of high nature conservation value occur close to, and indeed within, major cities, and if the aim is to provide a high level of protection to all such sites, then the critical levels should apply as air quality objectives. Nevertheless, the benefits of protecting these sites do need to be balanced against the additional costs in terms of air pollution control, and hence we propose that a more detailed assessment of the implications is conducted.

Ozone

The strengths and weaknesses of the AOT40 exposure index that is used to define a critical level for ozone have been explained in Section 7.6.2. At present, the AOT40 index is still the agreed basis for ozone risk assessment within Europe, and its application to the UK was fully described in PORG (1998), which included maps applying an empirical method to assess the effects of altitude in increasing values of AOT40 (see also Coyle *et al.,* 2001). These maps have recently been modified to include more recent monitoring data, covering the five-year period 1994-98. The results, shown in Figure 7.32 and 7.33, do not include any correction for the effect of elevated NO concentrations in and around urban areas in reducing ozone concentrations.

These maps show a much greater degree of exceedance of the critical level for crops and semi-natural vegetation (65% of the UK land area) than for forests (4% of the UK land area). However, the criteria used to define the critical levels for these different land uses are quite different. The approach adopted to derive the critical level of an AOT40 of 10,000 ppb h over a six month period for trees was to relate ozone exposures of young trees in open-top chambers, for periods of up to five years, to tree response in terms of biomass increment. The criterion used to define an adverse effect for both groups was statistical rather than biological, based on the size of effect that could be detected in these experiments. This led to a larger effect being used for trees (a 10% reduction in annual increment) than for crops, for which a mean yield loss over 5 years of 5% was used to derive the critical AOT40 of 3000 ppb h. This difference reflects the greater variability of experimental trees compared with crop species. However, the much greater lifetime of most tree species would suggest that, if anything, a more conservative approach was needed for trees than for arable crops; a 10% reduction in annual increment, accumulated over the lifespan of a typical tree species, would have an enormous effect on final yield. Thus, it is misleading to compare the two maps, as they give a false impression of the relative risks of significant ecological or economic damage. Future assessments of flux-based critical levels for both trees and crops, planned for discussion within UN/ECE in late 2002, may provide a stronger mechanistic basis for values which reflect the relative risks of adverse effects rather than the limitations of experimental design.

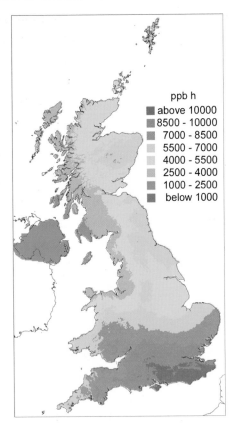

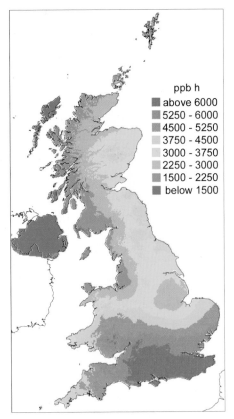

critical level 10000 ppb h (dark purple, ▪▪▪▪)

Figure 7.32 Mean AOT40 for forests, calculated for April-September inclusive, for the five years 1994-1998.

critical level 3000 ppb h (above yellow, ▪▪▪▪▪)

Figure 7.33 Mean AOT40 for crops and semi-natural vegetation, calculated for May-July inclusive, for the five years 1994-1998.

7.7.3 Critical Loads of Nutrient N

The ranges of empirical critical loads of nutrient nitrogen, which were agreed by the UNECE Task Force on Mapping in December 1995, are shown in Table 7.5. The range of values given reflects the fact that the effects of N deposition interact with many other factors, such as management, climate and phosphorus supply; thus an understanding of these interactions is needed when selecting an appropriate value within the range. Many of these critical load ranges (especially those classed as quite reliable or uncertain) still require further validation. A few recent studies have contributed new evidence, which is discussed below, although most experiments still use N application rates which are greater than the predicted critical load.

Studies of the abundance and physiology of mosses, and of vegetation composition, have shown the critical load for arctic alpine heath on Spitsbergen to be below 10 kg-N ha^{-1} y^{-1} (Gordon *et al.*, 2001b), at a site where the current deposition is only about 1 kg-N ha^{-1} y^{-1}. The ecosystem is analogous to dwarf shrub montane heath, which occurs on high mountain plateaus in northern Britain, and it seems reasonable to suggest that these communities may have a similarly low critical load, at the lower end of the range of 5-15 kg-N ha^{-1} y^{-1}, in Table 7.6.

Working at woodland edges in the vicinity of livestock farms, where N deposition is predominantly in the form of NH$_3$, Pitcairn *et al.* (1998) defined a critical load of 20 kg-N ha^{-1} y^{-1} to protect acidic coniferous woodland ground flora from change in species composition, confirming the value at the upper end of the UNECE range.

The critical load for upland acid grassland has been found to vary with grazing intensity, with heavy grazing having already shifted the vegetation towards reduced diversity such that there is less response to N and the critical load is thus increased (Gordon et al., 2001a). Several years' study of vegetation turves removed from the acid grassland described above suggests the critical load to be about 10 kg-N ha^{-1} y^{-1} for the protection of most bryophyte species (Jones et al., 1999). Critical loads suggested by these coordinated studies are 10 kg-N ha^{-1} y^{-1} for lightly grazed acid grassland (the lower end of the UNECE range of 10-15 kg-N ha^{-1} y^{-1}), but towards 20 kg-N ha^{-1} y^{-1} for heavily grazed vegetation (Gordon et al., 2001a). However, the background deposition at the site of this field experiment is greater than 20 kg-N ha^{-1} y^{-1} (Emmett et al., 1999), and so these suggested critical loads have not actually been empirically tested in the field. This illustrates a major problem in defining critical loads, namely that the total nitrogen inputs in most experiments are significantly greater than the actual critical load. There remains a need for investigation of long-term effects of low rates of addition of nitrogen to "pristine" vegetation. Also, the experiment with transplanted turves is primarily a recovery study, with N deposition rates in some treatments being lower than that previously received by the turves at the field site. Furthermore, experimental conditions differ from the field environment, such that extrapolation to the field situation is speculative. Nevertheless, there is some consistency between the conclusions drawn from the field and turf experiments.

The issue of the critical load for nutrient nitrogen varying with grazing management is an important one, and the relationship appears to be habitat specific. The upland acid grassland study cited above suggests an increase in critical load with increased grazing pressure because the vegetation is already degraded. Grazing has also been suggested to increase the critical load of N for lowland calcareous grassland, with species diversity being maintained by grazing even at high N inputs (reviewed by Wilson et al., 1995). In contrast, in an upland acid moorland in Scotland, reduced grazing levels have resulted in the typical moorland species composition being more resistant to N addition (Mitchell & Hartley, pers. comm.), such that the critical load would be lower at high grazing pressure. Computer simulation studies of lowland heath (Allchin et al., 1999) suggest that the critical load is reduced when mowing or burning is less intensive, and hence less N is removed from the system. This simulation model, parameterised for UK lowland heath, shows that under less intensive management regimes there is a significant risk of loss of Calluna dominance at 15 kg-N ha^{-1} y^{-1}. This value is at the lower end of the range in Table 7.5.

Phosphorus availability also affects the critical load of nutrient nitrogen for vegetation. Where phosphorus is in short supply the critical load may be larger because plant responses to nitrogen are constrained by phosphorus limitation. Some stands of vegetation are naturally phosphorus limited, or nitrogen and phosphorus co-limited; in others phosphorus limitation may develop as nitrogen limitation is alleviated by atmospheric nitrogen input. It has been suggested that for phosphorus limited calcareous grasslands, such as occur in the UK, the critical load of nitrogen should be calculated not on the basis of plant species composition change, but to prevent nitrate leaching through the very porous soil into the potable water supply (Wilson et al., 1995). Taking this approach the critical load was calculated to be 42-55 kg-N ha^{-1} y^{-1}. However, significant species changes in response to nitrogen addition have been observed in phosphorus limited calcareous grassland in the Peak District (Lee & Caporn, 1999), which argues for the quantification of the critical load required to protect calcareous grassland vegetation even in systems which are known to be phosphorus limited.

Determination of UK critical loads for nutrient nitrogen

The UNECE empirical critical load ranges (Table 7.5) are based on observed changes in abundance of particularly sensitive plant species, or on change in overall vegetation species composition. A recent Expert Workshop on Chemical Criteria and Critical Limits, held in York in March 2001, reviewed the ranges recommended by UN/ECE (cf. Table 7.5). The workshop concluded that a detailed scientific review of new evidence is needed prior to a revision of the recommended values, at a workshop planned for the autumn of 2002. However, the workshop also concluded that the new evidence was already sufficiently compelling to strongly suggest a change in the critical load for calcareous grasslands to 15-25 kg-N ha^{-1}, and for arctic heathlands to 5-10 kg-N ha^{-1}.

To date, UK critical loads mapping has used mid-range values from the UNECE proposed ranges, unless there was specific UK evidence to support an alternative value. The results of the York workshop, together with the recent field and experimental evidence from the UK such as that outlined above, suggest that the adoption of lower critical load values for some UK ecosystems is now justified. The mapping values for the UK have been modified to incorporate the results of the York workshop (Hall *et al.,* 2001a) and are presented in Table 7.6. They include a revised value for calcareous grasslands (for which previously a value of 50 kg-N ha^{-1} based on nitrate leaching was used), which now reflects the broadly comparable responses in acidic and calcareous grasslands, and for arctic/alpine heaths, reflecting the midpoint of the reduced range recommended at York.

However, the whole approach of taking species composition change as an indicator of critical load exceedance is very conservative. Soil microbial activity can respond to nitrogen inputs much more rapidly than plant community composition (e.g. Power *et al.,* 1998b; Lee & Caporn, 1999), and thus may also respond at lower nitrogen input rates. Nutrient cycling processes which are mediated by the quality (particularly C:N ratio) and quantity of litter produced by the vegetation, are also likely to be altered at a lower nitrogen input than that which changes species composition. The relationship between foliar nitrogen content and nitrogen deposition in the UK is linear for some species, such that in nutrient poor ecosystems there is no threshold of deposition below which no change occurs. Thus in theory the critical load may be zero, and we should be thinking rather in terms of target loads that accept a degree of ecosystem change. To substantiate this approach it is necessary to quantify relationships between N deposition, change in plant productivity and tissue quality, and processes such as decomposition and mineralisation, in a range of semi-natural vegetation communities. For these reasons, we consider that the empirical critical load values of nutrient nitrogen, which are currently used for mapping purposes in the UK, may not provide the optimal basis for assessing the long-term risk of ecological change from nitrogen deposition, or the benefits of measures to reduce this. These caveats need to be borne in mind when interpreting the maps of critical loads and exceedance that are presented in the next section. The review of the appropriateness of current critical load values which is now planned, using new data from throughout Europe, should lead to revised ranges of the values given in Table

7.6, and used in UN/ECE assessments, by the end of 2002. This will be followed by a formal review by DEFRA of the critical loads used in the UK. This revision could therefore have significant effects on the maps of the extent of both current and future critical load exceedance that are presented below.

Table 7.6 Summary of empirical critical loads to prevent changes in species composition recommended for use in the UK, modified to incorporate the results of the York workshop (Hall *et al.,* 2001a) as explained in the text.

Ecosystem	Critical load (kg-N ha^{-1} y^{-1})
Forests	
Deciduous woodland	17
Coniferous woodland	13
Grasslands	
Acid/neutral grassland	25
Calcareous grassland	25
Montane grassland	12
Heathland/moorland	
Lowland heaths	17
Upland Calluna heaths	15
Arctic/alpine heaths	7.5
Ombrotrophic bogs	10

UK Critical load and exceedance maps

UK habitat specific maps of critical loads of nutrient nitrogen are presented in Figure 7.34. These critical loads maps are based on land cover data for three broad ecosystem types – grassland, heathland/moorland, and woodland – for which mapping values are listed in Table 7.6. The critical loads for the specific ecosystems within these broad types (e.g. acid, calcareous and montane grasslands within grasslands) are incorporated as appropriate, according to the presence of groups of indicator species for that specific ecosystem. Indicator species data are only available on a 10 km square basis and this produces some "blockiness" in the maps. The critical loads within, for example, the grassland map are then derived by identifying the most sensitive specific grassland ecosystem occurring within each 1 km square in which grassland as a whole occupies more than 5% of the area. The critical load for that specific ecosystem is then applied to the entire 1 km square. Ombrotrophic bogs cannot readily be mapped using indicator species, and so the presence of peat is used as an indicator for this ecosystem. The critical load for these peat-based bogs is included within the heathland/moorland map.

For comparison with deposition, the 5 km square annual total nitrogen deposition data (using 1995-97 averages) are treated as 1 km x 1 km grid data, assuming that deposition values are constant across each 5 km square. Exceedance of the critical load is then calculated by subtraction of the critical load map data from the total nitrogen deposition map data. The deposition data used are habitat specific, such that deposition rates to woodland, which are larger than to non-wooded systems, are used for the woodland map, and deposition rates to short vegetation (typified by moorland) are used for the grassland and heathland maps. The derivation of these deposition data was described in Chapters 3, and it is important to consider any uncertainty in estimating deposition when assessing the implications of the exceedance maps.

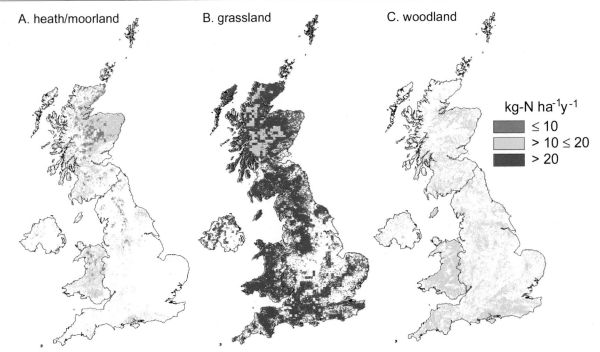

Figure 7.34 Nutrient nitrogen critical loads for (a) heath/moorland, (b) grassland and (c) woodland, based on the critical loads listed in Table 7.6.

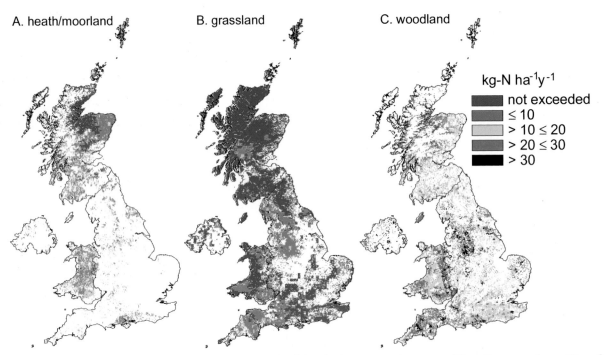

Figure 7.35 Exceedance of nutrient nitrogen critical loads by ecosystem-specific nitrogen deposition for 1995-97, based on the critical loads listed in Table 7.6.

Figure 7.35 provides UK maps of current exceedance of critical loads for nutrient nitrogen for grassland, heathland and woodland. The overall proportion of squares with grassland in which the critical load is exceeded is relatively small, reflecting the larger critical loads. Exceedance is concentrated in the acid grasslands of the Pennines, south-west England and parts of Wales, and montane grasslands in central Scotland. In contrast, the critical load for heathland/moorland/bog is exceeded throughout England and Wales, and in most of southern and eastern Scotland. A similar spatial pattern is seen for woodlands, but the degree of exceedance is markedly higher, reflecting the larger modelled deposition.

Although the maps indicate significant exceedance for woodland over a large proportion of the country it should be noted that these limits were set for the protection of ground flora, and the maps do not refer to woodland trees themselves. The studies of floristic changes on which the critical loads are based were made in continental Europe, and work is needed to confirm their applicability in the UK Modelled deposition (and hence critical load exceedance) refers to forest trees, but much of the nitrogen loading derives from the dry deposition of ammonia which is likely to be smaller to ground flora species as a result of uptake by the overstorey. There is also evidence that there can be high spatial variability in nitrogen deposition to forests, as described in Chapter 3. Hence critical loads exceedance maps for woodlands must be interpreted with caution.

7.8 Key Future Issues

The key conclusion from this chapter is that, while the effects of sulphur deposition have decreased significantly, both nitrogen deposition and ozone are currently significant problems for UK flora. More importantly, it appears that they will remain significant problems to 2010 and beyond.

Figure 7.36 provides UK maps of predicted exceedance of critical loads of nutrient nitrogen in 2010, with N deposition as predicted to occur under the Gothenburg Protocol and modelled as described in Chapter 4. Under this scenario, both the area and degree of exceedance is decreased compared to 1995-7, but the key feature of the map is that the critical loads for woodlands are still exceeded over all of England, Wales and southern Scotland. For heathlands and moorlands, critical loads are exceeded over most of England (apart from some areas close to the south coast) and a significant proportion of Wales. Even for grasslands, significant areas of exceedance remain under this modelled scenario.

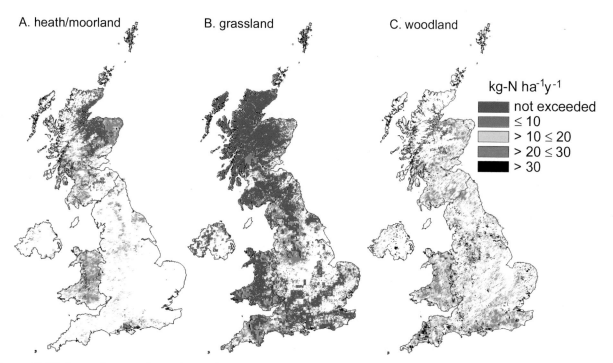

Figure 7.36 Exceedance of nutrient nitrogen critical loads, listed in Table 7.6, by predicted ecosystem-specific nitrogen deposition for 2010 (Gothenburg Protocol).

We emphasise again that the uncertainties in the current critical load values applied in the UK mean that considerable caution must be exercised in interpreting these maps. This is especially true for the 2010 scenario for which there may also be considerable uncertainty in the estimates of deposition. Nevertheless, the maps do suggest that there should be significant concern about the current and future impacts of N deposition on species composition, especially given our view that some of the critical loads currently applied may be too high. What is abundantly clear is the urgent need for more research to assess the evidence for species change in sensitive ecosystems, and to provide a more informed basis for assessment of appropriate critical load values.

Recovery from the effects of N deposition is also a crucial issue. The experience of re-invasion of lichen species as SO_2 concentrations have declined indicates that biological recovery may lag changes in atmospheric concentrations by decades. The evidence to date for nitrogen deposition suggests that, particularly where community composition has changed, the impacts may remain for many decades, or only be reversible with active management for restoration. A further urgent need is therefore for more detailed understanding of recovery processes and for more research on the effect of land use or site management in modifying the impacts of nitrogen.

It is predicted that ozone exposures will continue to increase through the first half of the next century, primarily because of changes in global background concentrations (Chapters 3 and 4). Although we have not provided a comprehensive analysis of the mechanisms of ozone impacts, it is clear that ozone cannot be considered in isolation from other climatic, edaphic and phenological factors. It is also clear that the AOT40 index, which is based on an empirical precautionary approach, does not provide an adequate analytical tool to assess the current and future impacts of ozone. It is likely that the current gradual increase in global background concentrations of ozone will lead to concentrations close to, or above, the threshold for effects on sensitive species and genotypes during this century (Ashmore & Bell, 1991), even if peak ozone concentrations occurring in regional photochemical episodes decline.

The impacts of any increase in ozone levels may be offset to some extent by the increase in atmospheric CO_2 levels. Furthermore, if this increase is accompanied by drier and warmer conditions, which may reduce the ozone flux, then the impacts may be further reduced. However, large-scale climatic change will also have important effects on cropping patterns, vegetation cover and species composition which would need to be considered in such a longer-term assessment of the impact of ozone in the UK.

In the case of both nitrogen deposition and ozone, considerable progress has been made over the past decade in developing methods of ecological risk assessment. A key challenge is to further develop and apply ecological risk assessment in policy development, by incorporating factors such as site management, and climatic and edaphic factors, so that both the extent of the national impact of these pollutants and the threats to particular local sites can be better valuated.

Chapter 8: The European Perspective

> Emissions of sulphur in Europe declined by 41% between 1990 and 1998. During the same period, emissions of NO_x declined by 21%, NH_3 by 14% and NMVOCs by 24%. European policy to decrease emissions was much more successful than that of the US.

> A substantial decrease in sulphur deposition and rainfall acidity has been recorded throughout Europe.

> Nitrogen deposition in Europe has changed little over the last two decades, and, in most countries of Europe, is dominated by reduced nitrogen as NH_3 and NH_4^+.

> Base cation deposition measured in the open field and in throughfall has declined during the last decade.

> Scenario studies show that by 2010 the Gothenburg protocol will lead to substantial reductions of the exceedances of critical loads of acidity in Europe. For nutrient nitrogen, however, critical load exceedances are unlikely to change very much.

> Non-linearities in the relationship between the emission and deposition patterns for sulphur and oxidised nitrogen have been detected, leading to slower reductions in critical loads exceedance in remote areas than expected.

> Ground-level ozone continues to exceed thresholds for effects on vegetation and human health. The peak concentrations have declined during the last decade, but mean ozone concentrations show signs of an upward trend.

> It is expected that global background ozone concentrations will continue to rise, due to increased precursor emissions, particularly in Eastern Europe and Asia. Emission control strategies in N America and Europe will lead to a reduction in peak episodic concentrations in those regions.

> Signs of recovery both of freshwater chemistry and biology have been shown in many ecosystems severely damaged by deposition during the 1970's and 1980's. The recovery is still limited and model calculations indicate that the recovery process may take many decades.

> Particulate matter has become an issue of increasing concern over Europe and North America and is considered to be the most important driving force for future control of the substances under the Gothenburg Protocol and the NECD.

8.1 Introduction

Acidification is the first environmental issue for which a European policy was developed to regulate the transport and deposition of pollutants between countries. In 1979 the UNECE Convention on the Long Range Transport of Transboundary Air Pollution (CLRTAP) was established after scientists in the 1960s established a link between sulphur emissions in continental Europe and the acidification of lakes in Scandinavia. The first protocol negotiated under the convention was the First Sulphur protocol in 1985 agreeing on a 30% emission reduction for each country that signed. 22 countries ratified the protocol. Since then several protocols have been signed (see Table 1.1):

1988 NO_x protocol, which prescribed that emissions in 1994 should not exceed those in 1987;

1991 The VOC protocol, requiring a 30% reduction by 1999;

1994 The second sulphur protocol by which exceedances of critical loads for acidification were expected to be reduced by 50% by 2010;

1999 The Gothenburg protocol aiming for substantial reductions of sulphur dioxide, nitrogen oxides, ammonia and NMVOCs.

The Gothenburg protocol, also known as the multi-pollutant multi-effect protocol, is unique in that it calls for reductions in four pollutants to abate three effects (acidification, eutrophication and the effects of tropospheric ozone). The protocol is based on a gap closure method aiming to decrease the exceedance of critical loads and levels in the most cost-efficient way. Individual countries estimate their own critical loads. Proposed reductions are listed in Table 1.1 in Chapter 1.

Apart from the protocols, the EU member states have to fulfil different Directives targeting precursor emissions. In May 1999 the European Commission presented a proposal for a Directive on national emission ceilings (NECD) for the same pollutants as CLRTAP and, for the first time, for ammonia. The proposed Directive uses a similar approach to the Second Sulphur Protocol, but extends it to include reduction in exceedance of critical limit values for ozone for human health and ecosystems. The approach is the same as used for the Gothenburg protocol. The targets in the NECD proposal, which has not yet been adopted, are much stricter than currently agreed targets in the EU. The targets for NECD are listed in Table 1.1 and are expected to be smaller than those agreed upon in the Gothenburg protocol.

In Europe there is wide variability in the problems encountered, with different areas having a different focus. In Scandinavia for example, acidification of soils and lakes was the most important driving force and it continues to be an important issue. In central Europe nitrogen related problems were the main focus and are expected to remain an important driving force even in the light of the control measures expected under the UN ECE Protocols and the EU Directives. In Southern Europe, photochemical pollution has been a topic of increasing importance for air pollution control and it will certainly remain for years to come. In addition, the health effects from fine particles have become an important issue and will certainly be included in future international strategies and agreements. It is clear that, despite the main emphasis on individual issues in specific regions, there is a strong interaction between the different pollutants and the different effects. With the new protocol a large step has been taken to integrate the different effects in a general abatement of pollution throughout Europe.

Within this chapter a European perspective on transboundary air pollution and the current major environmental problems associated with specific pollutants is presented. First an overview of current emissions, deposition and critical loads is presented. Special emphasis will be given to the evidence for trends in measurements. In the second part of this chapter some specific issues are considered. These include the observed trends in effects, the achievements in other continents, the non-linearity in sulphur emission – deposition relations and the increasingly important role of nitrogen in transboundary air pollution.

8.2 Emission

The protocols (Table 1.1) have had a major effect on the emission trends in Europe, especially for SO_2. European emissions are reduced with the clear objective that environmental loads, exposures and effects should decrease. So far very few studies have investigated the outcomes of various scenarios and reduction plans. The first scenario study on emission reductions and their outcome was presented as a Swedish case study for the UN environmental conference in Stockholm 1972. In this study, three scenarios were developed for European as well as Swedish emissions. These scenarios varied from an emission reduction of 60% by 1982 to a 2.5-fold increase over the same time.

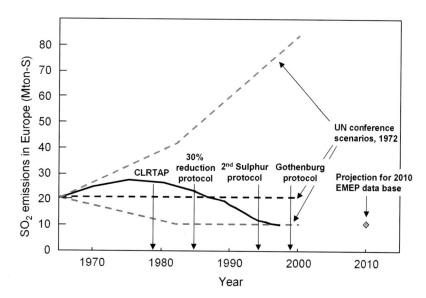

Figure 8.1 SO_2 emissions in Europe west of the Urals between 1965 and 2000 together with the predicted emissions at the UN conference in 1972. (Grennfelt pers. com.)

If these scenarios were compared with the actual emission figures, the emissions continued to increase until around 1980 when they started to decrease and reached the most optimistic scenario by 1995. The emission reductions have, however, continued since 1995. For Sweden, emissions started to decrease shortly after the UN Conference, followed the most optimistic emission reduction scenario until 1982 and have continued to decrease after that reaching about 90% reduction at the end of 1990's. Figure 8.1 shows the temporal variation in SO_2 emissions west of the Urals between 1965 and 2000. It shows the dates the three protocols were agreed and the effect the first two protocols had on European emissions. The emissions predicted at the 1972 conference are also displayed.

Figure 8.2 shows the change in total European yearly emissions between 1980 and 1996 (EEA, 1999). The European sulphur emissions declined by 55% between 1980 and 1997. In the same years NO_x was brought down by 13%, mainly after 1990. Ammonia emissions have very high uncertainties. Until recently only a few countries reported their NH_3 emissions but the situation has improved and now there seems to be a consistent dataset available in which emission data are available from 1980 and onwards. It shows that the emissions went down by 17% between 1980 and 1997. The most important message from Figure 8.2 is that GDP increased and total acid emissions decreased between 1990 and 1997. This means that the regulations to reduce emissions have not prevented economies from growing. In the next sections the changes in emissions in Europe and North America are described.

8.2.1 SO_2

Figure 8.3 shows the spatial distribution of emissions from European sources and from shipping. Large industrial areas show high emissions from processes or the combustion of solid and liquid fuels high in sulphur. Shipping emissions are significant in areas such as the Dover Strait and in the North Sea.

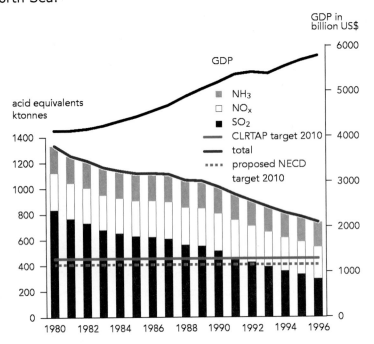

Figure 8.2 Trend in European emissions (Mton-S or-N per year).

Changes in emissions of sulphur since 1980 for the UK, Europe, North America and shipping are shown in Figure 8.4. In 1980 the USA, EU15 (European Union member countries) and non EU15 European countries including the former Soviet Union produced large quantities of S in the form of SO_2. These emissions had declined by 53% in 1997. Emission reductions in the EU15 countries have been the most significant, 66% between 1980 and 1997, through reduced S in fuels, fitting of flue gas desulphurisation (FGD) and a switch from coal and oil to natural gas for energy production and heating. The EU's target (-35% of 1985 emissions by 2000) was reached in 1992, and in 1998 the EU as a whole achieved the CLRTAP Second Sulphur Protocol target (-62% from 1980 emissions by 2000).

Emissions reductions are set to continue as the EU15 countries strive to meet their NECD and Gothenburg protocol targets in 2010. The agreed Gothenburg targets for 2010 appear to be attainable for the EU as a whole, although additional measures will be required in some EU Member States. Some EU countries have met, or nearly met, their target for 2010 (Germany, Finland, Austria), while others still need to achieve considerable additional reductions. For almost all PHARE Central and Eastern European countries, except Slovenia, SO_2 emissions declined substantially between 1990 and 1996 and are currently below the 2010 CRLTAP targets, except Slovenia, Czech Republic and Poland. This successful reduction is due to a combination of the economic restructuring process, a switch from coal to natural gas, construction of new power plants, use of low-sulphur coal and more FGD.

Emissions in the USA have declined more slowly, by only 24% of 1980 totals in 1997, and current planned reductions are set to reduce USA emissions by another 9% by 2010. Despite a 57% reduction since 1980 in emissions from Eastern European countries, emissions are forecast to increase over the next 5 to 10 years in the short term from relatively un-restricted economic growth.

Emissions from international shipping in the North Sea and the Atlantic are based on the EMEP 50 km x 50 km grid estimates and account for about 5% of the total emissions (Figure 8.4).

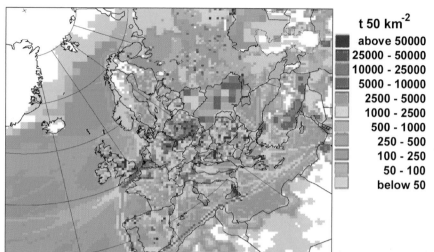

Figure 8.3 1998 European SO_2 emissions at 50 km x 50 km (t-SO_2), (from EMEP/MSC-W).

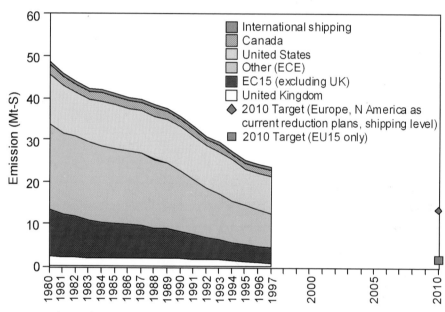

Figure 8.4 European and North American emissions of sulphur (Mt-S) 1980 – 2010 (from the UK NAEI at AEAT NETCEN).

8.2.2 NO$_x$

Figure 8.5 shows NO_x emissions from European countries and shipping at 50 km x 50 km. Road transport is responsible for a significant proportion of the high emitting areas located over most of the large European city centres. Shipping emissions are significant in areas such as the Dover Strait and in the North Sea.

NO_x emissions from North America, Europe and international shipping from 1980 – 2010 are shown in Figure 8.6. Emissions in the USA and Europe increased between 1980 and 1990 due to increased use of road transport. Since 1990, with the introduction of the catalytic converter for petrol vehicles and the use of low-NO_x burners in the power sector, European emissions have decreased. Emissions will decline further by 2010 as the use of vehicles with improved emission controls continues. However, projected growth in transport could reverse this trend in the more distant future.

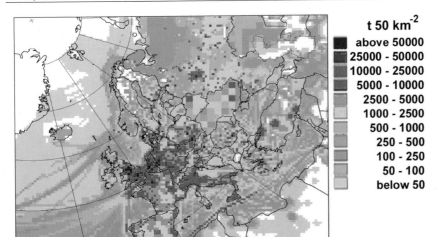

t 50 km^{-2}

■	above 50000
■	25000 - 50000
■	10000 - 25000
■	5000 - 10000
	2500 - 5000
	1000 - 2500
	500 - 1000
	250 - 500
	100 - 250
	50 - 100
	below 50

Figure 8.5 European emissions of NO$_x$ in 1998 at 50 km x 50 km (t-NO$_2$), (from EMEP/MSC-W).

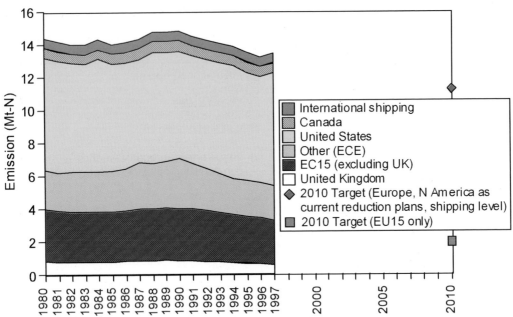

Figure 8.6 NO$_x$ (kt-N/y) emissions from North America, Europe and international shipping from 1980 – 2010 (from the UK NAEI at AEAT NETCEN).

The first CLRTAP Nitrogen Oxide Protocol target (Table 1.1) was achieved by the EU as a whole and by most Member States. However emissions in France, Greece, Ireland, Luxembourg, Portugal and Spain were, by 1996, not below their 1987 levels. Furthermore, the Fifth Environment Action Programme target, for the EU and all Member States, of a 30% reduction by 2000 with respect to 1990 will not be achieved.

Some EU Member States have reduced emissions substantially from 1990 (Germany, UK, Austria, Netherlands). Emissions from all PHARE countries have been reduced by between 30% and 60%, mainly due to a combination of the economic restructuring process and a switch from coal to natural gas. However most EU and various PHARE countries need substantial further reductions to meet the targets for 2010.

8.2.3 NH$_3$

Figure 8.7 shows the spatial distribution of NH$_3$ emissions in 1998 from Europe, at 50 x 50 km resolution, compiled by EMEP from reported country data. Areas of high agricultural activity in parts of France, Italy and the Netherlands show large emissions of ammonia.

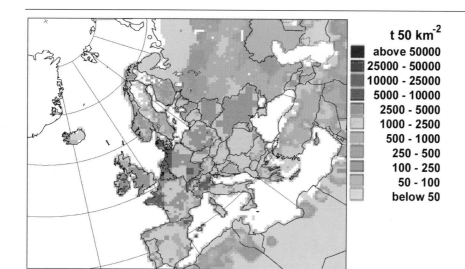

Figure 8.7 1998 European ammonia emissions at 50 km x 50 km (t-NH$_3$), (from EMEP/MSC-W).

Figure 8.8 shows ammonia emissions from Europe and the USA from 1990 to 1997 and targets for 2010. Ammonia emissions have not changed much since 1990 and are not expected to by 2010. Ammonia emissions are thought to have peaked in the mid eighties when animal numbers were at their height. Agricultural activity in the USA and Europe is the most significant source. Due to the uncertainty of ammonia inventories, data prior to 1990 has not been included.

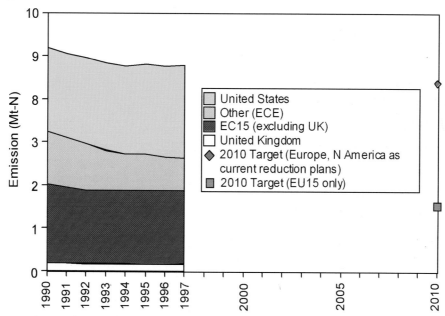

Figure 8.8 European and North American emissions of ammonia as Mt-N (from the UK NAEI at AEAT NETCEN).

Until recently no internationally agreed targets existed for ammonia. The proposed NECD target represents a 21% reduction across Europe and the Gothenburg Protocol requires a 12% reduction below 1990 emissions by 2010. Although some cost effective methods are available to reduce ammonia emissions, achieving reductions of more than around 20% would require both technical measures, and reductions in animal numbers and fertilizer use.

In the EU reductions have been small (7%), with emissions from some Member States increasing since 1990 (Spain, Sweden). Some countries report emissions reductions, which are at least partly the result of implementing technical abatement measures for ammonia emissions. These include: Denmark (19%), Germany (15%) and the Netherlands (35%).

However, there is currently debate on the magnitude of ammonia abatement already achieved, since none of the countries of Europe has published a satisfactory comparison between measured atmospheric concentrations and national emissions of ammonia. Part of the difficulty is that, as European sulphur dioxide emissions have decreased over the last decade, the atmospheric residence time of ammonia and ammonium aerosol has also changed, masking simple relationships between emissions and NH_x monitoring data (Sutton *et al.*, 2001e). It has been suggested for the Netherlands that the abatement measures may not have been as successful as anticipated (Erisman *et al.*, 1998a), although examples from Eastern Europe, where emissions must have reduced as a result of reduced agricultural activity, show similar uncertainty (Horváth and Sutton, 1998; Sutton *et al.*, 2001e). The key conclusion from these changes and analysis of air chemistry measurements is that it is necessary to identify realistic technical abatement efficiencies, as well as the importance of atmospheric interactions in assessing ammonia emission changes.

8.3 Concentrations and Deposition of S, N and Base Cations

8.3.1 S and N Compounds

Every year, EMEP calculates the present deposition maps for sulphur and nitrogen pollutants and ozone exposure maps based on meteorology driven theoretical models (see Chapter 4). The calculations are based on emission data. Until recently the model calculations were based on a Lagrangian model with a grid size of 150 km, with the EMEP emission inventory serving as input. Today the EMEP calculations are based on a Eulerian model and EMEP is running the model for all the years with available emissions. The Eulerian model has some advantages over the Lagrangian model, such as the improvement of scale (50 km x 50 km). Figure 8.9 shows the trend in calculated deposition averaged over Europe.

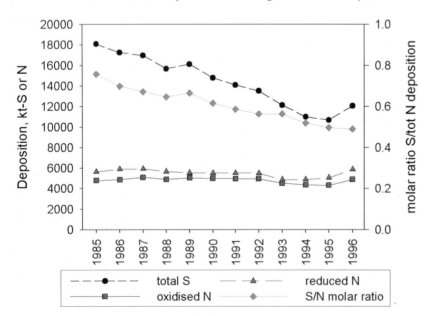

Figure 8.9 Total modelled deposition in Europe between 1985 and 1996 (t- S or -N per year, source: EMEP).

8.3.2 Base Cations

In relation to acidification, little emphasis is usually placed on the role of deposition of base cations such as Na^+, Mg^{2+}, Ca^{2+} and K^+. Besides their ability to neutralise acid input, base cations are important nutrient elements for ecosystems.

Hedin *et al.* (1994) from a variety of measurements of Ca^{2+} in precipitation made in Europe and North America detected a long-term decline. In a companion article, Gorham (1994) discussed the implications of these findings suggesting that if the decline of Ca^{2+} is from industrial sources, then emissions control for SO_2 would reduce Ca^{2+} emissions and thus, slow the recovery of ecosystems. At the time, no data on long-term Ca^{2+} aerosol concentrations were available.

Lee *et al.* (1998) re-analysed previously unreported long-term data sets of the atmospheric aerosol composition for the UK and showed a clear decline in Ca^{2+} over the period 1970 to 1995. Paralleling this decline were trends in scandium and arsenic. Scandium is often used as a tracer for non-combustion sources, whereas arsenic is often used as a tracer for combustion. Both metals clearly show a strong decline in fly-ash from industrial sources and hence the decline in Ca^{2+} can be understood.

In order to further understand the industrial component of Ca^{2+}, an emissions inventory for Ca^{2+} has been compiled (Lee and Pacyna, 1999), which is shown in Figure 8.10. Although highly uncertain, this inventory was the first attempt at estimating industrial emissions. Lee *et al.* (1999) then used this inventory in a long-range transport modelling study in order to estimate the industrial Ca^{2+} fraction of deposition. Modelled wet deposition on the European scale is shown in Figure 8.11. By comparing the measured Ca^{2+} deposition to the UK with modelled results, the modelling was able to account for approximately one third of the deposition. The results of the emission estimates and modelling were rather uncertain but indicated that a significant fraction of Ca^{2+} deposition arose from industrial emissions in the early 1990s.

Draaijers *et al.* (1997a and b) used the EDACS model to map base cations with a spatial resolution of 10 km x 20 km over Europe. Wet deposition was mapped on the basis of wet deposition measurements made at approximately 600 sites scattered over Europe. Dry deposition was calculated using air concentrations estimated from rain chemistry data and a scavenging model, together with deposition velocities derived from land-use and meteorological information using a detailed parameterisation of the dry deposition process. Generally, deposition fields found resemble the geographical variability of sources, land-use and climate. For Na^+ and Mg^{2+}, a clear pattern of increasing deposition with decreasing distance from the coast, in particular the Atlantic Ocean is observed, reflecting their seasalt origin. Large Na^+ deposition is also found e.g. northwest of the Black Sea, probably originating from wind erosion of salt containing soils. Large Mg^{2+}, Ca^{2+} and K^+ deposition in southern and south-eastern Europe results from a combination of wind erosion of calcareous and salt-containing soils, agricultural tillage practices, traffic on unpaved roads, and supply of Saharan dust. Relatively high Ca^{2+} deposition found in the border area between Germany, Poland and the Czech Republic, as well as in Estonia, for example, can be attributed to intensive industrial activity. Relatively large K^+ deposition in the border area between France, Germany and Switzerland is probably the result of open-cast mining activities. It was found that averaged over Europe, about 45% of the total base cation (Na^+, Mg^{2+}, Ca^{2+} and K^+) input is dry deposited.

Deposition of base cations counteracts the majority of the potential acid deposition in southern Europe. In Portugal, some areas of Spain, Sardinia, Sicily and the west coast of Ireland the amount of neutralization approaches or even exceeds 100%. In central and north western Europe base cation deposition usually amounts to less than 25% of the potential acid input. The smallest base cation deposition relative to potential acid deposition is found in southern Scandinavia, Denmark, the Netherlands, Poland and the Czech Republic. Whereas in eastern Scandinavia weathering is the dominant supplier of base cation to forest soils. In western Scandinavia, Scotland, the Netherlands, northern Germany, Poland and the former Yugoslavia forests rely heavily on atmospheric deposition for the supply of base cations. In these countries more than 80% of the base cation supply takes place via atmospheric deposition. In other areas of Europe, weathering and atmospheric deposition are equally important.

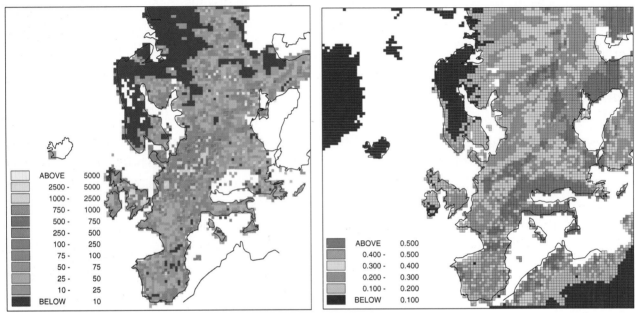

Figure 8.10 Calcium emissions from industrial sources (t y^{-1}), Lee and Pacyna, 1999.

Figure 8.11 Modelled European wet deposition of Ca^{2+} (kg-Ca^{2+} ha^{-1} y^{-1}).

8.4 Critical Loads and Exceedances

Critical loads for Europe are compiled from the information for individual countries. As deposition calculations are available for 150 x 150 km grid cells, a representative critical load value for an entire grid cell has to be determined. In order to do so the distribution of all critical load values for each ecosystem in the grid cell is made. From this distribution the 5th percentile is used as the critical load for that grid. In that way a map of critical loads is compiled (Posch *et al.*, 1995a). This map shows variability because each country chooses their important ecosystems with their respective protection levels.

It is important to show if a proposed emission reduction results in an effective critical load exceedance reduction and a significant decrease in effects. The effects of critical load exceedances are described in Chapters 5, 6 and 7 of this report. It is assumed here that a decrease in exceedances leads to a decrease in effects. At present a substantial decrease in acid deposition is calculated throughout Europe and both the actual exceedance and the area of ecosystems exposed to exceedance of critical loads have been considerably decreased. EMEP has calculated trends of emission, deposition and critical load exceedance (see Figure 1.2 in Tarrasson and Schaug, 1999). Since 1985 exceedances of critical acid loads have decreased by 76% (Tarrason and Schaug, 1999). The decrease is mostly due to the reduction in sulphur emissions and deposition, because nitrogen deposition was almost constant during the period. Consequently there is no significant change in the total eutrophying exceedance for these areas. Figure 8.12 shows that there is a non-linearity in emission and deposition for both sulphur and nitrogen (see also Chapter 3) and the percentage decrease in exceedance does not match the reduction in emission. For sulphur there seems to be a positive effect in some regions, because the exceedance decreases more than emission and deposition. The reason for this is that dry deposition has decreased much more than wet deposition (see Chapter 3) and thus the deposition is spread more over the EU area. For nitrogen the same is true for the exceedance of critical loads for acidity, but not for the eutrophication effects. The non-linearities are stronger for individual countries in Europe (see Section 8.11). It is noteworthy that the critical loads of acidity would not be exceeded if the total loads of acidifying components could be spread over the surface of Europe (RIVM, 2000). The European emissions reach 45% of the deposition target (excluding Russia). However, there are large regional differences in emissions and loads. The Netherlands, for example, would need about 5 times its own surface area to stay below the critical loads.

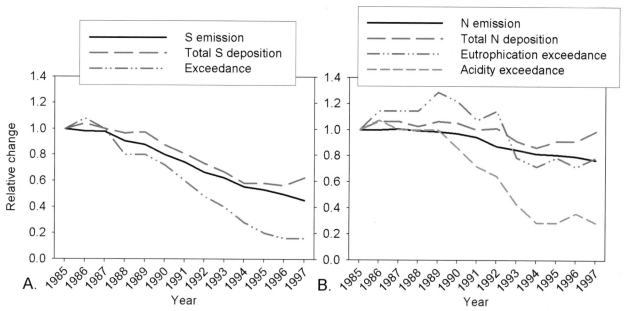

Figure 8.12 Relative changes in (a) total sulphur emissions and deposition and exceedance for acid loads and (b) in total nitrogen emission and deposition and exceedance of acid and nitrogen critical loads.

The critical load map used in the negotiation of the Gothenburg protocol for acidity and nitrogen is displayed in Figure 8.13. Also plotted in this Figure are the exceedances calculated with the depositions derived from the EMEP Lagrangian model. It shows that with implementation of the Gothenburg protocol the exceedance of critical acid loads will eventually be reduced to a minor problem, with only a few grids where the exceedance is above acceptable levels. However, for nitrogen the picture is very different: the areas with exceedance of critical nitrogen loads will hardly change. Note that the countries themselves specified the critical loads for these calculations and they can vary for comparable ecosystems between countries depending on the protection level and calculation method that was chosen.

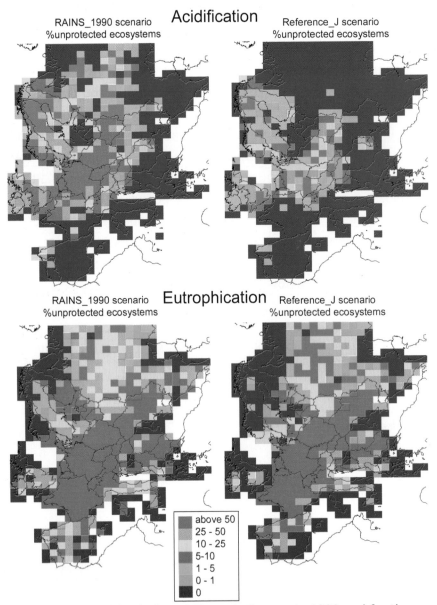

Figure 8.13 Exceedances of critical loads for acidity and nitrogen in 1990 and for the scenarios developed to underpin the Gothenburg protocol.

8.5 Ground-level Ozone

Individual countries have their own ozone monitoring networks, as well as taking part in international programme such as the EU-EUROAIRNET (to assess European air quality with respect to EU directives) and EMEP (as part of the CLRTAP). Figure 8.14a shows the locations of monitoring stations across Europe and Figure 8.14b those that report data to EMEP. The spatial distribution of monitoring sites is quite uneven, with the majority of sites being in NW Europe. Hence estimates of ozone concentration and effects threshold exceedance are quite uncertain for parts of the Mediterranean and Eastern Europe (EEA, 1998). In an assessment of how representative EU sites are of rural background and urban ozone concentrations, de Leeuw *et al.* (1997) estimated that rural stations cover 40-50% of the EU land area and only 30% of the urban population is covered. Table 8.1 lists the main ozone critical levels and standards that apply to European countries, the UK air quality strategy level is included for reference. The current ozone climate, level of exceedance of guidelines and future trends across Europe are briefly considered in the following discussion.

Many of the features seen in the UK ozone climate also occur across the rest of Europe:

- a diurnal cycle with an afternoon peak and night-time minimum at rural sites;

- a seasonal cycle with a spring or spring-summer maximum;

- episodic peaks in ozone concentration due to a combination of warm sunny weather systems and high levels of precursor emissions;

- ozone depletion in urban and industrial areas due to local NO emissions,

although there are considerable variations in the magnitude of ozone concentration in different regions and at different times of the year. Figure 8.15 (Collins *et al.*, 2000b) shows the global distribution of ozone during the year, modelled for a present-day atmosphere (nominally 1990). The seasonal NW-SE gradient in ozone concentration observed in the UK, as described in Chapter 3, extends to the rest of Europe. In general, ozone levels are highest in central and southern Europe (due to high precursor emissions, high UV radiation and warmer temperatures), and gradually reduce to the NW. In the winter months lower concentrations are often observed in central Europe as concentrations of ozone-depleting NO increase, leading to the negative NW to SE trend observed in the UK. Globally, ozone concentrations are generally higher over industrialised latitudes of the Northern hemisphere and lower in the Southern hemisphere. However, ozone levels are enhanced over parts of S America and Africa due to biomass burning in these regions (Collins *et al.*, 2000a & b, Lelieveld & Dentener, 2000).

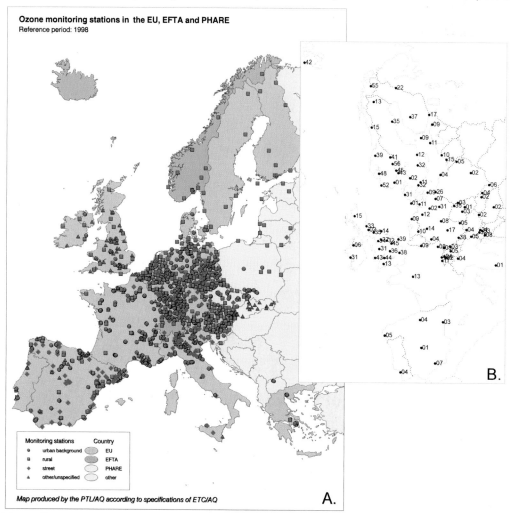

Figure 8.14 a. Ozone monitoring sites across Europe (EU = European Union, EFTA = European Free Trade Association, PHARE = countries in central and Eastern Europe participating in the EU PHARE program) and b. those that report data to EMEP.

Table 8.1 Ozone critical levels and guideline values that apply in the European region.

Set by	Description	Criteria	Value[i]
European Council Directive 92/72/EEC	population information threshold	1 hour average	$180 \ \mu g \ m^{-3} \approx 90$ ppb
	population warning threshold	1 hour average	$360 \ \mu g \ m^{-3} \approx 180$ ppb
	health protection threshold	fixed 8 hour means (0:00-8:00, 8:00-16:00,16:00-24:00,12:00-20:00)	$110 \ \mu g \ m^{-3} \approx 55$ ppb
UNECE-CLRTAP	critical level for crops and semi-natural vegetation	AOT40[ii] daylight[iii] hours May to July	3,000 ppb h
	critical level for forests	AOT40[ii] daylight[iii] hours April to September	10,000 ppb h
WHO	guideline for the protection of human health	running 8 hour maximum	$120 \ \mu g \ m^{-3} \approx 60$ ppb
	critical level for agricultural crops	AOT40[ii] daylight hours over 3 months	5,300 ppb h
	critical level for forests	AOT40[ii] all hours over 6 months	10,000 ppb h
UK Government - Air Quality Strategy Jan. 2000	provisional objective to be met by 2005 for the protection of human health	daily maximum of 8 hour running means to be exceeded no more than 10 times per year	$100 \ \mu g \ m^{-3} \approx 50$ ppb

i The method of converting $\mu g \ m^{-3}$ to ppb and vice-versa is given in Appendix C.
ii AOT40 is the accumulated concentration over a threshold of 40 ppb
iii daylight hours are defined as when solar radiation exceeds 50 Wm^{-2}

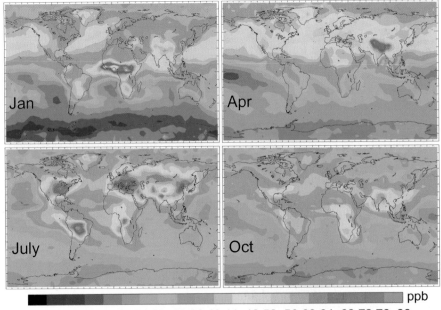

ppb

0 4 8 12 16 20 24 28 32 36 40 44 48 52 56 60 64 68 72 76 80

Figure 8.15 Present day (1990) modelled global ozone maps (Collins *et al.* 2000b).

8.5.1 Current Exceedance of Critical Levels for Ozone

Human Health

The EC health protection threshold of 110 $\mu g \ m^{-3}$ ($\approx$ 55 ppb) as a fixed 8 hour mean (0:00-8:00, 8:00-16:00,16:00-24:00,12:00-20:00) is similar to the UK standard, although as the UK uses a moving average and lower threshold value they are not directly comparable. The European Environment Agency reports that in 1996 (de Leeuw *et al.,* 1997), more than 50% of the population of the EU were exposed to at least one exceedance of the health threshold and more than 6% to exceedances over 50 days or more. Figure 8.16 shows the distribution of the exceedances between the urban and rural populations. As rural ozone concentrations are generally higher than urban, rural populations experience more exceedances. Figure 8.17 shows an analysis of the frequency distribution of 1200 - 2000 h averages over 110 µg m^{-3} during 1998 in countries across Europe. The UK has a similar distribution to Austria, Spain, the Netherlands, Germany, Luxembourg, the Czech Republic, Poland and Belgium. However it should be noted some of the variation will be due to differences in the proportion of rural, urban or industrial stations in each country.

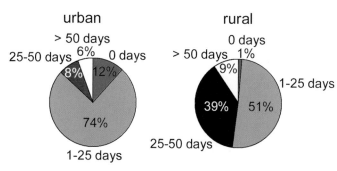

Figure 8.16 Number of exceedances (in days) and frequency distribution of urban and rural population exposed to eight-hourly concentrations exceeding 110 µg m^{-3}, 1 January-31 December 1996. Note that information on ozone exceedances which has been made available within the framework of the ozone directive, is estimated to be representative for a total urban population of 65.5 million (that is, about 32% of the EU population living in cities with more than 25000 inhabitants and 18% of the total population in the EU) and for a total rural population of about 90 million. From de Leeuw et al., 1997.

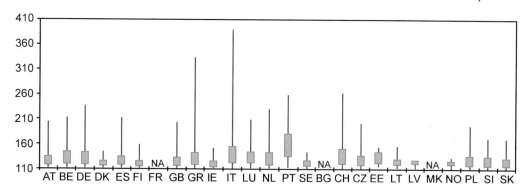

Figure 8.17 Frequency distribution of ozone concentrations (eight-hourly values; period 12.00-20.00; 1 January - 31 December 1998) in excess of the 110 µg m^{-3} threshold for hourly values. Frequency distributions are presented as Box-Jenkins plots indicating the minimum, the 25-Percentile, the 75-percentile and the maximum value. (For country codes see Appendix A). From de Leeuw et al., 2000.

Several assessments of the possible health impacts of exposure to ozone concentrations over the various critical levels have been made for individual countries or regions (for example Ponce de Leon et al., 1996; Medina et al., 1997; Anderson et al., 1996 & 1997; Stedman et al., 1999; Stedman et al., 1997c). In the EEA Second Assessment Report (EEA, 1998) approximately 0.3% of hospital admissions in the EU are attributed to high ozone concentrations, with individual countries ranging from almost 0% to 0.7%.

Vegetation

Figure 8.18a and b show maps of the 1998 AOT40 levels for the EMEP region (Hjellbrekke, 2000). These AOT40 maps have a similar spatial pattern to those shown in Chapter 7 Figures 7.32 and 7.33 but lower levels across the UK. The differences are due to: the UK only maps are interpolated from 1994 to 1998 averages to account for inter-annual variability whereas the EMEP map is for a single year, 1998; EMEP uses Kriging to interpolate and no adjustment is made for the enhancement of ozone concentrations at high altitudes.

The 1998 data indicate that critical levels are mainly exceeded in central and southern Europe. Assessment of data for other years gives a similar picture, although the magnitude and spatial extent of exceedance varies from year to year. As discussed in Chapter 7, these indices for effects on vegetation cannot be used to make an economic assessment of ozone damage, but only give an indication of areas at risk. Overall the data shows that current ozone levels are potentially affecting vegetation across the entire European region, with central and Southern Europe being most at risk.

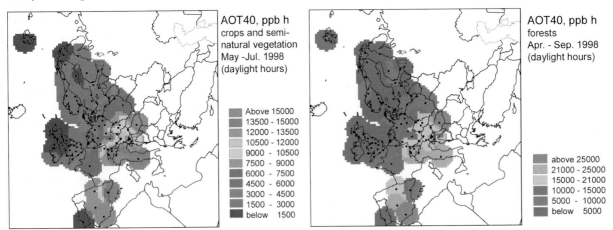

Figure 8.18 (a) AOT40 (ppb h) April–September 1998 (daylight hours) (b) AOT40 (ppb h) May, June and July 1998 (daylight hours) (Hjellbrekke, 2000). These maps are interpolated using the Kriging method.

8.5.2 Ozone Trends and Future Critical Level Exceedance

As shown in Chapter 2 and above, the decline in emissions of NO_x and NMVOCs across Europe that has occurred over the last few years is expected to continue, as a consequence of EU and UN-ECE abatement strategies (see Table 1.1). Modelling studies (Jonson et al., 2001; Collins et al., 2000a) have shown that this will lead to a reduction in the magnitude peak ozone concentrations in Europe, but as global background ozone is expected to continue increasing (Chapter 3 and Chapter 4) critical levels will continue to be exceeded (Collins et al,. 2000a & b).

The large spatial and temporal variability of ozone concentrations makes it difficult to detect any changes due to the reduction in precursor emissions that may have already occurred. Simpson et al. (1997) demonstrated, using the EMEP Lagrangian ozone model, that meteorological variations could alter the mean daily maximum June-July-August concentration by ±12 ppb and hence a 30 year time series might be needed to detect a trend due to European emission controls. As shown in Chapter 3, the 10 to 20 years of UK measurements do indicate that there has been a reduction in peak ozone concentrations and that background levels may be increasing. Results from other European countries vary considerably, however, although some have reported similar trends. For example, the EUROTRAC TOR-2 project reported statistically significant downwards trends in the May average, 50th percentile and 98th percentile ozone concentrations at sites in Norway, The Netherlands, Belgium, Germany, Switzerland, Hungary and Greece, correlating with a decline in peak summertime ozone production (Roemer, 2000). In the same study an increase in winter concentrations is seen at many sites supporting both an increase in the background concentrations and a decline in NO_x emissions, which would reduce ozone depletion due to NO titration. Laurila and Hakola (1999) reported an upward trend in ozone concentrations in "clean" air at the Finnish site Utö in the northern Baltic from 1989 to 1996. The remote location of this site and the removal of ozone measurements in "polluted" air masses support the conclusion that background ozone levels are increasing.

European data as a whole do illustrate some changes, for example Figure 8.19 shows the percentage of the EU population exposed to days when 8 hour running mean ozone exceeds 120 µg m^{-3} during 1990, 1995 and 1997. Although there has not been a significant reduction in the total population exposure, the magnitude has been reduced. This is indicated by the large increase in exposure for 20 days or less, relative to more than 60 days, which also implies that peak ozone levels have declined across the region.

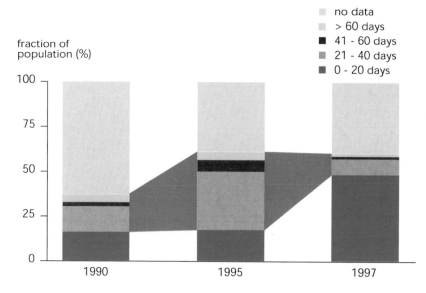

Figure 8.19 Population exposure in EEA member countries to ozone levels above EC targets (from EEA 2000a) Notes: Number of days per year with 8-hour rolling average concentration greater than 120 µg m^{-3}. Based on data from rural monitoring stations, so the population exposure may therefore be somewhat overestimated.

The possible changes to European and global ozone concentrations in the future have been considered in Chapters 3 and 4. In summary, it is expected that global background ozone concentrations will continue to rise due to increased precursor emissions, particularly in Eastern Europe, Asia and countries of the S hemisphere, but that emission control strategies (see Table 1.1) in N America and Europe will lead to a reduction in peak episodic concentrations in those regions. The EEA and EMEP have used models to study the implications for ozone critical level exceedance across Europe in 2010. In general the population exposed to potentially harmful levels of ozone is expected to decline, particularly on the northern and western fringes of Europe, but most vegetation will still be exposed to considerable exceedances of critical levels. Figures 8.20 and 8.21 from the EEA (2000b) illustrate the predicted changes to exceedances of the WHO threshold for the protection of human health and AOT40 for crops and semi-natural vegetation respectively. Looking past 2010, making further reductions in ozone concentrations will require action by all countries with significant emissions of precursor species.

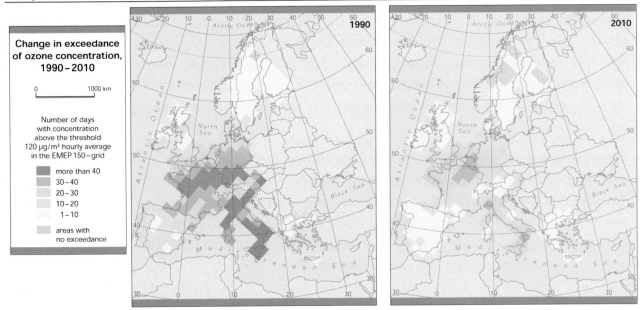

Figure 8.20 Number of days the WHO criterion is exceeded for emissions in 1990 and for projected emissions in 2010. Calculations represent the maximum of the three-year moving averages for the five-year period considered (EEA, 2000b).

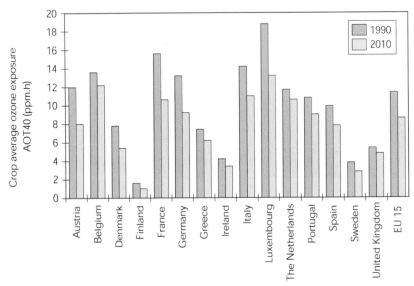

Figure 8.21 Predicted change in AOT40 levels by 2010 (EEA, 2000b). NB The critical level is 3 ppm h.

8.6 Is the calculated trend in deposition of S and N compounds supported by measurements?

8.6.1 Site Level

There are no long-term (>20 years) total deposition measurements available. Only long-term throughfall measurements (the total S deposition beneath forest canopies, measured in the water which falls through the canopy) are available for a few sites for such a long period. One of the longest series of throughfall measurements is available at the Sollingen site in Lower Saxony (Germany) (Meesenburg *et al.*, 1995). In the early 1970s the S input in this spruce forest amounted to about 3000 mol ha^{-1} y^{-1} (approximately 100 kg ha^{-1} y^{-1}), which decreased by about 70% to about 1000 mol ha^{-1} y^{-1} in 1996 (Figure 8.22). No clear trend in the N inputs was observed over the same period. The average annual throughfall flux of N equals 2360 mol ha^{-1} y^{-1} (33 kg ha^{-1} y^{-1}).

Throughfall has also been measured at Lake Gårdsjön (Sweden) since 1979 (Hultberg & Skeffington, 1998) and the data showed almost no trend in sulphur deposition between 1980 and 1990. Since 1990 the input by throughfall has decreased by approx. 60%. (Figure 8.23). For oxidised and reduced nitrogen, data show no significant trends.

In 1987 the University of Wageningen started a monitoring programme of gaseous exposure and gradient measurements on a tower in the Speulder forest in the centre of the Netherlands. Since then several deposition monitoring programmes have operated there using the throughfall method, micrometeorological methods and model estimates (van Aalst and Erisman, 1991; Duyzer et $al.$, 1994; Erisman and Draaijers, 1995; Erisman et $al.$, 1998c). The annual variation in SO_x, NH_x and NO_y fluxes is displayed in Figure 8.24. Despite year-to-year variations in meteorology and the different methods used the results indicate that the deposition of SO_x decreased between 1988 and 1995. For NO_y and NH_x no trend can be detected. The throughfall data for NH_4^+ show a slight decrease between 1987 and 1996, and no trend was apparent in the data of rates of NO_y deposition.

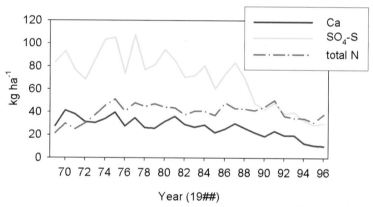

Figure 8.22 Annual variation in throughfall fluxes of SO_4^{2-}-S, N and Ca^{2+} at the Solling spruce site over the period 1973-1996 (Data from the Forest Experiment Station of Lower Saxony; Meesenburg, pers. comm.).

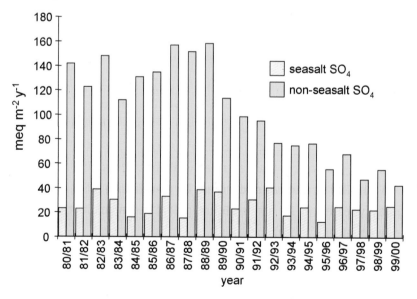

Figure 8.23 Annual variation in throughfall fluxes of seasalt and non-seasalt SO_4^{2-}-S, measured at Lake Gårdsjön since 1979 (Hultberg & Skeffington, 1998).

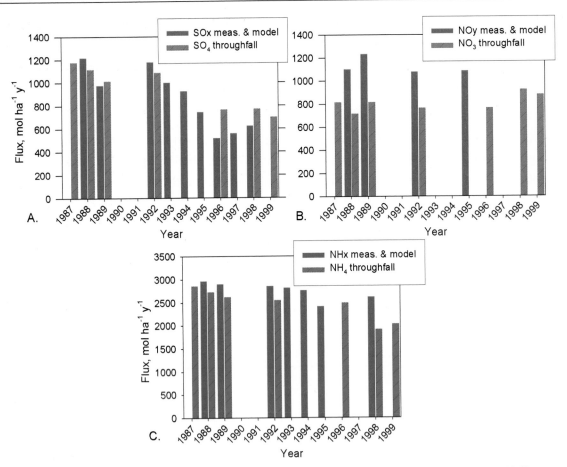

Figure 8.24 Annual variation in total deposition measured directly, by inferential modelling and by throughfall, over Speulder forest: a) SO_x (SO_2, SO_4^{2-} and wet SO_4^{2-}), b) NO_y (NO_2, HNO_2, HNO_3) and c) NH_x (NH_3, NH_4^+ and wet NH_4^+).

8.6.2 Transnational and European level.

Changes in N and S deposition have been derived from a comparison of annual throughfall fluxes assessed at some 120 plots in the 1980s (Ivens, 1990) and at more than 300 plots in 1996 and 1997 (de Vries *et al.*, 1999, 2000). The first set of data consists of a literature compilation, whereas the latter dataset is based on a European wide monitoring programme in forests (See also Section 8.7.3). The comparison required that stands with similar forest types (pine, spruce and broadleaves) were located within a distance of 10 km. Results for a total of 53 plots showed a clear decrease for both the total N and SO_4^{2-} input in throughfall (Figure 8.25a, b). The decrease in N inputs was due to a strong decrease of NO_3^- (Figure 8.25c), whereas values of NH_4^+ remained relatively constant (Figure 8.25d). A comparison of the N/S ratios in the 1980s and the 1990s showed, however, that at nearly all the plots the ratio has increased (De Vries *et al.*, (2000). A similar trend was derived by modelling the N and S deposition on forested plots based on a systematic 16 km x 16 km grid (See also Section 8.8), as illustrated in Figure 8.26 (Van Leeuwen *et al.*, 1999).

In the so-called 'Pan-European Programme for Intensive Monitoring of Forest Ecosystems' by the EC and ICP Forest, throughfall measurements are being conducted in more than 400 forest stands distributed over 23 countries in Europe (de Vries *et al.*, 1999). Annual throughfall fluxes for 1996 were calculated for 163 plots. Total deposition of S and N compounds ranged from 100 to 3000 mol ha^{-1} y^{-1} in approximately 90% of the plots, but values up to 4000-8000 mol ha^{-1} y^{-1} were also observed in some plots. If the uptake of N through the canopy is calculated correctly, the average N to S ratio varied between 0.5 and 2.7 (de Vries *et al.*, 1999). The calculated average total N deposition mostly exceeded that of S. The relative contribution of NH_4^+ and NO_3^- in N deposition varied over the plots, but in most countries, especially in northern and central Europe, NH_4^+ dominated N deposition. In western Europe, N deposition exceeded S inputs, whereas the reverse was observed at plots in central Europe. Approximately 50% of the plots received N inputs above 1000 mol ha^{-1} y^{-1}, which is a deposition level at which species diversity of the ground vegetation may be at risk (Heij and Erisman ,1997). Below this (long-term) rate of input, tree growth may be N limited. The total input of (potential) acidity, defined as the total input of N and S minus the base cation deposition corrected for Cl$^-$, all in eq mol ha^{-1} y^{-1}, ranged mostly between 200 and 4000 mol ha^{-1} y^{-1}. Adverse impacts by soil acidification and Al release are likely at very high deposition levels (>3000 mol ha^{-1} y^{-1}), which occur in approximately 15% of plots.

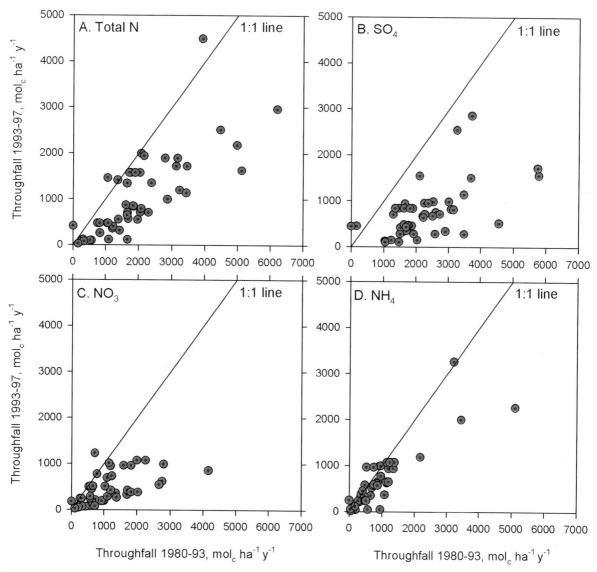

Figure 8.25 Comparison of throughfall of a) total N, b) SO_4^{2-}, c) NO_3^- and d) NH_4^+ measured at 53 plots located within 10 km in the eighties (1980-1993) and the nineties (1993-1997). The solid line represents the 1:1 line.

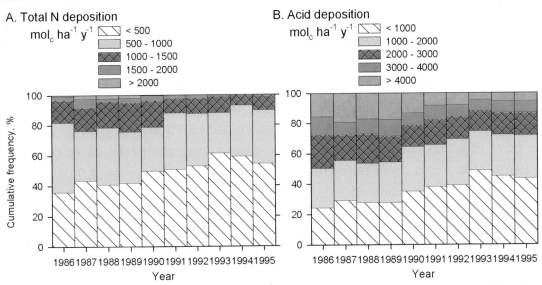

Figure 8.26 Temporal variation in annual average deposition of a) total nitrogen and b) potential acid, calculated on forested plots in a 16 km x 16 km grid over Europe in the period 1986-1995.

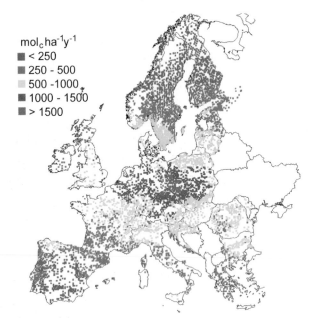

Figure 8.27 The calculated 10 years average N deposition (1985-1995) at forest monitoring plots on a systematic 16 km x 16 km grid.

Results of the inferential EDACS model for plots are presented in Figure 8.27 (van Leeuwen *et al.*, 1999). It shows the geographical variation in modelled N deposition on forested plots in Europe, where monitoring of crown condition takes place. The estimates are averages over the period 1985-1995. Figure 8.27 shows that elevated N deposition occurs in large parts of Europe (especially in western and central Europe), particularly when one considers that the N deposition is likely to be an underestimate in source areas (van Leeuwen *et al.*, 1999).

8.7 Pan European Monitoring Programme on Effects

The negotiations for the Protocols of CLRTAP rely on current scientific understanding of the effects of pollutants on the environment and health in Europe and North America. This information is provided for the Convention by the International Cooperative Programmes (ICPs) of the Working Group on Effects. Each ICP is led by a different country, and specialises in effects on different components of the environment (forests, rivers and lakes, buildings and cultural heritage, crops and semi-natural vegetation, ecosystems) and human health. Long-term monitoring of effects is an important part of the work of each ICP and provides an insight into the progress and success of abatement measures. The work is underpinned by scientific research on dose-response, critical loads and levels and damage evaluation. The monitoring and research programmes that have supported the development of the Gothenburg Protocol, and its proposed revision in 2004/05 are described in this section for the ICPs on surface waters, ecosystems, forests, and natural vegetation and crops.

8.7.1 ICP Surface Waters

The ICP on Assessment and Monitoring of Acidification of Rivers and Lakes (ICP Waters) was established in 1985. Its Programme Centre is at the Norwegian Institute for Water Research in Oslo. The main aim of the programme is to assess, on a regional basis, the degree and geographical extent of acidification of surface waters, evaluate dose-response relationships and long-term trends in aquatic chemistry and biota (ICP Waters, 2000). The ICP Waters database includes 142 sites with chemical data and 123 sites with biological data. Quality control is performed annually and most laboratories have participated in intercalibration exercises.

The sites cover most of the acid-sensitive areas in Europe. There are no sites in several regions that have been, or are potentially affected by acid deposition. Furthermore, Eastern Europe is not represented well to adequately assess both the risk of acidification and the sensitivity of surface waters.

Data from 98 sites were tested for trends in concentrations over the 10-year period 1989-1998. The (grouped) sites clearly showed significant decreases in SO_4^{2-} concentrations. Nitrate, however, showed no regional patterns of change, except maybe for Central Europe: decreasing trends occurred in the Black Triangle, while southwest Germany and Italy exhibited no or increasing NO_3^- trends. Concentrations of base cations declined in most regions. All of the regions showed tendencies towards increasing DOC.

Recovery from acidification reflected by an increase in surface water ANC and pH was significant in the Nordic Countries/UK region. In Central Europe there was a regional tendency toward increasing ANC, but large spatial differences were found: 10 out of 28 sites showed no significant changes. The low ANC sites showed the largest recovery. Non-forested sites showed clear and consistent signals of recovery in ANC and pH, and appropriate (relative to SO_4^{2-} trends) rates of base cation declines. Hence, it was concluded that the observed recovery was associated with declining SO_4^{2-} (ICP Waters, 2000).

For the UK and most sites in Germany no significant changes in acidification were recorded, but positive signals of improvements in the invertebrate fauna were observed. A clear positive trend was found for the Norwegian sites and most of the Swedish sites. In the most acidic sites in Central Europe improvements in water quality have not yet reached a level where improvements of biology can be detected. Biological improvements at these sites require considerable improvements in water quality with respect to acidification.

In many lakes in Scandinavia there is evidence of a small but significant recovery and many extinct species are now returning. The positive signs are mainly observed in lakes and streams with limited acidification. For the most acidified waters, the signs of recovery are still small and unclear. For those areas which have suffered from acid deposition, a key question is how extensive and how quickly recovery as a consequence of present agreements will be. The area has been the subject of several experimental and theoretical studies. At Lake Gårdsjön a plastic roof was built over a 0.7 ha catchment in 1991 by which the atmospheric deposition of pollutants was stopped (also discussed in Chapters 5 and 6). The experiment shows that the recovery of percolating water will be prolonged by desorption of adsorbed sulphur and probably also by mineralisation of organic sulphur. Model calculations based on the data from Lake Gårdsjön indicate that it may take several decades before ANC in soil water will return to positive values (if ever). There are several of these examples where recovery has been demonstrated.

In a study by Stoddard *et al.* (1999) data for 205 sites in eight regions in North America and Europe between 1980 and 1995 were used to test trends. The data they used were primarily from ICP Waters. They also found decreasing trends in SO_4^{2-} concentrations in all regions except the UK, and no or hardly any changes in NO_3^-. Trends in SO_4^{2-} varied from 0 to -4 µeq l^{-1} y^{-1} in the 1980s to -1 to -8 µeq l^{-1} y^{-1} in the 1990s. Recovery of alkalinity was associated with the decrease in SO_4^{2-} in all regions in Europe, especially in the 1990s.

The recovery found from the ICP data is very much in line with the expected recovery based on catchment studies with roofs to take away the sulphur deposition as e.g. the Lake Gårdsjön experiment in Sweden (Geisler *et al.*, 1998). The changes in chemistry clearly reflect the deposition reduction caused by emission abatement. The regional differences in trends are due to several factors, such as local emission changes, the total historical sulphur and nitrogen deposition, the soil buffering capacity and the rate at which base cations are supplied from primary weathering of bedrock. The degree and extent of recovery also depends on these factors as well as on the reduction of sulphur deposition. All these factors are highly variable even over relatively small areas, leading to difficulties in quantifying the response to emission reduction in time (Jenkins, 1999). We can, however, conclude that the observations indicate that the international legislation is having a positive effect on the natural environment. However, there is still a long way to go, especially if we look at nitrogen enrichment, before full recovery.

8.7.2 ICP Integrated Monitoring

The ICP IM sites (mostly forested catchments) are located in undisturbed areas, such as natural parks or comparable areas. The network presently covers 50 sites in 22 countries. Fluxes and trends of S and N compounds were recently evaluated for 22 sites (WGE, 2000). The site-specific trends were calculated for deposition and run-off water fluxes and concentrations using monthly data and non-parametric methods. Statistically significant downward trends of SO_4^{2-} and NO_3^- bulk deposition (fluxes and concentrations) were observed at 50% of the sites. Sites with higher N deposition and lower C/N-ratios clearly showed an increased risk of elevated N leaching. Decreasing SO_4^{2-} and base cation trends in output fluxes and/or concentrations of surface/soil water were commonly observed at the ICP IM sites. At several sites in Nordic countries decreasing NO_3^- and H^+ trends (increasing pH) were also observed. These results partly confirm the effective implementation of emission reduction policy in Europe. However, clear responses were not observed at all sites, showing that recovery at many sensitive sites can be slow and that the response at individual sites may vary greatly.

8.7.3 ICP Forests

ICP Forests, in close cooperation with the EC, monitored the defoliation and discolouration of stands on a regular 16 km x 16 km grid over Europe from 1986, the so-called Level I programme. The network presently covers 374,238 sample trees distributed on 18,717 plots in 31 countries. At about 900 sites in Europe key parameters such as deposition, growth, soil chemistry, leaf content, etc. have been monitored since 1994 to study cause effect relationships and to monitor the chemical and physical parameters determining forest ecosystem vitality (Level II). The duration of the Level II programme is too short for trend detection. These data are currently more relevant for studying cause-effect relationships. Figure 7.2 (Chapter 7) shows the annual variation in defoliation for different tree species in Europe as reported in the Extended Summary report by ICP Forests (ICP, 2000). It is concluded by ICP-F that in all parts of Europe defoliation of various extents is observed. Of the 1999 total transnational tree sample, mean defoliation was 19.7%. Of the main tree species, *Quercus robur* (European oak) has the highest defoliation with 25.1%, followed by *Picea abies* (Norway spruce, 19.7%), *Fagus sylvatica* (common beech, 19.6%) and *Pinus sylvestris* (Scots pine, 18.9%). The trend in defoliation over 14 years for continuously observed plots shows the sharpest deterioration of *Pinus pinaster* (maritime pine) and *Quercus ilexs* (Holm oak) in southern Europe. *Fagus sylvatica* (common beech) deteriorated in the Subatlantic, Mountainous (south) and Continental regions. *Picea abies* (Norway spruce) deteriorated in several parts of Europe, but has improved, particularly in the main damage areas of central Europe, since the mid 1990s (ICP, 2000).

As there are no specific symptoms of individual types of damage, defoliation reflects the impact of many different natural and anthropogenic factors. Countries mention weather conditions and biotic stresses most frequently. Several countries refer to air pollution as a predisposing, accompanying or triggering factor, but the degree to which air pollution explains the spatial and temporal variation of defoliation at the large scale cannot be derived from crown condition assessment alone (ICP, 2000). Statistical analysis of 262 of the 860 Level II plots indicate that defoliation is influenced mainly by stand age, soil type, precipitation, nitrogen and sulphur deposition. These factors explained only 30-50% of the observed variation. Nitrogen deposition correlated with defoliation of spruce and oak and sulphur deposition was found to correlate with defoliation of pine, spruce and oak (ICP, 2000). Impact of calculated drought stress was found for nearly all tree species, whereas impact of calculated ozone was mainly limited to broadleaves, specifically to common beech.

8.7.4 ICP Vegetation

The International Cooperative Programme on effects of air pollution on natural vegetation and crops (ICP Vegetation, formerly ICP Crops) was established in the late 1980s. It has primarily focussed on collaborative programmes to establish the impacts of ozone on vegetation, although its work has now expanded to consider nitrogen and heavy metal deposition. Since ozone levels have shown little clear trend over the past decade, the contribution of this ICP is more focussed on establishing the impact of ozone across Europe than on detecting evidence of recovery.

Participants in the ICP Vegetation have exposed white clover (*Trifolium repens*) to ambient ozone in 18 countries each summer since 1994, using a standardised protocol. The plants in this bioindicator system are harvested every 28 days by cutting back the foliage to a few centimetres above the soil surface, thus allowing several growth periods at each site in each year. From 1994 to 1996, ethylene diurea (EDU) was used to protect half of the white clover plants against ozone injury (e.g. Ball *et al*, 1998). Since then, ozone-resistant (NC-R) and ozone-sensitive (NC-S) clones of white clover have been exposed at the sites (e.g. Mills *et al.*, 2000b). The ratio of the biomass of plants in plots with or without EDU treatment, or NC-S to NC-R clover, decreased with increasing ozone exposure (Figure 8.28). As the slopes and intercepts of the regression lines for biomass ratio versus AOT40 for either system were not significantly different from each other, it is valid to compare the slopes for individual lines as presented in the figure. However, there were no significant differences between the regression lines for any of the years. Thus, these results confirm that there has been no evidence of recovery or reduction in magnitude of effect of ozone within the timescale of these experiments (1994 – 2000). However, effects on biomass at "high" ozone sites are clearly demonstrated.

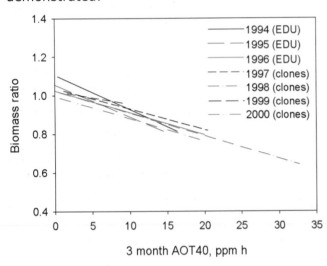

Figure 8.28 Biomass ratio of either non-EDU/EDU treated white clover (1994 - 1996) or NC-S/NC-R white clover (1997 - 2000) versus three-month AOT40 at ICP Vegetation sites in Europe. (Note biomass ratios and AOT40 were calculated from accumulation of data from harvests 1-2, 2-3 and 3-4).

The timing and magnitude of visible ozone injury (flecking of the upper surface of leaves) on white clover was also recorded at the ICP Vegetation sites (e.g. Benton *et al.*, 2000). It was present in at least one growth period at every site. Although there was a tendency for the frequency of injury to be greater at more southern latitudes, the contrast in the frequency of injury is much less than the contrast in ozone exposure across the continent. More detailed analysis of the data has demonstrated that other environmental conditions, such as lower vapour pressure deficits, increase the sensitivity to ozone at more northern sites. This explains why injury was present in 4 of the 6 years it was monitored at Finland-Jokioinen, and in every monitored year at Sweden- Östad even though the 28 day AOT40 rarely exceeded 1 ppm h at these sites.

Some of the participants in the ICP Vegetation have also carried out systematic surveys of commercial crops for characteristic visible symptoms of ozone damage, on days following visible injury in the clover bioindicator system. Table 8.2 provides a list of the wide range of commercial and horticultural crops on which injury has been found. Ozone injury has mainly been found in Mediterranean countries (Fumagalli *et al.*, 2001), but the cases in Table 8.2 include injury reported from Belgium, France and Switzerland.

The documentation by the ICP vegetation of the extent of visible injury due to ambient ozone, both in field surveys and in the bioindicator studies, together with effects on biomass of an ozone-sensitive species, provide important evidence for the significance of ozone as a phytotoxic pollutant across Europe.

Table 8.2 Commercial agricultural and horticultural crops injured by ambient ozone episodes in Europe.

Agricultural crops		Horticultural crops	
Bean	*Phaseolus vulgaris*	Courgette	*Cucurbita pepo*
Clover	*Trifolium repens*	Chicory	*Chicorium endiva*
Corn	*Zea mays*	Lettuce	*Lactuca sativa*
Grape-vine	*Vitis vinifera*	Muskmelon	*Cucumis melo*
Peanut	*Arachis hypogea*	Onion	*Allium cepa*
Potato	*Solanum tuberosum*	Parsley	*Petroselinum sativum*
Soybean	*Glycine maxima*	Peach	*Prunus persica*
Tobacco	*Nicotiana tabacum*	Pepper	*Capsicum anuum*
Wheat	*Triticum aestivum*	Radish	*Raphanus sativus*
	Triticum durum	Red beetroot	*Beta vulgaris*
		Spinach	*Spinacea oleracea*
		Tomato	*Lycopersicon esculentum*
		Watermelon	*Citrullus lanatus*

8.7.5 Biodiversity

Biodiversity has become a widely used term since the global Convention on Biological Diversity was signed in Rio de Janeiro in 1992. Within the Convention it is defined as the variability among all living organisms from all sources, including *inter alia*, terrestrial, marine and other aquatic ecosystems and ecological complexes of which they are part; this includes diversity within species, between species and of ecosystems (EEA, 1998). The EEA assessed the changes in biodiversity mainly of wildlife and semi-natural habitats and ecosystems. Atmospheric pollution, and more specifically acid deposition, is only one of the threats to biodiversity. However, it has not been possible so far to separate acid deposition effects from other causes. This has to be kept in mind when interpreting changes in biodiversity. Table 8.3 gives the share of Europe in the world-wide total species. The number of species that reside in Europe is only very large for amphibians and freshwater fish (Table 8.3). The Mediterranean area yields the highest biodiversity and is also one of the most species rich areas of the world.

The EEA concluded that the threat to Europe's wildlife species continues to be severe and the number of species in decline is growing. In many countries, up to half of the known vertebrate species are under threat. More than one third of the bird species in Europe are in decline, most severely in north-western and central Europe. This is mainly caused by damage to their habitats by land-use changes, particularly through intensification of agriculture and forestry, increasing infrastructure development, water abstraction and pollution.

However, the populations of a number of animal species associated with human activities are increasing and some plant species tolerant to high nutrient levels or acidity are spreading. There has also been some recovery in the number of breeding birds in areas where organic farming is practised. The introduction of alien species is causing problems in marine, inland water and terrestrial habitats.

Table 8.3 Share of European species to the worlds total (EEA, 1999).

	World Number of species	Europe Number of species	European share %	Only in Europe Number of species	Only in Europe %
Vascular plants	260,000	12,500	5	3,500	28
Fresh water fish	8,400	334	4	200	58
Reptiles	6,500	198	3	90	45
Amphibian	4,000	75	2	56	75
Butterflies	30,000	575	2	189	33
Breeding birds	9,600	514	5	30	6
Mammals	4,300	270	6	78	29

Wetland loss is greatest in southern Europe, but major losses are also still occurring in many agricultural and urbanised areas in north-western and central Europe. The main causes are land reclamation, pollution, drainage, recreation and urbanisation. Some large and many minor restoration projects in rivers, lakes, bogs and mires are, to some extent, compensating for these losses, though mostly on a small scale.

As agriculture has become more intensive and afforestation has continued in low-yielding areas, semi-natural agricultural habitats such as meadows are rapidly being lost or degraded. These habitats were formerly very widespread in Europe and depended on extensive agricultural management with low inputs of nutrients. They now suffer from excessive nutrient input and acidification. With the disappearance of their often very rich plant and animal life, the natural biodiversity of the open landscape has severely diminished.

A wide range of initiatives and legal instruments for the protection of species and habitats has been introduced internationally and nationally in all countries. All these have succeeded in protecting considerable land and sea areas and saving a number of species and habitats, but implementation is often difficult and slow and has not been able to counteract the general decline. At the European level, the implementation of the NATURA 2000 network of designated sites in the EU, and the upcoming EMERALD network under the Bern Convention in the rest of Europe, are currently the most important international initiatives.

8.8 The UK and the Rest of the World

Table 8.4 shows the emission trends in Europe and the USA. Europe shows the largest emission reductions in the world. Emission trends in the US between 1990 and 1998 are somewhat upward for the nitrogen components, whereas SO_2 and NMVOCs show a downward trend of respectively 18 and 14%. In Europe emissions of SO_2, NO_x, NH_3 and NMVOCs show a downward trend of 41, 21, 14 and 24% respectively.

Table 8.4 Changes in emissions between 1990 and 1998 in Europe and USA (%).

Component	Europe	USA
SO_2	-41	−18
NO_x	-21	+1
NH_3	-14	+4
NMVOCs	-24	-14

The blame matrices for SO_x, NO_y and NH_x for the different countries of Europe as calculated by EMEP show some changes between 1985 and 1997 (EMEP, 1998). These changes include both meteorological differences between the years and changes due to changes in emissions. The contribution of the UK's emissions to its deposition increased from 73 to 75% for SO_x, from 52 to 59% for NO_y and from 78 to 83% for NH_x. The contribution of France, Italy and Spain to the deposition in the UK increased for SO_x; the contribution of the other countries remained the same. For NO_x, Belgium, Ireland, France and Spain made a higher contribution to deposition in UK in 1997 compared to 1985, whereas for NH_x Belgium, France and Spain contributed more.

The first signs of acidification came from the Scandinavian countries. The UK was blamed for a large contribution of acidifying components to the deposition in Scandinavia. Table 8.5 shows the contribution of the UK to the deposition in Sweden, Finland and Norway in 1985 and 1997 as calculated by EMEP. The contribution of UK NO_y emissions to the deposition in Scandinavia decreased from 12.3% in 1985 to 11.8%. For SO_x the decrease ranged from 8.1% to 6.5% and for NH_x from 3.5% to 2.6%.

Table 8.5 Deposition in Scandinavian countries and the contribution of the UK to the deposition in Sweden, Finland and Norway in 1985 and 1997 as calculated by EMEP.

Species	year	Sweden	Norway	Finland	Total	reduction %	Emission UK	reduction %
			(100 t-S or –N)				(kt-S or -N)	
SO_x	1985	252	238	62	552		1865	
	1997	74	87	20	181	67%	828	56%
NO_x	1985	153	135	47	335		741	
	1997	90	98	35	223	33%	562	24%
NH_x	1985	26	31	7	64		274	
	1997	11	17	5	33	48%	266	3%

Besides the contribution of the UK to its own deposition, pollutants are both exported through long-range transport, contributing to the exceedances in other countries, and imported. In a study by Rachel Warren at Imperial College, London (ApSimon, pers. comm.), the degree to which the UK contributes to the exceedances in other countries is examined using the ASAM model. For this study the EMEP emissions data were used and the critical load maps produced by CCE (Posch *et al.*, 1995a). Taking the 1997 emissions as a base case, the calculations show that the UK contributes significantly to the exceedances of critical loads in Denmark, France, Germany, Ireland, the Netherlands and Norway. The UK ranks third, after Germany and Poland, in contributing to exceedance of critical loads for acidification in the entire ECE region. For eutrophication, the UK ranks seventh.

If the emissions in the UK could be set to zero, the areas with critical load exceedances, will decrease from 6.21% to 4.95% in Europe. In the UK the percentage of areas with acidity critical load exceedance would drop from 30 to 1% and in Norway from 17 to 11%. The UK emissions make a greater contribution to the exceedance of critical loads in Norway than those of any other single country in Europe. For eutrophication the areas of critical load exceedance when setting all the emissions to zero, drop from 13 to 0% for the UK and from 22% to 21% for Europe. Significant changes are found in Denmark, Finland, Ireland, Sweden, Norway and Latvia. For acidification in the UK, the most important changes occur when its own emissions are set to zero. This is unlike many other, especially smaller countries, where the neighbouring countries dominate. The biggest changes in the UK are calculated when: Irish emissions are set to zero, 3.4% less area exceeded; Germany, 1.8% less; France 1.7% less and the Netherlands 1.1% less, starting with 30.3% exceedance overall. For eutrophication the picture is similar; the exceedance is decreased to zero from 13% if the UK emissions are set to zero, by 2.9% by Ireland and 2.1% by France. All these calculations help understand where the focus of control measures should be directed.

With the same method predictions can be done for the year 2010. By 2010 the areas remaining unprotected in all the countries have shrunk considerably. The contributions of the different countries to the exceedances in other countries are rather similar in 1997 and 2010. In 2010 under the Gothenburg protocol, the UK ranks fourth in contributing to exceedance of critical loads for acidification in the entire ECE region. For eutrophication the UK ranks ninth.

8.9 Is the UK different from other countries in Europe?

To what extent are trends and situations in the UK congruent with those in the rest of Europe? The UK has a comparatively large gradient in terms of air pollution exposure compared to most countries in north west Europe. The situation in southern England is very similar to that on the opposite side of the English Channel, with high emission densities and a large influence from the deposition of nitrogen. Ozone episodes with concentrations above 50 ppb are quite frequent and ozone formation is to a large extent limited by the emissions of NMVOCs. Health effects are an important driving force in addition to the effects on ecosystems.

The conditions in the northern UK are more like those in Scandinavia. In these regions, the regional air problem is more associated with deposition of acidifying substances to sensitive soils and waters. Health effects are a problem of minor concern relative to the situation in the more polluted areas. Influences of regional air pollution are more episodic in nature and much of the deposition may arise from a limited number of occasions. In highland areas, snowmelt episodes may be the determining factor for ecosystem effects. The areas are also characterised by a very large influence from sources outside the actual countries, i.e. countries may be able to do very little themselves to solve the problem.

8.10 Non-Linearity in Sulphur Emission and Deposition

Sulphur emissions across Europe decreased by 41% between 1990 and 1998. The question is whether the emission reduction resulted in a similar deposition reduction in the most sensitive areas. Fricke and Beilke (1992) demonstrated that the decrease in emissions of sulphur in western Europe from 1980 onwards resulted in much larger decreases in observed concentrations of SO_2 in ambient air compared to the decrease in ambient SO_4^{2-} aerosol concentrations and SO_4^{2-} precipitation concentrations in Germany. This is an indication that non-linearities play a role in determining source-receptor relationships so that while, on a regional scale, the system appears linear, changes in the patterns of emission and deposition within the region may appear. Current models used for the formulation of abatement strategies assume linear relationships between emission and deposition changes over time (Tuovinen et al., 1994). Several explanations have been suggested for the cause of the non-linear processes (Alcamo et al., 1987). Non-linearities can be illustrated by using long-term measurements in the Netherlands, Germany and Sweden, as examples. Figure 8.29 shows the ratio between the relative change in measured ambient SO_2 over that of SO_4^{2-} aerosol concentrations and rainwater SO_4^{2-} concentrations. 1980 was taken as the reference year. The Figure shows similar results to those found by Fricke and Beilke (1992), i.e. the relative decrease in the observed SO_2 concentration is larger than that observed in SO_4^{2-} concentrations in aerosol and precipitation. The direction of the changes in sulphur concentrations in air and rain is similar to the changes in SO_2 emission, but the magnitude is different. Measurement errors and meteorological variation during the different years affect the measurements. However, these facts cannot explain the systematic difference in magnitude and the difference in SO_2 and SO_4^{2-} concentrations (Figure 8.29).

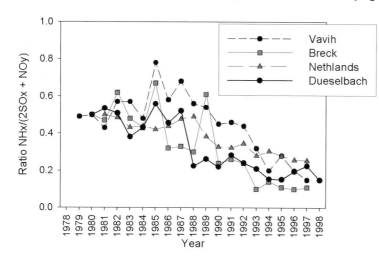

Figure 8.29 Ratio between the relative change in the period 1980 - 1995 in measured ambient SO_2 over that of SO_4^{2-} aerosol concentrations and rainwater SO_4^{2-} concentrations in the Netherlands, Sweden and Germany. 1980 was taken as the reference year.

The concentrations in air, aerosol and precipitation are of a different origin and transported over different distances. A likely explanation for the different trends in concentrations is that there is a non-linearity in atmospheric chemistry, cloud processes (Hov *et al.*, 1987) and surface processes (Erisman and Draaijers, 1995). Cloud processes can be non-linear as the result of cloud chemistry. Atmospheric or cloud chemistry can cause non-linearities when the components or mechanisms, which lead to conversion of SO_2 to SO_4^{2-}, are limiting, e.g. when the oxidising precursors (H_2O_2, O_3) are exhausted or when clouds are evaporated. In both cases the pH of droplets might fall below 4 and less SO_2 is converted to SO_4^{2-}. Thus, when there was an excess of SO_2, conversion was limited and with decreasing emissions (non-excess situations), the limitations do not occur any more. In this respect, the role of ammonia might be of importance. NH_3, being an alkaline gas, provides the neutralising capacity for aerosols, cloud droplets and precipitation. Furthermore, it might provide an 'alkaline environment' when deposited at comparable amounts or in excess over acid-forming components, which might further enhance the effect of non-linearities of SO_2 in the atmosphere (see Chapter 3 for evidence of non-linearity in the UK).

The important role of NH_3 can clearly be deduced from trends of wet and dry deposition of SO_2 in the Netherlands (Erisman and Draaijers, 1995). Through the strong decrease in SO_2 emission in western Europe, SO_2 concentrations show a strong decline. In most areas this has led to a decline in dry deposition of SO_2. However, wet deposition does not show the same decline (Figure 8.30). This might be explained by the lifting of the SO_2 excess as the result of increased neutralisation by ammonia. Ammonia emissions decreased to a much lesser extent than SO_2 emissions in this period. Ammonia can neutralise SO_2/SO_4^{2-} in the atmosphere, forming $(NH_4)_2SO_4$ particles. Before the steep decline of SO_2 emissions after 1987, SO_2 was in excess over NH_3. NH_3 was probably then the limiting factor in aerosol formation. After the emission decline, SO_2 and NH_3 are equally present in the atmosphere, which means that aerosol formation might be limited by either of the gases, depending on local patchiness in their concentrations. The aerosol formation has not decreased, thus the availability of condensation nuclei (e.g. $(NH_4)_2SO_4$ particles) and scavenging of aerosols has probably decreased in only a limited way. The only decrease in wet deposition of SO_4^{2-} is the decrease in below-cloud scavenging of SO_2. This however is not the most important factor determining wet deposition of SO_4^{2-}. The increase in atmospheric neutralisation by ammonia can be illustrated by the increased ratio of NH_4^+ over NO_3^- and SO_4^{2-} on a molar basis in precipitation as given in Figure 8.31. The ratio increased to complete neutralisation of NO_3^- and SO_4^{2-} in recent years in the Netherlands.

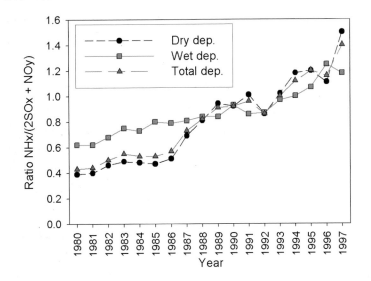

Figure 8.30 Ratio of NH_4^+ over (SO_4^{2-} plus NO_3^-) in dry, wet and total deposition in the Netherlands over the period 1980-1997.

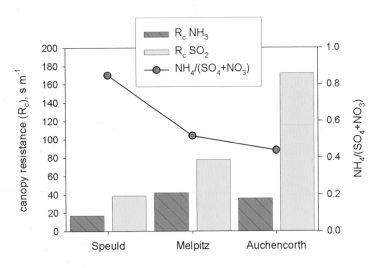

Figure 8.31 The dependence of the surface resistance of SO_2 on the neutralisation capacity of ammonia expressed as the ratio of NH_4^+ over (SO_4^{2-} plus NO_3^-) in precipitation.

The other role of NH_3 is to provide an 'alkaline environment' when deposited. In this respect the accumulation of SO_2 and NH_3, and the neutralisation capacity of the surface is important (Erisman and Wyers, 1993). If there is an excess of SO_2 over NH_3 in terms of deposition fluxes, the surface might become saturated and SO_2 uptake is retained. Evidence for this process is obtained from long-term dry deposition measurements at three different sites in Europe (Erisman *et al.*, 1996a; 1997a). Deposition parameters were obtained from measurements throughout the year (1995) at 3 contrasting sites; Melpitz (SE Germany; Spindler *et al.*, 1996), Speulder forest (Central Netherlands; Erisman *et al.*, 1996b & 1997b) and Auchencorth Moss (Southern Scotland; Fowler *et al.*, 1996). Figure 8.31 shows the median surface resistances of SO_2 at the three sites plotted against the molar ratio of NH_4^+ over (SO_4^{2-} + NO_3^-). The surface resistance is a measure for the uptake of gases at the surface, regulating dry deposition; zero surface resistances mean ideal uptake of gases at the surface (e.g. Chamberlain, 1966). The annual average ratio of $NH_4^+/(2\ SO_4^{2-}+NO_3^-)$ in precipitation measured at the sites is taken as a measure for the neutralisation capacity of ammonia at the sites; a low ratio means little neutralisation. Figure 8.31 shows that there is a clear relation between the surface resistance and the ammonia situation at the sites. At low ratios, the resistance to uptake of SO_2 at the sites is highest.

Synthesis

There is a complex interaction between SO_2 and NH_3, which becomes important when the emission of one of the two gases changes differently from the other, as has been the case in Europe and the USA during the last decade. In situations where NH_3 emission increased or SO_2 decreased, atmospheric and surface wetness chemistry induced higher SO_4^{2-} formation leading to important non-linearities in sulphur emission – deposition relationships. If the pH in aqueous solutions (cloud droplets, aerosols, surface wetness) increases, the solubility of SO_2 increases as well as its oxidation rate (Kruse-Plass *et al.*, 1993). The consequence of this is that despite the large SO_2 emission reductions, SO_4^{2-} aerosol and wet deposition in remote areas (yielding the most important input) has decreased much less. Furthermore, despite NO_x emission reductions, wet deposition of NO_3^- changed little in remote areas. Again this is the result of the SO_2 and NH_3 interactions: in SO_2 source areas excess SO_2 decreased due to the strong emission reductions. NH_3 primarily forms $(NH_4)_2SO_4$ in aerosol or cloud droplets and the excess NH_3 is in equilibrium with HNO_3 and HCl to form ammonium nitrate and chloride (Stelson and Seinfeld, 1982; Allen *et al.*, 1989). Because the SO_4^{2-} production is limited by the SO_2 availability, there is more NH_3 available to form nitrates. The transport distance of nitrate aerosol is substantially longer than the rapidly deposited HNO_3. Inputs in remote areas are dominated by aerosol input and wet deposition, which therefore declined much less than emissions.

A complicating factor is that the dry deposition of SO_2 did not decrease at the same rate as the decrease in SO_2 concentration. The dry deposition velocity increased because the surface is less saturated by SO_2 uptake, a similar process to that described for cloud droplets or aerosols (Erisman *et al.*, 1997a; Fowler *et al.,* 2001). The consequence of this is that more SO_2 is lost at the surface and in aerosols or clouds, thus the transport distance of SO_2 is decreased.

The consequence of this combination of processes is that despite strong reductions in SO_2 emissions and to a lesser extent in NO_x emissions, the decrease in deposition in remote areas, dominated by aerosol and wet deposition, was much smaller than the emission reduction. In source areas a substantial decrease in deposition is observed, whereas the reductions in deposition in areas between source and remote areas will be intermediate.

8.11 There is an increasing role of N

As shown in Section 8.3, the relative contribution of nitrogen compounds to the total deposition has increased. Furthermore, it is shown in Section 8.4 that acidification will be greatly reduced after full implementation of the Gothenburg protocol in 2010. On the contrary, eutrophication will not diminish much. Nitrogen is difficult to abate, because technological solutions are expensive. The most difficult sources to abate are traffic, small combustion sources and agricultural sources. Large industrial point sources are much easier to abate, because technology is well developed, even though it is rather expensive. Another problem, especially for reduced nitrogen, is that the emissions and deposition budgets even at a country scale are highly uncertain. In one of the most intensively studied countries, the Netherlands, there is still an 'ammonia hole' reflecting a difference between the estimated emissions based on activities and emission factors, and emissions derived from measurements.

To decrease the negative environmental effects of ammonia emissions, the Dutch government formulated legislation implemented in 1990 aimed at decreasing emissions of ammonia relative to the 1980 amounts by 50% in 2000 and 70% in 2005. The regulations include the placing of covers over slurry storage systems, prohibition of application of slurry in winter (to limit NO_3^- leaching and wash-off), and the obligatory incorporation of slurry in the soil after application. Furthermore, incentives were provided for investments in low emission housing systems. The intended effect of these measures was to decrease emissions from each individual source. These regulations were expected to decrease ammonia emissions in 1996 by about 37% compared to 1990 emissions and 38% relative to 1980 emissions (RIVM, 1997). These estimates were based on statistical data and assumptions about the effectiveness of the regulations (e.g. van der Hoek, 1994).

In 1997, five years of monitoring concentration and deposition of ammonia and ammonium were used to evaluate the effect of abatement policy to reduce ammonia emission in the Netherlands. It was found that the measured data did not show the expected reductions in emissions (Erisman et. al., 1998a). Actually the measurements showed hardly any downward trend between 1992 and 1997, as shown in Figure 8.32. Three reasons were suggested (van Jaarsveld et. al., 2000):

1. Meteorological conditions during these years were relatively dry with low wind speeds, inducing higher NH_3 emissions;

2. Due to the SO_2 emission reductions in west Europe during these years the SO_2 and SO_4^{2-} concentrations were reduced, leading to lower conversion rates of NH_3 into NH_4^+. In the 1980s NH_3 was the limiting factor in the conversion, leading to rates of 30% per hour. However, in the late 1990s the acid formation became the limiting factor for the conversion of NH_3 and the conversion rate reduced to about 10% per hour;

3. The emissions did not decline as much as expected and thus the concentrations and deposition remained fairly constant.

An extensive modelling study showed that the maximum emission decrease achieved was about 10-20%. The main contribution to the emission reductions would have been achieved by the techniques to inject manure into the soil or grass.

Erisman and Monteny (1998) postulated several hypotheses to explain the 'ammonia hole', mainly related to the application of manure in the field:

i)   the distribution of the manure was spread more over the country because of limits set to the application of the amount of P and N, increasing the effective emission area and therewith the emissions;

ii)   the periods or seasons that the manure/slurry is applied in the field have changed due to the limitations of the manure application period (prohibition of winter spreading). This has led to increased application of manure in spring and summer when temperatures are relatively high. The weather conditions under which manure is applied in the field are therefore different from those before the abatement, leading to higher emissions of ammonia (higher temperatures, no precipitation right after or during application, etc).

iii) Because of the forced winter storage of manure, the mineralisation of organic nitrogen might have increased the ammonia emission potential, leading to higher emissions when the manure is applied in the field.

iv) there might be a difference in the optimal application of low emission techniques, such as under test conditions, and the actual application (under field conditions).

v) it is reasoned that the amount of N fertilisation in the Netherlands is so high (> 400 kg-N ha^{-1} on the average), that injection of manure into the soil might have increased the stomatal emission of ammonia from grass and crops and this would have led to long-term emissions from e.g. grassland.

vi) Farmers did not follow the regulations.

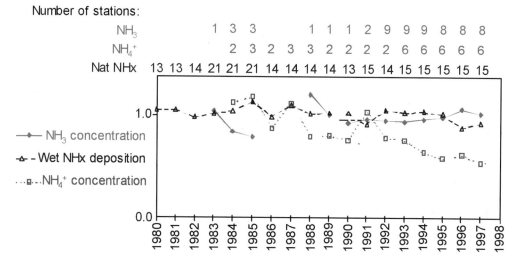

Figure 8.32 The relative change in wet deposition and concentrations of NH$_3$ and NH$_4^+$ in the Netherlands. The average of all stations with measurements is given in each year.

Since 1997 several attempts have been made to find the most reasonable explanation for the 'hole', but it has been concluded that there is no single explanation, and all of the above mentioned reasons might explain part of the gap.

Erisman *et al.* (2001) measured long-term emissions over two weeks from two test plots with a diameter of 50 m. At one plot manure was applied by conventional surface spreading and the other by sod injection. The measurements showed small emissions after three weeks from both plots. After about three days only 10% of the total emissions was measured, a very small contribution. The question is whether these results are representative for the more intensive areas in the Netherlands on sandy soils. Furthermore, temperatures were mild and it was wet most of the time.

A regional ammonia network was started in 1996 (Wyers *et al.*, 1996; Duyzer *et al.*, 1998). About 180 sites were equipped with passive samplers to measure the monthly average ammonia concentrations (Duyzer *et al.*, 1999). Figure 8.33 shows the monthly averages for three years averaged over 6 regions. The data show a strong decrease in 1998 relative to the two earlier years. Furthermore, even though the regions are different in emission characteristics and are located far apart, the temporal variations in concentrations show a high correlation. The 1998 concentrations are lower because of the meteorological conditions that were extremely wet preventing the application of manure in the field. It was estimated that about 30% less manure was applied during the year. These data show that the meteorological conditions determine the temporal variation in concentrations, whereas the level of concentrations is determined by the emission strength.

Based on different dispersion characteristics of source categories (housing systems; application; fertilisers) and foreign sources, the spatial distribution over the country and the temporal variation over the year, an investigation into the effect of emission source changes led to improved fits between modelled and measured concentrations. In all cases it was found that the increase in emission factors for manure/slurry application in the field led to the greatest improvements. The factors with which emissions after application had to be increased varied between 2 and 8, with 3 the optimum factor. Another way to improve the comparison between model and measurements is to reduce the dry deposition velocity in the country under dry and warm conditions, even changing it into emissions (van Jaarsveld *et al.*, 2000). This aspect has to be investigated further. It was concluded that only 45-70% of the claimed emission reduction between 1993-1997 was achieved.

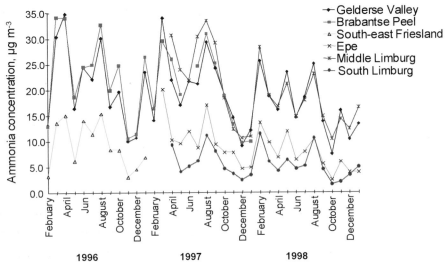

Figure 8.33 Monthly average NH$_3$ concentrations in six regions measured with passive samplers (from Duyzer *et al.*, 1999).

8.12 Future Air Pollution Control Initiatives in Europe

Even if the emissions of air pollutants in Europe decrease substantially, further control measures will be necessary if the long-term objectives of reaching critical loads and levels in the whole of Europe are to be achieved. In the Gothenburg Protocol and the NECD there are stipulations on renegotiation of the agreements within a certain time and it is expected that these re-negotiations will take place sometimes during the period 2004-2006. The Bodies under CLRTAP have already started this process and re-organised the work in order to fulfil the new tasks.

Within the European Commission the initiative has been slightly different. Instead of focusing only on transboundary air pollution, the European Commission found that reductions of air pollution in Europe were driven not only by regional problems but equally by urban and global air pollution problems. Therefore, in 1999 the commission formulated an initiative called Clean Air For Europe or CAFÉ. A feasibility study on the CAFÉ initiative was presented to the countries and various stakeholders in a process for the further development of European strategies and directives on air pollution in Europe. The work focuses on structures and deliverables and it also points out the importance of collaboration with the CLRTAP process. The report assumes that the protection of health will be the main driving force for air pollution control in Europe over the next decade. With respect to transboundary air pollution, an increased focus is expected on particulates and ozone, where the regional transport component is substantial.

8.13 Particulate Matter

Particulate matter has recently become an issue of increasing importance for air pollution control in Europe. Various studies on air pollution effects on health have indicated a strong relationship between air pollution concentrations and observed health effects. There is also strong evidence that small particles (2.5 μm diameter) play an important role in the observed effects. Since the concentrations of particles in this size fraction are to a large extent determined by secondary particles, i.e. particles formed in the atmosphere from sulphur dioxide, nitrogen oxides, ammonia and volatile organic compounds, particles became an issue for CLRTAP and the EU. Monitoring programmes and transport models are under development for both CLRTAP and the EU, and data on the regional pattern of particles and their origin may be expected within a couple of years.

8.14 Carbon Sequestration

The reduction of carbon dioxide (CO_2) emissions that is required to stabilise the global atmospheric concentrations might be offset by an increase in carbon storage (sequestration) in terrestrial and aquatic ecosystems. Forests could play an important role in sequestering carbon. De Vries *et al.* (2000) used ICP Forests Level I and Level II data to determine the carbon sequestered by European forests. An estimate of the net carbon sequestration at Level I plots was based on calculated nitrogen retention as a function of modelled N deposition and measured C/N ratio of the organic layer in the soils, multiplied by the C/N ratio of the forest soil. An estimate of carbon sequestration by trees was derived from stand age and available site quality characteristics, using forest yield tables to estimate the actual forest growth, assuming a carbon content of 50% (de Vries *et al.*, 2000). The total sequestration in tree wood and forest soil was estimated to be 279 Mt-C y^{-1} for the actual growth of tree wood, 115 Mt-C y^{-1} for the net growth of tree wood and 9.3 Mt-C y^{-1} for long-term forest soils. The results show that carbon sequestration by forests is mainly due to a net increase in forest growth, while carbon immobilisation in the soil is limited. This implies that the current sequestration may only be a relatively short transitory phenomenon.

8.15 Conclusions

The European policy to reduce emissions of acidifying and eutrophying compounds in Europe has been successful: emissions of sulphur declined by 41% between 1990 and 1998. During the same period, emissions of NO_x declined by 21%, NH_3 by 14% and NMVOCs by 24%. The decline in emissions of sulphur is reflected in a substantial decrease of concentrations in source areas, in sulphur deposition and thus critical load exceedance, and in surface water sulphate concentrations. For nitrogen the decreases in emissions have led to much smaller changes in N deposition than for S. Nitrogen deposition in most countries is dominated by reduced N. It is expected that ammonia emissions may increase in the future and therefore abating nitrogen emissions and deposition will be the challenge for the coming years.

Non-linearities in the relationship between the emission and deposition patterns for sulphur and oxidised nitrogen have been detected, leading to slower reductions in critical loads exceedance in remote areas than expected. Ammonia plays an important role in the non-linearities. The neutralisation capacity of ammonia in rainwater, surface wetness and aerosols determines the sulphate and nitrate formation. Ammonia is now frequently present in chemical excess over sulphate leaving more ammonia to neutralise nitric acid and form nitrates. Nitrate is transported further away than nitric acid because of its lower deposition rates. Therefore, remote areas show less reduction in deposition than source areas.

Ground-level ozone continues to exceed thresholds for effects on vegetation and human health, although the peak concentrations have declined during the last decade. It is expected that global background ozone concentrations will continue to rise, due to increased precursor emissions, particularly in Eastern Europe and Asia. Emission control strategies in N America and Europe will lead to a reduction in peak episodic concentrations in those regions.

The ICP monitoring programme has shown some recovery from acid deposition. The percentage of non-vital forest stands has decreased and surface water chemistry has improved. The recovery is still limited, however, and model calculations indicate that the recovery process may take many decades.

Chapter 9: Recovery From Acid Deposition

> Current (1995 to 1997) exceedance of critical loads for acidification extends over 71% of the area of sensitive ecosystems in the UK, and is expected to decline to 46% by 2010.

> Deposition of reduced nitrogen is a major part of the exceedance and will become the dominant component by 2010.

> There is evidence of chemical recovery in some upland soils from the effects of acidification, with the largest increases in soil pH in the uplands of England and Wales.

> There is evidence of chemical recovery of some freshwaters from the effects of acidification in Galloway, Cumbria, the Pennines, North Wales and the SE of England.

> Chemical recovery of UK freshwaters is not uniform and large areas show no recovery.

> Biological recovery of freshwaters is a slow process and signs of recovery are few in the UK. However, there are signs of recovery of epilithic diatoms in some areas of Scotland and Wales.

> Critical loads for eutrophication are currently (1995-1997) exceeded in ca 25% of UK 1 km x 1 km grid squares with sensitive grasslands and ca 55% with heathland. These percentages are expected to decline to ca 20% and ca 40% respectively in 2010, with reduced nitrogen (NH_3 and NH_4^+) being the main contributor.

> The reductions in nitrogen emissions have produced only small decreases in nitrogen deposition in the UK so far (16%). For eutrophying effects there is no evidence of chemical or biological recovery. When deposition is reduced sufficiently to allow recovery to begin, the recovery process is expected to be very slow.

> For ozone, there has been a substantial decline in the peak ozone concentrations (30% since the mid-1980s), although the mean concentrations show evidence of an increase and are expected to increase further over the coming decades. The net effect of these changes in the ozone climatology of the UK on terrestrial ecosystems remains unknown.

9.1 Introduction

The core chapters of this report present current understanding of emissions, long range transport, transformation, deposition and effects on soils, freshwaters and vegetation of the major pollutants contributing to acidification, eutrophication and photochemical oxidant formation. Each of these environmental problems was discovered long after the processes creating them began. In the case of freshwaters, diatom records in lake sediments show biological responses to acidification of some sensitive Scottish lochs early in the 19th century whereas the UK programme to monitor the deposition and effects of acidifying compounds throughout the country was not established until 1985. Similarly, the eutrophication resulting from nitrogen deposition, and production and effects of photochemical oxidants began long before the networks were established to monitor them, again about 1985 (RGAR, 1987; PORG, 1987). The peak in deposition of acidifying compounds occurred in about 1970 when UK (and European) sulphur emissions were at their maximum, more than a decade before our monitoring networks were properly established.

The deposition of nitrogen compounds peaked somewhat later than that of sulphur, corresponding with a maximum in the NO_x emissions in the 1990's and a peak in NH_3 emissions in the mid 1980s. Since 1970, sulphur emissions and deposition have been declining. For nitrogen compounds, emissions of both NO_x and NH_3 are smaller by the late 1990s, and records of deposition show a small decline to date. Peak concentrations of ozone have declined since the mid 1980's, but AOT40s have changed little and there is evidence of an increase in annual average concentrations.

There is therefore a background of declining emissions and deposition of acidifying pollutants in the UK, and a decline in emissions of oxidized nitrogen and volatile organic compounds. An examination of the evidence of improvements in air quality and reductions in the deposition and effects of the pollutant deposition is the focus of this chapter, which also includes estimates of the likely magnitude of environmental improvements over the coming decade.

This chapter draws together evidence of recovery from the observed decreases in acid deposition reported in the chapters on effects on soils, freshwaters and vegetation, beginning with the observed improvements in air quality during the last two decades from Chapter 3. This evidence is compared with the reductions in emissions and deposition. The major international protocol adopted at Gothenburg in 1999 will deliver further major decreases in emissions of sulphur, nitrogen oxides and volatile organic compounds. This chapter also summarises the likely magnitude of the decreases in critical load exceedances for acidification of soils and for ecosystem eutrophication by nitrogen, which result from emission reductions under the Gothenburg protocol.

9.2 Changes in Air Quality and Deposition

9.2.1 Sulphur

The reduction in emissions of sulphur has been large, from 3.2 million tonnes of SO_2 (as S) in 1970 to 0.6 million tonnes in 1999. Half of this 80% reduction in UK S emissions occurred before the monitoring networks were fully operational in 1986, however, since 1986 there has been a reduction in emissions of nearly 50% based on 1986 emissions. Deposition of sulphur within the UK declined by 52% during the period 1986 to 1997 corresponding to an average reduction in S deposition from 20 kg-S ha^{-1} to 10 kg-S ha^{-1}.

The ambient concentrations of SO_2 in Central Scotland, industrial regions of NW England, the Trent Valley, the Vale of York and large areas of SE England have declined from between 15 and 25 ppb (levels which have been shown to influence plant growth and crop yields) to between 1 and 3 ppb, an order of magnitude decline. Rural Britain is now largely free from SO_2 concentrations which damage or reduce the productivity of higher plants although there are still areas in which SO_2 may restrict the growth and survival of very sensitive lichens or bryophytes (see Chapter 7). A further consequence of the very large decline in SO_2 concentration has been a large reduction in dry deposition, especially in areas heavily polluted by SO_2 in the 1970's. Much of the arable cropland in the UK now receives less sulphur from the atmosphere than is required for optimum crop yield or quality and increasingly, sulphur must be applied along with the major fertilizer nutrients. The further 50% reduction in SO_2 emissions by 2010 will largely protect UK vegetation from direct effects of SO_2.

9.2.2 Acid Deposition

The reduction in sulphur emissions in the UK and Europe has led to a substantial reduction in wet and dry acid deposition throughout the UK. The contribution of nitrogen to acid deposition has remained fairly constant throughout the monitoring period (1986-present), so that almost all of the reduction in acid deposition from 1986 to 1997 in the UK, which amounts to about 30% in total, is attributable to the 50% reduction in sulphur deposition.

The reduction in deposition of acidifying compounds will reduce the magnitude of exceedance of critical loads, and the areas in exceedance throughout the UK. However, in quantifying the magnitude of critical loads exceedances, and their spatial distribution, it must be recognised that there is considerable uncertainty in the overall process, and large differences in the absolute values for exceedance are possible using different data sources. Care must therefore be taken in interpreting the maps, or statistics of critical load exceedances, recognising the uncertainties in the data sources and the methodology. For current exceedances, or those for years since the development of networks to monitor the deposition patterns, the measured deposition data provide the best estimates of deposition. Whereas for the future, it is necessary to use models to provide the deposition patterns. There are two important steps in providing the best estimate of the exceedance for 2010. First, models which simulate the long range transport and deposition of the pollutants are applied. For the UK deposition of sulphur and oxidized nitrogen, the HARM model is used and for reduced nitrogen the FRAME model is used, as described in chapter 4.

The second step is to calibrate the model against the measurements to provide the best estimate of the absolute values for deposition for future emission scenarios. Differences between the measurements and modelled deposition and their spatial distribution have been identified, with models underestimating deposition and therefore critical load exceedances. For example, the exceedances of acidity critical loads for ecosystems in the UK for 1995 using the HARM model for deposition of S, NO_x and NH_x shows 38% of the area in exceedance for all ecosystems, however, the measured deposition data show an exceedance of 71%. The main contributor to the difference in total acidifying deposition between HARM modelled deposition and the measurements is in the treatment of NH_3 and NH_4^+.

Many of the processes responsible for the differences between modelled and measured deposition are understood and future generations of the models will narrow the gap. Steps must be taken to correct for underestimates by the models to avoid interpreting differences between modelled and measured data as real trends in deposition and exceedance.

To illustrate this point, it is helpful to compare exceedances of critical loads using the models currently applied to simulate the transport, transformation and deposition of sulphur and nitrogen compounds, HARM and FRAME (which are described in Chapter 4) and the measured deposition data.

Following the implementation of the Gothenburg protocol, sulphur and oxidized nitrogen deposition will be considerably reduced, and the potential acidification from NH_3 and NH_4^+ will contribute a larger proportion of the total deposition. If the comparison of the current exceedance, with that of the future, following the implementation of the Gothenburg ceilings, relied solely on modelled values for both years, then the absolute values of exceedance would be underestimated, by approximately 50%. If however, the exceedances are based on measured deposition values for 1995 to 1997 and modelled for the future, then the underestimate by the model for the future date would imply a greater reduction than one would expect based on the magnitude of the reduction in emissions. It is therefore necessary to calibrate the model to correct for the underestimation of deposition.

It is possible to quantify the extent to which the models underestimate deposition by comparing models with measured deposition. The ratio of the measured deposition to the modelled can be used to correct maps of future deposition calculated by the model. Using the HARM and FRAME deposition calibrated in this way, the area of ecosystems exceeding the critical loads in 2010 is estimated to be 46%. If the model is not calibrated, the area would be 9%.

The exceedances for 2010, using the combination of HARM for SO_2 and NO_x, and FRAME for NH_3, calibrated against measured deposition are summarized in Table 9.1. These projections show that substantial progress will have been made by 2010, with a reduction in the effects of acid deposition, but the problems will not entirely be solved. The reduction in ecosystem exceedances of acid deposition is large, from 71% to 46%. These statistics illustrate the degree of improvement expected following the full implementation of the Gothenburg protocol. However, as noted above, the exceedances cannot be quantitatively translated with current knowledge into damage. The maps of exceedance show us where the probability of damage is greatest, and current survey data and experimental data show that the critical load values identify the thresholds beyond which damage may occur.

Table 9.1 Percentage of ecosystem areas that exceed critical loads for acidity in 1995-1997 and 2010.

Ecosystem type	1995 to 1997	2010
acid grassland	80	50
calcareous grassland	32	18
heathland	69	49
coniferous woodland	69	38
deciduous woodland	82	68
freshwaters*	18	9
all ecosystems	71	46

*The results for freshwaters are based on the catchment areas of 1610 upland lakes or headwater streams, sampled across the UK.

There remain many uncertainties in quantifying the exceedance of critical loads and their changes with time. There are continual improvements in all aspects of the underlying science and in the mapping procedures. These exceedance estimates show large reductions in the ecosystem threat from these pollutants, but they also show that the problems will not be entirely solved, even with the large scale of the reduction in emissions. The main contributor to the remaining exceedances in 2010 will be reduced nitrogen, as NH_3 and NH_4^+. This is not a surprising result, as the projected emissions of NH_3 are only expected to decline by 14% by 2010.

It is also important to distinguish between reducing the acidifying inputs sufficiently to allow recovery to begin and the actual recovery both chemical and biological. For acidified soils and freshwaters the base cations have been depleted and leached from upper soil horizons. Recovery, therefore, requires weathering of soil minerals to restore the base saturation of soils and alkalinity to the freshwaters. The weathering processes vary greatly according to the parent soil mineralogy and some acidified soils derived from granitic rock weather very slowly. Thus the chemical recovery in soils and freshwaters observed to date is spatially variable even though a substantial reduction in acidifying input has occurred.

9.3 Observed Recovery in Soils

The majority of the field evidence in the UK of repeated soil acidity measurements at the same location shows acidification of soils during the 20th Century (see Chapter 5). However, there have been no systematic national surveys of soil acidity which includes unmanaged land until quite recently. The Countryside Survey sampling was first completed in 1978 at a time close to the maximum in acid deposition and re-sampled in 1998/1999 (described in Chapter 5). These data show an increase in mean soil pH in all major soil groups except Pelosols, and in all environmental zones in the 20 year period, during which acid deposition has declined. The magnitude of the recovery which ranges from 0.1 and 0.3 pH units is small and has not been fully analysed to date. For example its association with the spatial changes in wet and dry deposition could be analysed. However, these data show the largest recovery from acidification in the uplands of England and Wales. The smallest changes in soil pH are in the Scottish Highlands which are among the regions to have experienced the smallest reduction in acid deposition. No biological indicators of recovery of soils from acidification have been reported.

9.3.1 Future Recovery of Soils

Experimental data and long-term model predictions indicate that soil water chemistry will respond relatively rapidly (up to 5 years) to decreases in acid deposition inputs and there is some limited, long-term field evidence to confirm this. However, in soils with a large pool of readily extractable sulphate, desorption of this sulphate will inhibit recovery of soil water ANC over a time scale of one to two decades. The experimental and modelling data suggest that recovery of soils by increases in base saturation will take much longer (decades) than for soil water chemistry. The majority of long-term modelling suggests that the base saturation of most acidified soils will not recover to those levels believed to exist prior to the industrial revolution. The rate of recovery is dependent on base cation supply from weathering and atmospheric inputs. Soils where the base saturation has been depleted by acid deposition will remain 'acid sensitive' for a considerable period of time as there will be little capacity to buffer acidity by cation exchange.

9.4 Freshwater Acidification

Chemical recovery

Good indicators of chemical recovery of freshwaters are increases in ANC (acid neutralising capacity, Appendix C), increases in pH and decreases in non-seasalt sulphate (SO_4^{2-}). In Galloway (SW Scotland) the long-term data (1979-1998) for these indicators show clear evidence of recovery (Figure 6.4). Reductions in non-seasalt sulphate have also been observed at some sites in the Pennines, Cumbria, SE England (Old Lodge) and in Central and North Wales. These data show that some recovery is beginning at sites in most of the acidified regions of the UK (Figure 9.1), especially those in areas of greatest acid deposition.

However, chemical recovery is not uniform. There are sites in regions close to the west coast where acid deposition has changed relatively little and therefore, they are where little response would be expected. There are other sites in regions where significant reduction in acid deposition has taken place but where there has been little chemical response in surface waters. In these latter cases delays in response may be due to the slow rate of base cation regeneration from the weathering of catchment minerals or to the continued desorption of sulphur from catchment soils. A further complication is the influence of climate variability especially in association with the North Atlantic Oscillation (NAO). Through its impact on the transport and deposition of pollutants and winter rainfall in particular, the NAO can cause inter-annual changes in pH and ANC that at some sites can mask the relatively weak response of surface waters to reductions in acid deposition.

Biological Recovery

The change in emission is followed immediately by changes in deposition since the acidifying pollutants have an atmospheric lifetime of only a few days at most. However, as Chapter 3 shows, the spatial pattern in acid deposition has changed in response to changes in emissions and while deposition has declined in response to emissions, the relative change is not the same everywhere. The chemical recovery of freshwaters, which are now taking place are further separated from changes in emission by chemical interactions within soils. Recovery is further delayed by the release of sulphur absorbed in soil and the signal of chemical change is confounded by non-stationarity in climate, as evidenced by the North Atlantic oscillations and consequent changes in the relative frequency of westerlies.

Biological recovery of freshwater ecosystems depends first on chemical recovery. As there is evidence that many sites are now showing signs of chemical recovery an equivalent biological response might be expected. However, the biological response is so far weak, mainly restricted to changes in epilithic diatom communities in Scotland (Round Loch of Glenhead, Loch Chon) and Wales (Llyn Llagi). The reasons for this patchy response are not fully understood but include the insufficiency of the chemical change so far and time-delays associated with the dispersal and recolonization of biota from distant source populations and refuges. These problems may be more acute for stream rather than lake populations where recurrent high flow acidic episodes in streams may prevent apparently successful colonists from sustaining their populations. The evidence of chemical and biological recovery from the effects of freshwater acidification described in this section is summarized in Figure 9.1.

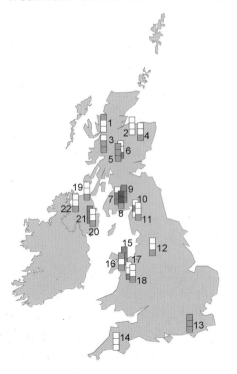

Figure 9.1 Sites in the UK Acid Waters Monitoring network showing changes during 1988 to 2000 in non-seasalt SO_4^{2-} deposition (bottom segment), acidity (middle segment), and biology (top segment) (inferred from diatom inferred pH and/or an increase in trout density), UK AWMN, (*2000*). Improvement (blue), no change (blank), deterioration (red). See Table B5 in Appendix B for site information.

Overall, there are signs of recovery in most of the areas of the UK in which widespread effects of surface water acidification have been reported, this evidence is believed to be the start of a process that will take many decades to complete, and there remain areas in which no improvements have yet been detected.

9.4.1 Future Recovery of Freshwaters 2001-2010

The approaches adopted to quantify responses of soils and freshwaters to the agreed emission reductions include comparison of areas of exceedance of critical loads and the application of dynamic models. Both approaches rely on atmospheric transport and deposition models to calculate the deposition resulting from emission reduction scenarios (considered in Chapter 4). A comparison of critical load exceedances for 2010 using the HARM plus FRAME models with current (1995 - 1997) exceedances shows the percentage of freshwaters in exceedance declines from 18% to 8%. However, among the many uncertainties in this comparison is the estimate of deposition. The observed decline in acid deposition to date in many of the wet deposition dominated uplands has been much smaller than the decline in emission. Since HARM and FRAME are essentially linear models, the reduction in exceedance may well prove to be optimistic. There are also large uncertainties in the critical load values, and their application in maps to quantify areas of exceedance.

For dynamic modelling of freshwaters the time course of past acidification has been simulated reasonably well, and model calibration in well-instrumented catchments provides acceptable results. Predictions for the future under the most recently agreed emission reductions indicate that chemical recovery is likely to take several decades and that leakage of nitrogen from catchment soils may exert a significant constraint on future recovery trends. The controls on nitrogen leaching remain uncertain. However, in the best-case scenario that assumes no further leakage of N and no additional complicating processes, a substantial chemical recovery of UK freshwaters from acidification effects could be expected by the middle of this century. The recovery of the biological status of these systems is likely to be further delayed.

9.5 Eutrophication

The problem of acidification is rather simpler and better understood than that of eutrophication. In part, this results from the earlier detection and study of the process, with acidification research beginning during the 1960s following the pioneering work of Odén (1968). Eutrophication by nitrogen over regional scales has been recognized only within the last decade (Galloway, 1998). Furthermore, the regional emissions of fixed nitrogen as NO_x and NH_3 lag those of sulphur, and only during the last few years have nitrogen emissions in the UK exceeded those of sulphur. In a mechanistic sense nitrogen accumulates within ecosystems prior to negative effects and some semi-natural ecosystems have the capacity to sequester very large quantities of nitrogen in vegetation and especially soils.

The emissions of oxidized nitrogen peaked around 1990 at 800 kt-N, and have declined by about 45% since then. However, the oxides of nitrogen are oxidized to HNO_3 rather slowly and NO_2 removal by dry deposition rates are also small, with the result that only a small fraction (20%) of UK NO_x emissions are deposited within the UK. The wet and dry deposition of oxidized nitrogen shows only a small decline since 1986. Emissions of reduced nitrogen have declined since the early 1980s, but the magnitude of the change is small relative to the uncertainty in emissions (Sutton *et al.,* 1998; Fowler *et al.,* 1990). The wet deposition measurements of reduced N show that there has been a decline in wet deposition of reduced N of about 10% from 120 kt-N in the mid 1980s to about 110 kt-N in 1995-1997.

Dry deposition of NH_3 has only been quantified accurately within the last 4 years following the development of an NH_3 monitoring network, and quantifying a change over the last 15 years would be a very speculative exercise.

There is no evidence of any recovery in response to the reduction in total nitrogen deposition over the past two decades, which is not surprising given the small magnitude of the reduction. On the contrary, there is some evidence of increasing problems of eutrophication due to nitrogen deposition. Evidence from long term nitrogen addition experiments, recovery experiments (including NITREX; Emmett *et al.*, 1998b) and re-assessment of previously abandoned fertilisation experiments leads us to suggest that there will be a long lag time between significant reduction in nitrogen deposition and ecological recovery (See Chapter 7). This is due to the fact that sensitive ecosystems of naturally low nutrient status have been accumulating excess deposited nitrogen over many decades and tend to retain this nitrogen tightly. Thus large pools of nitrogen have built up, mainly in the soil, which may take many decades (at least) to deplete back to natural levels, even if atmospheric nitrogen deposition were reduced now to below the critical load. In habitats where there have been **significant** changes in the species composition of the vegetation, it is possible that recovery to the original state may never occur. This is because the species gaining dominance due to eutrophication alter ecosystem nitrogen cycling in a self-perpetuating way, which may prove inimical to the re-establishment of the original species. Serious consideration needs to be given to the potential usefulness of habitat management techniques that remove the vegetation and/or soil to reduce the accumulated nitrogen pools of badly affected ecosystems, thus promoting their recovery.

Will the reduction in nitrogen deposition in Britain following full implementation of the Gothenburg Protocol by 2010 be sufficient to allow the recovery of ecosystems? Critical loads mapping can be used as a tool to predict the spatial extent of ecosystems adversely affected by nitrogen deposition under future deposition scenarios. All the uncertainties of critical loads mapping have to be borne in mind, and to these are added the uncertainties attached to the modelling of deposition patterns in the future. It should also be noted that the designation of critical load exceedance on a map does not mean that vegetation change is evident in that area, only that the potential for it exists. However, a comparison of the percentage area of four major ecosystem types for which the critical load of nutrient nitrogen is currently exceeded, and will still be exceeded in 2010, is shown in Table 9.2. It can be seen that implementation of the Gothenburg Protocol will result in a reduction in the proportion of the area of each ecosystem type receiving nitrogen deposition in excess of the critical load. However, very significant areas of semi-natural habitat in Britain could still be adversely affected by nitrogen deposition in 2010, the total area potentially impacted being reduced from the current 40% to 32% of the area of all ecosystems combined. This represents a reduction in the total area for which the critical load is exceeded of 8%. However, a reduction in deposition to below the critical load does not equate with recovery. Lags in recovery time mean that the date at which these areas show biological recovery will be much later than 2010, and the possibility remains that in some situations recovery may never occur without the aid of appropriate site management. This practical issue requires further investigation.

Table 9.2. Exceedances of critical loads* of ecosystems for eutrophication by nitrogen in the UK (%).

Ecosystem type	1995-1997	2010
acid grassland	27	19
heathland	56	42
coniferous woodland	88	79
deciduous woodland	96	92
all ecosystems	40	32

*This table is based on the official national critical loads; it is important to note that in some cases these differ from values used in Chapter 7, which incorporated recommendations from a recent international workshop (Hall *et al.,* 2001a).

9.6 Ground-level Ozone

In the case of vegetation, some of the limitations of the AOT40 index currently used in policy assessment have been identified in Chapter 7. It is likely that impacts are more closely related to absorbed dose than to AOT40, reflecting the impacts of variables such as vapour pressure deficit, soil water deficit and phenology as factors influencing the flux of ozone from the atmosphere to the site of damage in the leaf. Assuming that climate and hence flux does not change, it is possible to comment on the predicted changes in ozone concentrations and AOT40 exposures in a relative, if not in an absolute, sense.

Firstly, the clear signal of reduced peak concentrations of ozone should have benefits in terms of reducing the frequency with which critical levels for visible injury are exceeded. In theory, this would be of real economic benefit for some crop species, but in practice there is very limited evidence that major episodes produce visible injury in the UK even on the most sensitive crop species. Secondly, the reduction in peak concentrations by 2010 should have some benefit in parts of the UK in terms of increased crop yield and forest growth. On this basis, some recovery is to be expected.

However, the impact of increasing global background ozone concentrations, for which there is some evidence from the rural measurement network, is uncertain, because of the lack of experimental data on the impact of long-term exposure to ozone concentrations in the range 20-40ppb The effects of an ozone climate with higher background concentrations but lower peak concentrations are also unknown. Over the longer term, other changes in atmospheric concentration, particularly of CO_2, and climate are likely to significantly modify the impacts of ozone. A key objective for the next decade is therefore to improve risk assessments for future effects of ozone, including the use of flux-based approaches which integrate climatic factors with changes in ozone exposure patterns.

Chapter 10: Recommendations

Emissions (Chapter 2)

- Maintain and improve spatially disaggregated emission inventories and verify emission inventories where possible.

- Quantify uncertainty in emission inventories and their spatial distribution.

- Reduce uncertainty in emission inventories, especially for NH_3.

- Develop fully spatially disaggregated inventories for additional pollutants, such as metals and POPs.

Concentrations and deposition (Chapter 3)

- Maintain the wet deposition network and dry deposition monitoring stations through the period of emission reduction to quantify from measurements the reduction in deposition, its spatial pattern and any changes in underlying processes.

- The greatest uncertainty in N deposition and concentration arises through the spatial variability of NH_3 and deposition. This pollutant is the major contributor to nitrogen deposition and proposed emission reductions are modest. It is necessary therefore to further concentrate research effort on reducing uncertainties in UK NH_3 emission and deposition and the role of NH_x in acidification and eutrophication.

- Validate the peak deposition values present in UK maps.

- Provide site specific deposition data and links between the deposition measurement network and sites of effects work, to develop quantitative links in UK conditions, between critical load exceedance and actual effects.

- Provide annually, the UK and regional atmospheric mass budgets of the major pollutants, to identify the fate of UK emissions and changes with time.

- Develop low cost methods of monitoring deposition fluxes for each of the major pollutant gases.

- Provide improved spatial resolution in deposition estimates for catchments and develop methods to provide exposure and deposition estimates at scales appropriate for effects assessment.

- Quantify the uncertainty in deposition of S, N, acidity and O_3 at a scale appropriate for the assessment of terrestrial effects.

- Ensure that there is a process of frequent review of the measured concentration and deposition data, and comparison with models.

- To incorporate the latest developments in mechanistic understanding of deposition processes in the UK deposition models, and communicate these developments to other European research and application groups, especially those within EMEP.

Long range transport modelling (Chapter 4)

- Further develop long-range transport models to quantify the fate of the major air pollutants emitted within or advected into the UK (S, oxidised N, reduced N, O_3 and metals) at scales appropriate for effects assessment

- To improve model performance: take into account additional pollution sources, such as non-European emissions; include changes in the chemical behaviour of the atmosphere through time.

- Compare models with measured concentration and deposition fields, and recommend appropriate models and approaches for each pollutant and terrestrial ecosystem.

- Provide a review process to ensure application of the most appropriate models to the scientific issue in question.

Soils (Chapter 5)

- Monitor UK soils at time and space scales appropriate to quantify rates of recovery from acid deposition and the 'breakthrough' of nitrogen.

- Establish a UK network of soil monitoring to quantify the recovery from effects of acid deposition and provide early detection of future soil related environmental problems.

- Develop and apply models of soil processes which are appropriate to quantify the recovery of soils from the effects of acidification.

- Quantify the time scales for nitrogen storage and release in UK soils under a range of climates, land use and pollutant deposition.

Freshwaters (Chapter 6)

- Maintain freshwater chemical and biological monitoring through the period of emission reductions 2000 – 2010.

- Quantify the rate and spatial distribution of recovery in UK freshwaters from the effects of acidification.

- Quantify the importance of atmospheric N to freshwater quality and explain the mechanism leading to NO_3^- in non-agricultural areas.

- Quantify the effects of natural variability in climate on the rate of recovery of freshwaters from the effects of acidification.

- Review the scientific basis of the critical loads estimation for freshwaters.

- Separate effects of climate from those of chemistry and pollution.

- Understand the processes and timescales of biological recovery and develop the monitoring programme to identify recovery in the field.

Vegetation (Chapter 7)

- There is a need both to establish new monitoring programmes designed specifically to detect the biological effects of atmospheric deposition, using a range of appropriate sites, and to ensure that the data from existing monitoring exercises can be used effectively to assess changing impacts of air pollution. These programmes need to have a strong integration of soil and vegetation data in order to detect effects of changing rates of sulphur and nitrogen deposition.

- New field studies are required, specifically designed to compare vegetation composition and ecosystem processes at sites with different rates of nitrogen deposition, and thus to better assess the biological implications of exceedance of critical loads.

- A detailed critical review is urgently needed of whether the critical loads of nitrogen which are currently applied in UK mapping exercises are appropriate.

- It is essential to ensure that appropriate critical loads are assigned to sensitive species or habitats notified under the Habitats Directive, including new research for habitats for which critical loads do not exist.

- There is an urgent need to improve the scientific basis for predicting the magnitude and timescale of ecological recovery after reductions in nitrogen deposition, both through experiments and appropriate dynamic models. These studies must include the potential for active site management to reduce nitrogen status.

- The patterns of changing distributions of both lichen and bryophyte species over the last 20-30 years need to be examined in more detail using both national database and site-specific investigations, to identify the role of S and N deposition and the factors limiting re-invasion.

⊕ Risk assessment for ozone impacts needs to have a stronger mechanistic basis. The most immediate priority is the development of models based on cumulative stomatal flux, but it is also important to develop a basis for modelling long-term effects on growth of tree species. In both cases, field and experimental studies are needed to provide a basis for model development.

⊕ The UK Air Quality Strategy should take full account of the ecological impacts of air pollutants in developing and applying air quality objectives, and in assessing the need for emission control.

⊕ Experimental studies are required which are specifically designed to test the implications for vegetation of the predicted future patterns of ozone exposure, and specifically the effect of reduced frequencies of peak concentrations and increased levels of background concentrations.

⊕ Further research is needed to identify the key factors influencing the effects of ozone on semi-natural plant communities, to predict its impacts on species composition of sensitive communities and to test these predictions against observed changes in species composition in the field.

⊕ Site-specific assessments are urgently needed to ensure that protection of sites of high biodiversity under the Habitats Directive takes into account the impacts of local and regional air pollution.

⊕ Critical levels and loads represent a relatively crude method of assessing the risk of air pollution impacts on vegetation. Research is urgently needed to develop improved methods of ecological risk assessment for air pollution to be applied at international or local scales. This should focus on ozone and nitrogen deposition as the two pollutants for which current risk assessment methods suggest there will be continued impacts on vegetation after 2010.

European (Chapter 8)

⊕ Quantify effects of UK pollutants outside the UK (sulphur v nitrogen v photochemical oxidants).

⊕ Compare the responses of air quality, deposition and effects to changes in pollutant emissions elsewhere in Europe with those observed in the UK.

⊕ Develop closer links between UK research programmes and those of other European countries and EMEP.

References

Aber, J.D., Nadelhoffer, K.J., Steudler, P., Melillo, J.M. (*1989*) Nitrogen saturation in northern forest ecosystems. Bioscience, 29, 378-387.

Aber, J.D. and Federer, C.A. (*1992*). A generalized, lumped-parameter model of photosynthesis, evapotranspiration and net primary production in temperate and boreal forest ecosystems. Oecologia 92, 463-474.

Aber, J., McDowell, W., Nadelhoffer, K., Magill, A., Berntson, G., Kamakea, M., McNulty, S., Currie, W., Rustad, L. and Fernandez, I. (*1998*). Nitrogen saturation in temperate forest ecosystems - Hypotheses revisited. Bioscience 48, 921-934.

Abrahamsen, G., Bjor, K., Honvedt, R & Tveite, B. (*1976*). Effects of acid precipitation on coniferous forests. In, Impact of acid precipitation on forest and freshwater ecosystems in Norway. Edited by F. H. Brakke. Oslo-As: SNSf porojektet FR 6/76.

Abrahamsen, G. (*1985*). Assessment of the long-term effect of acid deposition on leaching from forets soils. A methodological study. In, Air Pollution and stability of coniferous forest ecosystems. Edited by R. Klimo and R. Saly. International Symposium, pp3-22. Brno: University of Agriculture, Brno.

Abrahamsen, G. & Stuanes, A. O. (*1986*). Lysimeter study of effects of acid deposition on properties and leaching of gleyed dystric brunisol soil in Norway. Water, Air and Soil Pollution 31, 865-878.

Abrahamsen, G., Seip, H.M. & Semb, A. (*1989*). Long-term acidic deposition studies in Norway. In, Acidic Precipitation Volume 1: Case Studies. Edited by D.C. Adriano and M. Havas. New York: Spinger Verlag.

Abrahamsen, G., Stuanes, A. O. and Tveite, B. (Eds.) (*1994*). Long-term experiments with acid rain in Norwegian forest ecosystems. Ecological Studies 104, New York: Springer Verlag.

Adamson, J. K., Rowland, A. P., Scott, A. A. & Hornung, M. (*1996*). Changes in soil acidity and related variables over 25 years in the North Pennine Uplands, UK. Soil Use and Management 12, 55-61.

Aerts R & Bobbink R, (*1999*).The impact of atmospheric nitrogen deposition on vegetation processes in terrestrial, non-forest ecosystems. In: The impact of nitrogen deposition on natural and semi-natural ecosystems (Ed. SJ Langan). Kluwer Academic Publishers, Dordrecht. pp 85-122.

Alban, D. H. (*1982*). Effects of nutrient accumulation by aspen, spruce and pine on soil properties . Soil Science Society of America Journal 46, 153-457.

Alcamo, J., ApSimon, H., Builtjes, P. (Eds.) (*1987*). Interregional Air Pollutant Transport: The Linearity Question. IIASA RR-87-20, Laxenburg, Austria.

Alcamo, J., Shaw, R. and Hordjik, L. (Eds.) (*1990*). The RAINS model of acidification. Science and strategies in Europe. Kluwer, Dordrecht.

Alewell, C. and Matzner, E. (*1993*). Reversibility of soil solution acidity and of sulphate retention in acid forest soils. Water Air and Soil Pollution 71, 155-165.

Alewell, C., Bredemeier, M., Matzner, E. and Blanck, K. (*1997*). Soil solution response to experimentally reduced acid deposition in a forest ecosystem. Journal of Environmental Quality 26: 658-665.

Allchin E, Power SA & Ashmore MR (*1999*). Impacts of enhanced inputs to Calluna systems: integration synthesis and modelling. Annual Report to DETR. Imperial College & Bradford University.

Allen, A.G., Harrison, R.M. and Erisman, J.W. (*1989*). Field measurements of the dissociation of ammonium nitrate and ammonium chloride aerosols. Atmospheric Environment, 23:1591-1599

Allott, T.E.H., Harriman, R. and Battarbee, R.W., (*1992*). Reversibility of acidification at the Round Loch of Glenhead, Galloway, Scotland. Environ. Pollut., 77, 219-225.

Allott, T.E.H., Battarbee, R.W., Curtis, C., Kreiser, A.M., Juggins, S. & Harriman, R. (*1995*). An empirical model of critical acidity loads for surface waters based on paleaolimnological data. In: M.Hornung, M.A.Sutton & R.B.Wilson (eds.) Mapping and modelling of critical loads for nitrogen – a workshop report. Institute of Terrestrial Ecology. pp50-54.

Alonso I & Hartley SE (*1998*). Effects of nutrient supply, light availability and herbivory on the growth of heather and three competing grass species. Plant Ecology 137 203-212.

Alonso I, Hartley SE & Thurlow M (*2001*). Competition between heather and grasses on Scottish moorlands: Interacting effects of nutrient enrichment and grazing regime. Journal of Vegetation Science 12, 249-260.

Anderson H.R., Ponce de Leon A., Bland J.M., Bower J.S. and Strachan D.P. (*1996*). Air pollution and daily mortality in London 1987-92. BMJ 312 pp 665-669.

Anderson H.R, Spix C, Medina S. (*1997*). Air pollution and daily admissions for chronic obstructive pulmonary disease in 6 European cities; results from the APHEA project. Eur. Respir. J. 10, pp 1064-1071.

Andersson, F. and Persson, T. (Eds) (*1988*). Liming as a Measure to Improve Soil and Tree Condition in Areas Affected by Air Pollution. Report 3518, Solna, Swedish Environmental Protection Board.

Anfossi D. & Sandroni S. (*1997*). Short communication: Ozone levels in Paris one century ago. Atmos. Env. 31(20), 3481-3482. 7.

Anfossi, D., Sandroni, S. and Viarengo, S. (*1991*). Tropospheric ozone in the nineteenth century: the Moncalieri series. Journal of Geophysical Research 96, D9, 17,349-17,352.

Angold PG (*1997*). The impact of a road upon adjacent heathland vegetation: effects on plant species composition. J.Appl.Ecol, 34, 409-417

ApSimon, H.M., Barker, B.M. & Kayin, S. (*1994*). Modelling studies of the atmospheric release and transport of ammonia - applications of the TERN model to an EMEP site in eastern England in anticyclonic episodes. Atmospheric Environment 28, 665-678.

Ashmore MR & Bell JNB (*1991*). The role of ozone in global change. Annals of Botany, 67, 39-48.

Ashmore MR & Davison AW (*1996*). Towards a critical level of ozone for natural vegetation. In: Critical Levels of Ozone for Europe: Testing and Finalising the Concepts Karenlampi L & Skarby L (eds.) pp. 58-71. University of Kuopio, Kuopio.

Atkinson, K.M. and Howarth, E.Y. (*1990*). Devoke Water and Loch Sionascraig: recent environmental changes and post-glacial overview. Phil. Trans. R. Soc. Lond., B, 349-355.

References

Avery, B.W. (*1980*). Soil Classification for England and Wales. Soil Survey Technical Monograph no. 14. Soil Survey, Harpenden.

Ayazloo M & Bell JNB (*1981*). Studies of the tolerance to sulphur dioxide of grass populations in polluted areas. I: Identification of tolerant populations. New Phytologist, 88, 203-222,

Bååth, E., Lundgren, B. and Söderström, B. (*1981*). Effects of nitrogen-fertilization on the activity and biomass of fungi and bacteria in a podzolic soil. Zentralblatt Fur Bakteriologie Mikrobiologie Und Hygiene I Abteilung Originale C-Allgemeine Angewandte Und Okologische Mikrobiologie 2, 90-98.

Baddeley, JA, Thompson, DBA & Lee, JA (*1994*). Regional and historical variation in the nitrogen content of Racomitrium lanuginosum in Britain in relation to atmospheric nitrogen deposition. Environmental Pollution 84, 189-196.

Ball, G.R., Benton, J.M., Palmer-Brown, D., Fuhrer, J., Skarby, L., Gimeno, B.S., and Mills, G.E. (*1998*). Identifying factors which modify the effects of ambient ozone on white clover (Trifolium repens L.) in Europe. Environmental Pollution 103:7-16.

Barrett, K. and Berge, E. (*1996*). Transboundary air pollution in Europe. EMEP/MSC-W Report 1/96.

Barrett, K., Schaug, J., Bartonova, A., Semb, A., Hjellbrekke, A-G. and Hanssen, J.E. (*2000*). Europe's changing air environment. Two decades of trends in acidifying atmospheric sulphur and nitrogen in Europe; 1978-1998. EMEP/CCC-Report 7/2000.

Bartnicki, J. and Tarrason, L. (*1998*). Comparison of the Lagrangian and the Eulerian model performance. In: Transboundary Acidifying Pollution in Europe, EMEP/MSC-W Report 1/98, 139-150.

Bartnicki (*2000*). Non-Linear Effects in the Source-Receptor Matrices Computed with the EMEP Eulerian Acid Deposition. EMEP/MSC-W Note 4/00, July 2000.

Bates, J.W., Bell J.N.B., Farmer, A.M., (*1990*). Epiphyte recolonisation of oaks along a gradient of air pollution in south-east England, 1979-1990. Environmental Pollution 68, 81-99.

Battarbee, R.W., Flower, R.J., Stevenson, A.C. and Rippey, B., (*1985*). Lake acidification in Galloway: a palaeoecological test of competing hyptheses. Nature, 314, 350-352.

Battarbee, R.W., Flower, R.J., Stevenson, A.C., Jones, V.J., Harriman, R. and Appleby, P.G. (*1988*). Diatom and chemical evidence for reversibility of acidification of Scottish lochs. Nature, 322, 530-532.

Battarbee, R.W., Mason, B.J., Renberg, I. and Talling, J.F. (Eds) (*1990*). Palaeolimnology and Lake Acidification. Royal Society, London, 445 pp.

Battarbee, R.W., Allott, T.E.H., Juggins, S., Kreiser, A.M., Curtis, C. & Harriman, R. (*1996*). Critical loads of acidity to surface waters – an empirical diatom-based palaeolimnological model. Ambio 25(5), 366-369.

Batty, K., (*1997*). Population dynamics of epiphytic lichens in relation to changing air quality. Ph.D. thesis, Imperial College, London.

Baxter D & Farmer A (*1993*). The control of Brachypodium pinnatum in chalk grasslands: Influence of management and nutrients. English Nature, Peterborough.

Beebee, T.J.C., Flower, R.J., Stevenson, A.C., Patrick, S.T., Appleby, P.G., Fletcher, C., Marsh, C., Natkanski, J., Rippey, B. and Battarbee, R. (*1990*) Decline of the natterjack Toad Bufo calamita in Britain: Palaeoecological, documentary and experimental evidence for breeding site acidification. Biological Conservation, 53, 1-20.

Beekmann,M; Ancellet,G; Blonsky,S; DeMuer,D; Ebel,A; Elbern,H; Hendricks,J; Kowol,J; Mancier,C; Sladkovic,R; Smit,HGJ; Speth,P; Trickl,T; VanHaver,P (*1997*): Regional and global tropopause fold occurrence and related ozone flux across the tropopause. J. Atmos. Chem. 28(1-3), 29-44.

Beier, C., Hultberg, H., Moldan, F. and Wright, R.F. (*1995*). MAGIC applied to roof experiments (Risdalsheia, N; Gardsjon, S; Klosterhede, DK) to evaluate the rate of reversibility of acidification following experimentally reduced acid deposition. Water Air And Soil Pollution 85, 1745-1751.

Beilke,S. and Wallasch,M. (*2000*) Die Ozonbelastung in Deutschland seit 1990 und Prognose der zukünftigen Entwicklung. Immissionsschutz 4, 5.Jahrgang, Dezember 2000, S.149-155.

Bell JNB, McNeill S, Houlden G, Brown VS & Mansfield PJ (*1993*). Atmospheric change: effects on plant pests and diseases. Parasitology, 106, 811-824

Benton, J.M., Fuhrer, J., Gimeno, B., Skarby, L., Palmer-Brown, D., Ball, G.R., Roadknight, C., and Mills, G.E. (*2000*). An International Cooperative Programme indicates the widespread occurrence of injury on crops caused by ambient ozone episodes in Europe. Agriculture, Ecosystems and Environment 78: 19-30.

Berden, M., Nilsson, I. S., Rosen, K. & Tyler, G. (*1987*). Soil Acidification extent, causes and consequences. Solna, Sweden; National Swedish Environmental Protection Board.

Berdowski JJM (*1993*) The effect of external stress and disturbance factors on Calluna dominated heathland vegetation. In: Heathlands: patterns and processes in a changing environment. (eds R Aerts & GW Heil). Kluwer Academic Publishers, Dordrecht. 85-124.

Berg, B., Eckbohm, G., Johansson, M, -B., Mc Claugherty, C., Rutigliano, F. & Virzo De Santo, A. (*1996*). Some foliar litter types have a maximum limit for decomposition – a synthesis of data from forest systems. Can. J. Bot. 74, 659-672.

Berg, B. and Matzner, E. (*1997*). Effect of N deposition on decomposition of plant litter and soil organic matter in forest systems. Environmental Reviews 5, 1-25.

Berge, E. and Tarrason, L. (*1992*). An evaluation of Eulerian advection methods for the modelling of long range transport of air pollution. EMEP/MSC-W Note 2/92.

Berge, E. (*1993*). Preliminary estimates of sulphur transport and deposition in Europe with a regional scale multilayer Eulerian model. EMEP/MSC-W Note 1/93

Bergmann E, Bender J & Weigel H (*1995*). Growth response and foliar sensitivies of native herbaceous species to ozone exposure. Water Air Soil Pollut., 85, 1437-1442.

Berntsen TK, Myhre G, Stordal F, Isaksen ISA. (*2000*). Time evolution of tropospheric ozone and its radiative forcing. J GEOPHYS RES-ATMOS 105: (D7) 8915-8930 APR 16 2000

Billett, M. F., FitzPatrick, E. A. & Cresser, M. C. (*1988*). Long-term changes in the acidity of forest soils in North-East Scotland. Soil Use and Management 4, 102-106.

Billett, M. F., Parker-Jervis, F., Fitzpatrick, E. A. & Cresser, M. S. (*1990*a). Forest soil chemical changes between 1949/50 and 1987. Journal of Soil Science 41, 133-145.

Billett, M. F., Fitzpatrick, E. A. & Cresser, M. S. (*1990*b). Changes in organic carbon and nitrogen status of forest soil organic horizons between 1949/50 and 1987. Environmental pollution 66, 67-79.

Bjornstad, O. N. (*1991*). Changes in forest soils and vegetation in Søgne, Southern Norway, during a 20 year period. Holarctic Ecology 14, 234-244.

Blake, I., Goulding, K.W.T., Mott, C.J.B. and Johnston, A.E. (*1999*). Changes in soil chemistry accompanying acidification over more than 100 years under woodland and grass at Rothamsted Experimental Station, UK. European Journal of Soil Science 50, 401-412.

Blaser, p., Zysset, M., Zimmermann, S. & Luster J. (*1999*). Soil Acidification in Southern Switzerland between 1987 and 1997: A case study based on the critical load concept. Environ. Sci. Technology 33, 2383-2389.

Bobbink, R., Hornung, M. & Roelofs, J.G.M. (*1996*). Empirical nitrogen critical loads for natural and semi-natural ecosystems. In: UNECE Manual on methodologies and criteria for mapping critical levels/loads and geographical areas where they are exceeded. Federal Environmental Agency (Umweltbundesamt) Berlin. Available online at: http://www.umweltbundesamt.de/mapping/

Boreham, S., (*1993*). A study of corticolous lichens on London plane Platanus x hybrida trees in West Ham Park, London. London Naturalist 71, 61-69.

Boxman AW, Blank K, Brandud T-E, Emmett BA, Gundersen P, Hogervorst RF, Kjønaas OJ, Persson H, Timmermann V (*1998*). Vegetation and soil biota response to experimentally-changed nitrogen inputs in coniferous forest ecosystems of the NITREX project. Forest Ecology and Management 101, 65-79.

Bradley, D.C. and Ormerod, S.J. (*2001*). Long-term effects of catchment liming on invertebrates in upland streams. Freshwater Biology, 48 (in press).

Brasier CM (*1999*). Phytopthora pathogens of trees: their rising profile in Europe. Forestry Commission Information Note 30, Edinburgh.

Braun S, Rihm B & Fluckiger W (*1999*). Growth of mature beech in relation to ozone: and epidemiological approach. In: Critical levels for ozone – level II (J Fuhrer & B Achermann, eds.), pp. 111-114. Swiss Agency for Environment, Forest and Landscape, Berne.

Bredemeier, M., Blanck, K., Dohrenbusch, A., Lamersdorf, N., Meyer, A.C., Murach, D., Parth, A. and Xu, Y-J. (*1998*a). The Solling roof project – site characteristics, experiments and results. Forest Ecology and Management 101, 281-293.

Bredemeier, M., Blanck, K., Xu, Y.-J., Tietema, A., Boxman, A.W., Emmett, B.A., Moldan, F., Gundersen, P., Schleppi, P. and Wright, R.F. (*1998*b). Input-output budgets at the NITREX sites. Forest Ecology and Management 101, 57-64.

Broadmeadow MSJ and Jackson SB (*2000*). Growth responses of Quercus petraea, Fraxinus excelsior and Pinus sylvestris to elevated carbon dioxide, ozone and water supply. New Phytologist 146:437-451.

Brown, K. A. (*1987*). Chemical effects of pH 3 sulphuric acid on a soil profile. Water Air Soil Pollut., 32, 201-218.

Brunet J, Diekemann M & Falkengrup-Grerup U (*1998*). Effects of nitrogen deposition on field layer vegetation in south Swedish oak forests. Environmental Pollution, 102, 35-40.

Buckton, S. T. & Ormerod, S. J. (*1997*). Effects of liming on the Coleoptera, Hemiptera, Araneae and Opliones of catchment wetlands in Wales. Biological Conservation, 79, 43-57

Buckton, S.T., Brewin, P.A., Lewis, A., Stevens, P. and Ormerod, S.J. (*1998*). The distribution of dippers (Cinclus cinclus) in the acid sensitive regions of Wales, 1984-1995. Freshwater Biology, 39, 387-396.

Cannell MGR, Thornley JHM, Mobbs DC & Friend AD. (*1998*). UK conifer forests may be growing faster in response to increased N deposition, atmospheric CO_2 and temperature,. Forestry71: 277-296.

Cannell MGR (*1999*). Relative importance of increasing atmospheric CO_2, N deposition and temperature in promoting European forest growth. In: Causes and consequences of accelerating tree growth in Europe. Eds. T Karjalainen, H Spiecker, O Laroussinie. Proceedings No 27. European Forest Institute, Joensuu, Finland.

Cape, J.N., Leith, I.D., Fowler, D., Murray, M.B., Sheppard, L.J., Eamus, D., Wilson, R.H.F., (*1991*). Sulphate and ammonium in mist impair the frost hardening of red spruce seedlings. New Phytologist 118, 119-126.

Cape, J.N., (*1993*). Direct Damage to Vegetation Caused by Acid Rain and Polluted Cloud - Definition of Critical Levels for Forest Trees. Environmental Pollution 82, 167-180.

Caporn SJM, Risager M & Lee JA (*1994*). Effects of atmospheric nitrogen deposition on frost hardiness in Calluna vulgaris. New Phytologist 128, 461-468.

Caporn SJM, Song W, Read DJ & Lee JA (*1995*). the effect of repeated nitrogen fertilization on mycorrhizal infection in heather [Calluna vulgaris (L) Hull]. New Phytologist 129, 605-609.

Carnol, M., Ineson, P., Anderson, J.M., Beese, F., Berg, M.P., Bolger, T., Couteaux, M.M., Cudlin, P., Dolan, S., Raubuch, M., and Verhoef, H.A. (*1997*). The effects of ammonium sulphate deposition and root sinks on soil solution chemistry in coniferous forest soils. Biogeochemistry 38, 255-280.

Carreira, J. A., Harrison, A. F., Sheppard, L. J. & Woods, C. (*1997*). Reduced soil P availability in a Sitka spruce (Picea sitchensis (Bong.) Carr) plantation induced by applied acid-mist: significance in forest decline. Forest Ecology and Management 92, 153-166.

Carroll JA, Caporn SJM, Cawley L, Read DJ & Lee JA (*1999*). The effect of increased deposition of atmospheric nitrogen on Calluna vulgaris in upland Britain. New Phytologist 141, 423-431.

CEC (Commission of the European Communities). (*1992*). CORINE Land Cover – technical guide. Luxembourg: CEC.

Chamberlain, A.C. (*1966*). Transport of gases from grass and grass-like surfaces. Proc. R. Soc. Lond., A290:236-265.

Chamberlain, D. E., Warren, R. W., Crick, H. Q. P., Hall, J., Metcalfe, S., Ormerod, S. J., Whyatt, D. & Vickery, J. A. (*2000*). Acidification and terrestrial birds. BTO Research Report No. 236. A Report to the DETR on Prject EPG 1/3/135. BTO, Thetford

Chao, T.T., Harward, M.E. and Fang, S.C. (*1962*). Adsorption and desorption phenomena of sulphate ions in soils. Soil Science Society of America Proceedings 26, 234-237.

Chalmers, A.G., Kershaw, C.D, and Leech, P.K. (*1990*). Fertilizer use on farm crops in Great Britain: results from Survey of Fertilizer Practice, 1969-88. Outlook on Agriculture 19, 269-278.

References

Choularton, T.W., Gay, M.J., Jones, A., Fowler, D., Cape, J.N. & Leith, I.D. (*1988*). The influence of altitude on wet deposition. Comparison between field measurements at Great Dun Fell and the predictions of a seeder-feeder model. Atmos. Environ. 22, 1363-1371.

CLAG (Critical Loads Advisory Group). (*1995*). Critical loads of acid deposition for United Kingdom freshwaters. Report prepared at the request of the Department of Environment.

CLAG (*1996*). Critical Levels of Air Pollutants for the United Kingdom. Department of the Environment, London.

CLAG (*1997*). Deposition Fluxes in the United Kingdom: A compilation of the current deposition maps and mapping methods (1992-1994) used for Critical Loads exceedance assessment in the United Kingdom. Critical Loads Advisory Group sub-group report on Deposition Fluxes. 45 pp. Penicuik: Institute of Terrestrial Ecology.

Clark, P.A., Fisher, B.E.A. & Scriven, R.A. (*1987*). The wet deposition of sulphate and its relationship to sulphur dioxide emissions. Atmos. Environ,., 21, 1125-1131.

Clymo, R.S., Foster, G.N., MacKay, J., Robertson, J., Shore, R. and Skidmore, D.I. (*1992*). Terrestrial biology in limed catchments. In: Restoring Acid Waters: Loch Fleet 1984-1992, Howells, G. and Dalziel, T.R.K. (Eds.), Elsevier, London.

Collen, P., Harriman, R., Morrison, B.R.S., Keay, E. and Watt, A.W., (*2000*). Restoration of a brown trout (Salmo Frutta. L.) population to Loch Enoch, an acidified loch in Galloway, SW Scotland. Freshwater Forum, 14, 3-14.

Collins, R. and Jenkins, A. (*1998*). Regional modelling of acidification in Wales; calibration of a spatially distributed model incorporating land use change. Hydrology and Earth System Sciences 2, 533-541.

Collins, W.J., Stevenson, D.S., Johnson, C.E. and Derwent, R.G. (*1997*) Tropospheric ozone in a global scale three-dimensional Lagrangian model and its response to NOx emission controls. Journal of Atmospheric Chemistry 26, 223-274.

Collins W.J., Derwent R.G., Johnson C.E. and Stevenson D.S. (*2000*a): The impact of human activities on the photochemical production and destruction of tropospheric ozone. QJR Met. Soc. 126, pp 1925-1951.

Collins W.J., Derwent R.G., Johnson C.E. and Stevenson D.S. (*2000*b): The European regional ozone distribution and its links with the global scale for the years 1992 and 2015. Atmos Env. 34 pp 255-267.

Cook, L.M., Rigby, K.D. and Seaward, M.R.D. (*1990*) Melanic moths and changes in epiphytic vegetation in north-west England and north Wales. Biological Journal of the Linnean Society, 39: 343-54.

Corsmeier U, Kalthoff N, Kolle O, Kotzian M, Fiedler F (*1997*). Ozone concentration jump in the stable nocturnal boundary layer during a LLJ-event. ATMOSPHERIC ENVIRONMENT 31: (13) JUL 1997

Cosby, B.J., Wright, R.F., Hornberger, G.M. and Galloway, J.N. (*1985*). Modelling the effects of acid deposition: estimation of long-term water quality repsonses in a small forested watershed. Water Resources Research 121, 1591-1601.

Cosby, B.J., Jenkins, A.,Ferrier, R.C., Miller, J.D. and Walker, T.A.B., (*1990*). Modelling stream acidification in afforested catchments: long-term reconstructions at two sites in central Scotland. J. Hydrol., 120, 143-162.

Coyle M., Smith R., Flechard C., Fowler D., Derwent R.G., Milton M.J.T. (*1999*). Trends in Rural Ozone Concentration in the UK. EUROTRAC-2 Symposium98 Proceedings. EUROTRAC International Scientific Secretariat, Garmisch-Partenkirchen. WIT Press.

Coyle M., Fowler D., Smith R. (*2000*). Trends in Rural Ozone Concentrations in the UK. EUROTRAC-2 Symposium2000 Proceedings. EUROTRAC International Scientific Secretariat, Garmisch-Partenkirchen. CD ROM and WIT Press, In press

Coyle, R.I. Smith, J. R. Stedman, K. J. Weston and D Fowler (*2001*). Quantifying the spatial distribution of surface ozone concentration in the UK. Atmospheric Environment. in press.

Cresser, M.S., Smith, C. & Sanger, L. (*1993*). Critical loads for peat soils. In: M.Hornung & R.Skeffington (Eds.), Critical loads: concept and application, ITE Symposium No. 28. HMSO, London.

Crittenden P & Read DJ (*1978*). The effects of air pollution on plant growth with special reference to sulphur dioxide. II. Growth studies with Lolium perenne L. New Phytologist, 80, 49-62.

Crocker, R.L. and Major, J. (*1955*). Soil development in relation to vegetation and surface age, Glacier Bay, Alaska. J. Ecol. 43, 427-448.

Cronan, C.S. and Grigal, D.F. (*1995*). Use of calcium/aluminum ratios as indicators of stress in forest ecosystems. Journal of Environmental Quality 24, 209-226.

Crossley, A., Wilson, D.B. & Milne, R. (*1992*). Pollution in the upland environment. Environ. Pollut. 75, 81-88.

Curtis, C.J., Whyatt, J.D., Metcalfe, S.E., Allott, T.E.H. and Harriman, R. (*1999*) Assessing the impact of international emissions reduction scenarios to combat the acidification of freshwaters in Great Britain with the First-order Acidity Balance (FAB) model and the Hull Acid Rain Model (HARM). Energy and Environment, 10, 571-596.

Curtis, C.J., Allott, T.E.H., Hughes, M., Hall, J., Harriman, R., Helliwell, R., Kernan, M., Reynolds, B. and Ullyett, J. (*2000*) Critical loads of sulphur and nitrogen for freshwaters in Great Britain and assessment of deposition reduction requirements with the First-order Acidity Balance (FAB) model. Hydrology and Earth System Sciences 4, 1-15.

Dahl, E. (*1988*). Acd9ification of soils in the Rondane Mountains, south Norway, due to acid precipitation. Økoforsk rapport 1988/1, 1-53.

David, M. B. & Mitchell, M. J. (*1987*). Transformations of organic and inorganic sulfur: Importance to sulphate flux in an Adirondack forest soil. JAPCA – The International Journal of Air pollution Control and Hazardous waste Management 37, 39-44.

Davison, AW and Barnes, JD (*1998*). Effects of ozone on wild plants. New Phytologist 139 (1) 135-151.

de Leeuw F., Sluyter R and van Zantvoort E. (*1997*). Air Pollution by Ozone in the European Union, Exceedance of threshold values in 1996 and summer 1997. EEA, Copenhagen.

de Leeuw F., Sluyter R and Camu A. (*2000*). Air Pollution by Ozone in Europe in 1998 and summer 1999. EEA, Copenhagen.

de Vries, W., G.J. Reinds, H.D. Deelstra, J. M Klap and E.M. Vel (*1999*). Intensive Monitoring of Forest Ecosystems in Europe. Technical report 1998. UN/ECE, EC, Forest Intensive Monitoring Coordinating Institute,193 pp.

de Vries, W., G.J. Reinds, H.D. Deelstra, J. M Klap and E.M. Vel (*2000*). Intensive Monitoring of Forest Ecosystems in Europe. Technical report 1999. UN/ECE, EC, Forest Intensive Monitoring Coordinating Institute,173 pp.

DeGraaf MCC, Verbeek PJM, Bobbink R & Roelofs JGM (*1998*). Restoration of species-rich dry heaths: the importance of appropriate soil conditions. Acta Botanica Neerlandica 47, 89-111.

Derome, J., Kukkola, M. and Malkonen, E. (*1986*). Forest Liming on Mineral Soils – Results of Finnish Experiments. Report 3084, Solna, Swedish Environmental Protection Board.

Diekmann, M., Brunet, J., Ruhling, Å. and Falkengren-Grerup, U. (*1999*). Effects of nitrogen deposition: results of temporal-spatial analysis of deciduous forests in South Sweden. Plant Biology 1, 471-481.

DoE (*1995*) Critical Loads of Acid Deposition for United Kingdom Freshwaters, Critical Loads Advisory Group Sub-group Report on Freshwaters. Institute of Terrestrial Ecology, Penicuik, Scotland.

DoE (*1997*) Department of the Environment. The United Kingdom National Air Quality Strategy. The Stationary Office, March 1997, CM 3587.

Dohmen GP, McNeill S & Bell JNB (*1984*). Air pollution increases Aphis fabae pest potential. Nature, 307, 52-53.

Dore, A.J., Choularton, T.W. & Fowler, D. (*1992*). An improved wet deposition map of the United Kingdom incorporating the seeder-feeder effect over mountainous terrain. Atmospheric Environment, 26A, 1375-1381.

Draaijers, G.P.J., Leeuwen, E.P. van, Jong, P.G.H. de en Erisman, J.W. (*1997*a). Base cation deposition in Europe - Part I. Model description, results and uncertainty. Atmospheric Environment,31,4139-4157.

Draaijers, G.P.J., Leeuwen, E.P. van, Jong, P.G.H. de en Erisman, J.W. (*1997*b). Base cation deposition in Europe - Part II. Acid neutralization capacity and contribution to forest nutrition. Atmospheric Environment,31,4159-4168.

Dragosits U., Sutton M.A., Place C.J. and Bayley A. (*1998*). Modelling the spatial distribution of ammonia emissions in the UK. Environ. Pollut. (Nitrogen Conference Special Issue). 102, S1, 195-203.

Driscoll, C.T. and Schaefer, D.A. (*1989*). Overview of nitrogen processes. In: The Role of Nitrogen in the Acidification of Soils and Surface Waters, Ed Malanchuk, J.L. and Nilsson, J., pp.4-1 - 4-12, NORD 1989:92, Nordic Council of Ministers, Copenhagen.

DTI (Department of Trade and Industry) (*1999*) Digest of United Kingdom Energy Statistics. HMSO.

Durka, W., Schulze, E., Gebauer, G. and Voerkelius, S. (*1994*). Effects of forest decline on uptake and leaching of deposited nitrate determined from ^{15}N and ^{18}O measurements. Nature 373, 765-767.

Durrant DWH, Waddell DA, Benham SE & Houston TJ (*1992*) Air quality and tree growth: results of the open-top chamber experiments 1991. Research Information Note 221. Forestry Commission, Edinburgh.

Duyzer, J.H., Weststrate, J.H., Diederen, H.S.M.A., Vermetten, A., Hofschreuder, P., Wyers, P., Bosveld, F.C. and Erisman, J.W. (*1994*). The deposition of acidifying compounds and ozone to the Speulderbos derived from gradient measurements in 1988 and 1989. TNO report R94/095, Delft.

Duyzer, J.H., J.H. Weststrate, J.W. Erisman, A. Bleeker, H. van Jaarsveld (*1998*). Karakterisering van regionale concentratievelden van ammoniak 2efase: Overzicht (Characterization of regional ammonia concentration fields, 2nd phase: overview), in DutchTNO MEP rapport R98/004

Duyzer, J.H., Nijenhuis, A. Bleeker (*1999*). Een analyse van metingen van de concentratie van ammoniak in de verschillende regio Concept rapport TNO-MEP Apeldoorn Oktober 1999

Edmunds, W.M. and Kinniburgh, D.G., (*1986*). The susceptibility of UK groundwaters to acid deposition. J. Geolog. Soc. of London, 143, 707-720.

EEA (*1998*). Europe's Environment, The Second Assessment. Office for Official Publications of the European Communities, Elsevier Science Ltd.

EEA (*1999*). Environmental in the European Union at the turn of the century. European Environmental Agency, Copenhagen, Denmark.

EEA (*2000*a). Environmental Signals 2000. EEA, Copenhagen, ISBN 92-9167-205-X.

EEA (*2000*b). Environment in the European Union at the turn of the century. EEA, Copenhagen.

Eliassen, A. and Saltbones, J. (*1983*). Modelling of long-range transport of sulphur over Europe: a two-year model run and some model experiments. Atmospheric Environment 17, 1457-1473.

Emberson LD, Ashmore MR, Cambridge H, Tuovinen J-P and Simpson D (*2000*). Modelling stomatal flux across Europe. Environmental Pollution, 109, 403-414.

EMEP (*1998*) Transboundary acidifying air pollution in Europe. Estimated dispersion of acidifying and eutrophying compounds and comparison with observations. MSC-W Status report 1998. Report 1/98. Norwegian Meteorological Institute, Oslo, Norway.

EMEP (*1999*). EMEP Emission Data, Status report 1999, Ed. S Mylona. Meteorological Synthesizing Centre, Norwegian Meteorological Institute.

Emmett, B.A., Stevens, P.A. and Reynolds, B. (*1995*). Factors influencing nitrogen saturation in Sitka spruce stands in Wales, UK. Water Air and Soil Pollution 85, 1629-1634.

Emmett, B.A., Cosby, B.J., Ferrier, R.C., Jenkins, A., Tietema, A. and Wright, R.F. (*1997*). Modelling the ecosystem effects of nitrogen deposition: Simulation of nitrogen saturation in a Sitka spruce forest, Aber, Wales, UK. Biogeochemistry 38, 129-148.

Emmett, B.A., Reynolds, B., Silgram, M., Sparks, T.H. and Woods, C. (*1998*a). The consequences of chronic nitrogen additions on N cycling and soilwater chemistry in a Sitka spruce stand, North Wales. Forest Ecology and Management 101: 165-175.

Emmett, B.A., Boxman, D., Bredemeier, M., Gundersen, P., Kjønaas, O.J., Moldan, F., Schleppi, P., Tietema, A. and Wright, R.F. (*1998*b). Predicting the effects of atmospheric nitrogen deposition in conifer stands: Evidence from the NITREX ecosystem-scale experiments. Ecosystems 1, 352-360.

Emmett BA, Williams D, Pugh B, Brittain SA & Woods C (*1999*). Grazing/nitrogen deposition interactions in upland acid moorland. Contract Report to DETR. 7 pp.

EPAQS, (*1994*). Department of the Environment, Expert panel on air quality standards: Ozone. HMSO, London.

Erisman, J.W. and Wyers, G.P. (*1993*) Continuous measurements of surface exchange of SO_2 and NH_3; implications for their possible interaction in the deposition process. Atmospheric Environment, 27A:1937-1949.

Erisman, J.W. and Draaijers, G.P.J. (*1995*). Atmospheric deposition in relation to acidification and eutrophication. Studies in Environmental Research 63, Elsevier, the Netherlands.

References

Erisman, J.W., Mennen, M.G., Fowler , D., Spindler, G, Duyzer, J.H., Ruigrok, W., Wyers, G.P. (*1996*a) Towards development of a deposition monitoring network for air pollution of Europe. Report no. 722108015. National institute of Public Health and the Environment, Bilthoven, The Netherlands.

Erisman, J.W., G.P.J. Draaijers, M.G. Mennen, J.E.M. Hogenkamp, E. van Putten, W. Uiterwijk, E. Kemkers, H. Wiese, J. H Duyzer, R. Otjes, G. P. Wyers. (*1996*b) Towards development of a deposition monitoring network for air pollution of Europe; Deposition monitoring over the Speulder forest, Report no. 722108014, National Institute of Public Health and the Environment, Bilthoven, The Netherlands.

Erisman J. W., Mennen M.G., Fowler D., Flechard C.R., Spindler G., Grüner A., Duyzer J.H., Ruigrok W., Wyers G.P. (*1997*a) Deposition monitoring in Europe. Environmental Monitoring and Assessment, in press.

Erisman, J.W., G.P.J. Draaijers, M.G. Mennen, J.E.M. Hogenkamp, E. van Putten, W. Uiterwijk, E. Kemkers, H. Wiese, J. H Duyzer, R. Otjes, G. P. Wyers. (*1997*b) Long-term continuous measurements of SO2 dry deposition over the Speulder forest. Water Air and Soil Pollut., in press.

Erisman J.W. and Monteny G.J. (*1998*) Consequences of new scientific findings for future abatement of ammonia emissions. Environ. Pollut. (Nitrogen Special Issue) 102, S1, 275-282.

Erisman J. W., Bleeker, A., and van Jaarsveld, J.A. (*1998*a). Evaluation of the effectiveness of the ammonia policy using measurements and model results. Environ. Pollut. 102, 269-274.

Erisman, J.W., Mennen, M., Fowler, D., Flechard, C.R., Spindler, G., Gruner, G., Duyzer, J.H., Ruigrok, W. and Wyers G.P. (*1998*b). Deposition monitoring in Europe. Environ. Monit. Assess. 53, 279-295.

Erisman, J.W., Draaijers, G.P.J., Steingröver, E., van Dijk, H., Boxman, A.W., de Vries, W., (*1998*c). Assessment of the exposure and loads of acidifying and eutrophying pollutants and ozone, as well as their harmful influence on the vitality of the trees and the Speulder forest ecosystem as a whole. Wat., Air and Soil Pollut., 105, 539-571.

Erisman, J.W., Mosquera, J. and Hensen, A. (*2001*) Two options to explain the ammonia gap in The Netherlands. Environ. Sci. & Pol., 4, 97-105.

EUROTRAC-2 (*1998*) Project description and handbook. EUROTRAC International Scientific Secretatiat, GSF-Forschungszentrum Für Umwelt und Gesundheit GmbH, München, Germany.

Evans P A & Ashmore M R (*1992*). The effects of ambient air on a semi-natural grassland community. Agric. Ecosyst. Environ., 38, 91-97.

Evans HF, McNamara DG, Braasch H, Chadoeuf J, Magnusson C (*1996*). Pest risk analysis (PRA) for the territories of the European Union (as PRA area) on Bursaphelenchus xylophilus and its vectors in the genus Monochamus. EPPO Bulletin 26:199-249.

Evans, C.D., Jenkins, A., Helliwell, R.C. and Ferrier, R.C., (*1998*). Predicting regional recovery from acidification; the MAGIC model applied to Scotland, England and Wales. Hydrol. Earth Syst. Sci., 2, 543-554.

Evans, C.D. and Jenkins, A. (*2000*) Surface water acidification in the South Pennines. II. Temporal trends. Environmental Pollution, 109, 21-34. Elsevier Science Ltd.

Evans, C.D. and Monteith, D.T. (*2000*) Natural and anthropogenically-driven changes in the chemistry of six UK mountain lakes, 1988 to 2000. Water, Air and Soil Pollution.

Evans, C.D., Jenkins, A. and Wright, R.F. (*2000*) Surface water acidification in the South Pennines. I. Current status and spatial variability. Environmental Pollution, 109, 11-20. Elsevier Science Ltd.

Evans, C.D. and Monteith, D.T. (*2001*) Chemical trends at lakes and streams in the UK Acid Waters Monitoring Network, 1988-2000: evidence for recent recovery at a national scale. Hydrol. Earth Syst. Sci., 5(3), 351-366.

Falkengren-Grerup, U. (*1986*). Soil acidification and vegetation changes in deciduous forest in southern Sweden. Oecologia, 70, 339-347.

Falkengren-Grerup, U. (*1987*). Long-term changes in pH of forest soils in southern Sweden. Environmental Pollution 43, 79-90.

Falkengren-Grerup (*1993*) Effects on beech forest species of experimentally enhanced nitrogen deposition. Flora 188, 85-91.

Farmer, A. M. (*1995*). Soil chemistry change in a lowland English deciduous woodland 1974-1991. Water, Air and Soil Pollution 85, 677-682.

Firbank LG, Smart SM, van de Poll HM, Bunce RGH, Hill MO, Howard DC, Watkins JW & Stark GJ (*2000*). Causes of Change in British Vegetation. ECOFACT Volume 3. Institute of Terrestrial Ecology, Grange-over-Sands.

Fisher, B.E.A. (*1978*). The calculation of long-term sulphur deposition in Europe. In: Sulphur in the Atmosphere, edited by R.B.Husar, J.P.Lodge, Jr. & D.J.Moore. Pergamon Press.

Fischer, R., De vries, W., Seidling, W., Kennedy, P., Lorenz, M. (*2000*). Forest Condition in Europe. 2000 Executive Report. Geneva/Brussels; UN/ECE and EC, 34 pp.

Fisk, M.C. and Schmidt, S.K. 1996. Microbial responses to nitrogen additions in alpine tundra soil. Soil Biology and Biochemistry 28, 751-755.

Flechard, C.R., Fowler, D., Sutton, M.A. & Cape, J.N. (*1999*). A dynamic chemical model of bi-directional ammonia exchange between semi-natural vegetation and the atmosphere. Q.J.R. Meteorol. Soc. 125, 1-33.

Flower, R.J. and Battarbee, R.W., (*1983*). Diatom evidence for recent acidification of two Scottish lochs. Nature, 20, 130-133.

Flückiger W & Braun S (*1999*). Nitrogen and its effect on growth, nutrient status and parasite attacks in beech and Norway spruce. Water Air & Soil Pollution 116, 99-110.

Fog, K. (*1988*). The effect of added nitrogen on the rate of decomposition of organic matter. Biological Reviews 63, 433-462.

Foot JP (*1996*). The effects of ozone and low temperatures upon the growth, physiology and frost hardiness of British upland plants. Ph.D Thesis University of Sheffield.

Foster, N.W., Hogan, G.D. and Morrison, I.K. (*1988*). Growth of Jack pine forest on an acid brunisol treated with lime. Communications in Soil Science and Plant Analysis 19, 7-12.

Fowler, D., Cape, J.N., Leith, I.D., Paterson, I.S., Kinnaird, J.W. & Nicholson, I.A. (*1982*). Rainfall acidity in northern Britain. Nature, Lond. 297, 383-386.

Fowler, D. (*1984*). Transfer to terrestrial surfaces. Phil. Trans. R. Soc.B 305, 281-297. [Also published in: The ecological effects of deposited sulphur and nitrogen compounds, eds J.W.L. Beament and others, 23-39. London: Royal Society.]

Fowler, D., Cape, J.N., Leith, I.D., Choularton, T.W., Gay, M.J. & Jones, A. (*1988*). The influence of altitude on rainfall composition at Great Dun Fell. Atmos. Environ. 22, 1355-1362.

Fowler, D., Cape, J.N., Deans, J.D., Leith, I.D., Murray, M.B., Smith, R.I., Sheppard, L.J., Unsworth, M.H., (*1989*). Effects of acid mist on the frost hardiness of red spruce seedlings. New Phytologist 113, 321-335.

Fowler, D., Morse, A.P., Gallagher, M.W. & Choularton, T.W. (*1990*). Measurements of cloud water deposition on vegetation using a lysimeter and a flux gradient technique. Tellus 42(b), 285-293

Fowler, D., Leith, I.D., Binnie, J., Crossley, A., Inglis, D.W.F., Choularton, T.W., Gay, M., Longhurst, J.W.S & Conland, D.E. (*1995*a). Orographic enhancement of wet deposition in the United Kingdom: continuous monitoring. Water Air and Soil Pollution, 85, 2107-2112.

Fowler, D., Flechard, C., Storeton-West, R.L., Sutton, M.A., Hargreaves, K.J. & Smith, R.I. (*1995*b). Long-term measurements of SO$_2$ deposition over vegetation and soil and comparison with models. In: Acid rain research: do we have enough answers? edited by G.J. Heij & J.W. Erisman, 9-19. Amsterdam: Elsevier.

Fowler, D., Flechard, C.R., Milford, C., Hargreaves, K.J., Storeton-West, R.L., Nemitz, E., Sutton, M.A. (*1996*) Towards development of a deposition monitoring network for air pollution in Europe; Measurements of pollutant concentration and deposition fluxes to moorland at Auchencorth Moss in Southern Scotland, 1995. Institute of Terrestrial Ecology, Edinburgh, Scotland.

Fowler, D., Smith, R.I., Crossley, A., Leith, I.D., Mourne, R.W., Brandford, D.D. & Moghaddam, M. (*1998*a). Quantifying fine scale variability in deposition of pollutants in complex terrain using ^{210}Pb inventories in soil. BIOGEOMON Special issue of Water, Air and Soil Pollution, 105, 459-470

Fowler, D., Flechard, C., Skiba, U, Coyle, M. and Cape, J.N. (*1998*b). The atmospheric budget of oxidized nitrogen and its role in ozone formation and deposition. New Phytol. 139, 11-23.

Fowler D., Pitcairn C.E.R., Sutton M.A., Flechard C., Loubet B., Coyle M. and Munro R.C. (*1998*c) The mass budget of atmospheric ammonia within 1 km of livestock buildings Environ. Pollut. (Nitrogen Conference Special Issue). 102, S1, 343-348.

Fowler (*1999*). Fertilizing the atmosphere with fixed nitrogen, the roles of fossil fuel combustion and agriculture. In: Macaulay Land Use Research Institute, Annual Report, 1998. Craigiebuckler, Aberdeen, pp 72-75.

Fowler, D., Sutton, M.A., Flechard, C., Cape, J.N., Storeton-West, R., Coyle, M. & Smith, R.I. (*2001*). The control of SO$_2$ dry deposition onto natural surfaces by NH$_3$ and its effects on regional deposition. Water, Soil and Air Pollutions.

Franzaring J, Dueck Th A & Tonneijck AEG (*1999*). Can plant traits be used to explain differences in ozone sensitivity between native European plant species? In: Critical Levels for Ozone – Level II (J Fuhrer & B Achermann, eds.), pp. 83-87. Swiss Agency for Environment, Forests and Landscape, Berne.

Fricke, W. and S. Beilke, (*1992*) Indications for changing deposition patterns in Central Europe. Environmental Pollution 75, pp. 121-127.

Frogner, T. (*1990*). The effect of acid deposition on cation fluxes in artificially acidified catchments in western Norway. Geochimica Comochimica Acta 54, 769-780.

Frossard, E., Brossard, M., Hedley, M.J. and Metherell, A. (*1995*). Reactions controlling the cycling of P in soils. In: Phosphorus in the Global Environment (Ed. H. Tiessen), 106-137, SCOPE 54, Chichester, Wiley.

Fuhrer J (*1996*). The critical levels for effects of ozone on crops, and the transfer to mapping. In: Critical Levels for Ozone in Europe: Testing and Finalising the Concept. L Karenkampi & L Skarby, eds., pp. 27-43. University of Kuopio, Kuopio.

Fuhrer J, Skarby L & Ashmore MR (*1997*). Critical levels for ozone effects on vegetation in Europe. Environmental Pollution, 97, 91-106.

Fuhrer J & Ashmore MR (*2000*). Use and abuse of the AOT40 concept. Atmospheric Environment, 34, 1157-1159.

Fuller, R.M., Groom, G.B. & Jones, A.R. 1994. The Land Cover Map of Great Britain: an automated classification of Landsat Thematic Mapper data. Photogrammetric Engineering and Remote Sensing 60, 553-562.

Fumagalli, I., Gimeno, B.S., Velissariou, D., De Temmerman, L. & Mills, G (*2001*). Evidence of ozone-induced adverse effects on crops in the Mediterranean region. Atmospheric Environment.

Galloway J.N. (*1998*). The global nitrogen cycle: changes and consequences. pp 15 - 24 in: Proceedings of the First International Nitrogen Conference. van der Hoek K, Erisman J.W., Smeudlers S., Wisniewski J.R. and Wisniewski J (Eds). Elsevier Science, Oxford, UK.

Gagnon ZE, Karnosky DF (*1992*). Physiological response of three species of Sphagnum to ozone exposure. Journal of Bryology 17: 81-91.

Gardner MW & Dorling SR (*2000*): Meteorologically adjusted trends in UK daily maximum surface ozone concentrations. ATMOS ENVIRON 34: (2) 171-176 2000

Garland J.A. and Derwent R.G. (*1979*). Destruction at the ground and the diurnal cycle of concentration of ozone and other gases. Quart. J.R. Met. Soc., 105, 169-183.

Garwood, T., Chambers, B., Mitchell, R. & Webb, J. (*1999*). Annex 1. Nutrient budget: Tillage land in England and Wales from 1967-1997. In: the Impact of Framing Practices on Sustainable Land Use. Contract report to MAFF. Contract code OC9403.

Geisler, R., Stuanes, A.O., Lundström, U.S., Kjønaas, O.J. and Moldan, F. (*1998*). Changes in the soil solution chemistry after exclusion of acid deposition. In: Experimental Reversal of Acid Rain Effects: The Gårdsjön Roof Project, eds. H Hultberg and R. A. Skeffington, Chichester, Wiley.

Gillespie J & Barnes JD (pers. comm.) Department of Agricultural and Environmental Science, University of Newcastle, Newcastle NE1 7RU.

Glatzel, G., Kilian, W., Sterba, H & Stoohr, D. (*1985*). Waldbodenversauerung in Österreich: Ursachen – Auswirkungen. Allgemeine Forstzeitung 96, 35-37.

Goodwin J.W.L, Eggleston, H.S, Stedman, J.R. (*1997*). The National Atmospheric Emissions Inventory 1995, Detailed spatial emission estimates and method, AEA Technology, AEAT-1835/RAMP/20090001/issue1,

References

Goodwin, J.W.L, Salway, A.G, Murrells, T.P., Dore, C.J., Passant, N.R. and Eggleston, H.S. (*2000*). UK Emissions of Air Pollutants 1970 - 1998, AEA Technology, AEAT/R/EN/0270, ISBN 0-7058-1794-6

Gordon C (*1998*). The effects of environmental change on competition between heather and bracken. PhD Thesis, University of Aberdeen.

Gordon C, Woodin SJ, Alexander IJ & Mullins CE (*1999*). Effects of increased temperature, drought and nitrogen supply on two upland perennials of contrasting functional type: Calluna vulgaris and Pteridium aquilinum. New Phytologist 142, 243-258.

Gordon C., Emmett, B.A., Jones, M.L.M., Barden, T., Wildig, J., Williams, D.L., Woods, C., Bell, S.A., Pugh, B., Norris, D.A., Blackstone, D.R., Sparks, T., Ashenden, T.W., Rushton, S.P. and Sanderson, R.A. (*2001*a). Grazing/nitrogen Deposition Interactions in Upland Acid Moorland. Report to Welsh Office (047/96), Countryside Council for Wales (FC/03/89) and the National Power/Powergen/Eastern Generation Joint Environment Programme (GT00084), CEH Bangor.

Gordon, C., Wynn, J.M. & Woodin, S.J. (*2001*b). Impacts of increased nitrogen supply on high Arctic heath: The importance of bryophytes and phosphorus availability. New Phytologist 149, in press.

Gorham E., (*1957*). The chemical composition of some natural waters in the Cairngorm-Strathspey district of Scotland. Limnol. Oceanog., 2, 143-154.

Gorham E. (*1994*) Neutralising acid rain. Nature 367, 321.

Goudling KWT, Bailey NJ, Bradbury NJ, Hargreaves P, Howe MT, Murphy DV, Poulton PR & Willison TW (*1998*). Nitrogen deposition and its contribution to nitrogen cycling and associated soil processes. New Phytologist, 139, 49-58.

Graedel T.E. and Crutzen P.J. (*1993*). Atmospheric Change, An Earth System Perspective. WH Freeman and Company, New York.

Graveland, J., Van der Waal, R., Van Balen, J. H., Van Noordwijk, A. J. (*1994*). Poor reproduction in forest passerines from decline of snail abundance on acidified soils. Nature, 368, 446-448

Green PRS, Ashmore MR, Power SA & Bobbink R (*1997*). Whole ecosystem nitrogen manipulation: a review study. English Nature, Peterborough.

Green, R. E. (*1998*). Long-term decline decline in the thickness of eggshells of thrushes, Turdus spp. In Britain. Proceedings of the Royal Society of London, 265, 679-684

Green, P.R.S, Ashmore, M.R., Power, S.A. and Bobbink, R. (*1999*). Whole ecosystem nitrogen manipulation: review study. Report to English Nature, Peterborough, English Nature.

Grenzius, R. von. (*1984*). Starke Versauerung der Waldböden Berlins. Forstw. Cbl. 103, 131-139.

Groenenberg, B-J., de Vries, W. and Kros, H. (*1998*). Simulation of the long-term carbon and nitrogen dynamics of Dutch forest soils under Scots pine. Hydrology and Earth System Sciences 2, 439-449.

Grubb, P. J., Green, H. E. & Merrifield, R. C. J. (*1969*). the ecology of chalk heath: its relevance to the calcicole-calcifuge and soil acidification problems. J, Ecol. 57, 175-212.

Grünhage L, Jager HJ, Haenel HD, Hanewald K, & Krupa S (*1997*). PLATIN (Plant Atmosphere Interaction) II Co-occurrence of high ambient ozone concentrations and factors limited plant absorbed dose. Environmental Pollution, 98, 51-60.

Guest, J. (*1989*). Further recolonisation of Cheshire by epiphytic lichens. British Lichen Society Bulletin, 64: 29-31.

Gundersen, P. (*1995*). Nitrogen deposition and leaching in European forests – preliminary results from data compilation. Water Air and Soil Pollution 85, 1179-1184.

Gundersen, P., Boxman, A.W., Lamersdorf, N., Moldan, F. and Andersen, B.R. (*1998*a). Experimental manipulation of forest ecosystems: lessons from large roof experiments. Forest Ecology and Management 101, 339-352.

Gundersen, P., Callesen, I., and de Vries, W. (*1998*b). Nitrate leaching in forest ecosystems is related to forest floor C/N ratios. Environ Pollution 102: 403-407.

Gundersen, P., Emmett, B.A., Kjønaas, O.J., Koopmans, C.J. and Tietema, A., (*1998*c). Impact of nitrogen deposition on nitrogen cycling in forests: a synthesis of NITREX data. Forest Ecol. Manage., 101, 37-55.

Haddad, N. M., Haarstad, J. & Tilman, D. (*2000*). The effects of long-term nitrogen loading on grassland insect communities. Oecologia, 124, 73-84.

Haines-Young R.H., Barr C.J., Black H.I.J.,. Briggs D.J, Bunce R.G.H., Clarke R.T., Cooper A., Dawson F.H., Firbank L.G., Fuller R.M., Furse M.T., Gillespie M.K., Hill R., Hornung M., Howard D.C., McCann T., Morecroft M.D., Petit S., Sier A.R.J., Smart S.M., Smith G.M., Stott A.P., Stuart R.C. and Watkins J.W. (*2000*) Accounting for nature: Assessing habitats in the UK countryside. DETR, London. ISBN 1 85112 460 8

Hall, J., Bull, K., Bradley, I., Curtis, C., Freer-Smith, P., Hornung, M., Howard, D., Langan, S., Loveland, P., Reynolds, B., Ullyett, J. & Warr, T. 1998. Status of UK Critical Loads and Exceedances (January *1998*). Part 1: Critical Loads and Critical Loads Maps. Report to the Department of Environment, Transport and the Regions. DETR/NERC Contract EPG1/3/116. Available in online and downloadable versions from: http://critloads.ceh.ac.uk

Hall, J., Ashmore, M., Curtis, C., Doherty, C., Langan, S. & Skeffington, R. (*2001*a). UN/ECE Expert Workshop: Chemical Criteria and Critical Limits. In: M. Posch, P.A.M. de Smet, J.-P. Hettelingh & R.J. Downing (eds.), Modelling and Mapping Critical Thresholds in Europe. Status Report 2001, Coordination Centre for Effects. National Institute for Public Health and the Environment, Bilthoven, Netherlands. pp 67 - 71.

Hall, J., Reynolds, B., Aherne, J. & Hornung, M. (*2001*b). The importance of selecting appropriate criteria for calculating acidity critical loads for terrestrial ecosystems using the simple mass balance equation. Water, Air and Soil Pollution: Focus 1, 29-41.

Hall, J., Ullyett, J., Hornung, M., Kennedy, F., Reynolds, B., Curtis, C., Langan, S. & Fowler, D.(*2001*c). Status of UK Critical Loads and Exceedances. Part 1: Critical Loads and Critical Loads Maps. Update to January 1998 report: February 2001. Report to Department for Environment, Food and Rural Affairs. DETR/NERC Contract EPG1/3/185. . Available in online and downloadable versions from: http://critloads.ceh.ac.uk

Hall, J., Broughton, R., Bull, K., Curtis, C., Fowler, D., Heywood, E., Hornung, M., Metcalfe, S., Reynolds, B., Ullyett, J. & Whyatt, D. (*2001*d). Status of UK Critical Loads and Exceedances. Part 2: Exceedances. Report to the Department of Environment, Transport and the Regions. DETR/NERC Contract EPG1/3/116. In preparation. On completion this report will be available in online and downloadable versions from: http://critloads.ceh.ac.uk

Hallbäcken L & Zhang L (*1998*) Effects of experimental acidification, nitrogen addition and liming on ground vegetation in a mature stand of Norway spruce (Picea abies (L.) Karst.) in SE Sweden. Forest Ecology and Management 108, 201-213.

Hallbacken, L. & Tamm, C. O. (*1986*). Changes in soil acidity from 1927 to 1982-1984 in a forest area of southwest Sweden. Scandinavian Journal of Forest Research 1, 219-232.

Harriman, R. and Morrison, B.R.S., (*1982*). The ecology of streams draining forested and non-forested catchments in an area of central Scotland subject to acid precipitation. Hydrobiologia, 88, 251-263.

Harriman, R., Morrison, B.R.S., Birks, H.J.B., Christie, A.E.G., Collen, P., Watt, A.W. (*1995*a) Long-term chemical and biological trends in Scottish streams and lochs. Water, Air and Soil Pollution., 85, 701-706.

Harriman, R., Allott, T.E.H., Battarbee, R.W., Curtis, C., Jenkins, A. & Hall, J.R. (*1995*b). Critical loads of nitrogen and their exceedance in UK freshwaters. In: M.Hornung, M.A.Sutton & R.B.Wilson (Eds.) Mapping and modelling of critical loads for nitrogen – a workshop report. Institute of Terrestrial Ecology. pp39-49.

Harriman, R., Watt, A.W., Christie, A.E.G., Collen, P., Taylor, D.W.M. and Watson, J., (*2001*). Interpretation of recovery trends in acidic deposition and surface waters in Scotland during the past three decades. Hydrol. Earth Syst. Sci., in press.

Hartley SE (*1997*). The effects of grazing and nutrient inputs on grass-heather competition. Botanical Journal of Scotland 49 317-326.

Hartley SE & Amos L (*1999*). Competitive interactions between Nardus stricta L. and Calluna vulgaris (L.) Hull: The effects of fertilizer and defoliation on above- and below-ground performance. Journal of Ecology 87, 330-340.

Hawksworth D & Rose (*1970*). Quantitative scale for estimating sulphur dioxide air pollution in England and Wales using epiphytic lichens. Nature, 227, 145-148.

Hawksworth, D.L., and McManus, P.M., (*1989*). Lichen recolonization in London under conditions of rapidly falling sulphur dioxide levels, and the concept of zone skipping. Botanical Journal of the Linnean Society 109, 99-109.

Hawksworth, D.L., and McManus, P.M., (*1992*). Changes in the lichen flora on trees in Epping Forest through periods of increasing and then ameliorating sulphur dioxide air pollution. In Epping Forest through the eye of the naturalist. Essex Naturalist, 11: 92-101

Hayman, G.D., Vincent, K., Hasler, S., Baker, S., Donovan, B., Smith, M., Sansom, L. & Page, H. (*2000*). Acid Deposition Monitoring in the UK: 1986-1998. AEA Technology Report AEAT/EEQC-0143. AEA Technology Abingdon, Oxfordshire.

Hedin L. O., Granat L., Likens G. E., Buishand T. A., Galloway J. N., Butler T. J. and Rodhe H. (*1994*) Steep declines in atmospheric base cations in regions of Europe and North America. Nature 367, 351–354.

Heij, G.J. and Erisman, J.W. (*1997*). Acidification research in the Netherlands; report of third and last phase. Studies in Environmental Sciences 69, Elsevier, Amsterdam, the Netherlands.

Helliwell, R.C., Ferrier, R.C. and Jenkins, A. (*1998*a). A two-layer application of the MAGIC model to predict the effects of land use scenarios and reductions in deposition on acid sensitive soils in the UK. Hydrology and Earth System Sciences 2, 497-507.

Helliwell, R.C., Ferrier, R.C., Evans, C.D. and Jenkins, A., (*1998*b). A comparison of methods for estimating soil characteristics in regional acidification models; an application of the MAGIC model to Scotland. Hydrol. Earth Syst. Sci., 2, 509-520.

Helliwell, R.C., Wright, R.F., Ferrier, R.C., Jenkins, A. and Evans, C.D. (*2000*) Acidification of lochs in the Cairngorm Mountains, NE Scotland. International Symposium on High Mountain Lakes and Streas. Indicators of a Changing World. September, Austria. (in press)

Hendershot, W.H., Warfvinge, P., Courchesne, F. and Sverdrup, H. (*1991*). The mobile anion concept – Time for a reappraisal? Journal of Environmental Quality 20, 505-509.

Henriksen, A., Kämäri, J., Posch, M. & Wilander, A. (*1992*). Critical loads of acidity: Nordic surface waters. Ambio 21(5), 356-363.

Henriksen, A., Hindar, A., Hessen, D. & Kaste, Ø. (*1997*). Contribution of nitrogen to acidity in the Bjerkreim River in Southwestern Norway. Ambio 26(5), 304-311.

Henriksen, A. (*1998*). Application of the first-order acidity balance (FAB) model to Norwegian surface waters. Report SNO 3809-98, Norwegian Institute for Water Research (NIVA), Oslo, Norway, 33pp.

Henriksen, A. and Posch, M., (*2001*). Steady-state models for calculating critical loads of acidity for surface waters. Water, Air and Soil Pollut., Focus, 1, 375-398.

Hesthagen, T., Sevaldrud, I.H. and Berger, H.M., (*1999*). Assessment of damage to fish population in Norwegian lakes due to acidification. Ambio, 28, 112-117.

Hettelingh, J.-P., Posch, M., de Smet, P.A.M. & Downing, R.J. (*1995*). The use of critical loads in emission reduction agreements in Europe. Water, Air and Soil Pollution 85, 2381-2388.

Heyes, C., Schopp, W., Amann, M., Bertok, I., Cofala, J., Gyarfas, F., Klimont, Z., Makowski, M. and Shibayev, S. (*1997*). A model for optimizing strategies for controlling ground-level ozone in Europe. IIASA Interim Report IR-97-002/January.

Hicks, W.K., Leith I.D., Woodin, S.J., & Fowler, D. (*2000*). Can the foliar nitrogen concentration of upland vegetation be used for predicting atmospheric nitrogen deposition? Evidence from field studies. Environmental Pollution, 107, 367-376.

Hill MO, Mountford JO, Roy DB & Bunce RGH (*1999*). Ellenberg's Indicator values for British Plants. DETR London.

Hill, T.J., Skeffington, R.A. and Whitehead, P.G. (*2000*). The Tillingbourne acidification study: recovery of low critical load areas in Southern England. Report No. ETSU N/01/00052/REP. Report commissioned by the Department of Trade and Industry under the Energy and Environment Programme.

Hjellbrekke A. (*2000*). Ozone measurements 1998. NILU, EMEP/CCC-Report 5/2000

Hodgson JM (1974). Soil Survey Field Handbook. Soil Survey Technical Monograph no. 5. Soil Survey, Harpenden.

Hodson, M.E., Langan, S.J., Kennedy, F.M. and Bain, D.C. (*1998*). Variation in soil surface area in a chronosequence of soils from Glen Feshie, Scotland and its implications for mineral weathering rate calculations. Geoderma 85, 1-18.

Hodson, M.E. and Langan, S.J. (*1999*). The influence of soil age on calculated mineral weathering rates. Applied Geochemistry 14, 387-394.

References

Högberg, P. and Jensén, P. (*1994*). Aluminium and uptake of base cations by tree roots: a critique of the model proposed by Sverdrup *et al*. Water Air and Soil Pollution 75, 121-125.

Holland MR, Forster D & King K (*1999*). Ozone Position Paper, Section 5.2, cost-benefit analysis. European Commission, Brussels.

Hornung, M. (*1985*). Acidification by trees and forests. Soil Use and Management 1, 24-28.

Hornung, M., Bull, K.R., Cresser, M., Hall, J., Langan, S., Loveland, P. & Smith, C. (*1995*a). An empirical map of critical loads of acidity for soils in Great Britain. Environmental Pollution 90, 301-310.

Hornung, M., Bull, K.R., Cresser, M., Ullyett, J., Hall, J.R., Langan, S., Loveland, P.J, Wilson, M.J. (*1995*b) The sensitivity of surface waters of Great Britain to acidification predicted from catchment characteristics. Environmental Pollution, 87, 207-214.

Hornung, M., Dyke, H., Hall, J.R. & Metcalfe, S.E. (*1997*). The critical load approach to air pollution control. In: R.E.Hester & R.M.Harrison (Eds.) Air Quality Management, Issues in Environmental Science and Technology, Number 8, The Royal Society of Chemistry, Cambridge, UK.

Horváth L. and Sutton M.A. (*1998*) Long term record of ammonia and ammonium concentrations at K-puszta, Hungary. Atmospheric Environment 32 (Ammonia Special Issue), 339-344.

Hough, A.M. & Derwent, R.G. (*1987*). The impact of motor vehicle control technologies onnfuture photochemical ozone formation in the United Kingdom. Environ. Pollut., 44, 109-118.

Hov, Ø., Allegrini, I., Beilke, S., Cox, R.A., Eliassen, A., Elshout, A.J., Gravenhorst, G., Penkett, S.A. and Stern, R. (*1987*). Evaluation of atmospheric processes leading to acid deposition in Europe. Report 10, EUR 11441, CEC, Brussels.

Howells, G. and Dalziel, T.R.K. (*1992*). Selection of a site for restoration. In: Restoring Acid Waters: Loch Fleet 1984-1992, Howells, G. and Dalziel, T.R.K. (Eds), Elsevier, London.

Hughes, S., Reynolds, B. and Roberts, J.D. (*1990*). The influence of land management on concentrations of dissolved organic carbon and its effect on the mobilization of aluminium and iron in podzol soils in Mid-Wales. Soil Use and Management 6, 137-144.

Hultberg H and Skeffington R .A. (Eds). (*1998*). Experimental Reversal of Acid Rain Effects: The Gårdsjön Roof Project, Wiley, Chichester.

Hurrell, J.W. (*1995*). Decadal trends in the North Atlantic Oscillation, regional temperatures and precipitation. Science, 269, 676-679.

Hyvärinen M & Crittenden, PD, (*1998*). Relationships between atmospheric nitrogen inputs and the vertical nitrogen and phosphorus concentrations gradients in the lichen Cladonia portentosa. New Phytologist 140, 519-540.

ICP (*2000*) Forest Condition in Europe, 2000 Executive Report. UN ECE Convention on Long-range Transboundary Air Pollution International Co-operative Programme on Assessment and Monitoring of Air Pollution Effects on Forests. Federal Research Centre for Forestry and Forest Products (BFH), Hamburg, Germany.

ICP Waters (*2000*). The 12-year report: Acidification of Surface Water in Europe and North America; Trends, biological recovery and heavy metals. NIVA, Norwegian Institute for Water Research, Oslo, Norway.

Inglis, D.W.F., Choularton, T.W., Wicks, A.J., Fowler, D., Leith, I.D., Werkman, B. & Binnie, J. (*1995*). Orographic enhancement of wet deposition in the United Kingdom: case studies and modelling. Water Air and Soil Pollution, 85, 2119-2124.

IPCC (*1994*). Radiative forcing of climate change. WMO/UNEP

IPCC (*1995*) Second Assessment Report: Climate Change. The Science of Climate Change Contribution of Working Group I to the Second Assessment of the Intergovernmental Panel on Climate Change JT Houghton, LG Meira Filho, BA Callender, N Harris, A Kattenberg and K Maskell (Eds) Cambridge University Press, UK. pp 572

IPCC (*2000*). Special report on emission scenarios. Special Report of Working Group III.

Ivens, W.P.M.F., (*1990*). Atmospheric deposition onto forests: an analysis of the deposition variability by means of throughfall measurements. PhD Thesis, Utrecht University, The Netherlands.

Jarrauld N (*2000*). The Effects of Ambient Air Pollution on Leaf Pathogens of Rose and Sycamore. PhD Thesis, University of London.

Jeffries, D.S. (Ed.), (*1997*). Canadian Acid Rain Assessment. Vol. 3, Aquatic Effects. National Water Research Institute, Burlington, Ontario.

Jenkin, M.E., Saunders, S.M. and Pilling, M.J. (*1997*). The tropospheric degradation of volatile organic compounds: a protocol for mechanism development. Atmospheric Environment 31, 81-104.

Jenkins, A., Ferrier, R.C. and Kirby, C. (*1995*). Ecosystem Manipulation Experiments: Scientific Approaches, Experimental Design and Relevant Results. Ecosystems Research Report No. 20, Brussels, European Commission.

Jenkins, A., Helliwell, R.C., Swingewood, P.J., Sefton, c., Renshaw, M. and Ferrier, R.C. (*1998*). Will reduced sulphur emissions under the Second Sulphur Protocol lead to recovery of acid sensitive sites in the UK? Environmental Pollution, B99, 309-318.

Jenkins, A. (*1999*). End of acid reign? Nature, 401, 537 – 538.

Johnson, D., Leake, J., Lee, J. and Campbell, C. (*1996*). Changes in the activity and size of the soil microbial biomass in response to simulated pollutant nitrogen deposition. In: Nitrogen Deposition and Acidification of Natural and Semi-Natural Ecosystems. The Macaulay Land Use Research Institute.

Johnson, D.W. (*1992*). Nitrogen retention in forest soils. Journal of Environmental Quality 2, 1-12.

Johnson, D.W. and Lindberg, S.E. (Eds.) (*1992*). Atmospheric Deposition and Forest Nutrient Cycling. Ecological Studies 91, New York, Springer-Verlag.

Johnston, A. E., Goulding, K. W. T. & Poulton, P.R. (*1986*). Soil acidification during more than 100 years under permanent grassland and woodland at Rothamsted. Soil Use and Management 2, 3-9.

Jonasson S (*1992*). Growth responses to fertilization and species removal in tundra related to community structure and clonality. Oikos 63, 420-429.

Jonasson S, Michelsen A, Schmidt IK & Neilson EV (*1999*). Response in microbes and plants to changed temperature, nutrient and light regimes in the Arctic. Ecology 80, 1828-1843.

Jones, V.J. Stevenson, A.C. and Battarbee, R.W., (*1986*). Lake acidification and the land-use hypothesis: a mid-post-glacial analogue. Nature, 322, 157-158.

Jones, V.J., Kreiser, A.M., Appleby, P.G., Brodin, Y.-W., Dayton, J., Natkanski, J.A., Richardson, N.G., Rippey, B., Sandoy, S. and Battarbee, R.W., (*1990*). The recent palaeolimnology of two sites with contrasting acid deposition histories. Philosophical Transactions of the Royal Society of London, Series B, 327, 397-402.

Jones M.L.M., Bambrick M. & Ashenden T.W. (*1999*). Critical loads of nitrogen for acidic and calcareous grasslands in relation to management by grazing. Contract Report to DETR. (EPG 1/3/52). CEH Bangor.

Jones MLM & Ashenden TW (*2000*). Critical loads of nitrogen for acidic and calcareous grasslands in relation to management by grazing. Contract Report to DETR (EPG 1/3/52). CEH Bangor.

Jonson, J.E. and Berge, E. (*1995*). Some preliminary results on transport and deposition of nitrogen components by use of the multi-layer Eulerian model. EMEP/MSC-W Note 4/95.

Jonson, JE, Sundet, JK, Tarrason, L. (*2001*). Model calculations of present and future levels of ozone and ozone precursors with a global and a regional model. Atmospheric Environment, 35, pp 525-537.

Jönsson, C., Schöpp, W., Warfvinge, P. and Sverdrup, H. (*1994*). Modelling long term impact on soil acidification for three sites in Europe. Technical Report, Department of Chemical Engineering II, Lund University, Lund, Sweden.

Jordan, C. and Enlander, I.J., (*1990*). The variation in the acidity of ground and surface waters in Northern Ireland. Int. Revue ges. Hydrobiol., 75, 379-401.

Kellner O & Mårshagen M (*1991*). Effects of irrigation and fertilization on the ground vegetation in a 130-year-old stand of Scots pine. Canadian Journal of Forest Research 21, 733-738.

Kennedy and Freer-Smith, (*2000*). Annual progress report May 2000 of Forestry Commission contract 'cause effect relationships for pollutant inputs to UK woodland ecosystems.' Forestry Commission Research Agency.

Kentarchos,AS; Roelofs,GJ; Lelieveld,J (*1999*). Model study of a stratospheric intrusion event at lower midlatitudes associated with the development of a cutoff low. Journal of Geophysical Research-Atmospheres 104(D1), 1717-1727.

Kerslake JE, Woodin SJ & Hartley SE (*1998*). Effects of carbon dioxide and nitrogen enrichment on a plant-insect interaction: the quality of Calluna vulgaris as a host for Operophtera brumata. New Phytologist 140, 43-53.

Killham, K. & Wainwright, M. (*1984*). Chemical and microbiological changes in soil following exposure to heavy atmospheric pollution. Environ. Pollut. Ser. A, 33, 121-31.

Klap J, Voshaar JO, De Vries W & Erisman JW (*1997*). Relationships between crown condition and stress factors. In: (Eds.) C Muller-Edzards, W dDe Vries, JW Erisman 'Ten years of monitoring forest condition in Europe – studies on temporal development, spatial distribution and impacts of natural and anthropogenic stress factors'. Convention on Long-Range Transboundary Air pollution International Co-operative Programme on Assessment and Monitoring of Air Pollution Effects on Forests and European Union Scheme on the Protection of Forests against Atmospheric Pollution. EC-UN/ECE Brussels, Geneva.

Kooijman AM, Dopheide JCR, Sevink J, Takken I & Verstraten JM (*1998*). Nutrient limitations and their implications on the effects of atmospheric deposition in coastal dunes; lime-poor and lime-rich sites in the Netherlands. Journal of Ecology 86, 511-526

Kreutzer, K., Reiter, H., Scheirl, A. and Gottlein, A. (*1989*). Effects of acid irrigation and liming in Norway spruce stand (Picea abies (L) Karst). Water Air and Soil Pollution 48, 111-125.

Kriebitzsch, W.U. (*1978*). Stickstoffnachlieferung in suare Waldboden Nordwestdeutschlands. Scr. Geobot. 14, 1-66.

Kristensen, H.L. and McCarty, G.W. (*1999*). Mineralization and immobilization of nitrogen in heath soil under intact Calluna, after heather beetle infestation and nitrogen fertilisation. Applied Soil Ecology 13, 187-198.

Krupa SV, Grünhage L, Jager H-J, Nosal M, Manning WJ, Legge AH, Hanewald K (*1995*). Ambient ozone (O_3) and adverse crop response: a unified view of cause and effect. Environ. Pollut., 87, 119-126.

Kruse-Plass, M., ApSimon H.M. and Barker, B. (*1993*). A modelling study of the effect of ammonia on in-cloud oxidation and deposition of sulphur. Atmospheric Environment, 27A, 223-234.

Kuylenstierna, J. C. I. & Chadwick, M. J. (*1991*). Increases in soil acidity in North West Wales between 1957 and 1990. Ambio 20, 118-119.

Langan, S.J. (*1989*). Sea-salt induced streamwater acidification. Hydrological Processes 3, 25-41.

Laurila T and Hakola H (*1999*). Ozone trends and source analysis of VOCs at the Finnish background stations. EUROTRAC-2 Symposium98 Proceedings. EUROTRAC International Scientific Secretariat. WIT Press.

Laws, J.B., Gilbert, J.H. & Pugh , E. (*1861*). On the sources of nitrogen for vegetation. Phil. Trans. R. Soc. Lond. 151, 431-577.

Lee J.A. & Webber, D. E. (*1982*). Effects of sulphuric acid rain on major cation and sulphate concentrations of water percolationg through two model hardwood forests. J. Environ. Qual., 11, 57-64.

Lee D.S, Cape J.N., Cupit M., Derwent R.G., Falls N.A.R., Holland M.R., Lewis P.M. and Mower K.G. (Dec. *1995*). The Effects of Ozone on Materials: First six-monthly progress report to the Department of the Environment. Contract EPG 1/3/50. AEA Technology plc.

Lee D.S., Espenhahn S. E. and Baker S. (*1998*). Evidence for long-term changes in base cations in the atmospheric aerosol. Journal of Geophysical Research 103, 21955–21966.

Lee J.A. & Caporn SJM (*1998*). Ecological effects of atmospheric reactive nitrogen deposition on semi-natural terrestrial ecosystems. New Phytologist 139, 127-134.

Lee D.S. and Pacyna J. M. (*1999*). A European industrial emissions inventory for calcium. Atmospheric Environment 33, 1687–1697.

Lee D. S., Kingdon R. D., Pacyna J. M., Bouwman A. F. and Tegen I. (*1999*). Modelling the atmospheric transport and deposition of calcium in the UK and Northern Europe. Atmospheric Environment 33, 2241–2256.

Lee J.A. & Caporn SJM (*1999*). Natural vegetation responses to atmospheric nitrogen deposition. Contract Report to DETR (EPG 1/3/52). 13 pp.

Lee D.S., Kingdon, R.D., Jenkin, M.E. and Garland, J.A. (*2000a*) Modelling the atmospheric oxidised and reduced nitrogen budgets for the UK with a Lagrangian multi-layer long-range transport model. Environmental Modeling and Assessment 5, 83-104.

References

Lee, D.S., Kingdon, R.D., Jenkin, M.E. and Webster, A. (*2000*b) Modelling the contribution of different sources of sulphur to atmospheric deposition in the United Kingdom. Environmental Modeling and Assessment 5, 105-118

Lee D.S., Kingdon, R.D., Garland, J.A. and Jones, B.M. (*2000*c) Parameterisation of the orographic enhancement of precipitation and deposition in a long-term, long-range transport model. Annales Geophysicae 18, 1447-1466.

Lee J. A., Caporn, S., Pilkington, M., Johnson, D, & Phoenix, G. (*2000*d). Natural vegetation responses to added nitrogen deposition, Report to the Department of the Environment, Transport and the Regions.

Lee J.A., Caporn SJM, Pilkington M, Johnson D & Phoenix G (*2000*e). Critical levels and loads of nitrogen for vegetation growing on contrasting native soils. Contract Report to DETR (EPG 1/3/11). 34 pp.

Lee D.S., Lewis P., Cape J. N., Leith I. D. and Espenhahn S. E. (*2001*). The effects of ozone on materials—experimental evaluation of the susceptibility of polymeric materials to ozone. In 'The Effects of Air Pollutants on the Built Environment' Edited by P. Brimblecombe (in press).

Leith I.D and Cape J.N. (March *1998*). Effects of Ozone on Materials: Interim Report to AEA Technology plc, for the Department of the Environment (ITE Project Code T07058M7). Institute of Terrestrial Ecology, Edinburgh.

Lelieveld J and Dentener F.J (*2000*): What controls tropospheric ozone?. J of Geophys. Res. 105 (D3) pp 3531-3551.

Lien, L., Raddum, G.G. & Fjellheim, A. (*1992*). Critical loads of acidity to freshwater – fish and invertebrates. Fagrapport No. 23, NIVA, Oslo, Norway, 36pp.

Lines R (*1984*) Species and seed origin trials in the industrial Pennines. Quarterly Journal of Forestry 78:9-23.

Lines R (*1985*) Pinus nigra in the Pennine hills of northern England. Quarterly Journal of Forestry 79:227-233.

Liu, S., Munson, R., Johnson, D.W., Gherini, S., Summers, K., Hudson, R., Wilkinson, K. and Pitkela, L.F. (*1992*). The nutrient cycling model (NuCM): Overview and application. In: Atmospheric Deposition and Forest Nutrient Cycling, Eds D.W. Johnson and S.E. Lindberg, 583-609, Ecological Studies 91, New York, Springer-Verlag.

Lökke, H., Bak, J., Falkengren-Grerup, U, Finlay, R.D., Ilvesniemi, H., Nygaard, P.H. and Starr, M.(*1996*). Critical loads of acidic deposition for forest soils: Is the current approach adequate? Ambio 25, 510-516.

Lundstrom, U. S., Nyborg, L., Danielsson, R., van Hees, P. A. W. & Andersson, M. (*1998*). Forest soil acidification: Monitoring on the regional scale, Varmland, Sweden. Ambio 27, 551-556.

Lyons TM, Barnes JD & Davison AW (*1997*). Relationships between ozone resistance and climate in European populations of Plantago major. New Phytologist, 136, 503-510.

Martin, A. & Barber, F.R. (*1984*). Acid gases and acid in rain monitored over 5 years in rural East-Central England. Atmos. Environ. 19, 1091-1102.

Mason, B.J. (Ed.), (*1990*). The surface waters acidification programme. Cambridge University Press, 522 pp.

Massman WJ, Mussleman RC & Lefohn AS (*2000*). A conceptual ozone dose-response model to develop a standard to protect vegetation. Atmos. Environ., 34, 745-759.

Mather R, Freer-Smith P, Savill P (*1995*). Analysis of the changes in forest condition in Britain 1989 to 1992. Bulletin 116, Forestry Commission. HMSO, Edinburgh.

McGrath & Zhao (*1995*). A risk assessment of sulphur deficiency in cereals using soil and atmospheric data. Soil Use & Management, 11, 100-114.

McKee IF, Bullimore JF & Long SP (*1997*). Will elevated CO_2 protect the yield of wheat from O_3 damage? Plant Cell and Environment, 20, 77-84.

McLaughlin SB & Downing DJ (*1995*). Interactive effects of ambient ozone and climate measured on growth of mature forest trees. Nature, 374, 252-254.

McLaughlin SB & Percy K (*1999*). Forest health in North America: some perspectives on actual and potential roles of climate and air pollution. Water Air and Soil Pollution, 116, 151-197.

McNulty, S.G., Aber, J.D. and Newman, S.D. (*1996*). Nitrogen saturation in a high elevation New England spruce-fir stand. Forest Ecology and Management 84, 109-121.

Medina S., le Tertre M.A., Dusseux E. and Carnard J.P (*1997*). Analyse des liens à court terme entre pollution atmosphérique et sante. Resultats 1991-1995. ERPURS, ORS, Ille-de-France, Paris.

Meesenburg, H., Meiwes, K.J. and Rademacher, P. (*1995*). Long-term trends in atmospheric deposition and seepage output in northwest German forest ecosystems. Water, Air and Soil Pollut., 85, 611-616.

Metcalfe, S.E., Whyatt, J.D. and Derwent, R.G. (*1995*). A comparison of model and observed network estimates of sulphur deposition across Great Britain for 1990 and its likely source attribution. Quarterly Journal of the Royal Meteorological Society 121, 1387-1411.

Metcalfe, S.E., Derwent, R.G., Whyatt, J.D. and Dyke, H. (*1998*a). Nitrogen deposition and strategies for the control of acidification and eutrophication across Great Britain. Water, Air and Soil Pollution 107, 121-145.

Metcalfe, S.E., Whyatt, J.D. and Derwent, R.G. (*1998*b). Multi-pollutant modelling and the critical loads approach for nitrogen. Atmospheric Environment 32, 401-408.

Metcalfe, S.E., Whyatt, J.D., Broughton, R., Derwent, R.G., Finnegan, D., Hall, J., Mineter, M., O'Donoghue, M. and Sutton, M. (*2001*) Developing the Hull Acid Rain Model: its validation and implications for policy makers. Environmental Science and Policy 4, 25-37.

Metcalfe, S.E., Whyatt, J.D., Derwent, R.G. and O'Donoghue, M. (*in prep.*) The regional distribution of ozone across the British Isles and its reponse to control strategies. (submitted to Atmospheric Environment, 2001)

Miles, J. (1978). The influence of trees on soil properties. Annual Report of the Institute of Terrestrial Ecology 1977, pp. 7-11. Huntingdon; Institute of Terrestial Ecology.

Miller, J. D., Duff, E., Hirst, D., Anderson, H. A., Bell, J. S. & Gauld, J. H. (*1999*). sampling strategies for ECN soil protocols. MLURI report.

Mills G, Hayes F, Buse A & Reynolds B (*2000*a). Air Pollution and Vegetation. UN/ECE ICP Vegetation. Annual Report 1999/2000. Centre for Hydrology and Ecology, Bangor.

Mills, G., Ball, G.R., Hayes, F., Fuhrer, J.,Skärby, L., Gimeno, B., De Temmerman, L. & Heagle, A., Members of the ICP Vegetation Programme (*2000*b). Development of a multi-factor model for predicting the effects of ambient ozone on the biomass of white clover. Environmental Pollution 109: 533 – 542.

Misselbrook TH, Van der Weerden TJ, Pain BF, Jarvis SC, Chambers BJ, Smith KA, Phillips VR, Demmers TGM., (*2000*). Ammonia emission factors for UK agriculture. Atmospheric Environment 34, 871-880.

Moldan, F., (*1999*). Reversal of Soil and Water Acidification in Sweden, Simulating the Recovery Process. Doctoral Thesis,Swedish University of Agricultural Sciences, Umeå.

Moldan, F., Hultberg, H. and Andersson, I., (*1995*). Covered catchment experiment at Gårdsjön: changes in runoff chemistry after four years of experimentally reduced acid deposition. Water, Air Soil Pollut., 85, 1599-1604.

Monteith, D.T. and Evans, C.D. (Eds.) (*2000*). UK Acid Waters monitoring Network Ten Year Report. Analysis and Interpretation of results, April 1988-March 1998. ENSIS Publishing, London.

Monteith, D.T., Evans, C.D. and Reynolds, R., (*2000*). Are temporal variations in the nitrate content of UK upland freshwaters linked to the North Atlantic Oscillation? Hydrol. Proc., 14, 1745-1749.

Monteith, D.T., Evans, C.D. and Patrick, S.T. (*2001*). Monitoring acid waters int he UK: analysis of results 1988-1998. Water, Air and Soil Pollution (in press).

Moore, T. M. (*1987*). The effect of simulated acid rain on the nutrient status of subarctic woodland soils in eastern Canada. Can. J. For. Res., 17, 370-378.

Morecroft, M.D., Sellers, E.K. and Lee, J.A. (*1994*). An experimental investigation inot the effects of atmospheric nitrogen deposition on two semi-natural grasslands. Journal of Ecology 82, 475-483.

Murley, L. (*1995*). Clean air around the world: national approaches to air pollution control. IUAPP/EPA

Nadelhoffer, K., Downs, M., Fry, B., Magill, A. and Aber, J.D. (*1999*). Controls on N retention and exports in a forested watershed. Environmental Monitoring And Assessment 55, 187-210.

Neal, C. and Reynolds, B., (*1999*). The impact of conifer harvesting and replanting on upland water quality. R&D Technical Report to the Environment Agency, Report P211, Environment Agency, Rivers House, Waterside Drive, Aztec West, Almondsbury, Bristol, BS32 4UD, UK, 137 pp.

Neal, C., Reynolds, B. and Robson, A.J. (*1999*). Acid neutralisation capacity measurements within natural waters: towards a standardised approach. The Science of the Total Environment 243/244, 233-241.

Nilsson, J. & Grennfelt, P. (Eds.). (*1988*). Critical loads for sulphur and nitrogen. Report 1988:15. UNECE/Nordic Council of Ministers, Copenhagen, Denmark.

Odén S. (*1968*). The acidification of air and precipitation and its consequences on the natural environment. Ecology Committee, Bull. 1, National Science Research Council of Sweden. (In Swedish).

OECD (*1977*). The OECD programme on long range transport of air pollutants. Measurements and findings. Organisation for Economic Cooperation and Development, Paris, France.

Olendrzynski, K., Bartnicki, J. and Jonson, J. (1998) Performance of the Eulerian Acid Deposition Model. In: Transboundary Acidifying Pollution in Europe, EMEP/MSC-W Report 1/98, 104-136.

Olendrzynski, K., Bartnicki, J. and Jonson, J. (*1998*) Performance of the Eulerian Acid Deposition Model. In: Transboundary Acidfying Pollution in Europe, EMEP/MSC-W Report 1/98, 104-136.

Olendrzynski, K. (*2000*). EMEP Eulerian Acid Deposition Model. Model performance for 1998. EMEP/MSC-W Note 3/2000.

Ollerenshaw J, Lyons T & Barnes JD (*1999*). Impacts of ozone on the growth and field of field-grown winter oil-seed rape. Environmental Pollution, 104, 53-59.

Ollinger SV, Aber JS & Reich PB (*1997*). Simulating ozone effects on forest productivity: interactions among leaf-, canopy-, and stand-level processes. Ecological Applications, 7, 1237-1251.

Ormerod, S.J., Donald, A.P., and Brown, S.J., (*1989*). The influence of plantation forestry on the pH and aluminium concentration of upland Welsh streams: a re-examination. Environ. Pollut., 62, 47-62.

Ormerod, S. J. and Rundle, S. D. (*1998*). Effects of experimental acidification and liming on terrestrial invertebrates: implications for calcium availability to vertebrates. Environmental Pollution, 103, 183-191

Ovington, J.D. (*1953*). Studies of the development of woodland conditions under different trees. I. Soil pH. J. Ecol. 41, 13-34.

Pain B.F., van der Weerden T.J., Chambers B.J., Phillips V.R. and Jarvis S.C. (*1998*) A new inventory for ammonia emissions from U.K. agriculture. (Ammonia Special Issue) Atmospheric Environment 32 (3), 309-313.

Patrick, S.T., Timberlid, J.A. and Stevenseon, A.C., (*1990*). The significance of land-use and land-management change in the acidification of lakes in Scotland and Norway: an assessment using documentary sources and pollen analysis. Philosophical Transactions of the Royal Society of London, Series B, 327, 363-367.

Pennington, W., (*1981*). Records of a lake's life in time: the sediments. Hydrobiologia, 79, 197-219.

Pennington, W., (*1984*). Long-term natural acidification of upland sites in Cumbria: evidence from post-glacial lake sediments. Freshwater Biological Association Annual Report, 52, 28-46.

Persson, T., Lundkvist, H., Wiren, A., Hyvonen, R. and Wessen, B. (*1989*). Effects of acidification and liming on carbon and nitrogen mineralisation and soil organisms in mor humus. Water Air and Soil Pollution 45, 77-96.

Pitcairn CER, Fowler D & Grace J (*1991*) Changes in species composition of semi-natural vegetation associatied with the increase in atmospheric inputs of nitrogen. Report to Nature Conservancy Council.

Pitcairn, C.E.R., Fowler, D. & Grace, J. (*1995*) Deposition of fixed atmospheric nitrogen and foliar nitrogen content of bryophytes and Calluna vulgaris. Environmental Pollution, 88, 193-205.

Pitcairn CER, Leith ID, Sheppard LJ, Sutton MA, Fowler D, Munro RC, Tang S & Wilson D (*1998*) The relationship between nitrogen deposition, species composition and foliar nitrogen concentrations in woodland flora in the vicinity of livestock farms. Environmental Pollution 102(S1), 41-48.

Pitcairn CER, Leith ID, Fowler D, Hargreaves KJ, Moghaddam M, Kennedy V & Granat L, (*2001*). Foliar nitrogen as an indicator of nitrogen deposition and critical loads exceedance on a European scale. Water, Air & Soil Pollution, in press.

Pleijel H, Danielsson H, Karlssson GP, Gelang J, Karlsson PE & Sellden G (*2000*). An ozone flux-response relationship for wheat. Environmental Pollution, 109, 453-462.

Plöchl M, Lyons T, Ollernshaw J and Barnes JD (*2000*). Simulating ozone detoxification in the leaf apoplast through the direct reaction with ascorbate. Planta, 210, 454-462..

Ponce de Leon A., Anderson H.R., Bland J.M., Strachan D.P. and Bower J (*1996*). Effects of air pollution on daily hospital admissions for respiratory disease in London between 1987-88 and 1991-92. J Epidemiol. Comm. Health 50 (supplement 1), pp S63-S70.

References

PORG (*1987*). Ozone in the United Kingdom. Interim report, Harwell Laboratory, UK.

PORG (UK Photochemical Oxidants Review Group) (*1993*): Ozone in the United Kingdom 1993, Third Report of the Photochemical Oxidants Review Group. 1st ed. The Department of the Environment.

PORG (UK Photochemical Oxidants Review Group) (*1998*): Ozone in the United Kingdom, Fourth Report of the Photochemical Oxidants Review Group. 1st ed. The Department of the Environment Transport and the Regions/ CEH Edinburgh.

Port GR & Thompson JR (*1980*) Outbreaks of insect herbivores on plants along motorways in the United Kingdom. Journal of Applied Ecology 17, 649-656.

Posch, M., de Smet, P.A.M., Hettelingh, J.-P. & Downing, R. (Eds.) (*1995*a). Calculation and mapping of critical thresholds in Europe: Status Report 1995. Coordination Centre for Effects, National Institute of Public Health and the Environment (RIVM), Bilthoven, The Netherlands. Available online at: http://www.rivm.nl/cce/

Posch, M., de Vries, W. & Hettelingh, J.-P. (*1995*b). Critical loads of sulphur and nitrogen. In: M.Posch, P.A.M.de Smet, J.-P.Hettelingh & R.J.Downing (Eds.), Calculation and mapping of critical thresholds in Europe: Status Report 1995. Coordination Centre for Effects, National Institute of Public Health and the Environment (RIVM), Bilthoven, The Netherlands. pp31-41. Available online at: http://www.rivm.nl/cce/

Posch, M. & Hettelingh, J.-P. (*1997*). Remarks on critical load calculations. In: M.Posch, P.A.M.de Smet, J.-P.Hettelingh & R.J.Downing (Eds.), Calculation and mapping of critical thresholds in Europe: Status Report 1997. Coordination Centre for Effects, National Institute of Public Health and the Environment (RIVM), Bilthoven, The Netherlands. pp25-28. Available online at: http://www.rivm.nl/cce/

Posch, M., Kämäri, J., Forsius, M., Henriksen, A. & Wilander, A. (*1997*). Exceedance of critical loads for lakes in Finland, Norway and Sweden: reduction requirements for acidifying nitrogen and sulphur deposition. Environmental Management 21(2), 291-304.

Posch, M., de Smet, P.A.M. & Hettelingh, J.-P. (*1999*). Critical loads and their exceedances in Europe: an overview. In: M.Posch, P.A.M.de Smet, J.-P.Hettelingh & R.J.Downing (eds.), Calculation and mapping of critical thresholds in Europe: Status Report 1999. Coordination Centre for Effects, National Institute of Public Health and the Environment (RIVM), Bilthoven, The Netherlands. pp3-11. Available online at: http://www.rivm.nl/cce/

Potter L, Foot JP, Caporn SJM, Lee JA (*1996*). The effects of long-term elevated ozone concentration on the growth and photosynthesis of Sphagnum recurvum and Polytrichum commune. New Phytologist 134: 649-656.

Power, S.A., Ashmore, M.R., Cousins, D.A. and Ainsworth, N. (*1995*). Long term effects of enhanced nitrogen deposition on a lowland dry heath in southern Britain. Water Air and Soil Pollution 85, 1701-1706.

Power SA & Ashmore MR (*1996*). Nutrient relations and root mycorrhizal status of healthy and declining beech (Fagus sylvatica L.) in southern Britain. Water Air Soil Pollution, 86, 317-333.

Power SA, Ashmore MR, Cousins DA & Sheppard LJ (*1998*a) Effects of nitrogen on the stress sensitivity of Calluna vulgaris. New Phytologist 138 663-673.

Power SA, Ashmore MR & Cousins DA (*1998*b). Impacts and fate of experimentally enhanced nitrogen deposition on a British lowland heath. Environmental Pollution 102(S1) 27-34.

Press, M.C., Woodin, S.J. & Lee, J.A. (*1986*). The potential importance of an increased nitrogen supply to the growth of ombrotrophic Sphagnum species. New Phytologist, 103, 45-55.

Prins AH, Berdowski JJM & Latuhihin MJ (*1991*) Effects of NH_4 fertilization on the maintenance of Calluna vulgaris vegetation. Acta Botanica Neerlandica 40, 269-279.

QUARG (*1996*). Airborne Particulate Matter in the United Kingdom. Third report of the Quality of Urban Air Review Group. The University ofBirmingham. Institute of Public and Environmental Health.

Rasmussen, L. and Wright, R.F. (*1998*). Large-scale ecosystem experiments: ecological research and European environmental policy. Forest Ecology and Management 101, 353-363.

Redfern D, Boswell R & Proudfoot J (*2000*) Forest condition 1999. Forestry Commission Information Note 33. Forestry Commission, Edinburgh.

Reiling K & Davison AW (*1992*). Spatial variation in ozone resistance of British populations of Plantago major L. New Phytologist, 122, 699-708.

Renberg, I. and Battarbee, R.W., (*1990*). The SWAP Palaeolimnology Programme; a synthesis. In: The Surface Waters Acidification Programme (B.J. Mason (Ed.)), 281-300. Cambridge University Press, Cambridge.

Reuss, J. O. & Walthall, P. M. (*1989*) Soil reaction and acidic deposition. In, Acidic Precipitation Volume 4: Soils, Aquatic processes and Lake Acidification. Edited by S. A. Norton, S. E. Lindberg & A. L. Page. New York; Springer-Verlag

Reuss, J.O. and Johnson, D.W. (*1986*) Acid deposition and the acidification of soils and waters. Ecological Studies, 59, Springer-Verlag, New York, 119 pp.

Reynolds, B., Ormerod, S.J. and Gee, A.S., (*1994*). Spatial patterns in stream nitrate concentrations in upland Wales in relation to catchment forest cover and forest age. Environ. Pollut., 84, 27-33.

Reynolds, B., Stevens, P.A., Hughes, S., Parkinson, J.A. and Weatherley, N.S., (*1995*). Stream chemistry impacts of conifer harvesting in Welsh catchments. Water, Air Soil Pollut., 79, 147-170.

Reynolds, B. (*1997*). Predicting soil acidification trends at Plynlimon using the SAFE model. Hydrology and Earth System Sciences 1, 717-728.

Reynolds, B., Fowler, D., Smith, R.I. & Hall, J.R. (*1997*). Atmospheric inputs and catchment solute fluxes for major ions in five Welsh upland catchments. J. Hydrol. 194, 305-329.

Reynolds, B. and Stevens, P.A. (*1998*). Assessing soil calcium depletion following growth and harvesting of Sitka spruce plantation forestry in the acid sensitive Welsh uplands. Hydrology and Earth System Sciences 2, 345-352.

RGAR (*1987*). Acid deposition Monitoring in the United Kingdom 1981-1985. A Second Report of the United Kingdom Review Group on Acid Rain, Department of the Environment, London.

RGAR (*1990*). Acid deposition in the United Kingdom 1986-1988. Third Report of the United Kingdom Review Group on Acid Rain, Department of the Environment, London

RGAR (*1997*). Acid deposition in the United Kingdom 1992-1994. Fourth report of the United Kingdom Review Group on Acid Rain, 176 pp. HMSO, London

Riebeling, R. & Shaefer, C. (*1984*). Jahres- und Langzeit-entwicklung der ph-Werte von Waldböden im hessischen Fichtenbestanden. Forst- und Holzwert 39, 177-182.

Rimes, C.A., Farmer,A.M. and Howell, D. (*1994*). A survey of the threat of surface water acidification to the nature conservation interest of fresh water sites on Sites of Special Scientific Interest in Britain. Aquatic Conservation: Marine and Freshwater Ecosystems, 4, 31-44.

RIVM (*1997*). Milieubalans 1997. Samson Tjeenk Willink, Alphen a/d Rijn, the Netherlands.

RIVM (*2000*). Environmental outlook 5. Samson, Tjeenk Willink, Alphen a/d Rijn, Netherlands.

Robinson, CH, Piearce, T.G. and Ineson, P. (*1991*). Burrowing and soil consumption by earthworms in limed and unlimed soils from Picea sitchensis plantations. Pedobiologia 35, 360-367.

Robinson, CH, Ineson, P., Piearce, T.G. and Rowland, A.P. (*1992*). Nitrogen mobilization by earthworms in limed peat soils under Picea sitchensis. Journal of Applied Ecology 29, 226-237.

Robinson CH, Wookey PA, Lee JA, Callaghan TV & Press MC (*1998*). Plant community responses to simulated environmental change at a high arctic polar semi-desert. Ecology 79, 856-866.

Roemer (*2000*). Trends in tropospheric ozone in Europe over the last 10 years. EUROTRAC-2 Symposium2000 Proceedings. In press EUROTRAC International Scientific Secretariat. WIT Press.

Rose, C.I. & Hawksworth, D.L., (*1981*). Lichen recolonization in London's cleaner air. Nature 289, 289-292.

Rosenqvist, I.T., (*1978*). Alternative sources for acidification of river water in Norway. Sci. Total Environ., 10, 39-49.

Roy, R.L. and Campbell, P.G.C., (*1997*). Reduced toxicity of Al to juvenile Atlantic salmon (Salmo salar) in acidic soft water containing natural organic matter: A test of the free-ion model. Environ. Toxicol. Chem., 16, 1962-1969.

Rundle, S.D., Weatherley, N.S. and Ormerod, S.J., (*1995*). The effects of catchment liming on the chemistry and biology of upland Welsh streams: testing model predictions. Freshwater Biol., 34, 165-175.

Salway, AG, Murrells, TP, Milne, R, Ellis, S, (*2001*). UK Greenhouse Gas Inventory, 1990 to 1999, Annual Report for submission under the Framework Convention on Climate Change. AEAT Report , AEAT/R/ENV/0524, ISBN 0-7058-1797-0., NETCEN, Culham.

Saunders (*1966*). The toxicity of sulphur dioxide to Diplocarpon rosae Wolf causing black spot on roses. Annals of Applied Biology, 58, 103-114.

Schindler, D.W., Kasian, S.E.M. and Hesslein, R.H., (*1989*). Biological impoverishment of lakes in the midwestern and northeastern United States from acid rain. Environ. Sci. Technol., 23, 573-580.

Schindler, D.W., Frost, T.M., Mills, K.H., Chang, K.H., Davies, I.J., Findlay, L., Malley, D.F., Shearer, J.A., Turner, M.A., Garrison, P.J., Watras, C.J., Webster, K., Gunn, J.M., Brezonik, P.L. and Swenson, W.A., (*1991*). Comparisons between experimentally- and atmospherically-acidified lakes during stress and recovery. Proceedings of the Royal Society of Edinburgh, 97B, 193-226.

Schoepp, W., Amann, M., Cofalar, J., Heyes, C. and Klimont, Z. (*1999*). Integrated assessment of European air pollution emission control strategies. Environmental Modeling and Software 14, 1-9.

Seaward MRD (*1998*). Time-space analyses of the British lichen flora, with particular reference to air quality surveys. Folia Crytop. Estomica, 32, 85-96.

Sefton, C.E.M. and Jenkins, A. (*1998*). A regional application of the MAGIC model in Wales: Calibration and assessment of future recovery using a Monte Carlo approach. Hydrology and Earth System Sciences, 2, 521-531.

Sheppard L.J. and Crossley A. (*2000*). Responses of a sitka spruce ecosystem after 4 years of simulated wet N deposition: effects of NH4NO3 supplied with and without acidity (H2SO4pH2.5).Phyton, 40, 169-174

Simmonds,PG; Seuring,S; Nickless,G; Derwent,RG (*1997*). Segregation and Interpretation of ozone and carbon monoxide measurements by air mass origin at the TOR station Mace Head, Ireland from 1987 to 1995. J. Atmos. Chem. 28(1-3), 45-59.

Simpson, D. (*1993*). Photochemical model calculations over Europe for two extended summer periods: 1985 and 1989. Model results and comparison with observations. Atmospheric Environment 27A, 921-943.

Simpson D., Krzysztof O., Semb A., Støren E and Unger S. (*1997*): Photochemical oxidant modelling in Europe: multi-annual modelling and source-receptor relationships. EMEP MSC-W Report 3/97, Norwegian Meteorological Institute, PO Box 43-Blindern, N-0313 Oslo 3, Norway.

Simpson D, Altendstedt j & Hjellbrekke AG (*1998*). The Lagrangian oxidant model: status and multi-annual evaluation. In: EMEP MSC-W Report 2/98, Norwegian Meterological Institute.

Simpson, D., Winiwarter, W., Borjesson, G., Cinderby, S., Ferreiro, A., Guenther, A.,Hewitt, C. N. , Janson, R., Khalil, M. A. K., Owen, S., Pierce, T. E., Puxbaum, H., Shearer, M., Skiba, U., Steinbrecher, R., Tarrason, L., and Íquist, M. G., (*1999*). Inventorying emissions from nature in Europe, J. Geophys. Res., 104, No. D7, 8113-8152.

Singles R.J. (*1996*). Fine resolution modelling of ammonia dry deposition over Great Britain. Ph.D. thesis, Department of Meteorology, University of Edinburgh. pp 209

Singles, R., Sutton, M.A. and Weston, K. (*1998*). A multi-layer model to describe the atmospheric transport and deposition of ammonia in Great Britain. Atmospheric Environment (Ammonia Special Issue) 32, 393-399.

Skartveit, A. (*1981*). Relationships between precipitation chemistry, hydrology and run-off acidity. Nordic Hydrology 12, 65-80.

Skeffington, R.A. (*1999*). The use of critical loads in environmental policy making: a critical appraisal. Environmental Science and Technology, June 1st, 245A-252A.

Skiba, U., Cresser, M. S., Derwent, R. G. & Futty, D. W. (*1989*). Nature 337, 68-69.

Skiba, U., Fowler, D. And Smith, K.A. (*1997*). Nitric oxide emissions from agricultural soils in temperate and tropical climates: sources, control and mitigation options. Nutrient Cycling in Agroecosystems 48, 75 - 90.

Skiba U, Sozanska M, Metcalfe S and Fowler D (*2001*). Spatially disaggregated inventories of soil NO and N2O emissions for Great Britain, Water Air and Soil Pollution (in press)

Skinner, R. J., Church, B. M. & Kershaw, C. D. (*1992*). Recent trends in nutrient status in England and Wales. Soil Use and Management 8, 16-20.

Skinner, R. J. & Todd, A. D. (*1998*). Twenty-five years of monitoring pH and nutrient status of soils in England and Wales. Soil Use and Management 14, 162-169.

References

Smith, C.S.S., Cresser, M.S. & Mitchell, R.D.J. (*1993*). Sensitivity to acid deposition of dystrophic peat in Great Britain. Ambio 22, 22

Smith, R I., Fowler, D., Sutton, M.A., Flechard, and Coyle, M. (*2000*). A model for regional estimates of sulphur dioxide, nitrogen dioxide and ammonia dry deposition in the UK. Atmospheric Environment 34, 3757-3777.

SORG, UK Stratospheric Ozone Review Group (Ed.) (*1999*). Stratospheric Ozone 1999. 1st ed. Vol. 1. Department of the Environment, transport and the regions, London. (99EP0458).

Soulsby, C., Turnbull, D., Hirst, D., Langan, S.J., and Owen, R. (*1997*). Reversibility of stream acidification in the Cairngorm region of Scotland. Journal of Hydrology, 195, 291-311.

Sozanska, M. (*1999*). Distribution and Amounts of Nitrous and Nitric Oxide Emissions from British Soils, PhD Thesis, The University of Edinburgh.

Spiecker H, Mielikainen K, Kohl M, Skovsgaard J (Eds.) (*1996*). Growth trends in European forests. European Forests. Springer-Verlag, Berlin.

Spindler, G. and Grüner, A (*1996*). Towards development of a deposition monitoring network for air pollution of Europe; The Melpitz site in Germany - Results of measurements made in 1995, IFT, Leipzig, Germany.

Stark, J.M. and Hart, S.C. (*1997*). High rates of nitrification and nitrate tunrover in undisturbed coniferous stands. Nature 385, 61-64.

Stedman J.R., Vincent K.J., and Campbell G.W. (*1997*a). New high resolution maps of background air pollutant concentrations in the UK in 1994. AEA Technology, National Environmental Technology Centre. Report AEA/RAMP/20008001/003

Stedman J.R., Vincent K.J., Campbell G.W., Goodwin J.W.L. and Downing C.E.H (*1997*b). New high resolution maps of estimated background ambient NO_x and NO_2 concentrations in the UK. Atmos Env, 31, 3591-3602. see also http://www.aeat.co.uk/netcen/airqual/laqm/index.html

Stedman J.R., Anderson H.R., Atkinson R.W. and Maynard R.L. (*1997*c). Emergency hospital admissions for respiratory disorders attributable to summer time ozone episodes in Great Britain. Thorax 52, pp 958-963.

Stedman J.R., Linehan E. and King K. (*1999*). Quantification of the health effects of air pollution in the UK for the review of the National Air Quality Strategy. AEAT Report 4175 Issue 1.

Stelson, A.W. and Seinfeld, J.H. (*1982*) Relative humidity and temperature dependence of the ammonium nitrate dissiciation constant. Atmospheric Environment, 16:983-992.

Stevens, P.A., Norris, D.A., Sparks, T.H. and Hodgson, A.L. (*1994*). The impacts of atmospheric N inputs on throughfall, soil and stream water interactions for different aged forest and moorland catchments in Wales. Water Air and Soil Pollution 73, 297-317.

Stevens, P.A., Ormerod, S.J. and Reynolds, B., (*1997*). Final Report on the Acid Waters Survey for Wales. Vol. 1, Main Text. Institute of Terrestrial Ecology, Bangor.

Stevenson DS, Collins WJ, Johnson CE and Derwent RG (*1998*). Intercomparison and evaluation of atmospheric transport in a Lagrangian model (STOCHEM), and an Eulerian model (UM), using Rn-222 as a short-lived tracer. Quarterly Journal of the Royal Meteorological Society, 124 (551), 2477-2491, Part A.

Stoddard, J. (*1994*). Long-term changes in watershed retention of nitrogen. In: (Ed. Baker, L.A.) Environmental Chemistry of Lakes and Reservoirs. American Chemical Society.

Stoddard, J.L., Jeffries, D.S., Lukewille, A., Clair, T.A., Dillon, P.J., Driscoll, C.T., Forsius, M., Johannessen, M., Kahl, J.S., Kellogg, J.H., Kemp, A., Mannio, J., Monteith, D.T., Murdoch, P.S., Patrick, S., Rebsdorf, A., Skjelkvale, B.L., Stainton, M.P., Traaen, T., van Dam, H., Webster, K.E., Wieting, J., Wilander, A. (*1999*). Regional trends in aquatic recovery from acidification in North America and Europe. Nature, 401, 575- 578.

Stohl, A., Williams, E., Wotawa, G. and Kromp-Kolb, H. (*1996*). A European inventory of soil nitric oxide emissions and the effect of these emissions on the photochemical formation of ozone. Atmos. Environ. 30, 3741 - 3755.

Straw NA (*1995*). Climate change and the impact of the green spruce aphid, Elatobium abietinum (Walker), in the UK. Scottish Forestry 49:134-145.

Stribley GH & Ashmore MR (in press). Quantitative changes in twig growth pattern of young woodland beech (Fagus sylvatica L.) in relation to climate and ozone pollution over ten years. Forest Ecology and Management

Stuanes, A. O., Abrahamsen, G., Strand, L. T. & Vestgarden, L.S. (*2000*). Forest soil recovery nearly 20 years after addition of elevated acid rain deposition. Poster paper presented at Eurosol 2000. British Society of Soil Science.

Stull,RB (*1989*). An introduction to boundary layer meteorology. 1st ed. Vol. 1. Kluwer Academic Publishers, The Netherlands.

Sullivan, T.J., Cosby, B.J., Norton, S.A., Charles, D.F., Wright, R.F. and Gjesing, E. (*1994*). Multi-site testing and evaluation of a geochemical model of acid-base chemistry: confirmation of the MAGIC model using catchment manipulation experiments and historical diatom inferences. In: Ecosystem Manipulation Experiments: Scientific Approaches, Experimental Design and Relevant Results. Eds. A. Jenkins, R.C. Ferrier and C. Kirby, 360-365, Ecosystems Research Report No. 20, Brussels, European Commission

Sutcliffe, D.W., Carrick, T.R., Heron, J., Rigg, E., Talling, J.F., Woof, C. and Lund, J.W.G. (*1982*). Long-term and seasonal changes in the chemical composition of precipitation and surface waters of lakes and tarns in the English Lake District. Freshwater Biology, 12, 451-506.

Sutton, M.A., Pitcairn, C.E.R. & Fowler, D. (*1993*). The exchange of ammonia between the atmosphere and plant communities. Advances in Ecological Research, 24, 301-393.

Sutton M.A., Place C.J., Eager M., Fowler D. and Smith R.I. (*1995*a) Assessment of the magnitude of ammonia emissions in the United Kingdom. Atmospheric Environment 29, 1393-1411.

Sutton M.A., Schjørring J.K. and Wyers G.P. (*1995*b) Plant - atmosphere exchange of ammonia. Philosophical Transactions of the Royal Society, London. Series A. 351, 261-278.

Sutton M.A., Milford C., Dragosits U., Place C.J., Singles R.J., Smith R.I., Pitcairn C.E.R., Fowler D., Hill J., ApSimon H.M., Ross C., Hill R., Jarvis S.C., Pain B.F., Phillips V.C., Harrison R., Moss D., Webb J., Espenhahn S.E., Lee D.S., Hornung M., Ullyett J., Bull K.R., Emmett B.A., Lowe J. and Wyers G.P. (*1998*). Dispersion, deposition and impacts of atmospheric ammonia: quantifying local budgets and spatial variability. Environ. Pollut. (Nitrogen Special Issue). 102, S1, 349-361.

Sutton M.A., Dragosits U., Tang Y.S. and Fowler D. (*2000*a). Ammonia emissions from non-agricultural sources in the UK. Atmos. Environ. 34 (6), 855-869.

Sutton M.A., Nemitz E., Fowler D., Wyers G.P., Otjes R.P., Schjoerring J.K., Husted S., Nielsen K., San José R., Moreno J., Gallagher M.W. Gut A. (*2000*b). Fluxes of ammonia over oilseed rape: Overview of the EXAMINE. Agric. For. Meteorol. (Ammonia Exchange Special Issue) 105 (4), 327-349.

Sutton M.A., Tang Y.S., Miners B. and Fowler D. (*2001*a). A new diffusion denuder system for long-term, regional monitoring of atmospheric ammonia and ammonium. Water Air and Soil Pollut. (in press).

Sutton M.A., Tang Y.S., Dragosits U., Fournier N., Dore T., Smith R.I., Weston K.J. and Fowler D. (*2001*b) A spatial analysis of atmospheric ammonia and ammonium in the UK. The Scientific World (under review).

Sutton M.A., Milford C., Nemitz E., Theobald M.R., Hill P.W., Fowler D., Schjoerring J.K., Mattsson M.E., Nielsen K.H., Husted S., Erisman J.W., Otjes R., Hensen A., Mosquera J., Cellier P., Loubet B., David M., Genermont S., Neftel A., Blatter A., Herrmann B., Jones S.K., Horvath L., Führer E., Mantzanas K., Koukoura Z., Gallagher M., Williams P., Flynn M. and Riedo M. (*2001*c). Biosphere-atmosphere interactions of ammonia with grasslands: experimental strategy and results from a new European initiative. Plant and Soil 228 (1):131-145.

Sutton M.A., Miners B., Tang Y.S., Milford C., Wyers G.P., Duyzer J.H. and Fowler D. (*2001*d). Comparison of low-cost measurement techniques for long-term monitoring of atmospheric ammonia. J. Environ. Monit. 3, 446-453.

Sutton M A, W A H Asman, J A van Jaarsveld, K Acker, V Aneja, J H Duyzer, L Horváth, S Paramonov, M Mitosinkova, Y S Tang, B Achermann, T Gauger, J Bartniki, A Neftel, J W Erisman (*2001*e). Establishing the link between ammonia emission control and measurements of reduced nitrogen concentrations and deposition. Background document. UNECE Ammonia Expert Group Meeting. (18-20 September 2000), BUWAL, Berne, Switzerland.

Sutton, M.A., Tang, Y.S., Dragosits, U., Love, L., Fowler, D., Hasler, S., Sansom, L. & Hayman, G. (*2001*f). Monitoring of nitric acid, particulate nitrate and other species in the UK. Interim report under the UK Acid Deposition Monitoring Network.

Sverdrup, H., de Vries, W. & Henriksen, A. (*1990*). Mapping Critical Loads: A guidance to the criteria, calculations, data collection and mapping of critical loads. Miljorapport (Enviromental Report) 1990:14. Nordic Council of Ministers, Copenhagen. NORD: 1990:98. 124pp.

Sverdrup, H. and Warfvinge, P. (*1993*). The effect of soil acidification on the growth of trees, grass and herbs as expressed by the (Ca+Mg+K)/Al ratio. Reports in Ecology and Environmental Engineering 2. Department of Chemical Engineering II, Lund University, Sweden.

Sverdrup, H. & de Vries, W. (*1994*). Calculating critical loads for acidity with the simple mass balance method. Water, Air and Soil Pollution 72, 143-162.

Sverdrup, H., Warfvinge, P., Blake, L & Goulding, K. (*1995*). Modelling recent and historic soil data from the Rothamsted Experimental Station, UK using SAFE. Agriculture, Ecosystems and Environment 53, 161-177.

Sweden (*1971*). Air pollution across national boundaries. The impact on the environment of sulfur in air and precipitation. Swedish Royal Ministry for Foreign Affairs and the Royal Ministry of Agriculture. Kungl. Boktryckeriet P.A. Norstedt & Söner 720277, Stockholm 1972.

Tarrason, L. and Schaug, J. (Eds.) (*1999*). Transboundary acid deposition in Europe. EMEP Report 1/99.

Tarrason, L. and Schaug, J. (*2000*). Transboundary acidification and eutrophication in Europe. EMEP summary report CCC and MSCW. Oslo (EMEP Report 1/2000).

Teigen, O., Abrahamsen, G. & Haugbotn, O. (*1976*). Eksperimentelle forsuringsforsøk I skog. 2. Lysimeterundersokelser (Acidification experiments in conifer forest. 2. Lysimeter investigations). SNSF Project IR 26/76, Oslo-Ås, 45p.

Ten Harkel MJ & Van der Meulen F (*1995*). Impact of grazing and atmospheric nitrogen deposition on the vegetation of dry coastal dune grasslands. Journal of Vegetation Science 6 445-452.

Thompson DBA & Baddeley JA (*1991*). Some effects of acidic deposition on montane Racomitrium lanuginosum heaths. In: The effects of acid deposition on nature conservation in Great Britain (eds SJ Woodin & AM Farmer). NCC, Peterborough. pp. 17-28.

Thornton F C, Bock B R and Tyler (*1995*). Soil emissions of NO and N2O from injected anhydrous ammonium and urea J Environ Quality 25, 6:1378 - 1384

Thurman, E.M. (*1985*). Organic Geochemistry of Natural Waters. Dordrecht, Nijhoff/Junk.

Thwaites R (*1996*). The effects of tropospheric ozone on calcareous grassland communities. PhD thesis, Imperial College, London.

Tietema, A. and Beier, C. (*1995*). A correlative evaluation of nitrogen cycling in the forest ecosystems of the EC projects NITREX and EXMAN. Forest Ecology and Management 71, 143-152.

Tietema, A. (*1998*). Microbial carbon and nitrogen transformations in litter from coniferous forest ecosystems along an atmospheric nitrogen input gradient. Forest Ecology and Management 101, 29-36.

Tietema, A., Emmett, B.A., Gundersen, P., Kjønaas, O.J. and Koopmans, C. (*1998*). The fate of ^{15}N-labelled nitrogen deposition in coniferous forest ecosystems. Forest Ecology and Management 101, 19-27.

Tilman D & Downing JA (*1994*). Biodiversity and stability in grasslands. Nature 367, 718-720.

Tipping, E. (*1994*). WHAM - A chemical-equilibrium model and computer code for waters, sediments, and soils incorporating a discrete site electrostatic model of ion-binding by humic substances Comput Geosci 20, 973-1023.

Tipping, E., Carrick, T.R., Hurley, M.A., James, J.B., Lawlor, A.J., Lofts, S., Rigg, E., Sutcliffe, D.W. and Woof, C. (*1998*). Reversal of acidification in upland waters of the English Lake District. Environmental Pollution, 103, 143-151.

Tipping, E., Bass, J.A.B., Bettney, R., Blackburn, J., Hurley, M.A., Isgren, F., James, J.B., Lawlor, A.J., Lofts, S., Rigg, E., Simon, B.M., Smith, E.J., Stidson, R., Tapia, G. and Woof, C. (*1999*). Reversal of surface water acidification in the Upper Dayton catchment (English Lake District). Report No. ETSU N/01/00051/REP. Report commissioned by the Department of Trade and Industry under the Energy and Environment Programme.

Tipping, E. and Smith, E.J. (*2000*). Assessment of acidification reversal in surface waters of the Pennines. Report No. ETSU N/01/00058/REP. Report commissioned by the Department of Trade and Industry under the Energy and Environment Programme.

References

Tipping, E., Hurley, M.A., Wills, G. and Haworth, E.Y. (*2000*). Chemical and biological changes in Cumbrian lakes due to decreases in acid deposition. Report No. ETSU N/01/00059/REP. Report commissioned by the Department of Trade and Industry under the Energy and Environment Programme.

Torseth, K, Semb, A, Schaug, J, Hanssen, JE and Aamlid, D (*2000*). Processes affecting deposition of oxidised nitrogen and associated species in the coastal areas of Norway. Atmospheric Environment, V34, pp207 - 217

Torssander, P. & Mörth, C-M. (*1998*). Sulfur dynamics in the roof experiment at Lake Gårdsjön deduced from sulfur and oxygen isotope ratios in sulfate. In: Experimental Reversal of Acid Rain Effects: The Gårdsjön Roof Project, Eds. H Hultberg and R .A. Skeffington, pp.185-206, Wiley, Chichester.

Tuovinen, J.P., Barrett, K. and Styve, H. (*1994*). Transboundary acidifying pollution in Europe: Calculated fields and budgets 1985 - 1993. EMEP/MSC-W, Report 1/94, Norwegian Meteorological Institute, Oslo.

Tyler, S.J. and Ormerod, S.J., (*1991*). The influence of stream acidification and riparian land-use on the breeding biology of Grey Wagtails Motacilla cinerea in Wales. Ibis, 133, 286-292.

UBA (UmweltBundesAmt). (*1996*). UNECE Manual on methodologies and criteria for mapping critical levels/loads and geographical areas where they are exceeded. Federal Environmental Agency (Umweltbundesamt) Berlin. Available online at: http://www.umweltbundesamt.de/mapping/

Uddameri, V., Norton, S.A., Kahl, J.S. and Schofiled, J.P. (*1995*). Randomized Intervention Analysis of the response of the West Bear Brook Watershed, Maine to chemical manipulation. Water Air and Soil Pollution 79, 131-146.

UK AWMN, (*2000*). UK Acid Waters Monitroing Network:10 Year Report. Published for the Department of the Envirionment, transport and the Regions, and the Environment and Heritage Service, Northern Ireland by ENSIS Publishing, London.

UKAWRG, (*1988*). Acidity in UK Freshwater, Second Report. HMSO, London.

Ulrich, B. (*1983*). An ecosystem oriented hypothesis on the effect of air pollution on forest ecosystems. In: Ecological Effects of Acid Deposition, eds. G. Perssonand A. Jernelov, 221-231, Stockholm, Swedish Environmental Protection Board.

Ulrich, B. (*1987*). Stability, Elasticity and the Resilience of Terrestrial Ecosystems with Respect of Matter Balance. Ecological Studies 61, Berlin-Heidelberg, Springer-Verlag.

Ulrich, B (*1989*). Effects of acidic precipitation on forest ecosystems in Europe. In, Acidic Precipitation Volume 2: Biological and Ecological Effects. Edited by D. C. Adriano & A. H. Johnson. New York; Springer-Verlag.

UNECE (*1993*). Workshop on critical levels for buildings, materials, including cultural heritage. DoE, London.

Uren, S. (*1992*). The Effects of Wet and Dry Deposited Ammonia on Calluna vulgaris. PhD Thesis, University of London.

van Aalst, R.M. and Erisman, J.W. (*1991*). Atmospheric Input. In: G.J. Heij and T. Schneider (Editors), Acidification research in the Netherlands: Studies in Environmental Science 46, Elsevier, Amsterdam.

van Dam, D. and van Breemen, N. (*1995*). NICCCE: a model for cycling of nitrogen and carbon isotopes in coniferous forest ecosystems. Ecological Modelling 79, 255-275.

van der Eerden L, De Vries W & Van Dobben H (*1998*). Effects of ammonia deposition on forests in the Netherlands. Atmospheric Environment 32 525-532.

van der Hoek, K.W. (*1994*) Berekeningsmethodiek ammoniakemissies in Nederland voor de jaren 1990, 1991 en 1992. Report No. 773004003, National Institute of Public Health and Environmental Protection, Bilthoven, The Netherlands.

van Dobben HF, ter Braak CJF & Dirske GM (*1999*) Undergrowth as a biomonitor for deposition of nitrogen and acidity in pine forest. Forest Ecology and Management 114, 83-95

van Jaarsveld J.A., Bleeker A. and Hoogervorst N.J.P. (*2000*) Evaluatie ammoniak emissieredukties met behulp van metigen en modelberekeningen. RIVM report 722108025. RIVM, Bilthoven, The Netherlands (in Dutch).

van Leeuwen, E., Hendriks, K., Klap, J., de Vries, W., de Jong, E., Erisman, J.W., (*1999*). Effects of environmental stress on crown condition in Europe: Estimation of stress induced by meteorology and air pollutants. Water, Air and Soil Pollut., in press.

van Vuuren MMJ, Aerts R, Berendse F & De Visser W (*1992*). Nitrogen mineralization in heathland ecosystems dominated by different plant species. Biogeochemistry, 16, 151-166.

Vincent, K., Goodwin, J. & Passant, N. (*2000*). The Impact of Proposed Emission Limits on Sulphur and Nitrogen Deposition in the United Kingdom. Report 3 (DTI JN 5/5/3) prepared for the Department of Trade and Industry on the Project Modelling the Long Range Transport of Reduced and Oxidised Nitrogen Pollutants, Total Acidity and Critical Loads (TRACK) – Phase 2.

Vinton MA & Burke IC (*1995*). Interactions between individual plant species and soil nutrient status in shortgrass steppe. Ecology 76, 1116-1133.

Vogel, B., Corsmeier, U., Vogel, H., Fiedler, F., Kűhlwein, R., Friedrich, A., Obermeier, J., Weppner, N., Kalthoff, D., Bäumer, A., Jay, K. (*2000*). Comparison of measured and calculated motorway emission data. Atmospheric Environment 34: 2437-2450.

Volz A; Kley D (*1988*). Evaluation of the Montsouris series of ozone measurements made in the nineteenth century. Nat 332, 240-241.

Wallenda T & Kottke I (*1998*). Nitrogen deposition and ecotmycorrhizas. New Phytologist 139 169-187.

Wang YH & Jacob DJ (*1998*). Anthropogenic forcing on tropospheric ozone and OH since preindustrial times. J GEOPHYS RES-ATMOS 103: (D23) 31123-31135 DEC 20 1998

Warburton LM & Allen EB (*2000*). Shifts in arbuscular mycorrhizal communities along an anthropogenic nitrogen deposition gradient. Ecological Applications 10 484-496.

Warfvinge, P., Falkengren-Grerup, U. and Sverdrup, H. (*1993*). Modelling long-term base cation supply in acidified forest stands. Environmental Pollution 80, 1-14.

Warren, R. and ApSimon, H. (*2000*). Selection of target loads for acidification in emission abatement policy: the use of gap closure approaches. Water, Air and Soil Pollution 121, 229-258.

Watson A, Miller GR, & Green FHW (*1966*). Winter browning of heather (Calluna vulgaris) and other moorland plants. Transactions of the Botanical Society of Edinburgh 40, 195-203.

Webster, R., Campbell, G.W. &Irwin, J.G. (*1991*). Spatial analysis and mapping the annual mean concentrations of acidity and major ions in precipitation over the United Kingdom in 1986. Environ. Monitor. Assess., 16, 1-17.

Weinstein DA, Samuelson LJ & Arthur MA (*1998*). Comparison of the response of red oak (Quercus rubra) seedlings and mature trees to ozone exposure using simulation modelling. Environmental Pollution, 102, 307-320.

WGE (*2000*). 9th Annual Report 2000. UN ECE Convention on Long-range Transboundary Air Pollution International Co-operative Programme on Integrated Monitoring of Air Pollution Effects on Ecosystems (Sirpa Kleemola and Martin Forsius (eds) Working Group on Effects of the Convention on Long-range Transboundary Air Pollution, HELSINKI 2000

White, C. C. & Cresser, M. S. (*1995*). A critical appraisal of field evidence for a regional survey of acid deposition effects on Scottish moorland podzols. Chemistry and Ecology 11, 117-129.

White, C. C. & Cresser, M. S. (*1998*). Sensitivity of Scottish upland moorland podzols derived from sandstones and quartzites to acidification: the potential importance of the mobile anion effect. Water, Air and Soil Pollution 103, 229-244.

WHO (*2000*). Air Quality Guidelines for Europe. Second Edition. World Health Organisation, Copenhagen.

Wilander, A. & Lundin, L. (*1999*). Recovery of surface waters and forest soils in Sweden. In, Recovery from Acidification in the Natural Environment. Edited by P.

Williams, E.J., Guenther, A. and Fehsenfeld, F.C. (*1992*). An inventory of nitric oxide emissions from soils in the United States. J. Geophys. Res. 97, 7511-7520.

Wilson EJ, Wells TCE & Sparks TH (*1995*). Are calcareous grasslands in the UK under threat from nitrogen deposition? – an experimental determination of a critical load. Journal of Ecology 83, 823-832.

Wilson GR & Bell JNB (*1985*). Studies on the tolerance to sulphur dioxide of grass populations in polluted areas. III. Investigations into the rate of development of tolerance. New Phytologist, 100, 63-77.

Wilson, E.J. and Emmett, B.A. (*1998*). Factors influencing nitrogen saturation in forest ecosystems: Advances in our understanding since the mid 1980s. In: The Impact of Nitrogen Deposition on Natural and Semi-Natural Ecosystems, Ed. S.J. Langan, 123- 152, Dordrecht, Kluwer Academic Publishers.

Woodin SJ & Alexander I (unpublished data). Department of Plant and Soil Science, University of Aberdeen.

Woodin SJ & Choy J (unpublished data). Department of Plant and Soil Science, University of Aberdeen.

Woodin, S.J. & Farmer AJ (*1993*). Effects of acidic deposition on sites and species of conservation importance in Great Britain. Biological Conservation, 10, 23-30.

Wookey, P.A. and Ineson, P. (*1991*). Chemical changes in decomposing forest litter in response to atmospheric sulphur dioxide. Journal of Soil Science 42, 615-628.

Wookey, P.A., Ineson, P. and Mansfield, T.A. (*1991*). Effects of atmospheric sulphur dioxide on microbial activity in decomposing forest litter. Agriculture, Ecosystems and Environment 33, 263-280.

Woolgrove, C.E. & Woodin, S.J. (*1996*). Current and historical relationships between the tissue nitrogen content of a snowbed bryophyte and nitrogenous air pollution. Environmental Pollution, 91, 283-288

Worrell R & Malcolm DC (*1990*). Productivity of Sitka spruce inn northern Britain. 2. Prediction from site factors. Forestry 63:119-128.

Worrell R (*1987*). Productivity of Sitka spruce on upland sites in northern Britain. Forestry Commission Bulletin No 72. HMSO, London.

Wright, R.F. and Henriksen, A., (*1980*). Regional survey of lakes and streams in southwestern Scotland, April 1979. Internal Report IR 72/80, SNSF-Project, Ås, Norway, 63 pp.

Wright, R.F., Lotse, E. and Semb, A. (*1988*a). Reversibility of acidification shown by whole-catchment experiments. Nature 334, 670-675.

Wright, R.F., Norton, S.A., Brakke, D.F. and Frogner, T., (*1988*b). Experimental verification of episodic acidification of freshwaters by sea salts. Nature, 334, 422-424.

Wright, R.F., Lotse, E. and Semb, A. (*1993*). Rain Project - Results After 8 Years of Experimentally Reduced Acid Deposition to a Whole Catchment. Canadian Journal of Fisheries and Aquatic Sciences 50, 258-268.

Wright, R.F., Lotse, E. and Semb, A., (*1994*a). Experimental acidification of alpine catchments at Sogndal, Norway: results after eight years. Water, Air Soil Pollut., 72, 297-315.

Wright, R.F., Cosby, B.J., Ferrier, R.C., Jenkins, A., Bulger, A.J. and Harriman, R. (*1994*b). Changes in the acidification of lochs in Galloway, SW Scotland, 1979-1988: the MAGIC model used to evaluate the role of afforestation, calculate critical loads and predict fish status. Journal of Hydrology, 161, 257-285.

Wright, RF & van Breemen, N (*1995*). The NITREX project: an introduction. Forest Ecology and Management 71: 1-6.

Wright, R.F. and Rasmussen, L. (Eds) (*1998*). The Whole Ecosystem Experiments of the NITREX and EXMAN Projects. Forest Ecology and Management 101, 1-363.

Wright, R.F., Emmett, B.A. and Jenkins, A. (*1998*a). Acid deposition, land-use change and global change: MAGIC 7 model applied to Aber, UK (NITREX project) and Risdalsheia , Norway (RAIN and CLIMEX projects). Hydrology and Earth System Sciences 2, 385-397.

Wright, R.F., Beier, C. and Cosby, B.J. (*1998*b). Effects of nitrogen deposition and climate change on nitrogen runoff at Norwegian boreal forest catchments: the MERLIN model applied to Risdalsheia (RAIN and CLIMEX projects). Hydrology and Earth System Sciences 2, 399-414.

Wyers G.P, Wayers J.J, Möls T.R, Thijsse J.H, Duyzer J.H, Verhagen H.L.M and Erisman J.W. (*1996*). Characterization of the regional concentration fields for ammonia: sampling and monitoring strategy. Report ECN-C-96-038, Netherland Energy Foundation, Petten, the Netherlands.

Xu, Y.-J., Blanck, K., Bredemeier, M. and Lamersdorf, N.P. (*1998*). Hydrochemical input-output budgets for a clean rain and drought experiment at Solling. Forest Ecology and Management 101, 295-306.

Yesmin, L., Gammack, S.M. and Cresser, M.S. (*1996*). Changes in N concentrations of peat and its associated vegetation over 12 months in response to increased deposition of ammonium sulfate or nitric acid. The Science of the Total Environment 177, 281-290.

Zhao F-J, McGrath SP, Crosland AR & Salmon SE (*1995*). Changes in the sulphur status of British wheat grain in the last decade, and its geographical distribution. J Sci Food Agriculture, 68, 507-514.

Appendix A: Glossary (with abbreviations and acronyms)

Unit prefixes:

T	tera	10^{12}	c	centi	10^{-2}	k	kilo	10^{3}	n	nano	10^{-9}
G	giga	10^{9}	m	milli	10^{-3}	h	hecto	10^{2}	p	pico	10^{-12}
M	mega	10^{6}	μ	micro	10^{-6} (u is substituted where the μ character is not available)						

The Encyclopaedia of the Atmospheric Environment at http://www.doc.mmu.ac.uk/aric/eae/index.html is a comprehensive source of background information on atmospheric issues for non-specialists and many of the definitions given below are taken from it.

5EAP: EU – 5th Environmental Action Programme, http://europa.eu.int/comm/environment/actionpr.htm

acid deposition: The removal of acidic or acidifying compounds from the atmosphere by precipitation (rain, cloud droplets, fog, snow or hail), also known as acid rain or acid precipitation.

acidification: The generation of more hydrogen-ions (H^+) than hydroxide-ions (OH^-) so that the pH becomes less than 7.

advection: The movement of an entity by a horizontal flow of air, e.g. pollution carried by wind.

aerosols: Solid or liquid particles dispersed in the air, and include dust, soot, sea salt crystals, spores, bacteria, viruses and many other microscopic particles. (from the Encyclopaedia of the Atmospheric Environment)

AOT40: Accumulated Ozone concentration above a Threshold of 40 ppb, AOT40 = $\sum$ (O_3c > 40) - 40 where O_3c = ozone concentration and the summation is made over a prescribed time period.

ASAM: Abatement Strategies Assessment Model (Imperial College, London)

AT: Austria

a priori: not derived from experience; not submitted to critical investigation, derived from latin.

AQS: National Air Quality Strategy for England, Scotland, Wales and Northern Ireland

BE: Belgium

BG: Bosnia Herzegovina

Brownian diffusion: Brownian movement is the rapid and random motion of particles caused by collision with molecules of the gas or liquid in which they are suspended. Brownian diffusion refers to this random motion bringing the particles into contact with a surface (such as a cloud droplet).

c. or ca: abbreviation of circa meaning about/approximately

cf.: compare (abbreviation of the Latin confer)

CH: Switzerland

cloud condensation nuclei: Small particles (0.1 μm < diameter < 1.0 μm) which act as centres for the accumulation of water molecules, eventually forming cloud droplets and rainfall. Acidic aerosols are often in the correct size range to act as nuclei.

Cl: chlorine

CLRTAP: Convention on Long-range Transboundary Air Pollution (http://www.unece.org/env/lrtap/welcome.html). This Convention was the first internationally legally binding instrument to deal with problems of air pollution on a broad regional basis. It was signed in 1979 and entered into force in 1983. It has greatly contributed to the development of international environmental law and created the essential framework for controlling and reducing the damage to human health and the environment of transboundary air pollution. It is a successful example of what can be achieved through intergovernmental cooperation.

CORINAIR: Acronym for the air emission inventory initially developed in the frame of the European Communities CORINE programme (COoRdination d'INformation Environmentale).

critical level: A critical level is the maximum pollutant concentration a part of the environment can be exposed to without significant harmful effects

critical load: A critical load is the maximum amount of pollutant deposition a part of the environment can tolerate without significant harmful effects.

CZ: Czech Republic

DE: Germany

denitrification: The regeneration of dinitrogen (N_2) or nitrous oxide (N_2O) from nitrate (NO_3^-).

deposition: Can be either wet or dry. In dry deposition a material is removed from the atmosphere by contact with a surface. In wet deposition material is removed from the atmosphere by precipitation.

DETR: The Department of the Environment Transport and the Regions, from June 2001 reformed as two new departments: the Department of the Environment and Rural Affairs (**DEFRA**) and The Department of Transport, Local Government and the Regions (**DTLR**).

DEFRA: The Department of the Environment, Food and Rural Affairs. http://www.defra.gov.uk/.

diffusiophoresis: The process by which particles move in the direction of the mean flow of vapour molecules in the air, e.g. water molecules condensing on a droplet (see **cloud condensation nuclei**) generate a flow towards the droplet, carrying particles with it.

dissolution: Chemical process by which compounds dissolve into a water droplet.

DK: Denmark

dms: dimethyl sulphide, $(CH_3)_2S$, which is produced in the oceans by microbiological processes and emitted into the atmosphere where it forms sulphate aerosol.

DNMI: Norwegian Meteorological Institute (http://www.dnmi.no/)

DOC: Dissolved Organic Compounds

DoE: The Department of the Environment. This was the UK government department responsible for environmental issues prior to 1997. From June 2001 it became part of **DEFRA**.

DTLR: The Department of Transport, Local Government and the Regions, http://www.dtlr.gov.uk/.

dry deposition: see **deposition**

EE: Estonia

EFTA: The European Free Trade Association (EFTA) is an international organisation comprising four states, Iceland, Liechtenstein, Norway and Switzerland, with headquarters in Geneva and offices in Brussels and Luxembourg. http://secretariat.efta.int/efta/

ELMO: Edinburgh-Lancaster Model for Ozone (see Chapter 4)

EMEP: European co-operative programme for Monitoring and Evaluation of the long-range transmission of air Pollutants in Europe (http://www.emep.int/). Provides Governments and subsidiary bodies under the **LRTAP** Convention with qualified scientific information to support the development and further evaluation of the international protocols on emission reductions negotiated within the Convention.

emissions: Normally refers to the release of **primary pollutants** directly to the atmosphere by processes such as combustion although many natural processes also release compounds into the atmosphere, such as **dms** from micro-organisms in oceans.

ESI: Electricity supply industry

eq H^+: units of equivalents for hydrogen ion (H^+) concentration (see Appendix C)

EU: European Union, http://europa.eu.int/index_en.htm

EU15: The first 15 members of the European Union.

EUREKA: A Europe-wide Network for Industrial R&D: strengthening European competitiveness by promoting 'market-driven' collaborative RTD; involving industry and research institutes across Europe; using advanced technologies; resulting in cost-effective products, processes and services. (http://www3.eureka.be/Home/)

EUROTRAC-2: EUREKA Project on the Transport and Chemical Transformation of Environmentally Relevant Trace Constituents in the Troposphere over Europe; Second Phase (http://www.gsf.de/eurotrac/)

ES: Spain

ESI: Electricity supply infrastructure

et al.: and others (abbreviation of the Latin *et alii, et alia* etc.)

Eulerian model: This type of model treats the atmosphere as a grid of points or boxes. The parameters being modelled are calculated for each point then these values passed between the points for the next calculation step.

eutrophication: An increase in the amount of nutrients in waters or soils.

FGD: Flue-Gas Desulphurisation is the process used to remove sulphur from industrial waste gases before they are emitted to the atmosphere. It is most commonly used on coal-fired power stations.

FI: Finland

FR: France

FRAME: Fine Resolution Ammonia Exchange model (see Chapter 4)

gap-closure: This refers to reducing the difference between pollutant deposition or concentration and the critical load or level (where they are exceeded).

GB: Great Britain (in the context of European Union ozone data reporting GB actually refers to the UK).

GMT: Greenwich Mean Time (GMT) is the local time on the Greenwich meridian, based on the hypothetical mean sun. As the Earth's orbit is elliptical and its axis is tilted, the actual position of the sun against the background of stars appears a little ahead or behind the expected position. The accumulated timing error varies through the year in a smoothly periodic manner by up to 14 minutes slow in February to 16 minutes fast in November. The use of a hypothetical mean sun removes this effect. GMT was used generally until 1925. At that time the reference point was changed from noon to midnight and it was recommended that, to avoid confusion, the term Universal Time should be used for the "new" GMT. GMT is the basis of the civil time for the UK.

http://www.npl.co.uk/npl/ctm/time_scales.html

Gothenburg protocol: The latest protocol to the UNECE Convention on the Long Range Transport of Transboundary Air Pollution (see **CLTRAP**) which aims for substantial reductions of sulphur dioxide, nitrogen oxides, ammonia and VOCs to reduce the effects of acidification, eutrophication and ground-level ozone.

GR: Greece

ground-level ozone: Ozone present in the lowest layer of the atmosphere, the troposphere, from 0 up to 10 km is called tropospheric ozone. Ground-level ozone refers to that in the bottom layer, known as the boundary layer, which is closely coupled to the surface.

h: units of hours

HARM: Hull Acid Rain Model (see Chapter 4)

HCl: Hydrogen Chloride

heavy metals: Generally used to encompass any metals that can cause human health problems, such as cadmium, mercury, lead and bismuth.

HIRLAM: HIgh Resolution Limited Area Model. This is the operational numerical weather Prediction model of the Norwegian Meteorological Institute (http://www.dnmi.no/), see Chapter 4.

IE: Ireland

impaction: Accumulation of particles in a cloud droplet by collision, where one is unable to follow the airflow around the other.

IPC: Integrated Pollution Control

IPCC: Intergovernmental Panel on Climate Change, established by the World Meteorological Organization (WMO) and the United Nations Environment Programme (UNEP) in 1988, to examine the science and implications of climate change.

IT: Italy

kt-N: **kilo**tonnes of nitrogen (see Appendix C)

kt-S: **kilo**tonnes of sulphur (see Appendix C)

Kyoto protocol: The Kyoto Protocol to the United Nations Framework Convention on Climate Change (http://www.unfccc.de/) is the agreement in development by the UN countries to reduce their emissions of the gases contributing to climate change; it has yet to be ratified by all the signatories (for ratification status see http://www.unfccc.de/resource/kpstats.pdf).

LADM: EMEP Lagrangian Acid Deposition Model (see Chapter 4)

Lagrangian model: This type of model takes an initial set of values for a point or parcel of air then moves that parcel through the model domain (e.g. a two dimensional surface or a three dimensional box covering a country), modifying the values in the parcel as goes (e.g. adding emissions or changing concentrations due to chemical processes).

LAM50E: Limited Area Model at 50 km resolution for Europe. This is a numerical weather prediction model developed by **DNMI** and **EMEP** for use in air pollution modelling (see Chapter 4). It was used up to 1996 when it was replaced by **PARLAM-PS**.

LCP: Large Combustion Plant, any technical apparatus in which fuels are oxidised in order to use the heat generated with an energy output above around 50 **MW**.

LMO: Lagrangian Model for Ozone (EMEP model, see Chapter 4)

LRTAP: see **CLTRAP**

LT: Lithuania

LU: Luxembourg

mol: Mole, the quantity of a substance which contains one gram formula weight of the substance. One mole of a substance contains Avogadro's number (6.0223×10^{23}) of molecules or atoms.

MK: Republic of Moldova

MW: **Mega** (see unit prefixes) Watts

NAEI: The UK National Atmospheric Emission Inventory, http://www.aeat.co.uk/netcen/airqual/naei/home.html

NAOI: North Atlantic Oscillation Index. Description http://www.ldeo.columbia.edu/NAO/; Data http://www.cru.uea.ac.uk/cru/data/nao.htm.

NH_3: ammonia gas

NH_4^+: ammonium ion

NH_x: Reduced nitrogen, ammonia (**NH_3**) and ammonium (**NH_4^+**).

nitrification: The conversion of ammonium ions (NH_4^+) to nitrate (NO_3^-).

NL: The Netherlands

NMVOCs: non-methane **VOC**

NO: Norway or nitric oxide.

non-linearities: Refers to the observed non-linear relationship between reductions in primary emissions and reductions in pollutant deposition. It had generally been assumed that a reduction in emissions would lead to a directly proportional decrease in deposition.

NO_x: sum of the oxides of nitrogen NO and NO_2

NSI: National Soil Inventory

O_3: ozone gas

OECD: Organisation for Economic Co-operation and Development (http://www.oecd.org/)

Op. cit.: as already cited, from the Latin *opere citato*.

oxidation: The removal of electrons from a chemical species. The species that has lost the electrons is said to be oxidised. The oxidant or oxidising agent is the species that brings about the oxidation by accepting electrons.

parallelised: When a piece of software is "split up" so that it can run on several computers simultaneously or a parallel computer it has been parallelised. This is often done with complex models to reduce their run-time.

PARLAM-PS: PARallel Limited Area Model with Polar Stereographic map projection. This is a dedicated version of **HIRLAM** developed for EMEP.

particulate: Particulate matter is a complex mixture of organic and inorganic substances, present in the atmosphere as both liquids and solids. Coarse particulates can be regarded as those with a diameter greater than 2.5 μm, and fine particles less than 2.5 μm. Coarse particles usually contain earth crustal materials and dust from road vehicles and industries. Fine particles contain the secondarily formed aerosols (often acidic), combustion particles and re-condensed organic and metallic vapours. (from the Encyclopaedia of the Atmospheric Environment)

PBL: planetary boundary layer, defined as "that part of the troposphere that is directly influenced by the presence of the earth's surface, and responds to surface forcings with a timescale of about an hour or less" (Stull, 1988)

PHARE: European Union programme of financial and technical cooperation with the countries of central and eastern Europe, who may potentially join the union (includes Albania, Bosnia and Herzegovina, Bulgaria, the Czech Republic, Estonia, Macedonia, Hungary, Latvia, Lithuania, Poland, Romania, Slovakia and Slovenia), http://europa.eu.int/comm/enlargement/pas/phare/index.htm.

photochemical oxidant: An **oxidising** chemical formed by **photochemistry** e.g. ozone (**O_3**) , peroxy acetyl nitrate (PAN) and hydrogen peroxide (H_2O_2).

photochemical smog: Natural and **anthropogenic** emissions of nitrogen oxides (**NO_x**) and **VOCs** can generate other compounds, known as **secondary pollutants**, through chemical reactions driven by sunlight (**photochemistry**). In sunny conditions with warm still air, such as summer anti-cyclones in the UK, this process can lead to the production of large concentrations of secondary pollutants. This mixture of primary and secondary pollutants is often called photochemical smog.

photolysis: decomposition or dissociation of molecules by light (photons)

PL: Poland

pollutant: Any substance in the wrong place or at the wrong time is a pollutant. Atmospheric pollution may be defined as 'the presence of substances in the atmosphere, resulting from man-made activities or from natural processes, causing adverse effects to man and the environment'. (see the Encyclopaedia of the Atmospheric Environment)

POPs: Persistent Organic Pollutants are compounds that persist in the environment, accumulate in the food chain, and pose a risk of causing adverse effects to human health and the environment.

ppb: parts per billion (see Appendix C)

primary pollutants: Those pollutants emitted directly into the atmosphere, e.g. sulphur dioxide (SO_2).

PT: Portugal

RAINS: Regional Air pollution INformation and Simulation model. RAINS is a tool for analysing alternative strategies to reduce acidification, eutrophication and ground-level ozone in Europe. It combines a variety of information relevant for the development of cost-effective emission control strategies in Europe: projections of future economic, agricultural and energy development in 38 European countries; the present and future emissions of SO_2, NO_x, VOC and NH_3 resulting from these activities; the options for reducing emissions and the costs of these measures; the atmospheric dispersion characteristics of sulphur and nitrogen compounds and the formation of ground-level ozone, and the environmental sensitivities of ecosystems towards acidification, eutrophication and ground-level ozone. (http://www.iiasa.ac.at/Research/TAP/)

RCTM: Development of the **TRACK** model with a modified treatment of reduced nitrogen

RGAR: Review Group on Acid Rain, set up by the DETR (then the **DoE**) in 1981 to review the extent and impact of acidification over the UK and Northern Europe.

RSS: Representative Soil Series

SE: Sweden

secondary pollutants: Those pollutants formed in the atmosphere by chemical reactions, e.g. ozone (O_3).

seeder-feeder effect: Process which enhances the concentration of pollutants in precipitation over hilltops. Hill (orographic) cloud is formed above uplands as the air is forced to rise by the orography. The orographic cloud forms largely within boundary layer air and so contains larger concentrations of pollutants. Precipitation from higher level cloud washes out the hill cloud, increasing rainfall amount and the concentrations of the pollutants reaching the ground. (see Chapter 3).

SK: Slovakia

SL: Slovenia

smog: A term first used to describe sooty or smoky fogs. In the 19th and early 20th century smogs were associated with the burning of coal. In calm weather concentrations of soot particles and sulphur dioxide became concentrated into thick fogs. **Photochemical smogs** are now more common in the UK as smoke control legislation has greatly reduced emissions of smoke and SO_2.

SO_2: sulphur dioxide gas

source sector: A range of angles at a location, usually taken from North, from which an air mass originates, often used to indicate the source of pollution.

SSSI: Site of Special Scientific Interest, these are areas of particular value for nature conservation because of high biodiversity, rare species and rare habitats for example. Under current UK legislation they are given some protection from development and other forms of disturbance or damage.

TOR-2: Tropospheric Ozone Research, EUROTRAC-2 sub-project. Aims to quantify crucial processes in the atmosphere in order to improve the scientific background for the development of effect-based control strategies for photochemical oxidants over Europe.

TRACK: TRajectory Model with Atmospheric Chemical Kinetics (see Chapter 4)

UK: United Kingdom (Great Britain and Northern Ireland)

UNECE: United Nations Economic Commission for Europe (http://www.unece.org/). UNECE was set up in 1947 and is one of five regional commissions of the United Nations. Its primary goal is to encourage greater economic cooperation among its member States. It focuses on economic analysis, environment and human settlements, statistics, sustainable energy, trade, industry and enterprise development, timber and transport.

UNFCCC: the United Nations Framework Convention on Climate Change (http://www.unfccc.de/)

universal time: Universal Time (UT) now has three separate definitions (UT0, UT1, UT2) depending on which corrections have been applied to the Earth's motion. Authorities are not agreed on whether GMT equates with UT0 or UT1, however the differences between the two are of the order of thousandths of a second. GMT is no longer used for scientific purposes. http://www.npl.co.uk/npl/ctm/time_scales.html

UTC: Since 1972, all broadcast time services distribute time scales based on Coordinated Universal Time (UTC). UTC is an atomic time scale that is kept in agreement with **Universal Time** (UT). Leap seconds are occasionally added or subtracted from UTC to keep it within 0.9 seconds of UT1. UTC is more or less equivalent to **GMT**. http://www.npl.co.uk/npl/ctm/time_scales.html

VOC: volatile organic compound, organic chemicals that easily vaporize at room temperature e.g. benzene.

weathering: Chemical weathering is the process by which precipitation dissolves soluble species from rock and so the rock is gradually eroded. Physical weathering processes include the break up of rock by the expansion of water as it freezes and abrasion by wind-carried material.

wet deposition: see **deposition**

y: units of years

$\mu g\ m^{-3}$: microgrammes per cubic metre (see Appendix C)

Appendix B: UK Monitoring Networks

Table B1 Sources of information and data on air quality, emissions, soils and freshwaters.	
Description	Contact information
UK National Air Quality Information	http://www.aeat.co.uk/netcen/airqual/welcome.html
Networks	http://www.aeat.co.uk/netcen/airqual/networks/index.html
Data archive (air pollutant concentrations and wet deposition)	http://www.aeat.co.uk/netcen/airqual/data/index.html
Forecasts and Bulletins	http://www.aeat.co.uk/netcen/airqual/forecast.html
Summary statistics	http://www.aeat.co.uk/netcen/airqual/statistics.html
Emissions	http://www.aeat.co.uk/netcen/airqual/naei/home.html
Ammonia and Nitric Acid	http://www.nbu.ac.uk/cara/UKNAMN/uknamn.htm
Current air pollution levels and forecasts	DEFRA Freephone 0800 556677 Ceefax 410-417, Teletext 155
European monitoring and modelling (EMEP)	http://www.emep.int/
ACE: Atmosphere, Climate and Environment Information Programme - a very useful site with lots of background information on air pollution, climate change and other environmental issues.	http://www.doc.mmu.ac.uk/aric/ace/ace_frames.html
BADC - British Atmospheric Data Centre (BADC) is the Natural Environment Research Council's (NERC) Designated Data Centre for the Atmospheric Sciences. Assists UK atmospheric researchers to locate, access and interpret atmospheric data and to ensure the long-term integrity of atmospheric data produced by NERC projects. The BADC has substantial data holdings of its own and also provides information and links to data held by other data centres.	http://www.badc.rl.ac.uk/ UKMO - http://www.badc.rl.ac.uk/data/ukmo.html ECMWF - http://www.badc.rl.ac.uk/data/ecmwf.html Atmospheric Chemistry - http://www.badc.rl.ac.uk/data/chemistry.html Stratosphere - http://www.badc.rl.ac.uk/data/stratosphere.html NERC - http://www.badc.rl.ac.uk/data/nerc_prog.html
Acid Waters Monitoring Network	http://www.geog.ucl.ac.uk/ukawmn/
National Waters Archive - The National Waters Archive is one of the NERCs eight Designated Data Centres. The aim of the Designated Data Centres is to provide a focus for NERC's environmental holdings and provide information and advisory services to a wide range of users.	http://www.nwl.ac.uk/ih/nwa/index.htm National River Flow Archive - http://www.nwl.ac.uk/ih/nrfa/index.htm National Groundwater Level Archive - http://www.nwl.ac.uk/ih/nrfa/groundwater/index.htm
British Society of Soil Science	http://www.bsss.bangor.ac.uk/
ECN – The UK Environmental Change Network, Monitoring and research to detect and interpret environmental change	http://www.ecn.ac.uk/

Air Quality Monitoring

The main source of UK air quality data is the National Air Quality Information Archive at:

http://www.aeat.co.uk/netcen/airqual/welcome.html

From here several networks can be accessed:

Automatic Networks

Ozone (O_3), nitrogen dioxide (NO_2), nitric oxide (NO), oxides of nitrogen (NO_x), carbon monoxide (CO), sulphur dioxide (SO_2), particulates (PM10), and 25 hydrocarbon species are monitored on an hourly basis using automatic gas analysers at over 100 sites across the country in rural and urban areas. The data are regularly downloaded from the sites by modem and made available on the internet, Teletext/Ceefax and a phone line (see Table B1). Daily bulletins are also available by email (see Table B1). A full quality control and assurance procedure is implemented by a QA/QC unit to provide fully ratified data sets. These ratified data are maximised for accuracy and comparability with past years and non-UK networks. Table B2 lists the sites and Figure B1 a to f shows the locations of those currently operating (September 2000).

Table B2 Automatic monitoring sites in the UK. NB Auchencorth Moss (4), Mace Head (107) and Sutton Bonnington (144) are not part of the UK national networks but are discussed in the report and so are included for reference. All species may not have been measured at a site for the whole of its operation.

Ref. No.	Full name	Class	Grid Ref*	Species	Operating Period
1	Aberdeen	UB	NJ944073	NO_x, CO, PM10	18/09/99 - present
2	Ascot	R	SU946688	O_3	1979 - 1984
3	Aston Hill	R	SO298901	O_3	26/06/86 - present
4	Auchencorth Moss	RR	NT221562	O_3	1995 - present
5	Barnsley	U	SE348094	SO_2	14/03/91 - 21/03/94
6	Barnsley 12	UB	SE342067	SO_2	21/03/94 - present
7	Barnsley Gawber	UB	SE325075	O_3, NO_x, CO, SO_2	07/07/97 - present
8	Bath Roadside +	UK	ST753657	NO_x, CO	18/11/96 - present
9	Belfast Centre	UC	J339744	O_3, NO_x, CO, SO_2, PM10	08/03/92 - present
10	Belfast Clara St +	SU	J336374	PM10	09/06/98 - present
11	Belfast East	UB	J357740	SO_2	06/09/89 - present
12	Belfast South	UB	J333726	HC	23/08/93 - present
13	Billingham	UI	NZ470237	NO_x	01/01/87 - present
14	Bircotes	U	SK629922	SO_2	14/09/89 - 11/03/91
15	Birmingham Centre	UC	SP064868	O_3, NO_x, CO, SO_2, PM10	18/03/92 - present
16	Birmingham East +	UB	SP116889	O_3, NO_x, CO, SO_2, PM10, HC	23/08/93 - present
17	Birmingham Kerb	UK	SP070870	CO	13/03/74 - 17/01/78
18	Bolton +	UB	SD710085	O_3, NO_x, CO, SO_2, PM10	03/02/97 - present
19	Bottesford	R	SK797376	O_3	01/10/77 - present
20	Bradford Centre	UC	SE166331	O_3, NO_x, CO, SO_2, PM10	28/11/97 - present
21	Brampton	R	SK843810	O_3	1981 - 1985
22	Brighton Roadside +	UK	TQ313043	NO_x, CO	10/02/98 - present
23	Bristol Centre	UC	ST594732	O_3, NO_x, CO, SO_2, PM10	04/01/93 - present
24	Bristol East	UB	ST599729	HC	01/04/94 - present
25	Bristol Old Market +	UK	ST595731	O_3, NO_x, CO, SO_2, PM10	01/07/97 - present
26	Bury roadside +	UK	SD809048	O_3, NO_x, CO, SO_2, PM10	20/01/97 - present
27	Bush	R	NT245635	O_3	01/04/86 - present
28	Cambridge	UK	TL450580	CO	01/11/74 - 01/03/78
29	Cambridge Roadside	UK	TL545558	O_3, NO_x, CO	01/08/98 - present
30	Cardiff Centre	UC	ST184765	O_3, NO_x, CO, SO_2, PM10	12/05/92 - present
31	Cardiff East	UB	ST193773	HC	01/11/93 - present
32	Cardiff Kerbside	UK	ST183766	O_3, CO	28/07/73 - 23/11/76
33	Central Lon.	UC	TQ292791	O_3, NO_x, CO, SO_2	01/07/72 - 20/08/90
34	Chigwell	U	TQ442919	O_3	1979, 1982 - 1985
35	Chilworth	SU	SU405183	O_3	18/04/75 - 10/10/75
36	Clatteringshaws	R	NX553779	O_3	1986 - 1990
37	County Hall	U	TQ306797	O_3	1975-76, 1978-1986 - 1989
38	Coventry Centre	UC	SP326796	O_3, NO_x, CO, SO_2	18/02/97 - present
39	Derry	UB	C429172	O_3, NO_x, CO, SO_2, PM10	29/04/97 - present
40	Devilla	R	NS957894	O_3	1977 - 1980
41	Dunslair Heights +	R	NT280430	O_3	13/06/92 - present
42	Dursley	R	ST755967	O_3	1987 - 1990
43	East Kilbride	SU	NS638534	O_3	08/05/75 - 09/10/75
44	East Malling	R	TQ712572	O_3	1984 - 1985
45	Edinburgh Centre	UC	NT254738	O_3, NO_x, CO, SO_2, PM10	04/10/92 - present
46	Edinburgh Med. School	UB	NT257730	HC	27/08/93 - present
47	Eskdalemuir	R	NT235028	O_3	23/04/86 - present
48	Exeter Roadside +	UK	SX929918	O_3, NO_x, CO, SO_2	02/07/96 - present
49	Fawley	U	SU474202	O_3	1988 - 1991
50	Featherstone	U	SE429195	SO_2	14/09/89 - 13/03/91
51	Glasgow	U	NS554678	O_3	1983 - 1987
52	Glasgow Centre	UC	NS558665	O_3, NO_x, CO, SO_2, PM10	03/07/96 - present
53	Glasgow City Chambers	UB	NS595653	NO_x, CO	06/01/87 - present
54	Glasgow Hope St	UK	NS587651	NO_x, CO, SO_2	27/06/73 - 28/10/82
55	Glasgow Kerbside	UK	NS587652	NO_x, CO, PM10	10/03/97 - present
56	Glazebury	R	SJ690959	O_3	01/04/88 - present
57	Great Dun Fell	RR	NY711322	O_3	09/05/86 - present

Ref. No.	Full name	Class	Grid Ref*	Species	Operating Period
58	Hainault	U	TQ460917	O_3	1974 - 1975
59	Harrow	SU	TQ143874	O_3, NO_x	30/07/79 - 03/10/80
60	Harwell	R	SU474863	O_3, NO_x, SO_2, HC	22/06/76 - present
61	Hazelrigg	R	SD492579	O_3	1981 - 1982
62	High Muffles	R	SE776939	O_3	16/07/87 - present
63	Hove roadside +	UK	TQ289047	NO_x, CO	16/09/97 - present
64	Hull Centre	UC	TA097288	O_3, NO_x, CO, SO_2, PM10	04/01/94 - present
65	Jenny Hurn	R	SK817986	O_3	1984 - 1988
66	Kew	U	TQ185779	O_3	1978 - present
67	Ladybower	R	SK164892	O_3, NO_x, SO_2	15/07/88 - present
68	Leamington Spa +	UB	SP319657	O_3, NO_x, CO, SO_2, PM10	26/07/96 - present
69	Leeds Centre	UC	SE299343	O_3, NO_x, CO, SO_2, PM10	04/01/93 - present
70	Leeds Potternewton	UB	SE307367	HC	13/01/95 - present
71	Leicester Centre	UC	SK587040	O_3, NO_x, CO, SO_2, PM10	04/01/94 - present
72	Lincoln	U	SK983729	O_3	1986 - 1988
73	Lincoln roadside +	UK	SK977712	NO_x	06/05/97 - present
74	Liverpool Centre	UC	SJ349908	O_3, NO_x, CO, SO_2, PM10	23/04/93 - present
75	Liverpool Speke	UB	SJ438835	HC	01/12/95 - present
76	Lon., A3 Roadside	UK	TQ193653	NO_x, CO, PM10	20/03/97 - present
77	Lon., Bexley +	SU	TQ518763	O_3, NO_x, CO, SO_2, PM10	01/05/94 - present
78	Lon., Bloomsbury	UC	TQ302820	O_3, NO_x, CO, SO_2, PM10	23/01/92 - present
79	Lon., Brent +	UB	TQ200840	O_3, NO_x, CO, SO_2, PM10	26/01/96 - present
80	Lon., Bridge Place	UB	TQ291790	O_3, NO_x, CO, SO_2	03/07/90 - present
81	Lon., Bromley +	UK	TQ405694	NO_x, CO	11/08/98 - present
82	Lon., Bromley +	UK	TQ406695	NO_x, CO	02/05/97 - 06/07/98
83	Lon., Camden +	UK	TQ267843	NO_x, PM10	16/05/96 - present
84	Lon., Canvey Island	UI	TQ782847	O_3, NO_x, CO	10/05/77 - 01/10/80
85	Lon., Cromwell Rd	UK	TQ264789	O_3, NO_x, CO, SO_2	22/02/73 - 12/09/96
86	Lon., Cromwell Rd New	UK	TQ266791	O_3, NO_x, CO, SO_2	20/05/98 - present
87	Lon., Eltham +	SU	TQ440747	O_3, NO_x, SO_2, PM10, HC	04/03/93 - present
88	Lon., Hackney+	UC	TQ348862	O_3, NO_x, CO	06/01/97 - present
89	Lon., Haringey 2 +	UC	TQ339907	O_3	16/05/96 - present
90	Lon., Haringey +	UK	TQ339906	NO_x, PM10	16/05/96 - present
91	Lon., Hillingdon +	SU	TQ078806	O_3, NO_x, CO, SO_2, PM10,	03/07/96 - present
92	Lon., Hounslow +	UK	TQ175781	NO_x, CO	16/09/97 - present
93	Lon., Islington	U	TQ321831	O_3, NO_x	09/07/76 - 11/10/78
94	Lon., Lewisham +	UC	TQ377738	O_3, NO_x, SO_2	16/04/97 - present
95	Lon., Marylebone Rd +	UK	TQ281820	O_3, NO_x, CO, SO_2, PM10, HC	17/07/97 - present
96	Lon., N.Kensington +	UB	TQ240817	O_3, NO_x, CO, SO_2, PM10	01/04/96 - present
97	Lon., Southwark +	UC	TQ324785	O_3, NO_x, CO, SO_2	28/02/97 - present
98	Lon., Southwark +	UK	TQ591768	NO_x, CO, SO_2	01/04/97 - present
99	Lon., Sutton 3 +	SU	TQ278648	O_3, NO_x	01/04/96 - present
100	Lon., Sutton +	UK	TQ256646	NO_x, CO, SO_2, PM10	01/04/96 - present
101	Lon., Tower Hamlets 2+	UK	TQ521816	NO_x, CO	01/04/96 - present
102	Lon., UCL (Bloomsbury)	UK	TQ299822	HC	11/02/93 - present
103	Lon., Wandsworth 2 +	UC	TQ264746	O_3, NO_x	01/04/96 - present
104	W. London	UB	TQ251788	NO_x, CO	01/01/87 - present
105	Lough Navar	RR	H065545	O_3, PM10	02/04/87 - present
106	Lullington Heath	R	TQ538016	O_3, NO_x, SO_2	04/10/86 - present
107	Mace Head	RR	L740320	O_3	09/06/87 - present
108	Manchester Piccadilly	UC	SJ843983	O_3, NO_x, CO, SO_2, PM10	18/12/95 - present
109	Manchester South +	SU	SJ839858	O_3, NO_x, SO_2	06/12/96 - present
110	Manchester Town Hall	UB	SJ838980	NO_x, CO	22/01/87 - present
111	Middlesbrough +	UI	NZ505194	O_3, NO_x, CO, SO_2, PM10, HC	01/01/93 - present
112	Narbeth	R	SN146127	O_3, NO_x, SO_2, PM10	20/01/97 - present
113	Nat West Tower	U	TQ331814	O_3	1983 - 1983
114	Newcastle Centre	UC	NZ251649	O_3, NO_x, CO, SO_2, PM10	08/03/92 - present
115	North Norfolk	R	TG141388	O_3	1989 - 1990
116	Norwich Centre	UC	TG230089	O_3, NO_x, CO, SO_2, PM10	24/07/97 - present
117	Norwich roadside +	UK	TG234078	NO_x	21/06/97 - present

Ref. No.	Full name	Class	Grid Ref*	Species	Operating Period
118	Nottingham Centre	UC	SK574400	O_3, NO_x, CO, SO_2, PM10	02/09/96 - present
119	Oxford Centre +	UK	SP514092	NO_x, CO, SO_2	15/04/96 - present
120	Plymouth Centre	UC	SX477546	O_3, NO_x, CO, SO_2, PM10	29/09/97 - present
121	Port Tablot +	UB	SS780882	O_3, NO_x, SO_2, PM10	09/01/97 - present
122	Reading	UB	SU727733	O_3, NO_x, CO, SO_2, PM10	17/07/97 - present
123	Redcar +	SU	NZ599246	O_3, NO_x, CO, SO_2, PM10	25/06/97 - present
124	Rochester +	R	TQ831762	O_3, NO_x, SO_2, PM10	26/01/96 - present
125	Rotherham centre +	UC	SK430930	O_3, NO_x, SO_2	20/06/97 - present
126	Rugeley	UB	SK043173	SO_2	21/03/91 - 17/09/92
127	Salford Eccles +	UI	SJ779987	O_3, NO_x, CO, SO_2, PM10	20/03/97 - present
128	Sandwell Oldbury	UB	SO989896	O_3, NO_x, CO, SO_2	27/06/97 - present
129	Sandwell W. Bromwich	UB	SP003915	O_3, NO_x, CO, SO_2	04/11/98 - present
130	Scunthorpe +	UI	SE905107	SO_2, PM10	15/12/97 - present
131	Sheffield Centre	UC	SK352869	O_3, NO_x, CO, SO_2, PM10	01/01/96 - present
132	Sheffield Tinsley	UI	SK402906	NO_x, CO	28/11/90 - present
133	Sibton	R	TM364719	O_3, NO_x, SO_2	01/07/73 - present
134	Somerton +	R	ST486268	O_3	26/01/96 - present
135	Southampton Centre	UC	SU440130	O_3, NO_x, CO, SO_2, PM10, HC	04/01/94 - present
136	St. Osyth	R	TM104183	O_3	1985 - 1987
137	St.Bartholomew's	U	TQ319821	O_3	1976 - 1976
138	Stevenage	SU	TL237225	O_3, NO_x, CO, SO_2, PM10	22/06/76 - 29/04/94
139	Stockport +	UB	SJ895908	NO_x, CO, SO_2, PM10	25/11/96 - present
140	Stodday	R	SD462587	O_3	1982 - 1984
141	Stoke-on-Trent	UC	SJ883468	O_3, NO_x, CO, SO_2, PM10	11/03/97 - present
142	Strath Vaich	RR	NH347750	O_3, NO_x, SO_2	18/03/87 - present
143	Sunderland	UB	NZ398570	SO_2	06/10/92 - present
144	Sutton Bonnington	R	SK505268	O_3, NO_x, SO_2	01/01/93 - present
145	Swansea +	UC	SS655931	O_3, NO_x, CO, SO_2, PM10	01/12/94 - present
146	Syda House	R	SK312696	O_3	1986 - 1988
147	Teddington	SU	TQ156706	O_3	1975-76, 1978, 1982 - 1985, 1987-1991
148	Teddington +	UB	TQ156706	O_3, NO_x, SO_2	20/08/96 - present
149	Thorney	R	SK858731	O_3	1981 - 1988
150	Thurrock +	UB	TQ611779	O_3, NO_x, CO, SO_2, PM10	01/09/96 - present
151	Walsall Alumwell	UB	SO994982	NO_x,	05/03/87 - present
152	Walsall Wilenhall +	SU	SJ978011	NO_x	29/04/97 - present
153	West Burton	R	SK804864	O_3	1981 - 1984
154	Weybourne +	R	TG110430	O_3	01/01/95 - present
155	Wharleycroft	R	NY698247	O_3	08/05/85 - 28/11/95
156	Wicken Fen	R	TL564692	O_3, NO_x, SO_2	12/08/97 - present
157	Wolverhampton Centre	UC	SO914989	O_3, NO_x, CO, SO_2, PM10	18/12/95 - present
158	Wray	R	SD619678	O_3	01/04/85 - 29/02/88
159	Yarner Wood	R	SX786789	O_3	26/06/87 - present
160	Yorkminster	U	SE603522	O_3	1986 - 1990

Lon. = London, R ≡ rural, RR ≡ remote rural, SU ≡ sub-urban, UB ≡ urban background, UC ≡ urban centre, UI ≡ urban industrial, UK ≡ urban kerbside, U ≡ urban. + ≡ local council site affiliated with the national networks.
*Grid references are on the UK ordinance survey grid except those for Ireland that are on the Irish grid (with single letters).

Figure B1 UK Automatic national network sites in operation as of September 2000.

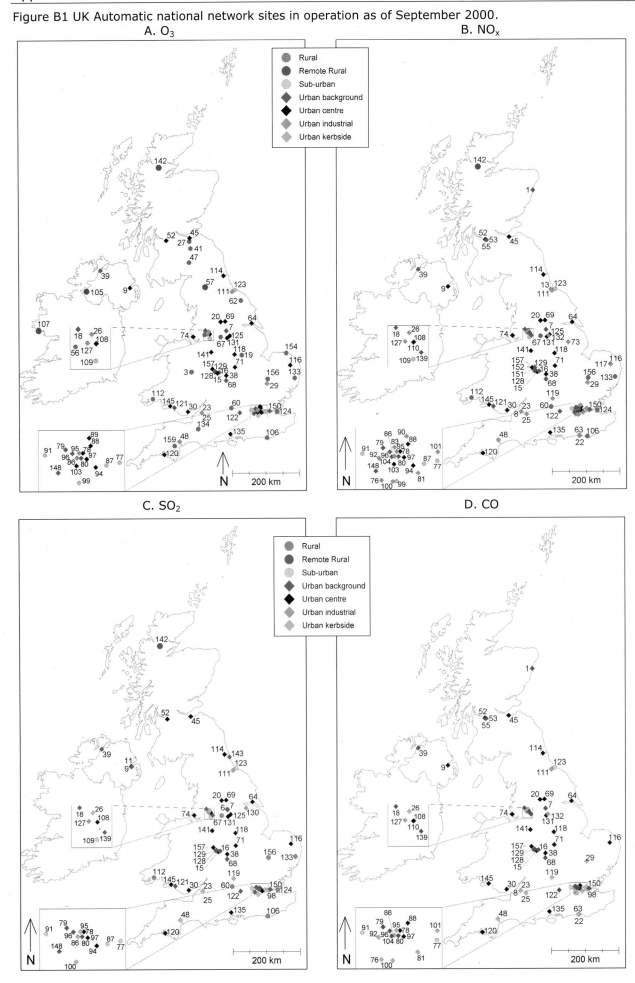

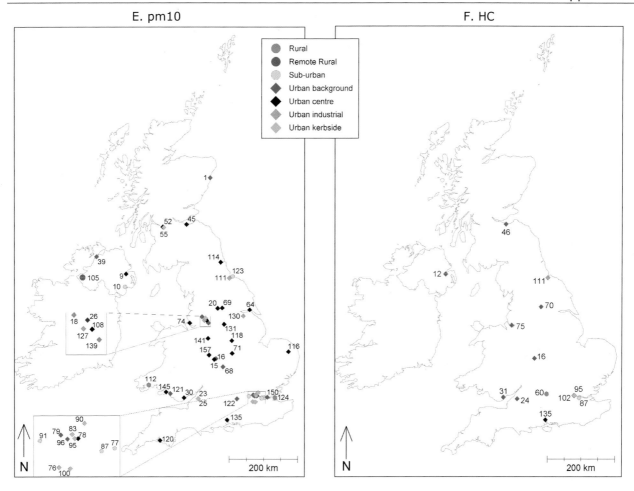

E. pm10

F. HC

Non-automatic Networks

There are five non-automatic networks, each of which has been set up to achieve a specific goal. The techniques employed, species measured and time scale of measurement all differ from network to network:

o   *Lead and other elements*
    Samples are collected by pulling air through a filter for a one week period, then the filter is subjected to analysis by spectrometric techniques. The network is set up to monitor the UK's compliance with the EC Directive on lead in air, to monitor the effect of the reduction of lead in petrol and the introduction of unleaded petrol, and to monitor the lead content of air in specific industrial areas. The samples are also analysed for other trace elements: Cadmium, Chromium, Copper, Iron, Manganese Nickel, Zinc, Vanadium and Cobalt.

o   *NO$_2$ Diffusion Tube Survey*
    Over 300 Local Authorities in the UK participate in this network, which provides a nationwide picture of concentrations of this important traffic-related pollutant. Monthly means of nitrogen dioxide are measured at over 1100 urban sites using diffusion tubes (see Figure B2). Each authority places samplers at one kerbside location (1 to 5 m from a major road), one intermediate site (20 - 30 m away from a major road) and two urban background sites (in residential areas more than 50 m from a major road). The primary aims of this survey are: to assess the distribution of NO$_2$ concentrations over time and space in the urban environment in the UK; to highlight areas where elevated concentrations of NO$_2$ occur, which may need further investigation by automatic monitoring.

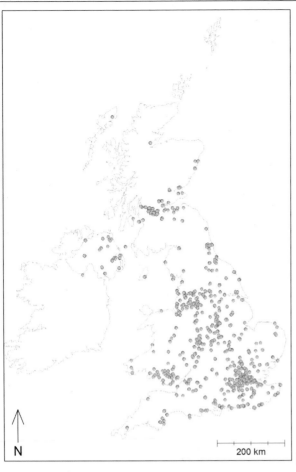

Figure B2 NO$_2$ diffusion tube sites operating in 1999.

o   *Smoke and Sulphur Dioxide Data*
This network has the longest history of all the UK Networks, having been in operation for over 30 years. The individual sites are mainly in urban areas and operated by local authorities, with the network managed and quality controlled by NETCEN, on behalf of the DEFRA. The network has recorded the decline in smoke and SO$_2$ concentrations that has followed from the implementation of the Clean Air Acts. There are currently over 220 sites in these networks, monitoring black smoke and SO$_2$ on a daily basis. The methods used to determine pollutant concentrations are: SO$_2$ by acid titration; black smoke by reflectance from a filter. The aims of this monitoring programme are: to provide information on long term trends and to calculate a national average concentration on a consistent basis; to monitor for compliance with EC Directive 80/779 on SO$_2$ and suspended particulate matter.

o   *Toxic Organic Micro Pollutants*
The objective of this network is to monitor a range of toxic organic micropollutants (Dioxins and PAHs) at selected sites around the UK. The samples are collected over two weeks, bulked together and then chemically analysed every 3 months for PAHs and every 6 months for dioxins.

o   *Acid Deposition Networks: Rainfall Composition (Acid rain), Rural Gases and Particles.*
See Table B3 and Figure B3 for site details.

   •   Acid deposition (rainfall concentrations of: acidity, sulphate, nitrate, ammonium, sodium, chloride, magnesium, calcium, potassium, phosphate and conductivity) is measured in precipitation collected at 40 sites (39 sample weekly and 1 daily) across the country.

   •   Rural sulphur dioxide concentrations are measured at approximately 38 sites across the UK using the wet chemistry bubbler method.

   •   Rural NO$_2$ concentrations are measured using diffusion tubes at about 21 sites.

   •   Sulphate particle concentrations are measured at 9 rural and 1 urban site.

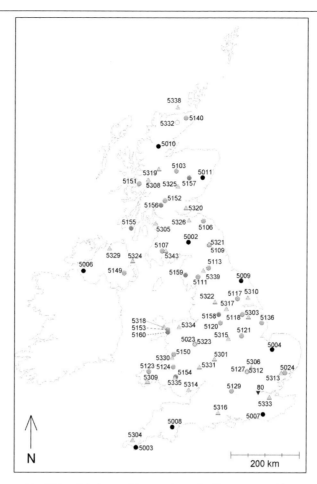

Figure B3 Non-automatic UK acid deposition network sites currently operating (July 2001).

Table B3 Acid Deposition Network Sites.

NB unless an end date is specified the site is still operating

Site Name	Ref. No.	Grid Ref.*	Rain Fall Composition Operating Period W	Rain Fall Composition Operating Period D	NO₂ Operating Period	SO₄²⁻ Particles Operating Period	SO₂ Freq.	SO₂ Operating Period
Eskdalemuir	5002	NT235032	09/01/86	DB 01/01/73 WOC 22/6/86	01/03/86	02/01/73	D	02/01/73
Goonhilly	5003	SW723214	08/01/86	DB 01/08/79 - 04/04/88	25/02/87	15/08/79 - 05/04/88	D	15/08/79 - 05/04/88
Stoke Ferry	5004	TL700988	08/01/86	DB 01/08/80 - 19/02/89 WOC 23/07/86 - 21/02/89 WSL 01/03/85 - 22/07/86	03/06/85	17/08/81	D	17/08/81
Ludlow	5005	SO570741	08/01/86 - 05/04/89	WOC 27/07/86 - 04/01/89 WSL 01/0184 - 22/07/86	02/01/87 - 22/03/89	-	-	-
Lough Navar	5006	H065545	08/01/86	WOC 12/08/86 - 04/04/99 WSL 01/04/86 - 11/08/86	01/04/85	02/04/85	D	02/04/85

NB unless an end date is specified the site is still operating

Site Name	Ref. No.	Grid Ref.*	Rain Fall Composition Operating Period W	D	NO$_2$ Operating Period	SO$_4^{2-}$ Particles Operating Period	SO$_2$ Freq.	SO$_2$ Operating Period
Barcombe Mills	5007	TQ437149	08/01/86	WOC 19/11/86 - 05/01/89	25/03/85	08/02/85	D	08/02/85
Yarner Wood	5008	SX786789	06/02/86	WOC 17/12/86 - 6/04/99	22/01/87	05/01/87	D	05/01/87
High Muffles	5009	SE776939	10/04/86	WOC 17/12/86 - 28/12/99	29/12/86	17/12/86	D	17/12/86
Strathvaich Dam	5010	NH347750	11/03/87	WOC 31/03/87 - 31/12/99	12/03/87	31/03/87	D	31/03/87
Glen Dye	5011	NO642864	04/02/87	WOC 05/02/87 - 04/04/89	04/02/87	05/02/87	D	05/02/87
Bridge Place	80‡	TQ291790	-	-	-	03/07/90	-	
Malham Tarn	5021	SD894672	08/01/86 - 11/01/89	-	25/02/87 - 11/01/89	-	-	-
Preston Montford	5023	SJ432143	08/01/86	-	25/02/87	-	-	-
Flatford Mill	5024	TM077333	08/01/86	-	25/02/87	-	-	-
Birds Hill	5029	ST056363	08/01/86 - 04/01/89	-	25/02/87 - 01/06/88	-	-	-
Beinn Eighe	5100	NH025629	08/01/86 - 10/01/89	-	25/02/87 - 01/06/88	-	-	-
Fort Augustus	5102	NH367091	07/01/86 - 04/01/89	-	16/06/87 - 13/06/88	-	-	-
River Mharcaidh	5103	NH876052	16/12/85	-	29/06/87	-	-	-
Lochnagar	5104	NO274858	01/07/86 - 30/12/88	-	-	-	-	-
Loch Ard	5105	NS470987	23/12/85 - 05/01/89	-	17/06/87 - 15/06/88	-	-	-
Whiteadder	5106	NT664633	31/01/86	-	29/05/91	-	-	-
Loch Dee	5107	NX468779	30/12/85	-	05/06/87	-	-	-
Waterhead	5108	NX752834	22/01/86 - 02/01/89	-	-	-	-	-
Redesdale	5109	NY833954	28/01/86	-	29/05/91	-	-	-
Kershope Forest	5110	NY492792	08/01/86 - 07/04/88	-	17/06/87 - 07/04/88	-	-	-
Bannisdale	5111	NY515043	08/01/86	-	10/06/87	-	-	-
Glassonby	5112	NY574387	08/01/86 – 04/1/89	-	10/06/87 - 08/06/88	-	-	-
Cow Green Reservoir	5113	NY817298	08/01/86	-	25/02/87	-	-	-
Isle of Man	5114	SC367861	10/10/86 - 01/01/90	-	25/02/87 - 25/05/88	-	-	-
Devoke Water	5115	SD163973	09/01/86 - 04/01/89	-	10/06/87 - 08/06/88	-	-	-
Hebden Bridge	5116	SE011327	09/01/86 - 04/01/89	-	25/02/87 - 01/06/88	-	-	-
Thorganby	5117	SE676428	08/01/86	-	25/02/87	-	-	-
Jenny Hurn	5118	SK816986	07/01/86	-	02/06/87	-	-	-
Beddgelert	5119	SH556518	22/01/86 - 29/07/96	-	03/06/87 – 27/07/96	-	-	-
Wardlow Hay Cop	5120	SK177739	15/01/86	-	25/02/87	-	-	-
Bottesford	5121	SK797376	07/01/86	-	02/06/87	-	-	-
Plynlimon	5122	SN822841	25/02/86 - 17/01/89	-	02/06/87 - 31/05/88	-	-	-
Tycanol Wood	5123	SN093364	08/01/86	-	04/03/87	-	-	-

NB unless an end date is specified the site is still operating

Site Name	Ref. No.	Grid Ref.*	Rain Fall Composition Operating Period		NO₂ Operating Period	SO₄²⁻ Particles Operating Period	SO₂	
			W	D			Freq.	Operating Period
Llyn Brianne	5124	SN807492	15/01/86	-	25/02/87	-	-	-
Broom's Barn	5125	TL753656	01/01/86 - 04/01/89	-	03/06/87 - 01/06/88		-	-
Ridgehill	5126	SO508353	10/10/86 - 29/12/88	-	26/02/87 - 25/05/88	-	-	-
Woburn	5127	SP964361	01/01/86	-	03/06/87	-	-	-
Bowood House	5128	ST953699	08/01/86 - 04/01/89	-	25/02/87 - 29/06/88	-	-	-
Compton	5129	SU512804	23/12/85	-	13/07/87	-	-	-
Plaxtol	5130	TQ618521	07/01/86 - 04/01/89	-	03/03/87 - 04/01/89	-	-	-
Altnaheglish Reservoir	5131	C698041	01/01/86 - 04/01/89	-	27/05/87 - 08/06/88	-	-	-
Fourmile Burn	5132	J227897	01/01/86 - 04/01/89	-	27/05/87 - 03/01/91	-	-	-
Silent Valley	5133	J306243	01/01/86 - 04/01/89	-	27/05/87 - 08/06/88	-	-	-
Gisla	5134	NB129258	09/04/86 - 04/01/89	-	04/03/87 - 06/07/88	-	-	-
Broadford	5135	NG652230	19/02/86 - 04/01/89	-	25/02/87 - 14/12/88	-	-	-
Driby	5136	TF386744	08/01/86	-	05/03/87	-	-	-
Pitsford	5137	SP763686	08/01/86 - 18/01/89	-	25/02/87 - 18/01/89	-	-	-
East Ruston	5138	TG341279	08/01/86 - 04/01/89	-	25/03/87 - 11/01/89	-	-	-
Hill of Shurton	5139	HU444400	02/07/86 - 04/01/89	-	01/07/87 - 15/06/88	-	-	-
Achanarras	5140	ND151550	14/05/86	-	01/07/87	-	-	-
Hartland Moor	5141	SY942855	07/05/86 - 13/01/89	-	17/06/87 - 15/05/90	-	-	-
Liphook	5142	SU859297	15/01/86 - 04/01/89	-	25/02/87 - 01/06/88	-	-	-
Loch Leven	5143	NT159990	09/07/86 - 12/01/89	-	25/02/87 - 12/01/89	-	-	-
Myres Hill	5147	NS569465	25/06/86 - 04/01/89	-	25/02/87 - 02/06/88	-	-	-
Baltasound	5148	HP609090	11/08/86 - 04/01/89	-	08/07/87 - 15/06/88	-	-	-
Hillsborough Forest	5149	J243577	01/02/89	-	30/05/91	-	-	-
Pumlumon	5150	SN823854	17/01/89	-	29/05/91	-	-	-
Polloch	5151	NM792689	10/10/90	-	29/05/91	-	-	-
Balquhidder 2	5152	NN545207	04/05/94	-	05/04/94	-	-	-
Llyn Llydaw	5153	SH638549	21/08/96	-	21/08/96	-	-	-
Crai Reservoir	5154	SN882219	13/01/99	-	-	-	-	-
Beaghs Burn	5155	ID345865	28/01/99	-	-	-	-	-
Loch Chon	5156	NN429084	24/02/99	-	-	-	-	-
Loch Nagar	5157	NO252859	25/03/99	-	-	-	-	-
River Etherow	5158	SK125986	04/03/99	-	-	-	-	-
Scoat Tarn	5159	NY158103	03/03/99	-	-	-	-	-
Llyn Llagi	5160	SH647483	01/03/99	-	-	-	-	-
Balquhidder	5200	NN521206	08/01/86- 04/05/94	-	26/02/87 - 13/04/94	-	-	-
Brockhill	5301	SP002702	-	-	-	-	W	16/08/91
Burham	5302	TQ730619	-	-	-	-	W	13/08/91 - 26/06/93
Caenby	5303	SK993900	-	-	-	-	W	13/08/91
Camborne	5304	SW628407	-	-	-	-	W	13/08/91
Camphill	5305	NS274546	-	-	-	-	W	15/08/91

NB unless an end date is specified the site is still operating

Site Name	Ref. No.	Grid Ref.*	Rain Fall Composition Operating Period		NO₂ Operating Period	SO₄²⁻ Particles Operating Period	SO₂	
			W	D			Freq.	Operating Period
Cardington	5306	TL082464	-	-	-	-	W	12/08/91
Carrickfergus	5307	J429899	-	-	-	-	W	13/08/91 - 12/11/91
Corpach	5308	NN054782	-	-	-	-	W	14/08/91
Cresselly	5309	SN064062	-	-	-	-	W	13/08/91
Etton	5310	SE980445	-	-	-	-	W	13/08/91
Husborne Crawley	5312	SP964361	-	-	-	-	W	13/08/91
Little Horkesley	5313	TL971312	-	-	-	-	W	14/08/91
Marshfield	5314	ST255830	-	-	-	-	W	13/08/91
Ratcliffe	5315	SK408278	-	-	-	-	W	15/08/91
Rockbourne	5316	SU116181	-	-	-	-	W	14/08/91
Wakefield	5317	SE352132	-	-	-	-	W	14/08/91
Waunfawr	5318	SH533607	-	-	-	-	W	14/08/91
Fort Augustus	5319	NH365091	-	-	-	-	W	29/11/91
Loch Leven	5320	NT159990	-	-	-	-	W	27/11/91
Redesdale	5321	NY833961	-	-	-	-	W	26/11/91
Hebden Bridge	5322	SE011327	-	-	-	-	W	01/01/92
Preston Montford	5323	SJ432143	-	-	-	-	W	20/11/91
Bentra	5324	J458923	-	-	-	-	W	12/11/91
Pitlochry	5325	NN918599	-	-	-	-	W	28/11/91
Bush	5326	NT246638	-	-	-	-	D	09/01/92
Great Dun Fell	5327	NY711322	-	-	-	-	W	10/02/92 - 15/11/96
Wharleycroft	5328	NY697246	-	-	-	-	W	10/02/92 - 03/11/95
Cam Forest	5329	C766221	-	-	-	-	W	22/04/92
Cwmystwyth	5330	SN772743	-	-	-	-	W	09/03/92
Rosemaund	5331	SO564476	-	-	-	-	W	02/04/92
Forsinard	5332	NC890425	-	-	1/12/96	-	W	23/02/93 - 08/10/96
Fairseat	5333	TQ622615	-	-	-	-	W	20/09/93
Bylchau	5334	SH974611	-	-	-	-	W	13/12/94
Crai	5335	SN861183	-	-	-	-	W	15/12/94
Forsinain	5338	NC906846	-	-	-	-	W	08/10/96
Appleacre	5339	NY665208	-	-	-	-	W	15/11/96
Garrary	5340	NX531790	-	-	-	-	W	07/11/97 - 02/08/99
Benniguinea	5343	NX570772	-	-	-	-	W	02/08/99

W ≡ weekly, D ≡ daily, Freq. ≡ frequency, DB = daily bulk collector, WOC = Hydrolog wet only collector, WSL = Warren Spring Laboratory wet only collector, ‡ Bridge Place is site 80 in the automatic network, see Table B2
*Grid references are on the UK ordinance survey grid except those for Ireland that are on the Irish grid (with single letters).

National Ammonia and Nitric Acid Monitoring Networks

Following concern about the possible environmental impacts of atmospheric ammonia, DEFRA is supporting work to monitor the air concentrations of ammonia and ammonium across the UK. A network of NH_3 monitoring sites was set up in 1996 and in 1999 monitoring was extended to NH_4^+, HNO_3, SO_2, HCl, NO_3^-, SO_4^{2-}, Cl^-, Mg^{2+}, Na^+ and Ca^{2+} at selected sites (Sutton et al. 2001f, known as the nitric acid network). Sampling is on a monthly basis using either the active denuder method (which requires mains power) or passive diffusion samplers (calibrated with the denuder measurements) (Sutton et al. 2001a, d) for NH_3; active denuders for HNO_3, SO_2, HCl; filter packs for the NO_3^-, SO_4^{2-}, Cl^-, Mg^{2+}, Na^+ and Ca^{2+} aerosols. Table B4 and Figure B4 below describe the sites and show their locations; many are also part of the other automatic and non-automatic networks. The networks are run by CEH-Edinburgh, for more information see:

http://www.nbu.ac.uk/cara/UKNAMN/uknamn.htm.

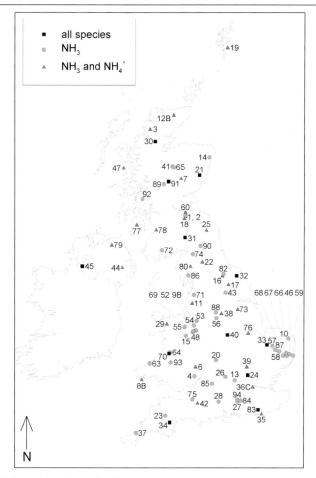

Figure B4 Ammonia and nitric acid network sites.

Table B4 Ammonia network monitoring sites. Those in italics are no longer operating and where a letter is given with the site number the site has been moved to a similar area close to the original.

Num.	Name	Grid Ref.[1]	Species[2]	Num.	Name	Grid Ref.[1]	Species[2]
1	Bush 1	NT245635	all	46	Sibton	TM363722	NH_3
2	Bush 2	NT247638	NH_3	47	Rum	NM408992	NH_x
3	Inverpolly	NC187088	NH_x	48	Wem Moss	SJ473343	NH_3
4	Penallt	SO523095	NH_3	49	*Frodsam*	SJ525795	NH_3
5	*Priddy*	*ST525526*	NH_3	50	*Swettenham Meadows*	SJ804674	NH_3
6	Holme Lacy	SO554357	NH_x	51	*Wybunbury Moss*	SJ698502	NH_3
7	Glen Shee	NO117693	NH_x	52	Fenn's Moss 1	SJ490365	NH_3
8	*Stackpole*	*SR982947*	NH_3	53	Little Budworth	SJ584658	NH_3
8B	Orielton	SR954992	NH_x	54	Bickerton HIll	SJ498527	NH_3
9	*Brown Moss 1 (Beehive Cottage)*	SJ559396	NH_3	55	Ruabon	SJ225489	NH_3
9B	Brown Moss 2 (Honeysuckle Cottage)	SJ563390	NH_3	56	Wardlow Hay Cop	SK177737	NH_3
10	Bure Marshes	TG334161	NH_3	57	Stanford	TL858948	NH_3
11	Mere Sands Wood	SD447157	NH_x	58	Redgrave and Lopham Fens	TM050797	NH_3
12	*Halladale 1*	*NC894514*	NH_3	59	Dunwich Heath	TM470680	NH_3
12B	Halladale 2	NC902488	NH_x	60	Edinburgh-Johnston Terrace	NT253734	NH_x
13	Aston Rowant	SU727979	NH_3	61	*Much Hoole*	SD473231	NH_3
14	Ellon Ythan	NJ945304	NH_3	62	*Midge Hall*	SD508231	NH_3
15	Llynclys Common	SJ273237	NH_3	63	Cardigan	SN185453	NH_3
16	North Allerton	SE360930	NH_x	64	Pen Y Garn	SN798771	NH_3
17	Easingwold	SE540675	NH_x	65	Allt a Mharcaidh	NH895024	NH_3
18	Auchencorth Moss	NT221562	NH_x	66	Dennington	TM276669	NH_3
19	Shetland	HU500400	NH_x	67	Fressingfield	TM261759	NH_3

Num.	Name	Grid Ref.[1]	Species[2]	Num.	Name	Grid Ref.[1]	Species[2]
20	Drayton	SP165549	NH_3	68	Bedingfield	TM173684	NH_3
21	Glensaugh	NO664799	all	69	Fenn's Moss 2	SJ478368	NH_3
22	Moor House	NY751334	NH_x	70	Cwmystwyth	SN771742	all
23	North Wyke	SX659983	NH_3	71	Myerscough	SD498399	NH_3
24	Rothamstead	TL123129	all	72	Dumfries	NX546658	NH_3
25	Sourhope	NT867218	NH_x	73	Jenny Hurn	SK816986	NH_x
26	Wytham Woods	SP452083	NH_3	74	Carlisle	NY468554	NH_3
27	Alice Holt	SU809379	NH_3	75	Westhay Moor	ST455440	NH_3
28	Porton Down	SU253365	NH_3	76	Pointon	TF128313	NH_x
29	Dyffryn Mymbyr	SH695572	NH_x	77	Carradale	NR798378	NH_x
30	Strathvaich Dam	NH348750	all	78	Auchincruive	NS379234	NH_x
31	Eskdalemuir	NT235030	all	79	Coleraine	C884211	NH_x
32	High Muffles	SE776939	all	80	Lyulphs Tower	NY403202	NH_x
33	Stoke Ferry	TL700988	all	81	*Pitmedden*	*NJ883278*	*NH_3*
34	Yarner Wood	SX789788	all	82	Brompton	SE389988	NH_3
35	Lullington Heath	TQ538016	NH_x	83	Barcombe Mills	TQ438149	all
36	*Bloomsbury*	*TQ264789*	NH_3	84	Thursley Common	SU910404	NH_3
36B	*Victoria*	*TQ291790*	NH_3	85	Savarnake	SU055888	NH_3
36C	Cromwell Road	TQ266791	NH_x	86	Lakes	SD337941	NH_3
37	Five Acres	SW794486	NH_3	87	Thetford	TL944841	NH_3
38	Sheffield	SK332870	NH_x	88	Sherwood	SK163905	NH_3
39	Silsoe	TL088356	NH_x	89	Rannoch	NN603533	NH_3
40	Sutton Bonington	SK505268	all	90	Coalburn	NY693782	NH_3
41	Lagganlia	NH856037	NH_3	91	Tummel	NN744611	NH_3
42	Castle Cary	ST609319	NH_x	92	Loch Awe	NM966115	NH_3
43	Tadcaster	SE452455	NH_3	93	Llynn Brianne	SN816484	NH_3
44	Hillsborough	J243577	NH_x	94	Alice Holt 2	SU805427	NH_3
45	Lough Navar	H065545	all				

1 Grid references are on the UK ordinance survey grid except those for Ireland that are on the Irish grid (with single letters).

2. NH_x = NH_3 and NH_4^+; all = NH_3, NH_4^+, NO_3^-, HNO_3, SO_2, HCl, SO_4^{2-}, Cl^-, Mg^{2+}, Na^+ and Ca^{2+}

Acid Waters Monitoring Network

The United Kingdom Acid Waters Monitoring Network (UKAWMN), funded by DEFRA, and the Department of the Environment Northern Ireland, was established in 1988 to monitor the ecological impact of acid deposition in areas of the UK believed to be sensitive to acidification. Over a decade on, its data-base provides a long-term record of water chemistry and biology which is unique for upland freshwater systems in the UK.

The Network consists of 11 lakes and 11 streams (Figure B5 and Table B5) which are monitored chemically and biologically. At all sites, regular spot samples are taken for laboratory analysis of an extensive range of chemical determinands, including pH, conductivity, and a standard suite of base cations, anions and metals. At a subset of streams, pH, conductivity and stream flow are also continuously monitored to provide a more detailed record of acid episodes. Epilithic diatoms, aquatic macrophytes and benthic invertebrates are sampled annually in the spring/summer and fish surveys for stream sites and the outflow streams of lakes are conducted each autumn.

Figure B5 AWMN site map.

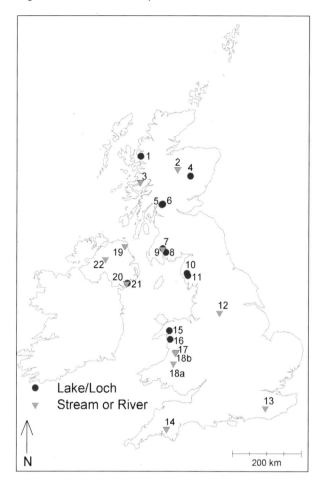

Table B5 AWMN sites.

Site No	Name	Grid Ref	Type
1	Loch Coire nan Arr	NG808422	L
2	Allt a'Mharcaidh	NH881045	S
3	Allt na Coire nan Con	NM793688	S
4	Lochnagar	NO252859	L
5	Loch Chon	NN421051	L
6	Loch Tinker	NN445068	L
7	Round Loch of Glenhead	NX450804	L
8	Loch Grannoch	NX542700	L
9	Dargall Lane	NX449786	S
10	Scoat Tarn	NY159104	L
11	Burnmoor Tarn	NY184043	L
12	River Etherow	SK116996	S
13	Old Lodge	TQ456294	S
14	Narrator Brook	SX568692	S
15	Llyn Llagi	SH649483	L
16	Llyn Cwm Mynach	SH678238	L
17	Afon Hafren	SN844876	S
18a	Nant y Gronwen	SN771556	S
18b	Afon Gwy	SN824854	S
19	Beagh's Burn	D173297	S
20	Bencrom River	J304245	S
21	Blue Lough	J327252	L
22	Coneyglen Burn	H640885	S

L ≡ Loch/Lake, S ≡ stream or river

Appendix C: Units and conversion methods

Emissions and Deposition

Annual total emissions are often given as the tonnage of the particular compound, e.g. mega-tonnes of sulphur dioxide, Mt-SO_2 or moles of the compound, e.g. giga-moles of nitrogen oxides Gmol-NO_2. Maps of emission are given as mass emitted per a prescribed area, e.g. kilo-tonnes of oxidised nitrogen per hectare, kt-NO_2 ha^{-1}; where no area is specified it should be assumed to be the size of the map's grid squares. Where related compounds are being compared the mass may be converted to a common atom e.g.:

compound	units	conversion	common unit
Oxidised nitrogen NO_x	a t-NO_2 (tonnes of NO_2)	$\frac{14}{46} \times a$	b t-N (tonnes of N)
Ammonia NH_3	a t-NH_3 (tonnes of NH_3)	$\frac{14}{17} \times a$	b t-N (tonnes of N)
compound XY	a t-XY	$\frac{\text{atomic weight X}}{\text{total atomic weight of XY}} \times a$	b t-X

As with emissions, deposition is often given as a mass or mass per area and may be converted into a common unit.

Equivalents (eq)

Wet deposition may also be shown as a concentration or deposition in equivalents per litre (eq l^{-1}) or per prescribed area (e.g. keq ha^{-1}) respectively which relates to the acidifying or neutralising capacity of the compound, i.e. it is the equivalent concentration of hydrogen ions. In general, for a compound XY with valency v and molecular weight A:

$$1\ \mu mol\ l^{-1} = v\ \mu eq\ l^{-1} = A \times 10^{-3}\ mg\text{-}XY\ l^{-1}$$

For example, z mg-SO_4^{2-} l^{-1}, where sulphate has a valency of -2, are converted to μeq l^{-1} as follows:

$$z\ mg\text{-}SO_4^{2-}\ l^{-1} = \frac{z}{96} \times 1000\ \mu mol\text{-}SO_4^{2-}\ l^{-1} = 2 \times \frac{z}{96} \times 1000\ \mu eq\ l^{-1}$$

This unit is commonly used to describe concentrations of acidifying/neutralising compounds in precipitation or other aqueous samples to allow easy comparison between them. It may also be expressed as mol$_c$, i.e. 1 μeq l^{-1} = 1 mol$_c$ l^{-1}

pH as equivalents of hydrogen ions per litre:

$$\mu mol\text{-}H^+\ l^{-1} = \mu eq\text{-}H^+\ l^{-1} = antilog_{10}(6.0 - pH) = 10^{(6.0\ -\ pH)}$$

pH	μeq-H^+ l^{-1}
3.0	1000
4.0	100
5.0	10

Gaseous Concentrations

The expression of air pollutant concentrations in more than one unit of measurement can cause confusion for those not professionally involved in the field. There are two main systems of unit in common use:

Mass per unit volume: usually μg m^{-3}. The mass of pollutant is expressed as a ratio to the volume of air. Since the volume of a given parcel of air is dependent upon the temperature and pressure at the time of sampling, the pollutant concentration expressed in these units should, strictly speaking, specify the conditions at the time of sampling.

Volume mixing ratio: usually ppm - parts per million (10^6); or ppb - parts per billion (10^9); or ppt - parts per trillion (10^{12}). This unit expresses the concentration of a pollutant as the ratio of its volume if segregated pure, to the volume of the air in which it is contained. Ideal gas behaviour is assumed and thus the concentration is not dependent upon temperature and pressure as these affect both the pollutant and the air to the same extent. As a consequence of the gas laws, a gas present at a volume mixing ratio of 1 ppm is not only 1 cm^3 per 10^6 cm^3 of polluted air, it is also 1 molecule per 10^6 molecules and has a partial pressure of one millionth of the atmospheric pressure.

Some pollutants (e.g. sulphate, nitrate) are present as particles in the air and the concept of a volume mixing ratio of gases is not obviously applicable. Their concentrations are normally expressed only in $\mu g\ m^{-3}$ units.

Conversion Factors

Interconversion of the two sets of units can be achieved as follows:

$$\frac{\mu g\ m^{-3}}{1000} = ppb \times \frac{\text{molecular weight (g mol}^{-1})}{\text{molecular volume (litres)}}$$

where, molecular volume $= 22.41 \times \frac{T}{273} \times \frac{1013}{P}$ litres

in which T = absolute temperature (K)

P = atmospheric pressure (hPa)

Similarly, ppb $= \frac{\mu g\ m^{-3}}{1000} \times \frac{\text{molecular volume (litres)}}{\text{molecular weight}}$

As mentioned above, volume mixing ratios (ppb, etc.) are invariant with temperature and pressure, whilst $\mu g\ m^{-3}$ concentrations change with temperature and pressure. The magnitude of this variation can be gauged from the variability of the molar volume (above). Generally, the molar volume is affected to the greatest degree by changes in temperature; a variation from 0°C to 27°C causes a change of 10% in molar volume, and thus $\mu g\ m^{-3}$ concentrations. A rather extreme change in atmospheric pressure from 950 mb to 1020 mb gives a 7% change. Thus errors due to these factors can be significant, but are not massive.

At 25°C and 1013 hPa pressure, the conversion factors are as follows:

	ppb to $\mu g\ m^{-3}$ multiply by	$\mu g\ m^{-3}$ to ppb multiply by
NO	1.23	0.81
NO_2	1.88	0.53
O_3	1.96	0.51
SO_2	2.62	0.38
NH_3	0.69	1.44
HNO_3	2.60	0.38
H_2O_2	1.39	0.72

At 20°C and 1013 mb pressure, the conversion factors are as follows:

	ppb to $\mu g\ m^{-3}$ multiply by	$\mu g\ m^{-3}$ to ppb multiply by
NO	1.25	0.80
NO_2	1.91	0.52
O_3	2.00	0.50
SO_2	2.66	0.38
NH_3	0.71	1.42
HNO_3	2.62	0.38
H_2O_2	1.41	0.71

ANC - Acid Neutralising Capacity

ANC is a fundamental measure of soil or stream water acidity. It is a pragmatic parameter which is readily estimated from relatively simple measurements and is reliably predicted by process models. In contrast to pH, it behaves conservatively when two or more waters are mixed together; it is unaffected by: i) degassing of dissolved CO_2 ii) precipitation/dissolution reactions involving aluminium hydroxide species, iii) precipitation/dissolution of H-organic and Al-organic (humic) substances. These properties make the concept of ANC extremely valuable in predictive modelling of soil and stream water acidification.

ANC (measured in units of $\mu eq\ l^{-1}$) is defined as:

ANC = Σ(strong base cations) - Σ(strong acid anions); that is: (1)

ANC = $[Na^+] + [K^+] + 2[Ca^{2+}] + 2[Mg^{2+}] + [NH_4^+] - [Cl^-] - [NO_3^-] - 2[SO_4^{2-}] - [F^-]$ (2)

Using charge balance constraints, this is approximately equivalent to:

$$ANC = 2[CO_3^{2-}] + [HCO_3^-] + [OH^-] - [H^+] - 3[Al^{3+}] - 2[Al(OH)^{2+}] - [Al(OH)_2^+] \qquad (3)$$

Where [] indicate micromolar concentrations. In acidic waters, $[CO_3^{2-}]$ and $[OH^-]$ are negligible.

The ANC of a water sample can be estimated from alkalinity measured by Gran titration $\{Alk_{Gran}\}$ and the concentrations of total dissolved aluminium $\{Altot\}$ and dissolved organic carbon [DOC]:

$$ANC \cong \{Alk_{Gran}\} - \{Altot\} + \Delta[DOC] \qquad (4)$$

Where {} denote micro-equivalent concentrations, Δ is an empirical constant with an approximate value of 0.07 and DOC is expressed in μmol C l^{-1} (Neal et al., 1999).

Appendix D: Critical load methodologies

Critical loads are generally defined as: " a quantitative estimate of exposure to one or more pollutants below which significant harmful effects on specified sensitive elements of the environment do not occur according to present knowledge" (Nilsson & Grennfelt, 1988).

This appendix briefly summarises the methods currently used in the UK to calculate acidity and nutrient nitrogen critical loads. Further details on the methods, including equations and maps, can be found on the UK National Focal Centre web site (http://critloads.ceh.ac.uk) and in the papers and reports referred to in the text below.

Critical Loads of Acidity

Two methods are used in the UK for calculating acidity critical loads for terrestrial ecosystems: the empirical approach is used for estimates for non-woodland ecosystems and the simple mass balance (SMB) equation for woodland ecosystems. Both methods provide critical loads for systems at steady-state. For freshwater ecosystems, three steady-state models are used: the Diatom model, the Steady-State Water Chemistry (SSWC) model and the First-order Acidity Balance (FAB) model. These methods are described briefly below.

Empirical critical loads of acidity for soils

Mineral weathering in soils provides the main long-term sink for deposited acidity. Using this principle, critical loads of acidity can be based on the amount of acid deposition which could be buffered by the annual production of base cations from mineral weathering (Nilsson & Grennfelt, 1988).

In the UK, empirical critical loads of acidity for soils have been assigned to each 1km grid square of the country based upon the mineralogy and chemistry of the dominant soil series present in the grid square (Hornung *et al.*, 1995a). The data are mapped in five classes representing ranges of critical load values, with low critical loads for soils dominated by minerals such as quartz and high critical loads for soils containing free carbonates. Where a single critical load value is required, for example, when calculating the excess deposition above the critical load (i.e., the exceedance), the mid-range values are applied, with the exception of those with the highest critical load, where the value at the top of the range is used (Hall *et al.*, 1998). However, this classification, based on weathering rates and mineralogy, is inappropriate for peat soils, which contain little mineral material. For these, the critical load was set using an approach (Smith *et al.*, 1993) which assumes that peat acidity comes to an equilibrium with the acidity of rainfall. The critical load was calculated as the amount of deposited acidity which would result in a decrease in peat pH of no more than 0.2 pH units, compared to a pH obtained under pristine conditions. Together, these empirical critical loads are assigned to the 1km grid squares of the country representing the following ecosystems: acid grassland, calcareous grassland and heathland. The distribution of these ecosystems are defined from land cover data (Hall *et al.*, 1998): the CEH Land Cover map for Great Britain (Fuller *et al.*, 1994) and CORINE Level 3 data (CEC, 1992) for Northern Ireland. In addition, the distribution of calcareous grassland is further refined using species distribution data (Hall *et al.*, 1998).

The application of these methods in the UK represent a precautionary approach, setting the critical loads for mineral soils to prevent any further change in soil chemistry as a result of deposited acidity (Hornung *et al.*, 1997).

The simple mass balance (SMB) equation for calculating acidity critical loads for woodland ecosystems

The SMB equation is the most commonly used model in Europe for the calculation of acidity critical loads for woodland ecosystems. This model is based on balancing the acidic inputs to and outputs from a system, to derive a critical load that ensures a critical chemical limit (related to effects on the ecosystem) is not exceeded (Sverdrup *et al.*, 1990, Sverdrup & De Vries, 1994). The equation has been derived from a charge balance of ions in leaching fluxes from the soil compartment, combined with mass balance equations for the inputs, sinks, sources and outputs of sulphur and nitrogen (Posch *et al.*, 1995b).

In the UK we apply the SMB equation to coniferous and deciduous woodland ecosystems, except for wooded areas on peat soils, where the SMB is inappropriate; in such areas empirical acidity critical loads for peat soils are applied (Cresser *et al.*, 1993; Smith *et. al.*, 1993). The application of the SMB equation to non-woodland systems needs further development and testing because of uncertainties in the applicability of the critical chemical criteria to other ecosystems.

The SMB equation is parameterised according to the appropriate critical chemical criteria and critical limits that will protect the receptor from the adverse effects of acidification. A critical molar ratio of calcium to aluminium of one in soil solution is a common criterion applied in the SMB to protect the fine roots of trees. This criterion is more appropriate for mineral soils than organic soils; for the latter a critical pH is considered to be more suitable (Hall *et al.*, 2001b). Therefore, in the UK we have parameterised the model to use a Ca:Al=1 criterion for woodland on mineral soils and a critical pH of 4.0 as the criterion for woodland on organic soils. The equations currently being used are given in Hall *et al.*, 2001c. In the case of peat soils, the empirical critical loads are still applied.

Acidity critical loads for freshwater ecosystems

The three steady-state models used to derive acidity critical loads for freshwaters are described briefly below. The calculations use data from a national survey of lakes or headwater streams, where a single site, judged to be the most sensitive (in terms of acidification) was sampled in each 10km grid square of the country. In less sensitive regions (e.g., south-east England) the sampling generally consisted of one site in each 20 km grid square. To date the models have been applied to 1470 sites in Great Britain and 140 in Northern Ireland. It should be noted that the critical load value mapped for a given 10 km grid square is only applicable to the waterbody or stream sampled and cannot be applied to other waters within the same grid square.

The Diatom model

This model has been developed from palaeolimnological data and diatom-based pH reconstructions. The model uses a dose-response relationship between total acid deposition and changes in diatom composition, taking into account variations in site sensitivity as represented by water calcium concentrations (Allott *et al.*, 1995; Battarbee *et al.*, 1996; CLAG, 1995; Hornung *et al.*, 1997). Acidification is indicated by a shift to a more acid-tolerant diatom flora. The model is based on the point of onset of acidification and is therefore said to set a "base critical load" for a site (CLAG, 1995). Only water chemistry data are required to apply the calibrated model.

The Steady-State Water Chemistry (SSWC) model

This model is based on the principle that excess base cation run-off reflects the net weathering processes in the catchment (Henriksen *et al.*, 1992; Henriksen *et al.*, 1997). The acidic input should be less than or equal to the critical load calculated by this method, in order to prevent exceedance of the selected chemical threshold. By setting the critical limit for Acid Neutralising Capacity (ANC) to a biologically significant level, a critical load can be calculated for any target organism. ANC is defined as the difference between base cations and strong acid anions in solution (Reuss & Johnson, 1986). In the UK an ANC limit of zero is currently used in the calculation of critical loads (Harriman et al., 1995b, Hornung et al., 1997), indicating a 50% probability of damage to brown trout populations (Lien et al., 1992).

The First-order Acidity Balance (FAB) model

FAB is a catchment-based model used to derive linked critical loads of sulphur and nitrogen (Henriksen, 1998; Posch et al., 1997; UBA, 1996). It is a process orientated model which can be used to quantify the proportion of total nitrogen deposition which is transported through the terrestrial part of a catchment into the surface waters (Curtis et al., 2000). The FAB model employs a simple charge balance for nitrogen and sulphur, along with the original base cation leaching rate from the SSWC model. The charge balance equates the deposition inputs of acid anions with the sum of processes which control their long term storage (e.g., in-lake retention of sulphur and nitrogen), removal (e.g., net growth uptake of nitrogen by forest vegetation, long-term immobilisation of nitrogen and nitrogen lost through denitrification in catchment soils) and leaching exports (e.g., catchment runoff). The equations currently being used in the model are given in Curtis et al., 2000 and Hall et al., 1998.

Critical Loads for Nutrient Nitrogen

Enhanced nitrogen deposition to terrestrial and freshwater ecosystems can lead to acidification or eutrophication. The latter can have major impacts on plant communities leading to changes in species composition and the sensitivity of vegetation to environmental stresses, such as drought, frost or insect predation (Hornung et al., 1997). Therefore methods have been developed to set critical loads to protect against these adverse effects. Two approaches are currently in use: empirical and mass balance, and these are described briefly below.

Empirical critical load for nutrient nitrogen

Empirical nutrient nitrogen critical loads have been set for a number of grassland, heathland, wetland and forest ecosystems based on the results of experimental studies and field observations, or on "expert judgement". Ranges of critical load values are given for each ecosystem type to take account of: (i) intra-ecosystem variations due to factors such as climate and management practice; (ii) the range of experimental treatments where an effect was observed or not observed; (iii) uncertainties in deposition values, where critical loads are based on field observations (UBA, 1996). The UNECE Mapping Manual (UBA, 1996) includes advice on where within these ranges, if insufficient national data are available, the critical load should be set. The ranges of critical load values recommended in the Mapping Manual are also accompanied by one of the following "reliability" scores: "reliable" where a number of published papers of various studies show comparable results; "quite reliable" when the results of some studies are comparable; and "expert judgement" or "best guess" where no data are available for a particular ecosystem type (Bobbink et al., 1996).

UK experts have agreed on appropriate values within these ranges to assign critical loads to UK ecosystems. Tables of the agreed values are given in Hall et al. 1998 and will not be repeated here. In the national mapping exercise, empirical critical loads have been assigned to acid grassland, calcareous grassland and heathland ecosystems, whilst for coniferous and deciduous woodland, the minimum value of the empirical or mass balance critical loads have been applied to individual grid squares (Hall et al.,

1998, Hall *et al.*, 2001b). However, it should be noted that empirical critical loads for woodland ecosystems are set to protect the woodland ground flora from adverse effects, rather than to protect the trees themselves.

Chapter 7 of the main report presents nutrient nitrogen critical load and exceedance maps for grassland, heathland/moorland and woodland ecosystems. These woodland maps are based on empirical critical loads only. In addition, the maps for grassland and heathland/moorland include some new, lower, critical load values (see Table 7.6 in Chapter 7) proposed at a UNECE Expert Workshop on Chemical Criteria and Critical Limits held in the UK in Spring 2001. These proposed values will be considered further at an expert workshop to be held under the UNECE Convention on Long-range Transboundary Air Pollution in the Autumn of 2002. This workshop will evaluate, update and revise the empirical critical loads of nutrient nitrogen for (semi-)natural ecosystems given in the Mapping Manual (UBA, 1996), on the basis of additional scientific information available for the period 1996 to 2001. Critical loads for UK ecosystems may be revised in light of the results of this expert workshop.

Mass balance critical loads for nutrient nitrogen

This method is based on an equation, which balances all significant long-term inputs and outputs of nitrogen for terrestrial ecosystems. In this context, long-term is defined as at least one forest rotation or 100 years (UBA, 1996). Critical loads calculated using this method are set to: (i) prevent an increase in leaching of nitrogen compounds, particularly nitrate, which may result in damage to the terrestrial, or linked aquatic systems; (ii) ensure sustainable production by limiting nitrogen uptake and removal to a level which will not result in deficiencies of other nutrient elements (Hornung *et al.*, 1997).

In principle, this approach could be used for any terrestrial ecosystem, but to date its use has been largely restricted to forest ecosystems. In the UK, the mass balance equation has been used to calculate nutrient nitrogen critical loads for coniferous and deciduous woodland ecosystems (Hall *et al.*, 1998). However, the national maps are currently based on the minimum of the empirical or mass balance critical loads values (Hall *et al.*, 2001b).

Calculating Exceedance of Critical Loads

Critical loads are compared with acidifying or eutrophying deposition to determine the excess deposition above the critical load, i.e., the exceedance. Current work for DEFRA and for the UNECE Convention on Long-Range Transboundary Air Pollution requires the impacts of acidification and eutrophication to be considered, and in terms of acidification, the contribution of both sulphur and nitrogen deposition to critical loads exceedance. To examine the acidifying effects of both sulphur and nitrogen deposition simultaneously, the Critical Loads Function (CLF) was developed in Europe (Posch *et al.*, 1999; Posch & Hettelingh, 1997; Posch *et al.*, 1995a; Hettelingh *et al.*, 1995). The CLF defines separate acidity critical loads in terms of sulphur and nitrogen, referred to as the "minimum" and "maximum" critical loads of sulphur and nitrogen. These critical loads incorporate some of the acidity critical loads values described above, together with data on base cation and nitrogen uptake, non-marine base cation deposition, nitrogen immobilisation and leaching and denitrification. The derivation and use of these critical loads is described elsewhere (Hall *et al.*, 1998; Hall *et al.*, 2001d) and will not be repeated here. These "new" critical loads can then be compared with sulphur and nitrogen deposition. This method is used by the UK National Focal Centre to examine the impacts of possible future emission reduction scenarios and to calculate the areas of sensitive ecosystems where critical loads are exceeded (Hall *et al.*, 2001d). The effects of excess nitrogen as a nutrient are considered separately by comparing the nutrient nitrogen critical loads with nitrogen deposition values and calculating the ecosystem areas exceeded.

However, it should be noted that the critical loads data on which exceedance calculations are currently based, are derived from empirical or steady-state mass balance methods, which are used to define **long-term** critical loads for systems at **steady-state** (Hall *et al.*, 2001d). Therefore, exceedance is an indication of the potential for harmful effects to systems at steady-state. This means that current exceedance does not necessarily equate with damage. In addition, achievement of non-exceedance of critical loads does not mean the ecosystems have recovered. Chemical recovery will not necessarily be accompanied by biological recovery; and the timescales for both chemical and biological recovery could be very long, particularly for the most sensitive ecosystems.

Appendix E: Ground-level ozone linear regression trend statistics

Trend statistics for UK rural ozone monitoring sites for the periods starting *ca* 1980 to 2000: annual maxima; the number of days per year the 8 hour running mean exceeds 50 ppb (8hrm); AOT40 crops and forests (W40 and F40); annual averages. Only years with data capture ≥ 75% are included, *italicised red numbers* are statistically significant.

Site name	Site Ref.	Variable	Period	No. of Years	Trend, $x^{ii} y^{-1}$	R^2	Probability
Sibton	*SB*	*Annual Max*	*1981 - 00*	*15*	*-3.63*	*0.53*	*0.00*
Yarner Wood	*YW*	*Annual Max*	*1988 - 00*	*13*	*-4.27*	*0.59*	*0.00*
Aston Hill	*AH*	*Annual Max*	*1988 - 00*	*13*	*-2.55*	*0.46*	*0.01*
Ladybower	*LB*	*Annual Max*	*1989 - 00*	*10*	*-3.58*	*0.64*	*0.01*
Bush	*BU*	*Annual Max*	*1986 - 00*	*15*	*-1.70*	*0.33*	*0.03*
Lough Navar	*LR*	*Annual Max*	*1988 - 00*	*13*	*-2.20*	*0.38*	*0.03*
Lullington Heath	*LH*	*Annual Max*	*1988 - 00*	*13*	*-3.05*	*0.32*	*0.04*
Harwell	*HR*	*Annual Max*	*1984 - 00*	*15*	*-1.81*	*0.27*	*0.05*
Glazebury	GZ	Annual Max	1989 - 00	12	-1.42	0.14	0.22
High Muffles	HM	Annual Max	1988 - 00	13	-0.93	0.09	0.31
Eskdalemuir	ES	Annual Max	1987 - 00	14	-0.76	0.06	0.40
Bottesford	BT	Annual Max	1981 - 00	18	-0.50	0.04	0.42
Mace Head	MH	Annual Max	1988 - 98	11	-0.79	0.06	0.48
Dunslair Heights	DH	Annual Max	1993 - 99	7	0.65	0.03	0.69
Strath Vaich	SV	Annual Max	1988 - 00	12	-0.09	0.00	0.86
Aston Hill	*AH*	*8hrm*	*1988 - 00*	*13*	*-3.12*	*0.66*	*0.00*
Bottesford	*BT*	*8hrm*	*1981 - 00*	*18*	*-2.29*	*0.53*	*0.00*
Ladybower	*LB*	*8hrm*	*1989 - 00*	*10*	*-3.45*	*0.77*	*0.00*
Lough Navar	*LR*	*8hrm*	*1988 - 00*	*13*	*-1.51*	*0.67*	*0.00*
Glazebury	*GZ*	*8hrm*	*1989 - 00*	*12*	*-1.80*	*0.55*	*0.01*
Lullington Heath	*LH*	*8hrm*	*1988 - 00*	*13*	*-3.57*	*0.45*	*0.01*
Sibton	*SB*	*8hrm*	*1981 - 00*	*15*	*-1.97*	*0.46*	*0.01*
Yarner Wood	*YW*	*8hrm*	*1988 - 00*	*13*	*-3.49*	*0.45*	*0.01*
High Muffles	*HM*	*8hrm*	*1988 - 00*	*13*	*-1.91*	*0.41*	*0.02*
Harwell	*HR*	*8hrm*	*1984 - 00*	*15*	*-2.08*	*0.31*	*0.03*
Bush	*BU*	*8hrm*	*1986 - 00*	*15*	*-1.17*	*0.26*	*0.05*
Eskdalemuir	*ES*	*8hrm*	*1987 - 00*	*14*	*-1.18*	*0.28*	*0.05*
Strath Vaich	SV	8hrm	1987 - 00	14	-0.90	0.10	0.28
Mace Head	MH	8hrm	1987 - 98	12	0.39	0.01	0.77
Dunslair Heights	DH	8hrm	1992 - 99	8	-0.23	0.01	0.84
Ladybower	*LB*	*W40*	*1989 - 00*	*10*	*-369.72*	*0.49*	*0.03*
Glazebury	*GZ*	*W40*	*1989 - 00*	*12*	*-157.72*	*0.34*	*0.05*
Bottesford	BT	W40	1981 - 00	18	-119.37	0.17	0.08
Yarner Wood	YW	W40	1988 - 00	13	-406.05	0.21	0.12
Lough Navar	LR	W40	1987 - 00	14	-115.77	0.17	0.14
Lullington Heath	LH	W40	1988 - 00	13	-315.56	0.15	0.20
High Muffles	HM	W40	1988 - 00	12	-130.62	0.12	0.26
Mace Head	MH	W40	1987 - 98	12	110.97	0.12	0.28
Dunslair Heights	DH	W40	1992 - 98	7	-484.87	0.19	0.33
Aston Hill	AH	W40	1987 - 00	13	-178.65	0.08	0.34
Bush	BU	W40	1986 - 00	15	-50.80	0.04	0.46
Harwell	HR	W40	1983 - 00	18	-49.12	0.01	0.69
Strath Vaich	SV	W40	1987 - 00	14	-38.88	0.01	0.70
Sibton	SB	W40	1981 - 00	18	32.72	0.01	0.75
Eskdalemuir	ES	W40	1986 - 00	15	-26.32	0.01	0.77
Ladybower	*LB*	*F40*	*1989 - 00*	*10*	*-442.23*	*0.46*	*0.03*
Lough Navar	LR	F40	1987 - 00	14	-179.59	0.33	0.03

Site name	Site Ref.	Variable	Period	No. of Years	Trend, x^{ii} y^{-1}	R^2	Probability
Mace Head	MH	F40	1987 - 98	12	267.27	0.28	0.08
Bottesford	BT	F40	1981 - 00	19	-185.69	0.16	0.09
Yarner Wood	YW	F40	1988 - 00	13	-580.54	0.24	0.09
Sibton	SB	F40	1981 - 00	18	-205.66	0.14	0.13
Lullington Heath	LH	F40	1988 - 00	13	-432.35	0.17	0.16
Glazebury	GZ	F40	1990 - 99	10	-186.20	0.21	0.18
High Muffles	HM	F40	1988 - 00	13	-138.17	0.09	0.32
Aston Hill	AH	F40	1987 - 00	13	-201.90	0.08	0.36
Bush	BU	F40	1986 - 00	14	-52.90	0.04	0.51
Dunslair Heights	DH	F40	1992 - 98	7	-342.75	0.09	0.51
Eskdalemuir	ES	F40	1986 - 00	15	-12.25	0.00	0.91
Harwell	HR	F40	1984 - 00	17	-16.54	0.00	0.93
Strath Vaich	SV	F40	1987 - 00	13	-9.54	0.00	0.94
Dunslair Heights	*DH*	*Annual Mean*	*1993 - 99*	*7*	*0.71*	*0.76*	*0.01*
High Muffles	*HM*	*Annual Mean*	*1988 - 00*	*13*	*0.25*	*0.40*	*0.02*
Bush	*BU*	*Annual Mean*	*1986 - 00*	*15*	*0.21*	*0.29*	*0.04*
Sibton	SB	Annual Mean	1981 - 00	15	0.08	0.21	0.09
Strath Vaich	SV	Annual Mean	1988 - 00	12	0.15	0.23	0.12
Mace Head	MH	Annual Mean	1988 - 98	11	0.19	0.23	0.13
Glazebury	GZ	Annual Mean	1989 - 00	12	0.14	0.15	0.21
Ladybower	LB	Annual Mean	1989 - 00	10	0.16	0.18	0.22
Lough Navar	LR	Annual Mean	1988 - 00	13	-0.11	0.13	0.22
Yarner Wood	YW	Annual Mean	1988 - 00	13	-0.11	0.05	0.45
Lullington Heath	LH	Annual Mean	1988 - 00	13	0.06	0.01	0.70
Aston Hill	AH	Annual Mean	1988 - 00	13	0.03	0.01	0.82
Harwell	HR	Annual Mean	1984 - 00	15	0.06	0.04	0.47
Bottesford	BT	Annual Mean	1981 - 00	18	0.08	0.03	0.51
Eskdalemuir	ES	Annual Mean	1987 - 00	14	0.10	0.04	0.51

i statistically significant at the 95% confidence level
ii Annual maximum and average: ppb y^{-1}; AOT40 :ppb h y^{-1}; 8hrm: number of days y^{-1}.

Appendix F: Inputs for HARM backcasts

Year	UK emissions	EMEP emissions*	Rainfall	Status
1970	1970 SO_2 NO_x scaled from 1995 1996 NH_3	1970 SO_2, others scaled from 1995	10 km GB 1941-70 for N. Ireland	✓
1980	1983 SO_2 NO_x scaled from 1995 1996 NH_3	1980 SO_2, others scaled from 1995	10 km GB 1941-70 for N. Ireland	✓
1983	1983 SO_2 NO_x scaled from 1995 1996 NH_3	1980 SO_2, others scaled from 1995	10 km GB 1941-70 for N. Ireland	✓
1986	1983 SO_2 NO_x scaled from 1995 1996 NH_3	Scaled from 1997	10 km GB 1941-70 for N. Ireland	✓
1990	1990 SO_2 1990 NO_x 1996 NH_3	Scaled from 1997	10 km GB 1941-70 for N. Ireland	✓
1991	1991 SO_2 1991 NO_x 1996 NH_3	Scaled from 1997	10 km UK excluding the Outer Hebrides	✓
1992	1992 SO_2 1992 NO_x 1996 NH_3	Scaled from 1997	10 km UK	✓
1993	1993 SO_2 1993 NO_x 1996 NH_3	Scaled from 1997	10 km UK	✓
1994	1994 SO_2 1994 NO_x 1996 NH_3	Scaled from 1997	10 km UK	✓
1995	1995 SO_2 1995 NO_x 1996 NH_3	Scaled from 1997	10 km GB 1941-70 for N. Ireland	✓
1996	1996 SO_2 1996 NO_x 1996 NH_3	Scaled from 1997	10 km UK	✓
1997	1997 SO_2 1997 NO_x 1996 NH_3	1997 official	10 km UK excluding the Outer Hebrides	✓

*scalings applied on a country by country basis, volcanic and dms emissions fixed at 1995 values, shipping emissions based on values in EMEP reports.

Appendix G: NEGTAP Membership

Professor David Fowler (Chairman)
Mhairi Coyle (Secretary)
Centre for Ecology and Hydrology Edinburgh
Bush Estate, Penicuik
Midlothian, EH26 0QB
http://www.nbu.ac.uk/

Professor Helen ApSimon
DEST (Department of Environmental Science
and Technology)
Imperial College of Science, Technology and
Medicine
Prince Consort Rd,
London, SW7 2PB
http://www.env.ic.ac.uk/

Professor Mike Ashmore
University of Bradford
Dept of Environmental Sciences
Bradford
West Yorkshire, BD7 1DP
http://www.brad.ac.uk/acad/envsci/

Mr Simon Bareham
Cyngor Cefn Gwlad Cymru/Countryside Council
for Wales
Plas Penrhos
Ffordd Penrhos
Bangor
Gwynedd, LL57 2LQ
http://www.ccw.gov.uk/

Professor Rick Battarbee
University College London
Environmental Change Research Centre
26 Bedford Way
London, WC1E 0AP
http://www.geog.ucl.ac.uk/ecrc/

Dr R G Derwent OBE
Meteorological Office
London Rd
Bracknell
Berkshire, RG12 2SZ
http://www.meto.govt.uk/home.html
rgderwent@meto.gov.uk

Dr Jan Willem Erisman
Energy research Center of the Netherlands, ECN
PO Box 1
1755 ZG Petten
The NETHERLANDS
http://www.ecn.nl/main.html

Mr Justin Goodwin
AEA Technology Environment
Culham
Abingdon
Oxon. OX14 3ED
http://www.aeat-env.com/

Professor Peringe Grennfelt
Swedish Environmental Research Institute
PO Box 47086
S-402 58 Goteborg
SWEDEN
http://www.ivl.se/

Professor Mike Hornung
Centre for Ecology and Hydrology Merlewood
Grange-over-Sands
Cumbria, LA11 6JU
http://www.nmw.ac.uk/

Professor Jimi Irwin
Environment Agency
Kings Meadow House
Kings Meadow Road
Reading
RG1 8DQ
http://www.environment-agency.gov.uk/

Dr Alan Jenkins
Centre for Ecology and Hydrology Wallingford
MacLean Building
Crowmarsh Gifford
Wallingford
Oxon. OX10 8BB
http://www.nwl.ac.uk/

Professor Sarah Metcalfe
University of Edinburgh
Dept of Geography
Drummond St
Edinburgh, EH8 9XP
http://www.geo.ed.ac.uk/

Professor Steve Ormerod
Cardiff University
School of Biosciences
Main Building
PO Box 915
Cardiff, CF1 3TL
http://www.cf.ac.uk/uwcc/biosi/

Dr Brian Reynolds
Centre for Ecology and Hydrology Bangor
University of Wales, Bangor
Deiniol Rd
Bangor, Gwynedd LL57 2UP
http://www.nmw.ac.uk/

Dr Sarah Woodin
University of Aberdeen
Dept of. Plant and Soil Science
Cruickshank Building
St Machar Drive
Aberdeen, AB24 3UU
http://www.abdn.ac.uk/pss/

Appendix H: Acknowledgements

Thanks go to Professor Keith Bull for his participation as a group member prior to taking a new post outside the UK and to Jane Hall for attending meetings on his behalf.

Contributors:

Jane Hall, CEH Monks Wood

Ed Tipping, CEH Windemere

Mark Sutton, CEH Edinburgh

Ulrike Dragosits, CEH Edinburgh

Chris Evans, CEH Wallingford

Jonathan Foot, Joint Nature Conservation Committee

Ron Harriman, Freshwater Fisheries Laboratory

Don Monteith, Environmental Change Research Centre, University College London

Mark Broadmeadow, Forestry Commission

Simon Langan, MLURI

Rachel Helliwell, MLURI

Duncan Whyatt, Lancaster University

David S. Lee, DERA

Chris Curtis, ECRC, UCL